Dynamical Properties of Solids

Volume 2

Dynamical Properties of Solids

Volume 2

Crystalline Solids, Applications

edited by

G.K. Horton
Rutgers University
New Brunswick, USA

A.A. Maradudin
University of California
Irvine, USA

1975

North-Holland Publishing Company – Amsterdam, Oxford
American Elsevier Publishing Company, Inc. – New York

Library of Congress Catalog Card Number: 73-81536
North-Holland ISBN: 0 7204 0284 0 (Vol. 2)
North-Holland ISBN: 0 7204 0285 9 (complete series)
American Elsevier ISBN: 0444 10970 6

Publishers: North-Holland Publishing Company, Amsterdam
North-Holland Publishing Company, Ltd., Oxford

Sole distributors for the U.S.A. and Canada:
American Elsevier Publishing Company, Inc.
52 Vanderbilt Avenue, New York, N.Y. 10017

Library of Congress Cataloging in Publication Data (Revised)

Horton, George K
Dynamical properties of solids.

Includes bibliographies and indexes.
CONTENTS: v. 1. Crystalline solids, fundamentals.--
v. 2. Crystalline solids, applications.
1. Lattice dynamics. 2. Solids. I. Maradudin, A. A. joint author. II. Title.
QC176.8.L3H67 548'.81 75-501105
ISBN 0-444-10536-0 (American Elsevier)

Printed in the Netherlands

Preface

This second volume continues the plan to make a comprehensive presentation of the dynamics of crystalline and non-crystalline solids. The authors are theoretical physicists. But they have tried to compensate for this bias by weaving appropriate experimental results into the fabric of the articles. In addition, important articles by experimental physicists are scheduled for publication in volume 3, the final volume of this series.

We were most grateful to many readers of the first volume for comments and suggestions. We again welcome feedback so that the final volume of this series will have better balance and be more complete.

We thank Dr. Berend Kolk for kindly preparing the Subject Index for volume two. The high professional competence of Drs. W. H. Wimmers and P. S. H. Bolman and their colleagues of the North-Holland Publishing Company has been an essential ingredient in the preparation of volume two.

September 1975

G.K. Horton
New Brunswick, N.J.
USA

A.A. Maradudin
Irvine, Cal.
USA

Contents

Volume 2

List of Contributors

H. Beck*, Institut für Theoretische Physik der Universität Zürich, Schönberggasse 9, 8001 Zurich, Switzerland

R.J. Elliott, Department of Theoretical Physics, Oxford University, Oxford OX1 3PQ, England, UK

N.S. Gillis, Physics Department, Colorado State University, Ft. Collins, Colorado 80521, USA

N. Jacobi, Department of Chemistry, University of Southern California, Los Angeles, California 90007, USA

T.R. Koehler, IBM Research Laboratory, San Jose, California 95193, USA

P.L. Leath, Rutgers University, New Brunswick, New Jersey 08903, USA

O. Schnepp, Department of Chemistry, University of Southern California, Los Angeles, California 90007, USA

D.W. Taylor, Physics Department, McMaster University, Hamilton, Ontario, Canada

R.F. Wallis, Department of Physics, University of California, Irvine, California 92664, USA

* New address: Institut für theoretische Physik, Klingelbergstrasse 82, CH-4056 Basel, Switzerland.

CHAPTER 1

Lattice Dynamics of Quantum Crystals

T.R. KOEHLER

IBM Research Laboratory
San Jose, California 95193
USA

Dynamical Properties of Solids, edited by
G.K. Horton and A.A. Maradudin

Contents

1. Introduction

1.1. Introductory remarks

Interest in both the experimental and theoretical properties of solid helium has increased dramatically during the last decade. Of special importance to lattice dynamics, improvements in crystal growing techniques during the past few years have permitted measurements of the velocity of sound and of complete phonon dispersion curves in single crystal specimens. Meanwhile, a completely satisfactory theoretical explanation of these and other experimental data has been surprisingly hard to develop.

The theory of the lattice dynamics of solid helium contains an intriguing combination of the simple and the difficult. On one hand, solid helium should be the simplest lattice dynamical system because with only two tightly bound (24.5 eV) electrons per atom it is the closest physical example of an ideal, simple Van der Waals solid. One should be able to model the solid quite accurately as a collection of atoms which interact through a spherically symmetrical, two-body potential and thus completely ignore atomic polarizibilities, long-range Coulomb interactions, band structure and other electronic effects.

On the other hand, the same physical characteristics which allow one to treat solid helium on the basis of this idealized physical model, are themselves responsible for the introduction of great complications. Because of the high binding energy of the atomic electrons, helium atoms are almost chemically inert and the interaction between two atoms is quite weak. The diatomic molecule He_2 does not exist at all and the solid exists only under pressure. This is of course as much a result of the light mass as of the weak attraction; the physical picture is that the kinetic energy required to localize one helium atom in the potential well of another is approximately equal to the energy gained from the binding. This localization energy is kinetic energy or, equivalently, zero-point energy and as such is strictly a quantum-mechanical effect.

In section 2, some of the introductory remarks of this section will be amplified in order to present a phenomenological theoretical picture of solid helium and relevant experimental work will be reviewed. The picture that will emerge is that of solid helium as a substance whose basic behavior is dominated by quantum-mechanical effects – for example, the zero-point energy is such that the mean-square deviation of an atom from its lattice site at 0 K is about 30% of the lattice spacing. Hence, the solid isotopes of helium are commonly called quantum solids or quantum crystals. These terms will be used in this chapter and also helium, ^{3}He or ^{4}He will be taken to be synonymous with solid helium, solid ^{3}He or solid ^{4}He, respectively.

Only a limited amount of experimental work prior to 1967 will be discussed here. However, two comprehensive and predominantly experimentally oriented surveys of the properties of solid helium are available in the works of Dugdale (1965) and Wilks (1967). In addition, much of the subsequent experimental work is discussed in the recent review article of Trickey et al. (1972a).

In contrast to the quantum crystals, the lattice properties of most other simple solids can be obtained from classical mechanics coupled with quantum statistics. It will be assumed in the remainder of this chapter that reference to quantum mechanical effects will refer only to the effect of zero-point energy or to the fact that the dynamics is governed by the Schrödinger equation and will not apply to statistical effects. In the latter regard, the quantum crystals are little different from ordinary crystals.

The symmetry properties of the wavefunction are generally unimportant for topics which will be treated in this chapter. These properties, of course, are quite important when one is interested in the effects of exchange on the nuclear spin system of ^{3}He. The question of exchange is treated in detail in the recent review articles by Guyer (1969b), and Guyer et al. (1971).

As is indicated by the titles of other chapters in these volumes, much recent work in the lattice dynamics of ideal crystals has been concerned with the development and application of the microscopic theory and with the treatment of anharmonic effects. In the case of an ideal Van der Waals solid, the implications of the microscopic theory can be ignored and anharmonic effects then present the leading difficulties.

The development and computational implementation of various self-consistent phonon theories, of perturbative treatments of anharmonic effects and of methods for the proper treatment of the hard-core problem are specialized topics related to anharmonicity which have been the subject of recent activity. One of the uniquely challenging features of the quantum crystal problem is that all of these special topics are important for its solution; in fact, much work in these areas has been specifically motivated by the desire to contribute to the solution of this problem.

Two other unique aspects of the quantum crystals which increase their interest as topics of theoretical study can be observed if one refers to the phase diagrams shown in figs. 1a, 1b. Each of the isotopes exists in all three of the simple phases – bcc, fcc and hcp – and, additionally, a molar volume change of a factor of two can be achieved by the application of experimentally accessible pressures.

The theory of the lattice dynamics of helium will be treated in sections 3, 4 along with various allied topics. Section 4 will consider the details of what are currently the most successful approaches toward this theory. A comparison of the predictions of these theories with experimental results will be given in section 5.

Section 3 will be in large part a review of material which is preparatory for section 4. It will consist of a tutorial introduction to the self-consistent phonon formalism based on the pedagogical example of an atomic linear chain – a system of particles which interact with nearest neighbors only through the one-dimensional analogue of an interatomic potential. This will be followed by a brief discussion of the extension of the one-dimensional results to three dimensions and of the treatment of anharmonicity in conventional lattice dynamics.

The material in section 3 actually forms the basis for the simplest of all theories of the lattice dynamics of quantum crystals – the approach in which one simply takes all of the expressions from the self-consistent harmonic approximation and replaces the hard-core potential with a softened, effective potential. Theories based on this idea will be called effective potential theories.

The organization of the sections represents a somewhat restructured history of the development of the theory of the lattice dynamics of solid helium. One first attempted to obtain a qualitative picture of the behavior of the substance and to understand its essential features. In order to appreciate that this was accomplished considerably before reliable quantitative theoretical results were available, one should read the review by Domb and Dugdale (1957). From today's vantage point, two noteworthy features of this review are the attention called by these authors to the work of Born (1951) and their suggestion that this work could very likely be important for the theory of solid helium. The work referred to was the original theoretical derivation of what was to be rediscovered several years later and termed the self-consistent phonon theory.

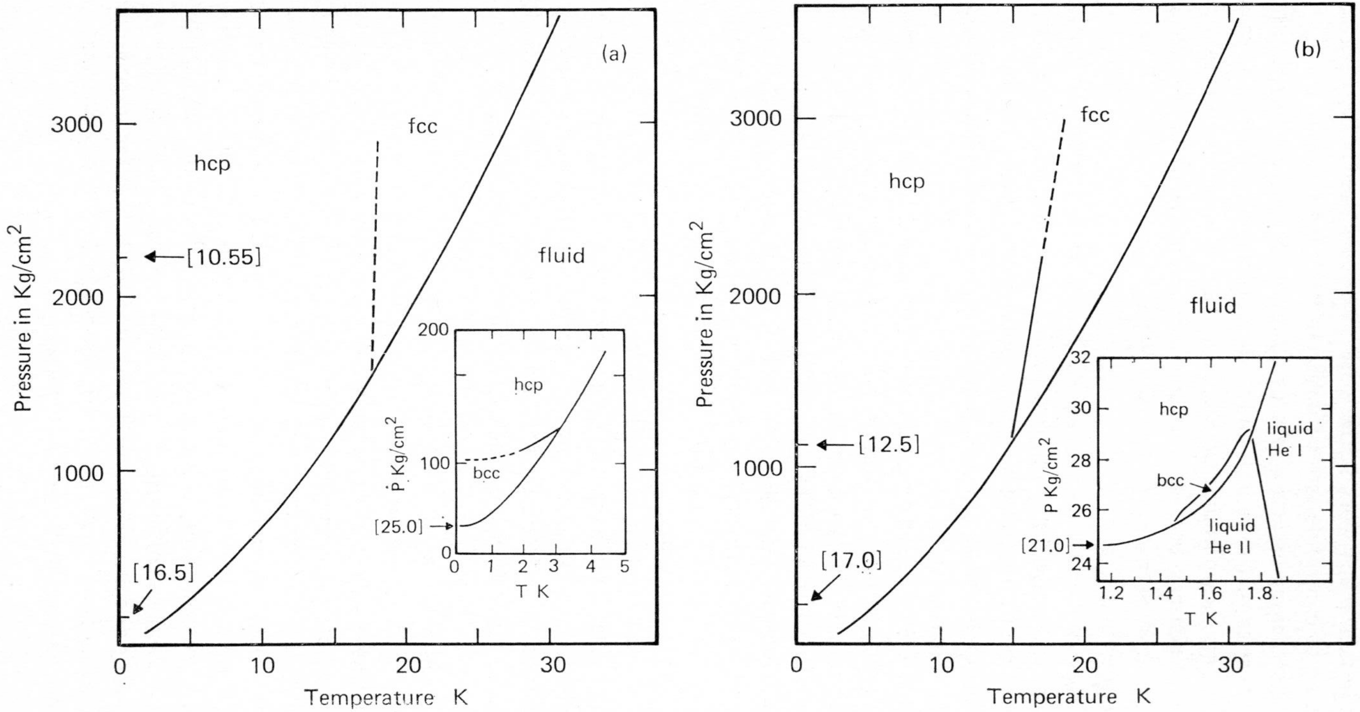

Fig. 1. (a) Phase diagram for ^{4}He. (b) Phase diagram for ^{3}He. Both diagrams are after Dugdale (1965). The numbers in square brackets indicate approximate molar volumes in cc/mole at 0 K as taken from Wilks (1967).

The development of more quantitative theories required both refinement of theoretical concepts and increased capabilities of electronic computers. It was first necessary to devise methods for the calculation of the ground-state or cohesive energy. Next one needed a formalism which, as opposed to the conventional quasi-harmonic approximation, could be validly used for obtaining phonon energies in the quantum crystals. Finally, it was necessary to find a way to account for interactions among phonons – that is, anharmonic effects.

By now, several methods are available by which one can calculate renormalized phonon propagators; these methods are described in subsections 4.3–4.5. However, even after the computational implementation of these anharmonic theories, certain experimental results could not be adequately explained. The resolution of these unexpected, additional difficulties was quick to come as is described in subsections 5.6 and 5.7. Finally, after all of the pieces have been assembled, phonon spectral line shapes in satisfactory agreement with the results of inelastic neutron scattering experiments are now obtained.

This, finally, is the state of the art in the theory of the lattice dynamics of the quantum crystals.

1.2. Terminology and notation

Although the Born–Huang notation will be followed as closely as possible, it is not always a convenient notation for expressions arising in anharmonic perturbation theory and in the non-traditional approaches to lattice dynamics which will be featured in this chapter. Therefore, a few modifications will be introduced as needed. Thus it is convenient, in this introductory section, to describe the notation and to discuss some terminology which will be used. For simplicity, all of the expressions in this chapter will be for the case of one atom per unit cell. The appropriate generalizations which must be made to treat hcp helium can be found in Gillis et al. (1968).

The equilibrium positions of the atoms are at $\boldsymbol{R}(i)$, $i=1, \cdots, N$, where N will always denote the number of atoms in the system. The true positions are at $\boldsymbol{r}(i)$ and $\boldsymbol{u}(i)=\boldsymbol{r}(i)-\boldsymbol{R}(i)$ is the displacement of the ith atom from equilibrium. Then $u_\alpha(i)$ is the α-cartesian component of $\boldsymbol{u}(i)$ and similarly for $\boldsymbol{R}(i)$ and $\boldsymbol{r}(i)$. Differences in vector quantities will be denoted by, for example, $\boldsymbol{r}(ij)=\boldsymbol{r}(i)-\boldsymbol{r}(j)$. The magnitude of $\boldsymbol{R}(ij)$, when i and j are nearest neighbors, will be $R(ij)=R_0$. Gradients will be indicated by $\nabla_\alpha(i)=\partial/\partial r_\alpha(i)$.

The notation for tensors and tensor products will be such that

$$\sum_{\alpha=1}^{3}\sum_{\beta=1}^{3}\sum_{i=1}^{N}\sum_{j=1}^{N} u_\alpha(i)\,\Phi_{\alpha\beta}(ij)\,u_\beta(j) = \sum u_\alpha(i)\,\Phi_{\alpha\beta}(ij)\,u_\beta(j) \tag{1.1a}$$

$$= \sum \boldsymbol{u}(i)\cdot\boldsymbol{\Phi}(ij)\cdot\,\boldsymbol{u}(j) \tag{1.1b}$$

$$= \sum \boldsymbol{u}(1)\cdot\boldsymbol{\Phi}(12)\cdot\boldsymbol{u}(2). \tag{1.1c}$$

Several conventions are implied in the above: a) A modified form of the Einstein summation convention is used in which a summation sign indicates that all repeated indices in the following expression are to be summed over. b) All summations are over the full range of the variable unless the contrary is indicated explicitly. c) Boldface type means that cartesian indices are suppressed. d) A centered dot (·) between two adjacent boldface symbols indicates summation over the appropriate cartesian indices. e) Numerals with superscripts or subscripts (1, 2, 1′, for example) can replace letters (such as i or j) in summations. The sense of this is for i_1 to be replaced by 1. This usage affords a considerable simplification of anharmonic expressions.

Functions of $r(ij)$ or $u(ij)$, such as interatomic potentials, will often be written, for example, as $v(ij)$ rather than $v[r(ij)]$. Thus (ij) will appear in a different sense in $v(ij)$, $r(ij)$ and $\Phi(ij)$. A similar ambiguity is whether $v(ij)$ means $v[r(ij)]$ or $v[u(ij)]$. In general, the precise meaning of such expressions will be clear from the symbols involved and from the context. Whatever slight ambiguity remains is worth tolerating for the avoidance of clumsy expressions.

The energy, usually expressed in dimensionless units, or the frequency of a phonon of wavevector $\boldsymbol{q}$ from the jth branch is given by $\omega_j(\boldsymbol{q})$. The α-cartesian component of the polarization vector $\boldsymbol{e}\binom{\boldsymbol{q}}{j}$ associated with this phonon is $e_\alpha\binom{\boldsymbol{q}}{j}$. In summations over the $\binom{\boldsymbol{q}}{j}$ indices, $\boldsymbol{e}(1)$ and $\omega(1)$ will represent $\boldsymbol{e}\binom{\boldsymbol{q}}{j}$ and $\omega_j(\boldsymbol{q})$, respectively, in analogy with (1.1c).

A notation which will be implicitly introduced in (2.2) and (2.3) will be followed throughout this chapter – a Roman H will always denote a harmonic hamiltonian and a script $\mathscr{H}$ will refer to a true crystal hamiltonian, that is, one in which there is an interatomic rather than a harmonic potential.

In addition to the quantum crystals, other classes of substances will be considered. They will be grouped as follows: Rare gas solids will designate solid Ne, Ar, Kr and Xe collectively, solid hydrogen (or simply hydrogen) will mean solid H_2, D_2 and HD and simple Van der Waals solids will include the rare gas solids, solid hydrogen and the quantum crystals.

There are currently a variety of approaches to the theory of lattice dynamics and it will be necessary to distinguish between them. The traditional quasi-harmonic approximation will be designated by QHA. The self-consistent harmonic approximation SHA will denote a perturbative theory based on an arbitrary harmonic hamiltonian which will have undamped phonon states as eigenstates. The self-consistent phonon approximation SPA will be taken to be very general and to include all of the more modern theories which will be discussed here. In particular, SPA will include theories in which damped phonons are introduced from the start. Thus, QHA is included in SHA and both are included in SPA.

Traditionally, QHA is used to denote a strictly harmonic theory in which the eigenstates are independent phonons. Perturbative corrections which introduce interactions among the phonons are called anharmonic effects. In the quantum crystals, anharmonicity is so important that there is no point in even considering a theory which is strictly harmonic. Therefore, it is useful to use QHA and SHA to designate different approaches to the lowest order of a theory in which the inclusion of anharmonic corrections is tacitly assumed. Anharmonicity will then be taken to mean interaction among phonons or perturbative corrections to a lowest order quantity for any theory.

Many body, variational wavefunctions are used explicitly in several versions of the SPA. The correlated-gaussian CG wavefunction is defined by

$$|0\rangle = C\exp[-\tfrac{1}{2}\textstyle\sum \boldsymbol{u}(i)\cdot\boldsymbol{G}(ij)\cdot\boldsymbol{u}(j)], \tag{1.2}$$

where $\boldsymbol{G}$ is a matrix and C a normalization constant. Although this wavefunction is the ground-state eigenfunction of some harmonic hamiltonian, in practice the $G_{\alpha\beta}(ij)$ are often determined variationally without specific reference to this hamiltonian. The closely related non-correlated gaussian NCG wavefunction is obtained from (1.1) by setting $G_{\alpha\beta}(ij) = A\delta_{\alpha\beta}\delta_{ij}$, where A is a constant. The NCG function is appropriate to an Einstein oscillator model in which each particle is bound to its lattice site by a harmonic force so that the entire frequency spectrum is replaced by a single frequency. This function is also a specialized case of a Hartree-type wavefunction

$$\Phi_{\rm H}[\boldsymbol{r}(1), \cdots, \boldsymbol{r}(N)] = \prod_i \varphi_i[\boldsymbol{u}(i)], \tag{1.3}$$

which in a lattice dynamics application is the product of single particle functions (or orbitals) which restrict each particle to the vicinity of a lattice site. The symbol $|0\rangle$ will always denote a normalized gaussian wavefunction, A will be used for the diagonal element in the exponential of a NCG and the notation for the Hartree wavefunction Φ_H will be as shown in (1.3). Another important function, the Jastrow-function, will be introduced in section 4.

2. Qualitative theories

2.1. Introduction

Broadly speaking, there are two levels of complexity at which one can approach the theory of the lattice dynamics of the quantum crystals. Initially one attempts to gain a qualitative understanding of their behavior by making intuitive generalizations of results from conventional lattice dynamics. Next one attempts to obtain quantitative results from a first principles theory. The latter approaches are analytically and numerically complex so that too rapid an exposure to them can easily obscure the essential physics. Consequently, a discussion of these theories will be postponed until section 4 and the necessary background will be presented in this section.

Selected experimental results for the quantum crystals and the simple theoretical interpretation of these results will be emphasized here. The qualitative theories are useful mainly for the interpretation of thermal data. The results of some experiments, especially inelastic neutron scattering experiments, are essentially quantitative and must be compared with the quantitative theories of section 4. This comparison will be made in section 5.

2.2. Law of corresponding states

An instructive and historically meaningful way to approach the quantum crystals is to follow De Boer (1957) and consider them as the limiting case of the system of simple Van der Waals solids. He was interested in obtaining a quantum-mechanical extension of the classical law of corresponding states. Briefly, this law implies that appropriately reduced thermodynamical quantities, expressed in reduced units, for a class of substances are all the same provided: a) The potential energy due to the intermolecular forces in the lth substance can be written as a sum of pair interactions $V_l(ij)$. b) For each substance there exists an energy unit ε and a distance unit σ such that $V_l(r/\sigma_l)/\varepsilon_l = v(r)$, where $v(r)$ is independent of l. Note that r is used here to denote both the true distance and the distance in reduced units. Since reduced units will be used in all expressions which are not explicitly dimensioned, this should lead to no confusion.

An example of such a system is what will be called the Lennard–Jones solids – substances in which the two-body potential is the Lennard–Jones (12–6) potential

$$v(r) = 4\varepsilon\left[(\sigma/r)^{12} - (\sigma/r)^{6}\right], \tag{2.1}$$

which is shown as the solid curve of fig. 2a. This potential has a zero at $r=\sigma$ and a minimum of $-\varepsilon$ at $r=2^{1/6}\sigma$. For helium, the values $\varepsilon=10.22$ K

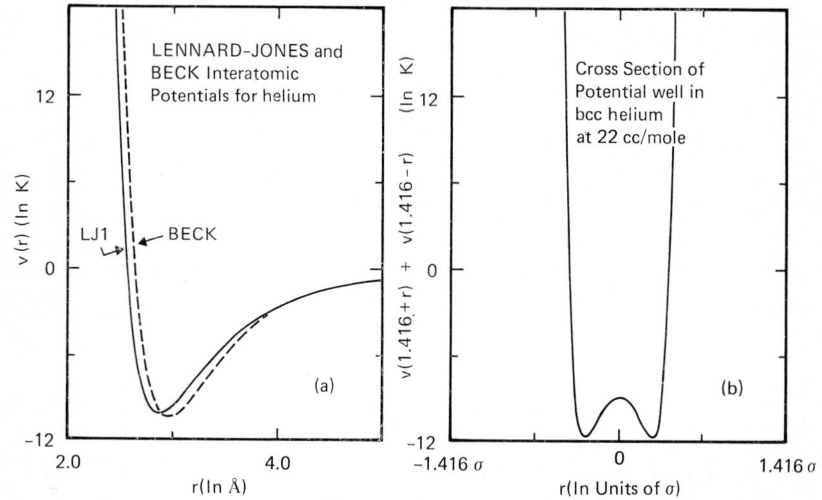

Fig. 2. (a) The Lennard–Jones potential LJ1 with the most commonly used parameters $\varepsilon = 10.22$K, $\sigma = 2.556$ Å is shown by the solid curve. The dashed curve is the Beck (1968) potential. (b) The potential well seen by a helium atom located at the center of the plot due to two neighbors located at the edges. The LJ1 potential is used and the nearest-neighbor distance 1.416 σ corresponds to bcc He at 22.0 cc/mole.

and $\sigma=2.556$ Å have been used extensively, although we will see in section 5.1 that another choice of σ gives better values for the ground-state properties of the solid.

Until recently, the bulk of the theoretical work on the simple Van der Waals solids has used the Lennard–Jones potential and its use will be assumed in all numerical work discussed in this chapter unless the contrary is indicated. Even though this potential is obviously too simple to be entirely correct, its extensive use in the past was entirely justifiable for several reasons: a) It is analytically simple. b) It has the essential features of an intermolecular potential between spherically symmetric molecules – a steeply rising short-range repulsive part or hard core, an attractive potential well with a minimum only slightly beyond the hard-core region, and a long-range attractive part which falls off like $1/r^6$. c) The use of a common potential in calculations facilitates comparison between various theoretical results. d) It is only recently that calculations of the properties of solids and liquids have become accurate enough to be very sensitive to the precise form of the potential. e) It has the right dependence on ε and σ for the application of the idea of corresponding states.

The extension of the law of corresponding states to a quantum lattice dynamics system becomes apparent if the hamiltonian for the crystal is written in units of ε and σ as

$$\mathscr{H} = \tfrac{1}{2}\lambda^2 \sum \nabla^2(i) + \tfrac{1}{2} \sum_{i \neq j} v(ij), \tag{2.2}$$

where $\mathscr{H}$ =(true hamiltonian)/ε and $\lambda^2 = \hbar^2/(m\sigma^2\varepsilon)$. This definition of the quantum parameter λ differs from De Boer's by a factor of 2π.

In this form, $\mathscr{H}$ defines a family of hamiltonians which depend on the parameter λ. Certain selected solids from among this family corresponding to particular values of λ are then models for the simple Van der Waals solids. Representative values of λ for these solids are given in table 1. Other values are found in the literature, but these are adequate here.

TABLE 1

Lennard–Jones parameters[a], experimental ground-state energy[b] $E_0(\text{exp})$, and theoretical ground-state energy[c] $E_0(\text{NS})$ for the rare gas solids and the quantum crystals.

	λ	ε	σ	$E_0(\text{exp})$	$E_0(\text{NS})$
^{3}He	0.492	10.22	2.556	−1.0	18.7
^{4}He	0.426	10.22	2.556	−5.5	7.24
Ne	0.0911	35.9	2.831	−22.6	−21.7
Ar	0.0293	122	3.400	−93.1	−93.6
Kr	0.0164	165	3.604	−130	−132
Xe	0.0102	230	3.920	−193	−193

a. From Zucker (1961).

b. From Pandorf and Edwards (1968) for bcc ^{3}He at 23.5 cc/mole. As quoted in Wilks (1967) for hcp ^{4}He at 20.8 cc/mole. The remaining data are those used by Nosanow and Shaw (1962) and are obsolete by now, but are valid for the comparison here.

c. From the Nosanow and Shaw (1962) variational calculation with the optimum spherically symmetric Hartree wavefunction. Their results are for bcc ^{3}He at 23.5 cc/mole and fcc ^{4}He at 20.8 cc/mole. The latter is contrasted with experimental results on the fcc phase, but this makes little difference.

It is clear that the importance of zero-point energy in the model system depends on the value of λ; $\lambda \to 0$ turns off the kinetic energy operator and the system becomes completely classical. The philosophy of the quantum-mechanical law of corresponding states is simply that the properties of the systems represented by the hamiltonian of (2.2) will be smoothly varying functions of λ.

One example can be quite easily demonstrated. The harmonic approximation to $\mathscr{H}$ is

$$\mathrm{H} = \tfrac{1}{2}\lambda^2 \sum \nabla(i)^2 + V_0 + \tfrac{1}{2} \sum \boldsymbol{u}(i) \cdot \boldsymbol{\Phi}(ij) \cdot \boldsymbol{u}(j), \tag{2.3}$$

where

$$\Phi_{\alpha\beta}(ij) = \nabla_\alpha(i)\, \nabla_\beta(j)\, V\big|_{\text{equil}}, \tag{2.4}$$

$$V_0 = V\big|_{\text{equil}}, \tag{2.5}$$

$$V = \tfrac{1}{2} \sum_{i \neq j} v(ij), \tag{2.6}$$

and $|_{\text{equil}}$ means the expression is to be evaluated in the equilibrium configuration: all $\boldsymbol{u}(i) = 0$.

The ground-state energy of H is $E_0 = V_0 + \frac{1}{2} \sum \omega_j(\boldsymbol{q})$. The squares of the phonon frequencies are obtained from

$$\sum_\beta \boldsymbol{D}_{\alpha\beta}(\boldsymbol{q})\, e_\beta \begin{pmatrix} \boldsymbol{q} \\ j \end{pmatrix} = e_\alpha \begin{pmatrix} \boldsymbol{q} \\ j \end{pmatrix} \omega_j(\boldsymbol{q})^2, \tag{2.7}$$

with the dynamical matrix $\boldsymbol{D}$ given by

$$D_{\alpha\beta}(\boldsymbol{q}) = (\lambda^2/N) \sum \Phi_{\alpha\beta}(ij) \exp[\mathrm{i}\boldsymbol{q} \cdot \boldsymbol{R}(ij)]. \tag{2.8}$$

It is clear that, at constant volume, the force-constant matrix $\boldsymbol{\Phi}$ is independent of λ and the frequencies are proportional to λ. Therefore, if the harmonic approximation were strictly correct, one would find $E_0(\lambda) = V_0 + c\lambda$, where c is a constant.

Two effects change this simple picture. First of all, the leading anharmonic corrections are readily shown to be strictly proportional to λ^2 and higher order terms can be grouped to make explicit contributions to cubic and higher powers of λ. Second, the kinetic energy or zero-point energy has an effect which is similar to that of an internal pressure and the crystal expands as λ increases. This changes the value of V_0, of the $\boldsymbol{\Phi}(ij)$ and of the coefficients which enter into the anharmonic contributions. Nevertheless, since the total range of λ values for the simple Van der Waals crystals is only $0 < \lambda < 0.5$, one could hope that the properties of the crystals could be represented by a low order power series in λ in which the leading terms would dominate throughout the entire range. The power series representation is of course phenomenological for the Van der Waals solids, but should be mathematically accurate for the analytical system, the Lennard–Jones solids.

The four graphs shown in fig. 3a–d illustrate the systematic variation of certain reduced thermodynamic quantities with the quantum parameter λ at 0 K. The pressure was the minimum required to produce a solid for the quantum crystals and zero for the remaining substances. These graphs are quite similar to those originally shown by De Boer (1957) except for the altered definition of the quantum parameter and the use, for some points, of slightly different Lennard–Jones parameters or experimental data. Even though the points obviously do not fall exactly on a smooth curve, the systematic behavior with λ is quite clear; in fact, it was used by De Boer and Lunbeck (1948) to predict the critical temperature of ^{3}He before experimental measurements were performed.

The second derivative of the Lennard–Jones potential vanishes at $r = 1.24\sigma$. A nearest-neighbor distance of this magnitude corresponds to a reduced specific volume of 1.48 or $1.46\sigma^3$/atom for the bcc or fcc–hcp phases respectively. From fig. 3c this is seen to correspond to a λ value of approximately 0.28. Beyond this density and presumably for larger values of λ, the force constant matrix of (2.4) is no longer positive definite, some or all of the frequencies determined from (2.7) are imaginary and QHA is no longer valid.

The physical picture is even clearer with reference to fig. 2b. Here is shown a cross section of the potential well seen by one helium atom due to contributions to the crystal potential from diametrically opposite nearest-neighbors. In the plot, the two neighbors would be located at the right and left-hand ends of the horizontal axis. The nearest-neighbor distance is $R_0 = 1.416\sigma$ which corresponds to bcc He at 22.0 cc/mole. In this density regime (in fact, for molar volumes $\gtrsim 12.5$ cc/mole) each atom sits in a classically unstable position where the potential has negative curvature. It has been shown by De Wette and Nijboer (1965) that, as one might expect, the frequencies as obtained from QHA are imaginary throughout the entire Brillouin zone when the solid is more than marginally within the classically unstable density range.

The fact that none of the graphs of fig. 3 show the slightest evidence of discontinuous behavior at this λ value is experimental evidence that a different theory is needed. The over-all smooth behavior indicates that the quantum crystals are quite similar to other solids even if they are more

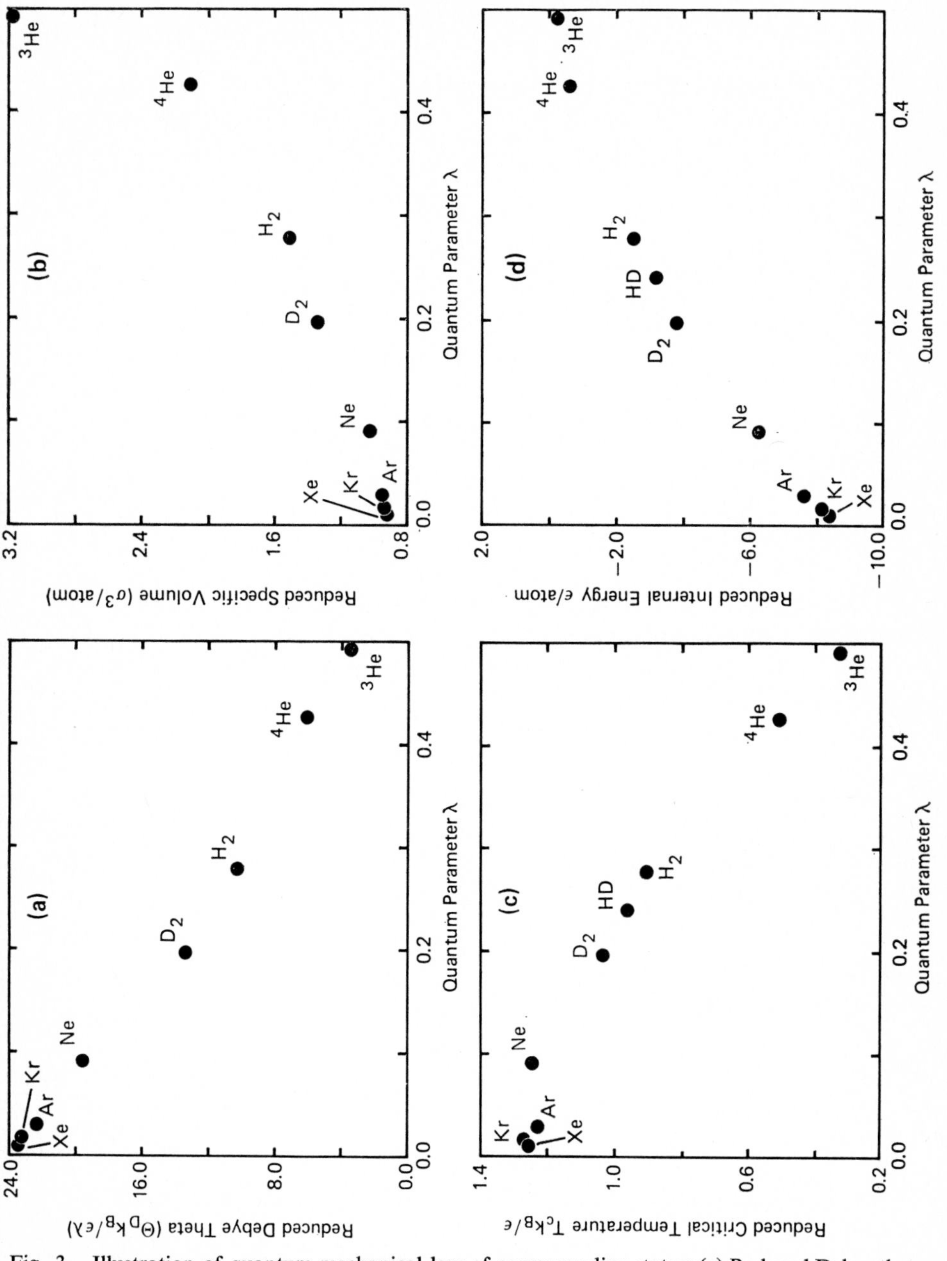

Fig. 3. Illustration of quantum-mechanical law of corresponding states: (a) Reduced Debye theta, (b) reduced specific volume, (c) reduced critical temperature, (d) reduced internal energy, all as a function of the quantum parameter λ. The λ values are obtained from the Lennard–Jones parameters of Zucker (1961). The experimental data are taken from Wilks (1967), Zucker (1961), De Boer (1957), and London (1954). More modern data is available, but these are adequate for this qualitative purpose.

difficult to treat analytically. In section 4 we will find that the frequencies in the quantum solids can be determined from formulas which are qualitatively similar to (2.7) and (2.8) but with a generalized definition of the force constants.

2.3. High-temperature Debye theta

A good example of a situation in which the basic physical ideas of conventional lattice dynamics are found to be sound, although the conventional QHA theory does not work, is the calculation of the high-temperature Debye theta θ_∞ for ^{4}He given by Domb and Dugdale (1957). According to QHA one should have

$$\theta_\infty = 0.41 \frac{h}{k_B}\left[\frac{1}{mN}\frac{d^2V_0(R_0)}{dR_0^2}\right]^{1/2}. \tag{2.9}$$

Here, $V_0(R_0)/N$ is the static lattice energy per particle as in (2.5). If one uses the Lennard–Jones potential to calculate $V_0(R_0)$, the dotted line curve in fig. 4 is obtained. The experimental values are given by the solid curve.

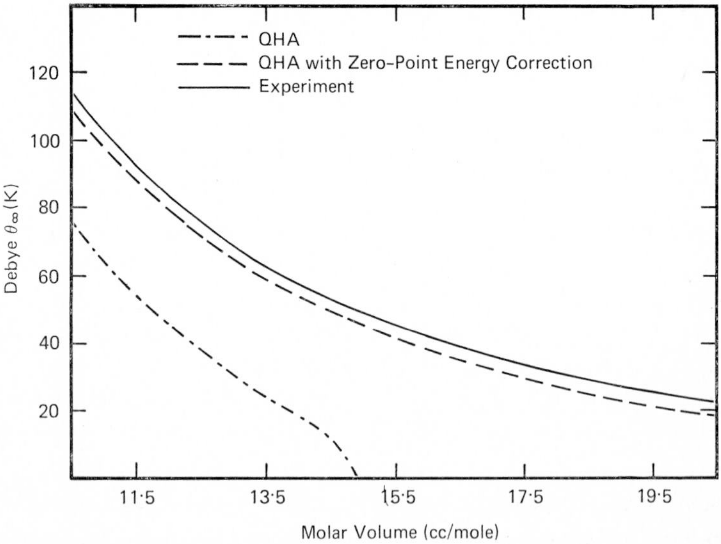

Fig. 4. The high-temperature Debye θ of solid ^{4}He as a function of molar volume after Domb and Dugdale (1957). The dot-dash curve is according to an expression derived from the quasi-harmonic approximation. The dashed curve has a correction for zero-point energy added and the solid curve shows the experimental values.

There is clearly a serious discrepancy between the two curves and the inadequacy of QHA beyond the inflection point in the potential is again demonstrated as it is obvious in (2.9) that $\theta_\infty = 0$ when the second derivative of the static lattice energy vanishes. This essentially where the second derivative of the potential is zero.

In ^{4}He, the zero-point energy is as important as the potential energy. If one follows the suggestion of Domb and Salter (1952) for expressing the zero-point energy in terms of θ_∞ and then adds the result to $V_0(R_0)$, (2.9) becomes

$$\theta_\infty = 0.41 \frac{h}{k_B} \left[\frac{1}{mN} \frac{d^2 V_0(R_0)}{dR_0^2} + \frac{9}{8} \frac{k_B}{m} \frac{d^2 \theta_\infty}{dR_0^2} \right]^{1/2} . \tag{2.10}$$

The derivative of θ_∞ on the right-hand side of (2.10) can be estimated from the experimental values of the Grüneisen parameter $\gamma = -V(\partial \ln \theta_\infty)/\partial V$. When this estimate is used to evaluate (2.10), the dashed curve in fig. 4 results. Thus, the 'true' potential which the particles see in a classical sense is the interatomic potential and the volume dependent zero-point energy. The expanded lattice is stabilized by the latter.

2.4. Specific heat anomalies

Other experiments which reveal unusual behavior in the quantum crystals are the specific heat measurements of Sample and Swenson (1967) for bcc He which are shown in fig. 5. Later results of Pandorf and Edwards (1968) are not shown, but are in excellent agreement with these. Note that the curves for ^{3}He are unusually low both at the lower and higher temperatures. This is the equivalent of excess heat capacity in these temperature regimes. These are called the two specific heat anomalies of solid ^{3}He.

An analysis of the high-temperature anomaly has been performed by De Wette and Werthamer (1969). This anomaly has generally been attributed to vacancies; however, a recent study by Guyer (1972a) indicates that vacancy contributions can account for at most 20% of the excess specific heat. The subject of vacancies in solid He is currently an interesting area of research. It has been suggested by Hetherington (1968) that vacancy waves should exist in the quantum crystals, as spin waves do in magnetic materials, and the implications of the existence of such waves has been investigated theoretically in several papers. However, the subject will not be treated further here and appropriate references may be found in Guyer et al. (1971), and Guyer (1972b).

The low-temperature specific heat anomaly is still a subject of some

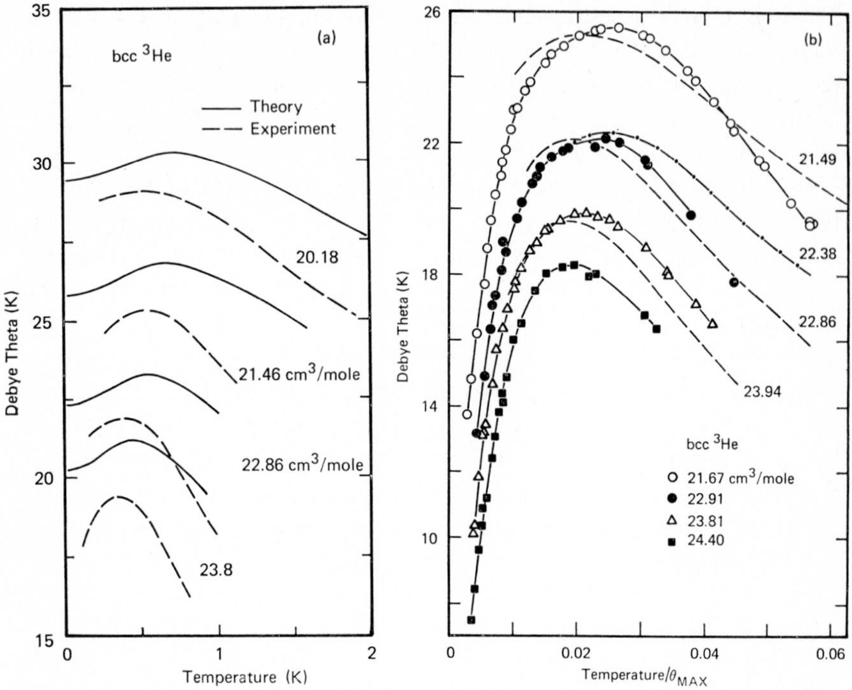

Fig. 5. Low-temperature specific heat anomaly in bcc ^{3}He. (a) The dashed lines show the experimental results of Sample and Swenson (1967); the results of a later experiment by Pandorf and Edwards (1968) are not shown here but are in excellent agreement with these. The solid lines are from the calculation of Horner (1972a). Earlier results by Horner (1970c) are similar is shape to these, but differ somewhat in magnitude. (b) The points are the experimental results of Castles et al. (1972). Also plotted are the results of Sample and Swenson (dashed curves) and Pandorf and Edwards (dot-dash curve).

controversy. References to complementary experimental evidence which supports the existence of this anomaly can be found in Guyer (1972a). An explanation of the anomaly in terms of interactions among the nuclear spins was proposed by Varma (1970); this explanation has been subsequently criticized by Guyer (1970). The possibility that the anomaly could result from lattice dynamics effects was noted by Henriksen et al. (1969). The precise way in which this possibility can be realized is: If one phonon branch is unusually low-lying it will dominate the specific heat at low temperature. If, in addition, it has upward dispersion as opposed to the normal downward dispersion, it will give rise to a specific heat in excess of the dispersionless Debye model. That this is indeed a possibility will be discussed in section 5.4.

3. *Self-consistent phonon theory and anharmonicity*

3.1. One-dimensional example

As will be seen in section 4, many of the calculations of the properties of solid helium have used theories which are either extensions of the SHA or are most readily understood in the context of the SHA. This approach leads very naturally to the introduction of phonons and provides a straightforward, lowest-order theory of the lattice dynamics of the quantum crystals.

Unfortunately, the implicit nature of the self-consistent phonon method obscures some of the important physical results because of the extensive calculations required to obtain them. However, there is one problem in which the self-consistent equations can be expressed in a simple, closed form that still contains most of the crucial dynamical aspects of the solid helium case: the atomic linear chain.

This one-dimensional problem is interesting historically: it was the model for which calculations were performed by Hooton (1955a, b) in the first numerical application of the self-consistent technique and, appropriately, the specific system he had in mind was solid helium. However, he used a truncated Taylor series expansion of the potential and his treatment did not bring out the methods which are currently used for the evaluation of ground state or ensemble averages of the potential and its derivatives.

The first more modern calculation by Koehler (1965) using the SHA also treated a linear chain, but did elucidate these techniques. Since the latter calculation can be performed entirely by hand and requires very little numerical effort beyond that which is well documented in the standard textbook example of the harmonic linear chain, it provides an appropriate, useful and simple introduction to the essential features of a complete three-dimensional self-consistent phonon theory calculation.

The first part of this section will be devoted to the linear chain at 0 K. The notation which will be used is readily extended to the treatment of a three-dimensional crystal and this will be done in the second part of this section. The restriction to 0 K is not important for this model; however, it simplifies the work somewhat and the proper extension of the 0 K self-consistent phonon theory is discussed in other chapters of this volume. The one-dimensional SHA theory has also been treated by Siklós (1971). This author has been associated with a large amount of work in the general area of self-consistent phonon theories; the references can be obtained from the paper just cited.

The hamiltonian for the atomic linear chain can be written as

$$\mathscr{H} = -\tfrac{1}{2}\lambda^2 \sum \nabla^2(i) + \sum v[r(i+1) - r(i)]. \tag{3.1}$$

This is the one-dimensional analogue of (2.2) with the additional restriction of nearest-neighbor interactions only. Periodic boundary conditions are used so that $u(i+N)=u(i)$. The notation is an obvious one-dimensional version of that described in section 1.2.

Even though the linear chain is a fairly simple physical system, the eigenvectors and eigenvalues of (3.1) cannot be found exactly even by brute-force numerical methods. However, those of a closely related hamiltonian

$$\mathrm{H} = -\tfrac{1}{2}\lambda^2 \sum \nabla^2(i) + V_0 + \tfrac{1}{2}\Omega^2 \sum [u(i+1) - u(i)]^2, \tag{3.2}$$

the harmonic linear chain, are so well known that the study of the properties of (3.2) generally constitutes the first step in a text-book introduction to phonons. Despite the fact that the diagonalization of H is a standard problem, it will be reviewed here in order to provide an introduction to the less conventional treatment which will follow and to establish the notation.

The canonical transformations

$$p(i) = -i\nabla(i) = (1/\sqrt{N}) \sum_q \exp[-iqR(i)]\, P(q), \tag{3.3}$$

and

$$u(i) = (1/\sqrt{N}) \sum_q \exp[iqR(i)]\, Q(q) \tag{3.4}$$

can be used to transform H into

$$\mathrm{H} = -\tfrac{1}{2}\lambda^2 \sum |P(q)|^2 + \tfrac{1}{2} \sum [2\Omega \sin(\tfrac{1}{2}q)]^2 \, |Q(q)|^2 + V_0, \tag{3.5}$$

the appropriate form for a now independent set of harmonic oscillators whose frequencies are

$$\omega(q) = 2\Omega\lambda \sin(\tfrac{1}{2}q). \tag{3.6}$$

The allowed values of q are obtained from the cyclic boundary conditions as $q=2\pi n/N$, $n=1, 2, \cdots, N$.

Since the oscillators are independent, the phonon contribution to the ground state energy is $\tfrac{1}{2}\sum \omega(q)$. The indicated sum can be performed exactly and one can show that

$$\lim_{N\to\infty} \tfrac{1}{2} \sum \omega(q) = (2/\pi)\, \Omega\lambda N. \tag{3.7}$$

Thus the ground state energy per particle is

$$E_0 = V_0/N + (2/\pi)\, \Omega\lambda. \tag{3.8}$$

It is clear that, if Ω is determined according to QHA as $\Omega^2 = \nabla\nabla v(R_0)$, it will be imaginary when the second derivative of the potential is negative. Then (3.8) is no longer physically meaningful. This is the situation which prevails for the quantum crystals, as has been illustrated in fig. 2b.

Nevertheless, it might still be appropriate to model the crystal hamiltonian for the quantum crystals by a soluble harmonic hamiltonian. First of all, simply because a soluble model generally provides a useful starting point, and, secondly, the results of inelastic neutron scattering experiments show that phonons are a physical reality in solid helium. Therefore a harmonic model, other than QHA, which automatically includes phonons is physically reasonable. The foregoing line of reasoning leads one to consider H not as given by QHA but simply as a model for $\mathscr{H}$ with the parameters of the model, the force constants, to be determined in some appropriate way. A variational determination is the most obvious choice and certain properties of the CG wavefunction will be explored in (3.9)–(3.18) in preparation for a subsequent variational calculation.

In the traditional approach to lattice dynamics calculations, the ground-state energy is taken to be that of the model harmonic hamiltonian; however, in a variational calculation, it is determined from the expectation value of $\mathscr{H}$. It is in the evaluation of this expectation value that the SPA theories make a significant departure from the QHA treatment and we will discuss the contrasting methods after first noting that the expectation value of the kinetic energy operator can be obtained quite easily and is not of immediate concern.

In QHA, the quantity $\langle 0|\, V\,|0\rangle$ is never really evaluated. The procedure to do so is well defined, however, and is outlined briefly in the following. The potential is first expanded in a Taylor series in the $u(i)$ and all of the terms are retained. The $u(i)$ are then transformed into $P(q)$ and $Q(q)$ by (3.3) and (3.4). These in turn are transformed into creation and annihilation operators‡, which increases the number of terms considerably. After this, the expectation value of each term may be obtained using the known properties of the operators and the final result is then gotten by adding all of the individual contributions. Since atomic potentials are singular, or very nearly so, the contribution from higher order terms may actually be divergent and arguments to avoid this difficulty add another complication to the procedure.

‡ Since second quantization will not be needed elsewhere in this chapter, we do not wish to formally introduce creation and annihilation operators. This topic is adequately treated in, for example, March et al. (1967) or Kittel (1963).

Fortunately, the process described above is unnecessary; it is merely an alternative way of performing a calculation which is most readily done directly in coordinate space. There, the contribution to $\langle 0| V |0\rangle$ from $\langle 0| v(ij) |0\rangle$ can be obtained if one first integrates the square of the ground-state wavefunction over all coordinates but i and j and then performs the integrals over these variables numerically. As a preliminary step to doing these integrals, we recognize that the ground-state eigenfunction of H is

$$|0\rangle = C \exp[-\tfrac{1}{2}Q(q)\,\omega(q)\,Q^*(q)], \tag{3.9}$$

where this form is identifiable as the product of the ground-state wavefunctions of each of the independent oscillators in (3.5). If one performs the summation on q in (3.9), a CG function as defined in (1.2) results with

$$G(ij) = (1/N) \sum \omega(q) \exp[iqR(ij)], \tag{3.10}$$

and this constitutes a derivation of (1.2) for the one-dimensional case. The sum indicated in (3.10) can be performed exactly and the result is given in Koehler (1966a). However, an approximate form

$$G(ij) \approx (4\Omega/\lambda\pi)\,\{1 - 4[R(ij)/NR_0]^2\}^{-2}, \quad |R(ij)|/NR_0 \ll 1, \tag{3.11}$$

valid for large N, is all that is required here.

The expectation value of $\mathscr{H}$ with respect to $|0\rangle$ is now readily evaluated as a preliminary to the variational calculation. The result is

$$\mathscr{E}_0 \equiv \langle 0| \mathscr{H} |0\rangle = \tfrac{1}{4}\lambda^2 NG(11) + N\langle 0| v(12) |0\rangle, \tag{3.12}$$

where symmetry has been used to rewrite the last term as $N\times$ (a single term involving particles 1 and 2 only). Also, it is clear from (3.11) that $G(ij)$ depends only on $R(ij)$ so that $NG(11)$ is an alternative way of writing tr $G \equiv \text{trace}(G)$.

It is now convenient to define the harmonic pair function $g(12)$ such that

$$\langle 0| v(12) |0\rangle = \int g(12)\, v(12)\, \mathrm{d}u(12), \tag{3.13}$$

where, obviously,

$$g(12) = C \int \exp[-\tfrac{1}{2}\sum u(i)\, G(ij)\, u(j)] \times \mathrm{d}[u(1) + u(2)]\, \mathrm{d}u(3), \cdots, \mathrm{d}u(N). \tag{3.14}$$

Once the pair function is found, the integral required to evaluate the rhs of (3.12) can be evaluated by standard numerical methods. The fact that the many-body integral of (3.14) can be performed with reasonable simplicity even in the three-dimensional, finite-temperature version of the theory is a key factor in the numerical application of the SHA theory. In the example under consideration here, the integral can be evaluated without performing any actual integration, an analytical simplification which makes this a particularly instructive example. The evaluation is accomplished as follows: First, one uses H instead of $\mathscr{H}$ in (3.12) to obtain

$$E_0 = \tfrac{1}{4}N\lambda^2 G(11) + V_0 + \tfrac{1}{2}\Omega^2 \int g(12)\, u(12)^2\, \mathrm{d}u(12). \qquad (3.15)$$

In the harmonic oscillator problem, the kinetic and potential energy contributions (excluding V_0) to E_0 are known to be equal; thus each dynamical contribution to the rhs of (3.15) must equal $\frac{1}{4}\sum \omega(q)$. Accordingly, $G(11)= =4\Omega/\pi\lambda$, as obtained before, and the term involving the integral must equal $\Omega\lambda/\pi$.

This integral can be evaluated in two ways and each of the methods is instructive. In one approach, we note that the wave-function $|0\rangle$ is a CG function and that integrals involving products of CG functions and polynomials can be evaluated quite readily. The techniques, which are discussed in Koehler (1968), can be used to obtain the result

$$\langle 0|\, u^2(12)\, |0\rangle = \tfrac{1}{2}[G^{-1}(11) - G^{-1}(12)], \qquad (3.16)$$

where $G^{-1}(ij)$ is the (ij) component of G^{-1}. This is the approach that is used to obtain the expressions which must be evaluated numerically in a three-dimensional calculation. Although it is not needed here, an analytic expression for the rhs of (3.16) may be found in Koehler (1966a).

In the other approach, we note that the integrals required to obtain $g(12)$ directly from (3.14) can be performed one at a time by completing the square in the exponent and evaluating the resulting gaussian integral over one variable. It is an easy matter to show that each successive integration retains the functional form of a CG, but with a modified matrix G' connecting the coordinates which have not been integrated out. The original matrix has the property $\sum_i G(ij)=0$, which is a consequence of the translational invariance of H. It can also be shown that G' has the same property, where the sum is restricted to only the remaining coordinates. This piecewise integration is impossible to carry out for a chain with even moderately large N. However, these considerations show that the final functional form of $g(12)$ must be a correlated gaussian which depends only on $u(12)$. Thus it can be written as

$$g(12) = [2/\pi\Lambda(12)]^{1/2} \exp[-u^2(12)/\Lambda(12)]. \tag{3.17}$$

The integral in (3.15) can now be evaluated analytically and the result equated to $\frac{1}{4}\sum \omega(q)$ to give

$$\Lambda(12) = 4\lambda/\pi\Omega. \tag{3.18}$$

Now, (3.12) can be rewritten more explicitly to give

$$\mathscr{E}_0/N = (\Omega\lambda/\pi) + \tfrac{1}{2}(\Omega/\lambda)^{1/2} \int \exp[-(\pi\Omega/4\lambda)\, u^2(12)]\, v(12)\, \mathrm{d}u(12). \tag{3.19}$$

The minimization of $\mathscr{E}_0$ with respect to Ω can be carried out analytically and the result $\partial\mathscr{E}_0/\partial\Omega = 0$, if

$$\Omega^2 = \int g(12) \frac{\mathrm{d}^2 v(12)}{\mathrm{d}u^2(12)}\, \mathrm{d}u(12), \tag{3.20}$$

is obtained after some algebraic manipulation. This is a special version of the self-consistent equation, but it shows the essential contrast between the SHA and the QHA: the force constants are the ground-state average of the second derivative of the potential rather than the equilibrium value. The self-consistency arises because Ω is involved explicitly on the lhs and implicitly on the rhs of (3.20).

An additional point that can be obtained from this analysis is especially meaningful in the case of solid helium. Consider the NCG function described in subsection 1.2 as an alternative trial wavefunction to the CG. In this case, the pair function is readily found to be

$$g(12) = (A/2\pi)^{1/2} \exp[-\tfrac{1}{2}Au^2(12)]. \tag{3.21}$$

Since the pair function for the three-dimensional NCG wavefunction (or for any Hartree wavefunction) is also easily found, this wavefunction is an attractive alternative to the CG as a variational wavefunction.

A comparison of the NCG with the CG can be made as follows: The expression for the ground-state energy with NCG is

$$\mathscr{E}_0(\mathrm{NCG})/N = \tfrac{1}{4}\lambda^2 A + (A/2\pi)^{1/2} \exp[-\tfrac{1}{2}Au^2(12)]\, v(12)\, \mathrm{d}u(12). \tag{3.22}$$

Suppose that a value of A has been found which minimizes $\mathscr{E}_0$(NCG). Now, one can use the CG wavefunction and simply set $\Omega = 2\lambda A/\pi$ rather than determine Ω variationally. The contributions to the potential energy in each case are then identically equal, but for the kinetic energy,

$$K(\text{CG}) = 2\lambda^2 A/\pi^2 = (8/\pi^2)\, K(\text{NCG}) \approx 0.81\, K(\text{NCG}), \tag{3.23}$$

where K(CG) from (3.19) has been expressed in terms of A. Thus, $\mathscr{E}_0$(CG) is always lower than $\mathscr{E}_0$(NCG) by approximately 20% of K(NCG).

In an actual numerical calculation, $\mathscr{E}_0$(CG) is minimized with respect to Ω; the resulting energy improvement is somewhat (but not much) greater than found above and is proportioned almost equally between an improvement in kinetic and potential energies. Thus, Ω as determined from (3.20) is about 10% larger than $2\lambda A/\pi$.

In this simple example, the change in ground-state energy from the use of a correlated wavefunction has been related to a percentage decrease in kinetic energy. This is a useful artifice because it enables us to immediately see two reasons for the importance of a correlated wavefunction in the treatment of the quantum crystals. First, the kinetic energy is large so a fixed percentage reduction will be larger in magnitude than for other substances. Second, because of the near cancellation between kinetic and potential energy contributions, the percentage reduction in the ground-state energy will be even larger. The perspective on the proper treatment of correlations will be sharpened in section 4 when attention is focused on the hard-core problem.

The foregoing can be applied to a simple, but instructive, numerical example if one uses a Morse potential

$$v(r) = \exp[-2c(r - r_{\text{m}})] - 2\exp[-c(r - r_{\text{m}})] \tag{3.24}$$

in (3.1). With this potential, exactly integrable expressions are obtained. This feature was also noted by Siklós (1971). If $r_{\text{m}} = 2^{1/6}$ and $c = (\ln 2)/(2^{1/6} - 1)$, the minimum and zero in the potential occur at the same place as in the Lennard–Jones potential and the depth of the minimum is the same. These values will be used in the numerical work. A more detailed account of the analytical and numerical application of the SHA theory to the atomic linear chain has recently been given in Koehler (1973a). Here, the numerical results will be presented without any elaboration.

The values of the ground-state energy per particle and the optimum nearest-neighbor distance as obtained from the numerical solution of (3.19), (3.20) are shown in figs. 6a, 6b. The dependence on R_0 is implicit and results from the definition of the $u(i)$. Also shown are the results of the QHA treatment of the same system. In each case there is an upper limit to the λ values for which stable solutions can be found. The limit is indicated by the termination of the curves. In QHA, it is almost the value at which $v''(R_0)=0$. In SHA, it is the value at which simultaneous solutions of (3.19), (3.20) do not exist.

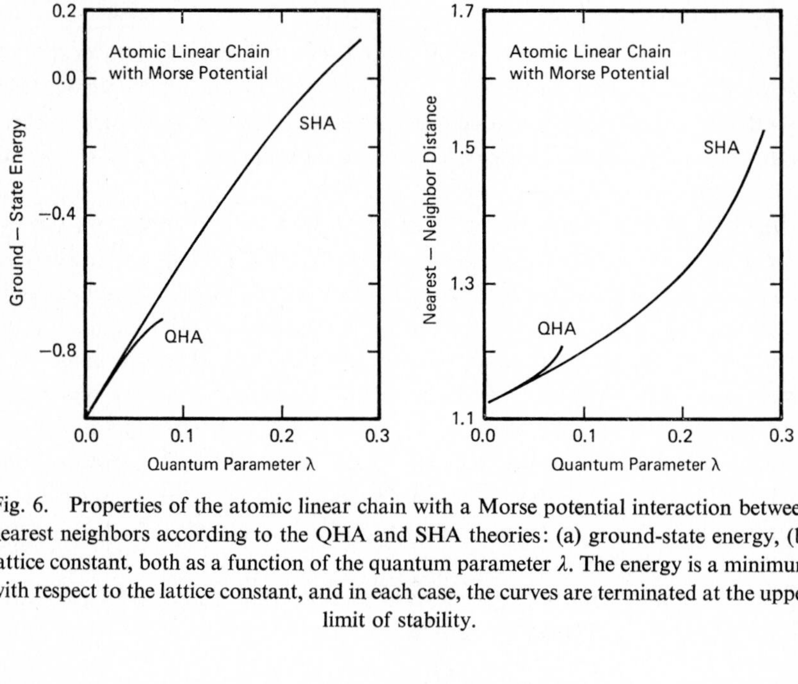

Fig. 6. Properties of the atomic linear chain with a Morse potential interaction between nearest neighbors according to the QHA and SHA theories: (a) ground-state energy, (b) lattice constant, both as a function of the quantum parameter λ. The energy is a minimum with respect to the lattice constant, and in each case, the curves are terminated at the upper limit of stability.

The over-all behavior of $\mathscr{E}_0$ and R_0 resembles the plots of fig. 3 for the law of corresponding states. However, the system becomes unstable at what is probably too small a value of λ. The SHA treatment is able to cope with the hard core of the potential somewhat better than the QHA treatment as evidenced by the greater range of stable λ values. Presumably, the stability range would be extended even further if one of the theories of section 4 were to be applied to this problem.

3.2. Three-dimensional extension

Most of the expressions in section 3.1 were written in such a way that the generalization to three-dimensional notation is straightforward, often involving only the addition of a cartesian index. However, certain expression will be important in section 4 and are written out explicitly here.

The ground-state energy in the lowest order of SHA is

$$\mathscr{E}_0 = \tfrac{1}{4}\lambda^2 \operatorname{tr} G + \langle 0 | V | 0 \rangle , \tag{3.25}$$

where the harmonic ground-state eigenfunction is as indicated in (1.2) with $\lambda^2 G^2 = \Phi$, which in turn is determined from the self-consistent equation

$$\Phi_{\alpha\beta}(ij) = \langle 0 | \nabla_\alpha(i) \nabla_\beta(j) V | 0 \rangle . \tag{3.26}$$

With the relationship between G and Φ established, it should be noted that (1.2) is the ground-state eigenfunction of the harmonic hamiltonian (2.3). The matrix G is determined from

$$G_{\alpha\beta}(ij) = \sum e_\alpha \begin{pmatrix} \boldsymbol{q} \\ l \end{pmatrix} e_\beta \begin{pmatrix} \boldsymbol{q} \\ l \end{pmatrix} \omega_l(\boldsymbol{q}) \exp[\mathrm{i}\boldsymbol{q}\cdot\boldsymbol{R}(ij)] , \tag{3.27}$$

in analogy with (3.10). The frequencies and polarization vectors are given by (2.7). In contrast to (3.10), the summation in (3.27) must be done numerically. The harmonic pair function $g_\mathrm{h}(ij)$, in a notation which will be introduced in section 4, is defined by an expression similar to (3.14). The explicit form of the function is

$$g_h(ij) = [\pi^3 |\boldsymbol{\Lambda}(ij)|]^{-1/2} \exp\{-\boldsymbol{u}(ij)\cdot[\boldsymbol{\Lambda}(ij)^{-1}]\cdot\boldsymbol{u}(ij)\} . \tag{3.28}$$

The precise form of $\boldsymbol{\Lambda}(ij)$ may be obtained if one evaluates two expressions

$$\begin{aligned} &\langle 0 | [u_\alpha(i) - u_\alpha(j)] [u_\beta(i) - u_\beta(j)] | 0 \rangle \\ &\qquad = \tfrac{1}{2}[G^{-1}_{\alpha\beta}(ii) - G^{-1}_{\alpha\beta}(ij) - G^{-1}_{\alpha\beta}(ji) + G^{-1}_{\alpha\beta}(jj)] , \end{aligned} \tag{3.29}$$

and

$$\int g_h(ij)\, u_\alpha(ij)\, u_\beta(ij)\, \mathrm{d}\boldsymbol{u}(ij) = \tfrac{1}{2}\Lambda_{\alpha\beta}(ij) , \tag{3.30}$$

which by definition must be equal. Then, equating the rhs of (3.29) and (3.30), one obtains

$$\boldsymbol{\Lambda}(ij) = \boldsymbol{G}^{-1}(ii) - \boldsymbol{G}^{-1}(ij) - \boldsymbol{G}^{-1}(ji) + \boldsymbol{G}^{-1}(jj) . \tag{3.31}$$

The $G^{-1}_{\alpha\beta}(ij)$ are obtained in a similar way to the $G_{\alpha\beta}(ij)$ but with $1/\omega_j(\boldsymbol{q})$ replacing $\omega_j(\boldsymbol{q})$ in (3.35). The notation for matrix inverses is similar to that used in (3.16).

All of the material reviewed in this subsection may be found in Koehler (1966a, 1968).

3.3. Anharmonicity

The study of anharmonic effects might be regarded as a luxury in some systems, but in solid helium, it is a necessity. Since the detailed theory of anharmonicity will be treated elsewhere in this book, no more than the essential ideas will be discussed here.

In either the QHA or the SHA, the hamiltonian may be rigorously split into a harmonic and an anharmonic part. The harmonic part provides a basis set of non-interacting phonons. The anharmonic part, which by definition is the total hamiltonian minus the harmonic part, introduces interactions among the phonons. Usually, the total anharmonic term is broken up into terms which introduce interactions between a particular number n of phonons, or alternatively, provide an n-phonon vertex in a diagrammatic perturbation expansion.

The magnitude of the contribution from an n-phonon vertex is assumed to be proportional to some expansion parameter to the nth power – in QHA this arises from the expansion of the hamiltonian in powers of the displacement. The frequencies, which enter into the energy denominators, are proportional to the first power of the expansion parameter. Thus, perturbative corrections are ordered both with respect to the number of phonons involved as well as to their order in perturbation theory.

The two-phonon vertex is usually identically zero. Then the leading corrections are expected to be four-phonon processes to first-order and three-phonon processes to second-order. These are commonly called the quartic and cubic contributions respectively. The quartic term is generally absorbed into the zeroth-order terms in the SPA theories and thus will be ignored here. The cubic term makes a second-order contribution to the ground-state energy of

$$\delta\mathscr{E}_0^{(3)} = -\tfrac{1}{6}\sum |\langle 0|\,\mathscr{H}\,|123\rangle|^2/[\omega(1)+\omega(2)+\omega(3)] \tag{3.32}$$

and a contribution, which is illustrated diagrammatically in fig. 29a, to the phonon self-energy

$$M_{jl}(\boldsymbol{q},\Omega) = -\,\Delta_{jl}(\boldsymbol{q},\Omega) + \mathrm{i}\Gamma_{jl}(\boldsymbol{q},\Omega) \tag{3.33}$$

of

$$\begin{Bmatrix}\Delta_{jl}(\boldsymbol{q},\Omega)\\ \Gamma_{jl}(\boldsymbol{q},\Omega)\end{Bmatrix} = -\tfrac{1}{2}N\sum\left\langle \begin{matrix}-\boldsymbol{q}\\ j\end{matrix}\middle|\mathscr{H}\middle| 12\right\rangle\left\langle 12\middle|\mathscr{H}\middle|\begin{matrix}\boldsymbol{q}\\ l\end{matrix}\right\rangle \times\begin{Bmatrix}P[\omega(1)+\omega(2)+\Omega]^{-1}+P[\omega(1)+\omega(2)-\Omega]^{-1}\\ \pi\delta[\omega(1)+\omega(2)+\Omega]-\pi\delta[\omega(1)+\omega(2)-\Omega]\end{Bmatrix}, \tag{3.34}$$

where an obvious notation has been used to indicate matrix elements of $\mathscr{H}$ between normalized phonon eigenstates and P indicates that the principal value is to be taken. The matrix elements involve the cubic force constants

$$\Phi(123) = \langle 0| \nabla(1)\, \nabla(2)\, \nabla(3)\, V\, |0\rangle \tag{3.35}$$

in the following way:

$$\langle 0| \mathscr{H} |123\rangle = \sum_{i_1 i_2 i_3} \prod_{l=1,3} \left[\left(\frac{\lambda^2}{2N\omega(l)} \right)^{1/2} \exp\left[\mathrm{i}\boldsymbol{q}_l \cdot R(i_l) \right] e(l) \right] \cdot \boldsymbol{\Phi}(i_1 i_2 i_3). \tag{3.36}$$

In (3.36), one of the summations over lattice vectors gives a factor $N\Delta(\boldsymbol{q}_1 + \boldsymbol{q}_2 + \boldsymbol{q}_3)$, where $\Delta(\boldsymbol{q}) = 0$ unless $\boldsymbol{q} = 0$ or a reciprocal lattice vector. This is not exhibited explicitly in (3.32) and (3.34). The matrix elements in (3.34) are obtained from (3.36) from the relationship $\langle {}_j^{-\boldsymbol{q}}| \mathscr{H} |12\rangle \propto = \langle 0| \mathscr{H} |{}_j^{\boldsymbol{q}}\, 12\rangle$.

The self-energy enters into the one-phonon Green's function $\boldsymbol{G}(\boldsymbol{q}, \Omega)$ as

$$\sum_k \{[\omega_j(\boldsymbol{q})^2 - \Omega^2]\, \delta_{jk} - 2\omega_j(\boldsymbol{q})\, M_{jk}(\boldsymbol{q}, \Omega)\}\, \boldsymbol{G}_{kl}(\boldsymbol{q}, \Omega) = 2\omega_j(\boldsymbol{q})\, \delta_{jl}. \tag{3.37}$$

In the case where $M_{jl}(\boldsymbol{q}, \Omega) \ll \omega_j(\boldsymbol{q})$, $M_{jj}(\boldsymbol{q}, \Omega)$, evaluated only at $\Omega = \omega_j(\boldsymbol{q})$, may be considered to provide a shift in the bare phonon energy (from the real part) and a linewidth or lifetime (from the imaginary part). In the case where the anharmonicity is substantial, one must evaluate $\boldsymbol{G}(\boldsymbol{q}, \Omega)$ as a function of Ω and then plot the spectral function $\boldsymbol{A}(\boldsymbol{q}, \Omega) \propto \mathrm{Im}\, \boldsymbol{G}(\boldsymbol{q}, \Omega)$. Such a plot is shown in fig. 19 and is discussed in more detail in subsection 5.2. The spectral function is essentially what one should measure in an inelastic neutron scattering experiment, although this concept requires some modification in the case of the quantum crystals as we will see in subsections 5.6 and 5.7.

The application of the above to solid helium requires that one view anharmonicity in the generalized sense which was discussed in (1.2). Still, one would like to think in terms of the framework provided by (3.32)–(3.37) for at least the following two reasons: a) If the concept of reasonably independent phonons as quasi-particles in solid helium is sensible at all, there should be some ordering of the strengths of various interactions in accord with the ordering used in QHA. b) For practical reasons, as discussed in Koehler (1972), three-phonon to second-order processes represent about the limit of what can be achieved computationally today.

Thus the theory of the lattice dynamics of the quantum crystals will be based as much as possible on equations similar to (3.25), (3.26), (3.32)–(3.37), but one must find a way to rigorously determine quantities which will appear as generalized force-constants, generalized three-phonon vertices and, possibly, modified forms of the interatomic potential. Various attempts to do this will be discussed in section 4.

For a detailed, formal derivation from which the results of this section may be obtained, consult Werthamer (1969a, 1970a) or Choquard (1967).

4. *Quantitative theories*

4.1. Pre-Nosanow treatments

The introduction of the era of reliable quantitative theoretical results in the theory of quantum crystals can be attributed to the work of Nosanow (1964, 1966). While this work was a significant advance, it was not an entirely new departure. In incorporating certain elements of previous treatments, it unified them and provided insight into why these treatments had been less successful. In addition, it happened to coincide in time with independent developments in the self-consistent phonon formalism and provided the vehicle for the speediest application of those ideas to quantum crystals. Even though the results of previous theories are no longer those one would choose to compare with experiment and none of them have been used in lattice dynamics calculations, a brief review of pre-Nosanow attempts to calculate the binding energy of solid helium is instructive.

In work which was first directed at obtaining the properties of the rare gas solids at 0 K and was later extended to the quantum crystals, Bernardes (1958) used a variational wavefunction to estimate the ground-state energy of the Lennard–Jones solids. The variational approach was a philosophical departure from purely phenomenological theories or treatments based on QHA and the fact that he choose the Lennard–Jones potential may have been responsible for its extensive use in subsequent variational calculations. He used a Hartree-type wavefunction with the single-particle functions taken to be linear combinations of the two lowest, spherically-symmetric eigenfunctions of a particle confined in a spherical region of radius a surrounded by an infinite potential. His wavefunction was thus of the form (1.3) with

$$\begin{aligned} \varphi(r) &= \sin(\pi r/a) + b\sin(2\pi r/a), \quad & r < a, \\ &= 0, & r > a. \end{aligned} \tag{4.1}$$

the parameters a and b were chosen variationally with the restriction $a \leqslant \frac{1}{2}R_0$.

A series expansion of the integrals required to evaluate the potential energy was devised by Bernardes (1959).

This work was extended in an attempt to derive an analytic form for the quantum-mechanical law of corresponding states, (Bernardes 1960a), and to calculate certain properties of the quantum crystals (Bernardes 1960b). In these last two papers, the work was simplified by setting $b=0$ in (4.1).

These calculations gave reasonable results for certain properties of the heavier rare gas solids, but because of the numerical approximations, were less reliable for solid Ne and were very open to suspicion when applied to the quantum crystals. Nevertheless, the idea of obtaining the properties of a Van der Waals solid from a variational calculation was somewhat novel at the time even if the spirit of the variational approach was violated by the introduction of some unreliable numerical approximations. Further comments on Bernardes' results will follow the discussion of the work of Nosanow and Shaw.

An attempt to calculate the properties of solid ^{3}He alone was made by Bernardes and Primakoff (1960). This work can be viewed as an effort to extrapolate the known properties of solid ^{4}He to predict those of ^{3}He. This was an ambitious undertaking, because at the time, very little was known experimentally about solid ^{4}He and the theory of solid ^{3}He was in a primitive state. Nevertheless, these authors tried to explain virtually all of the known experimental facts about solid ^{3}He and the paper is a useful reference to the known theoretical problems of that date.

Their treatment introduced two ideas which are with us today: a NCG as a variational wavefunction and an effective potential v_{eff}. Results based on this variational wavefunction were recently used by Guyer (1969b) to interpret the systematics of the Lennard–Jones solids and the effective potential is important in the Nosanow theory and the t-matrix theories.

The concept of an effective potential can be appreciated on physical grounds. The NCG wavefunction (or, from a later perspective, the CG wavefunction) is a mathematically simple wavefunction which contains much of the physics of the problem. However, this function cannot be used to evaluate the expectation value of the potential energy of the crystal. The Lennard–Jones potential has an infinitely hard core and any realistic interatomic potential has, at least, a quite hard core, while the gaussian wavefunction never vanishes. Thus $\langle 0|\, V\,|0\rangle$ either diverges or is many times too large. However, this variational wavefunction could be expected to represent the true motion of the atoms fairly well except for the very unlikely motion when two atoms overlap. The true wavefunction will be shaped so the atomic motion will avoid the hard core of the potential. The effective potential attempts to reshape the true potential, to remove the hard core and to permit the use of an analytically simple, approximate wavefunction. Ideally, the replacement is such as to make the final calculated value for the internal energy of the crystal correct.

In the later work of Nosanow (1966) and in the various t-matrix treatments there is a technique for the construction of v_{eff}. Bernardes and Primakoff, however, simply took $v_{\mathrm{eff}}(r) = v(r)\exp(-\beta/r^{10})$. Their estimate of the ground-state energy then depends on A (from the NCG) and β. They chose β so that the mean-square deviation of an atom from its lattice site in ^{4}He was correct for the optimum value of A. This β value was then used in the ^{3}He effective potential.

This calculation did not take account of the fact that the softening of the potential must be accompanied by an increase in kinetic energy because the softening implies that a change in the shape of the wavefunction has been made. Consequently, they underestimated the kinetic energy, found a rather large mean-square deviation and obtained an exchange integral which was far too large.

There are two aspects of this work which are deserving of further comment. a) It is clear that the logical rational for the replacement of v by v_{eff} that was presented here is similar in spirit to the arguments that are used for the introduction of a t-matrix. It is interesting to speculate how the course of theoretical work on the quantum crystals might have been altered had this aspect of the work of Bernardes and Primakoff been followed immediately. The numerical work in the t-matrix approach is considerably less than in the Nosanow approach. b) With the current availability of a large body of experimental knowledge concerning the quantum crystals and the development of more refined theories, it would be interesting to see if a semi-phenomenological theory could be developed which would explain most or all of the experimental data and which would combine a cleverly chosen, but empirical, effective potential with, perhaps, the SHA formalism with anharmonic corrections. Such an approach could provide an easily accessible theory of quantum crystals which could furnish a framework for correlating experimental data.

Another theory was developed by Saunders (1962) who attempted to solve the correlation problem in quantum crystals by extending the method of Pluvinage (1950) in which the independent variables of the system are taken to be the $r(ij)$ in addition to the $\boldsymbol{r}(i)$. Since V involves $r(ij)$ this simplifies part of the problem but at the expense of introducing a large number of constraint equations $r(ij)=|\boldsymbol{r}(i)-\boldsymbol{r}(j)|$. Saunders' theory agreed surprisingly well with the thermodynamic properties and, especially, with the exchange integral, but the theory contained many analytical difficulties. Therefore, Garwin and Landesman (1965) re-examined the theory and improved certain aspects of the approximations and of the numerical calculations.

This whole approach was later analyzed by Mullin (1968) in considerable detail. He showed that the theory was either inconsistent or wrong in several places, and numerical results of the previous papers are consequently in doubt. This method would therefore seem to be a dead end.

Very useful information about the ultimate limitations of a Hartree-type variational wavefunction was presented in the work of Nosanow and Shaw (1962) who carried out the variational calculation exactly, with the restriction that the wavefunction be spherically symmetric. In other words, they used a numerically obtained, optimum spherically symmetric form for the single-particle functions. Since their results are reliable upper bounds from a well-defined variational calculation, we have listed them in table 1 (see page 12). Note that the results for the rare gas solids agree fairly well with experiment although there is some discrepancy for solid neon. These results for helium are higher than those of Bernardes (which are not shown in table 1), thus indicating that there was a numerical error introduced by one of his approximations.

The most important result is that the energy for solid helium is far too high. The kinetic energy for ^{3}He came out to be about 80 cal/mole whereas it is estimated from θ_D to be about 30. The conclusion is that the uncorrelated nature of the Hartree wavefunction confines the atoms in too small a region, forcing the kinetic energy to become unrealistically high. It is therefore necessary to use some form of correlated wavefunction.

There is some space excluded because of the restriction to spherical symmetry on the single particle orbitals. The work of Rosenwald (1967) indicates that this restriction is probably not the major source of error. He used a non-spherically symmetric Hartree wavefunction and found that the variational ground-state energy of ^{3}He decreased by only 3.5 cal/mole, a result that was nearly density independent.

Strong evidence of the necessity for treating correlations properly can be deduced from two papers on solid neon. Mullin (1964) used a NCG wavefunction* and obtained essentially the same energy as Nosanow and Shaw,

* He actually used a wavefunction similar to that which will be introduced in (4.2). However, his handling of the cluster expansion was not quite correct and he, in effect, just used the Hartree wavefunction.

which showed that the NCG wavefunction was a good choice for a variational wavefunction.

A later calculation by Koehler (1966b) used a CG wavefunction and obtained a reduction of 7 cal/mole. This represented a decrease of about 12% of the kinetic energy and was due to the effect discussed in section 2.1. This energy improvement can be attributed to a better handling of correlations. This was for neon in which correlations are not as important as they are for helium.

It should be emphasized that neither of the calculations based upon gaussian wavefunctions can be directly extended to quantum crystals. These wavefunctions simply do not cut off rapidly enough to prevent hard-core overlap (even approximately) except with an unreasonable expenditure of kinetic energy. In fact, the wavefunctions do not cut off rapidly enough even in the case of solid neon. However, one can make a physical argument that, when the wavefunction becomes extremely small before hard-core overlap occurs, the modification in the function necessary to completely prevent overlap is minor and would produce negligible changes in the ground-state energy. In section 4.2, the description of the approach of Nosanow will make it clear that this physical argument can be put on firmer mathematical grounds.

4.2. Nosanow theory

The theory of Nosanow (1964, 1966) was based upon two assumptions. First, he used a variational wavefunction

$$\Psi_0 = \Psi_J \Phi_H \tag{4.2}$$

which was the product of a Jastrow function

$$\Psi_J^2 = \prod_{i<j} f(ij), \quad f(r \to 0) \to 0, \quad f(r \to \infty) \to 1 \tag{4.3}$$

and a Hartree function Φ_H as defined in (1.3). Second, he introduced a cluster expansion, which was a generalization of the method of Van Kampen (1961), as an approximation technique for obtaining the pair function, whose exact determination requires performing a many-body integration. In (4.2), the Hartree wavefunction part provides the lattice structure and the property $f(r \to 0) \to 0$ prevents hard-core overlap (or, equivalently, provides for short-range correlation). Usually, Ψ_J rather than Ψ_J^2 is defined as a product of $f(ij)$; however, the notation used in (4.3) leads to some notational simplification in the following and facilitates the comparison of $f(ij)$ with the pair function used in other theories.

Before discussing the exact form of f and φ, we will derive the variational expression for the ground-state energy $\mathscr{E}_0$ and will give a brief discussion of the cluster expansion. The expansion has been treated in great detail by Nosanow and more recently by Guyer (1969b) so that a shorter description is appropriate here.

When Ψ_0 is a product function, one can use a technique for the evaluation of the expectation value of the kinetic energy operator which was first exploited by Jackson and Feenberg (1961). That is, one notes that $-i\nabla$ is a hermitian operator and therefore $\langle\Psi_0|\,\nabla_\alpha^2(i)\,|\Psi_0\rangle = -\langle\nabla_\alpha(i)\,\Psi_0\,|\,\nabla_\alpha(i)\,\Psi_0\rangle$. Thus one can write

$$\langle\Psi_0|\,\nabla_\alpha^2(i)\,|\Psi_0\rangle = \tfrac{1}{2}[\langle\Psi_0|\,\nabla_\alpha^2(i)\,|\Psi_0\rangle - \langle\nabla_\alpha(i)\,\Psi_0\,|\,\nabla_\alpha(i)\,\Psi_0\rangle] \tag{4.4a}$$

$$= -\tfrac{1}{2}\langle\Psi_0|\,\{\nabla_\alpha^2(i)\ln\Psi_0\}\,|\Psi_0\rangle, \tag{4.4b}$$

where the curly brackets indicate that the enclosed quantity $\nabla_\alpha^2(i)\ln\Psi_0$ is to be considered as a function and the operator does not act outside the brackets. The utility of this approach is that, in the case of a product wavefunction the logarithm becomes a sum of logarithms. Now, with $\mathscr{E}_0 = \langle\Psi_0|\,\mathscr{H}\,|\Psi_0\rangle/\langle\Psi_0\,|\,\Psi_0\rangle$ we obtain

$$\mathscr{E}_0 = \langle\Psi_0| - \tfrac{1}{4}\lambda^2 \sum \nabla_\alpha^2(i)\ln\Psi_0 + \tfrac{1}{2}\sum_{i\neq j} v(ij)\,|\Psi_0\rangle/\langle\Psi_0\,|\,\Psi_0\rangle. \tag{4.5}$$

With an eye towards the ultimate introduction of the SPA, we wish to discuss a somewhat generalized version of the cluster expansion of Nosanow. Suppose that we temporatily identify Φ_{H} in (4.2) with any function (a CG, for example) for which we can perform the integral $\int \Phi_{\mathrm{H}}^2\,\mathrm{d}\{\boldsymbol{r}(i)\}$ where $\{\boldsymbol{r}(i)\}$ denotes any arbitrary subset of all the $\boldsymbol{r}(i)$.

When V is the sum of at most pair interactions, which is the only case that will be considered here, it is clear from (4.5) that the evaluation of $\mathscr{E}_0$ requires a knowledge of the pair function defined by

$$g_{\Psi_0}(12) = \int \Psi_0^2\,\mathrm{d}\boldsymbol{r}(3),\cdots,\mathrm{d}\boldsymbol{r}(N)/\int \Psi_0^2\,\mathrm{d}\boldsymbol{r}(i),\cdots,\mathrm{d}\boldsymbol{r}(N). \tag{4.6}$$

In the notation for the pair function, the subscript Ψ_0 will be omitted when the particular function on the rhs of (4.6) is clear from the context. In (4.6) and most of the following, a simplification of notation is achieved by the use of (12) instead of (ij) to designate two arbitrary particles. Note that g as defined by (4.6) will be normalized and, apart from normalization factors, is identical with the diagonal component of the density matrix or the pair function as defined in March et al. (1967).

The cluster expansion can be viewed as a way of constructing successive approximations $g^{(n)}(12)$, $n=1, 2, \cdots$ to $g(12)$ such that $g^{(n+1)}$ is a better approximation and a more complicated function than $g^{(n)}$. The construction will be based on three mathematical properties of Ψ_0: 1) The essential short-range behavior is accounted for by $f(12)$. 2) As noted before, Φ_{H}^2 can be integrated over any arbitrary set of coordinates. 3) The various $f(ij)$ are equal to unity throughout most of space so their presence should not greatly alter the result of exact integrations on Φ_{H}^2.

With the above in mind, it is clear that the simplest starting point is

$$g_{\Psi_0}^{(1)}(12) = g_{\mathrm{H}}(12)\, f(12) \Big/ \int g_{\mathrm{H}}(12)\, f(12)\, \mathrm{d}\boldsymbol{u}(12), \tag{4.7}$$

where g_{H} is the pair function for Φ_{H}. The next approximation could be

$$g_{\Psi_0}^{(2)}(12) = \frac{f(12)}{\sum\limits_{j\neq 1,2} \alpha^j} \sum \alpha^i \frac{\int g_{\mathrm{H}}(12i)\, f(1i)\, f(2i)\, \mathrm{d}\boldsymbol{r}(i)}{\int g_{\mathrm{H}}(12i)\, f(12)\, f(1i)\, f(2i)\, \mathrm{d}\boldsymbol{r}(i)\, \mathrm{d}\boldsymbol{u}(12)}. \tag{4.8}$$

Then the leading correction to $g^{(1)}$ is

$$\delta g^{(1)}(12) = f(12) \left\{ \frac{g_{\mathrm{H}}(12)}{\int g_{\mathrm{H}}(12)\, f(12)\, \mathrm{d}\boldsymbol{u}(12)} - \frac{1}{\sum\limits_{j\neq 1,2} \alpha^j} \sum \alpha^i \frac{\int g_{\mathrm{H}}(12i)\, f(1i)\, f(2i)\, \mathrm{d}\boldsymbol{r}(i)}{\int g_{\mathrm{H}}(12i)\, f(12)\, f(1i)\, f\ 2i)\, \mathrm{d}\boldsymbol{r}(i)\, \mathrm{d}u(12)} \right\}. \tag{4.9}$$

If all the $f(1i)$ and $f(2i)$ equal unity, $\delta g^{(1)}=0$. The triplet function $g_{\mathrm{H}}(12i)$ is obtained from an obvious generalization of the definition (4.6).

In the Nosanow cluster expansion, all of the α^i are unity. In this development it is not clear that they should be, but they will be taken to be so in the following. The use of the partially integrated functions $g_{\mathrm{H}}(12)$ and $g_{\mathrm{H}}(12i)$ is allied to the approach of Massey and Woo (1968), except they treat the Jastrow rather than the Hartree part as exactly integrable and use techniques from the theory of liquids to effect the integration.

The Nosanow cluster expansion involves fully correlated clusters, meaning that no indices appear only once. For example, the next approximation to g

would use $f(12)\times\sum f(1i)\,f(2j)\,f(1j)\,f(2i)\,f(ij)$. An alternative cluster expansion was proposed by Brueckner and Frohberg (1965). This was used in numerical calculations by these authors, by Frohberg (1967) and by Brueckner and Thieberger (1969). This expansion used both correlated and uncorrelated clusters. Thus, their second approximation to g uses the terms $f(12)\,f(1i)$ and $f(12)\,f(2j)$, which are completely absent in the Nosanow expansion. Their third approximation uses the terms $f(12)f(1i)f(2i)$, which are present Nosanow expansion, as well as terms like $f(12)\,f(1i)\,f(2j)$, which are not. The leading approximation is identical in either case.

There has been a certain amount of controversy about the relative merits of the two cluster expansions; however, this issue will not be pursued further here because all of the lattice dynamics calculations to date either have been restricted to the lowest-order cluster expansion or have used an entirely different method. The connection between the two expansions was pointed out by Trickey (1968) and comments on the relative merits of each approach can be found in Hetherington et al. (1967) and in Guyer (1969b).

It should be pointed out that both methods are completely correct when carried out to the last term in the expansion, the only debatable point is the comparative reliability of calculations which are truncated after a few terms. This is especially crucial when truncated cluster expansions are used to derive expressions for the optimum form of the Jastrow function.

The development of the Nosanow theory will now be continued and questions about the convergence of the cluster expansion will be deferred until later. It is convenient to immediately introduce two features of the analytical form of Ψ_0 which have been used in nearly all calculations and then to obtain in (4.11) and (4.12), the working expressions of the Nosanow theory. First, with Ψ_0 of the form (4.2), one easily finds that

$$\nabla_\alpha^2(i)\ln\Psi_0^2 = \nabla_\alpha^2(i)\ln\varphi(i) + \sum_{j\neq i}\nabla_\alpha^2(i)\ln f(ij)\,. \tag{4.10}$$

Second, Φ_{H} will be taken to be a gaussian of the form (1.2). For the original Nosanow theory, it is a NCG and for the SPA it is a CG. In either case,

$$\sum_{\alpha,i}\nabla_\alpha(i)\ln\Phi_{\mathrm{H}} = \sum_{\alpha,i}G_{\alpha\alpha}(ii) = (1/N)\,\mathrm{tr}\,G\,.$$

The gaussian approximation is useful for three reasons: 1) It is analytically convenient. 2) It simplifies introducing SPA. 3) It was shown by Nosanow (1966) that the gaussian orbitals are very nearly as good as the optimum spherically-symmetric Hartree orbitals.

With all of these assumptions, we find that

$$\mathscr{E}_0 = \tfrac{1}{4}\lambda^2 \operatorname{tr} G + \langle 0|\, V_{\text{eff}}\, |0\rangle / \langle 0|\, \Psi_J^2\, |0\rangle\,, \tag{4.11}$$

where

$$V_{\text{eff}} = \Psi_J^2 \left[V - \tfrac{1}{4}\lambda^2 \sum \nabla_\alpha^2 (i) \ln \Psi_J \right]. \tag{4.12}$$

Since Ψ_J contains factors which cut off the potential as $r(ij) \to 0$, we now have a theory in which the ground-state energy involves the gaussian average of an effective potential; however, as opposed to the simple cut-off ansatz used by Bernardes, an additional term whose average value is positive is introduced. This, of course, simply means that one cannot just cut off the potential arbitrarily but has to pay the price for it somewhere.

In the lowest order cluster expansion, the expression for $\mathscr{E}_0$ is

$$\mathscr{E}_0 = \tfrac{1}{4}\lambda^2 \operatorname{tr} G + \tfrac{1}{2} \sum_{i \neq j} \langle 0|\, v_{\text{eff}}(ij)\, |0\rangle / \langle 0|\, f(ij)\, |0\rangle\,, \tag{4.13}$$

where

$$v_{\text{eff}}(ij) = f(ij) \left[v(ij) - \tfrac{1}{8}\lambda^2 \nabla^2 (i) \ln f(ij) \right]. \tag{4.14}$$

For the NCG, tr $G = NA$ and for the CG, tr $G = \sum_{j,\boldsymbol{q}} \omega_j(\boldsymbol{q})$. Since experience has shown that $\langle 0|\, f(ij)\, |0\rangle \approx 1$, (4.13) is very nearly an expression in which the true interatomic pair potential is simply replaced by an effective pair potential. Thus, at this order the theory looks attractively simple. It appears that one can use an effective potential and can still work with the gaussian wavefunction. However, several questions remain unanswered: a) How good is the approximation? b) What do we use for f? c) Can we replace $v(ij)$ by $v_{\text{eff}}(ij)$ in, for example, anharmonic calculations? The answer to (c) requires a detailed discussion which will be given in subsection 4.3. The answer to (a) is that it depends on (b), so let us now consider (b).

One is immediately tempted to minimize $\mathscr{E}_0$, as defined in (4.13), with respect to both A (or G) and f independently. Unfortunately, this procedure leads to zero as the optimum value of A. The part of the wavefunction that localizes the solid becomes a constant and the solid 'melts'. This point is discussed in some detail by Guyer (1969b). The main observation is that one cannot make the cluster expansion and then freely vary f and A. Another point is that, if f is totally free, there is no need to have a g_{H}.

Nosanow avoided this difficulty by performing a restricted variation on f. He choose $f = \exp(-cv)$, where c is a variational parameter and v is the interatomic potential. The restricted variation worked and optimum values of both A and c could be found at each density.

This particular choice of f was originally made for a variety of physical reasons: it was simple, it cut off the potential and it tended to increase the particle density at the potential minimum. However, another feature was equally important. Later work by Hetherington et al. (1967) showed that the cluster expansion apparently converged for this particular form of f but not for all forms. In particular, the desirable form $f=\exp(-c/r^5)$, which asymptotically satisfies the Schrödinger equation for the Lennard–Jones potential at small r, is unsuitable for the cluster expansion. Similar conclusions were reached with greater rigor in studies of an atomic, linear-chain model quantum solid by Trickey and Nuttall (1969), and Kuebbing and Trickey (1972).

Since the cluster expansion and the Nosanow form for f were used in later lattice dynamics calculations, a more careful statement of the results of Hetherington et al. is relevant. They established that the sum of all of the three-body corrections to the ground-state energy was small compared to the lowest-order approximation. Most of the three-body corrections were themselves small, but over-all convergence was aided by a good bit of cancellation when the individual terms were summed. They had no reason to investigate the problem of the convergence of the cluster expansion for the evaluation of the matrix elements $\langle 0|\, \nabla_\alpha^2(i)\, V_{\text{eff}}\, |0\rangle$ and $\langle 0|\, \nabla_\alpha^3(i)\, V_{\text{eff}}\, |0\rangle$, which are used in lattice dynamics work. These questions will arise again in discussions of the work of Koehler and Werthamer in subsection 4.3 and section 5.

Since (4.2) has been widely used as a variational ground-state wavefunction in quantum crystal theory, it is useful to establish a nomenclature which will distinguish between various related methods. The general method will simply be called the Jastrow approach and specific techniques will be termed, for example, the Jastrow–CG method. The theory of Nosanow will be interpreted in a restricted sense and will refer to what, in essence, was the working model rather than the complete Jastrow–CG theory. The key features of the Nosanow theory are: a) The introduction of short-range correlations by the Jastrow wave function. b) The evaluation of many-body integrals by a cluster expansion. c) The use of the NCG wavefunction to give the crystal structure.

The original theory of Nosanow was aimed at the ground-state energy of solid helium. However, parallel theoretical developments provided the proper framework for its immediate application to lattice dynamics. Brenig (1963), and Fredkin and Werthamer (1965) had developed a formalism, based on a single-particle (or Hartree) picture, for the calculation of the phonon spectrum of crystals. Since this theory and its further development by Gillis and Werthamer (1968), and Kerr and Sjölander (1970) are quite involved, the work will not be presented here in any detail. The essential feature, the expression that was used in calculations of the phonon spectrum of helium by De Wette et al. (1967) is the use of the ground-state average of the second derivative of the potential for the force constants. The single-particle representation of the ground-state was used to evaluate the average. This was the first calculation using a realistic model potential to give real phonon energies for helium. However, the phonon concept emerges more clearly in the collective or SPA picture and the calculated dispersion curves are very similar. Consequently, the results of the single-particle picture will not be quoted here.

One limitation of the Nosanow theory is really of a mathematical nature and is not an essential feature of (4.2): the cluster expansion approximation to the many-body integral. This approximation can, in fact, be avoided by the use of Monte-Carlo techniques. In doing so, one gains an enormous advantage because one is no longer restricted to the class of wavefunctions for which the cluster expansion is known to converge. One pays the price, of course, because the Monte-Carlo method requires a considerable amount of computer time. However, the work of Hetherington et al. (1967) exploring the convergence of the cluster expansion was also a major computer effort which had to be accompanied by an analytical and programming effort of considerably more complexity than is required for Monte-Carlo calculations.

As will be seen in section 5.1, the additional variational freedom in the wavefunction which is possible when the Monte-Carlo integration technique is used, produces a significant improvement in the ground-state energy. Since the discussions of the results of lattice dynamics calculations in section 5 will make it clear that one would like to get away from the Nosanow wavefunction, it seems that the cluster expansion has been a useful tool, but one which should be gradually abandoned either in favor of the Monte-Carlo method or other techniques. As examples of the latter, the t-matrix approach avoids the many-body integral altogether and various methods which have been used in the theory of liquids such as the BBGKY method, the PY equation, and the perturbation theory of Barker and Henderson (1971) could perhaps be adapted to the hard-core solid problem.

4.3. Correlated basis function method

The incorporation of the Nosanow theory into the SPA formalism was accomplished by Koehler (1967, 1968) and Horner (1967). An extension of this SPA theory to include anharmonic effects (in the generalized sense described in section 1.2) was made by Koehler and Werthamer (1971) who also noted the strong parallel between their theory of solid helium and the correlated basis function CBF method which has been applied to the theory of liquid helium by Feenberg and co-workers. Because of this similarity, the Koehler–Werthamer theory will be referred to as the CBF approach. A comprehensive review of the CBF method for liquid helium has recently been provided by Feenberg (1969).

The development of the CBF theory will be discussed in this sub-section while the numerical results of the theory, as reported by Koehler and Werthamer (1972), will be given in section 5. The appropriate reference for each individual topic in the discussion will not be given; however, each of the points is treated in more detail in at least one of the Koehler and Werthamer papers cited above. The work of Horner (1967) has by now evolved into the theory which will be treated in subsection 4.5.

The formulas for the lowest-order KW theory have already been given implicitly. One simply takes the Nosanow wavefunction and substitutes a CG for the NCG part. The expression for $\mathscr{E}_0$ of (4.11) remains the same as does the lowest-order cluster expansion expression of (4.13), providing one uses the cluster expansion given in this chapter. The fact that the CG function can be integrated over an arbitrary number of coordinates so that $g_h(1, 2, \cdots, n)$ can be obtained for any n allows the cluster expansion. The pair function for a harmonic, CG wavefunction will always be denoted by g_h.

One can now consider (4.11) as a variational expression for the ground-state energy and minimize with respect to the $\boldsymbol{G}(ij)$ while keeping Ψ_J fixed. The result is analogous to the self-consistent expression (3.26) for the usual SHA:

$$\boldsymbol{\Phi}(ij) = \frac{\langle 0 | \boldsymbol{\nabla}(i) \boldsymbol{\nabla}(j) V_{\text{eff}} | 0 \rangle}{\langle 0 | \Psi_J^2 | 0 \rangle} - \frac{\langle 0 | \nabla(i) \boldsymbol{\nabla}(j) \Psi_J^2 | 0 \rangle \langle 0 | V_{\text{eff}} | 0 \rangle}{\langle 0 | \Psi_J^2 | 0 \rangle^2}, \tag{4.15}$$

with $G^2 = \lambda^2 \Phi$ in $|0\rangle$, as usual. Thus for any reasonable choice of Ψ_J the minimization condition for the $\boldsymbol{G}(ij)$ can be fulfilled; although if Ψ_J is chosen poorly, the resulting trial wavefunction $\Psi_0 = \Psi_J |0\rangle$ will not be a good one.

It is now tempting to define the phonon frequencies as the roots of G, in analogy with the SHA theory. However, two alternative definitions are possible in the SHA theory and both of these lead to identical expressions for the phonon energy when extended to the CBF theory. The latter definitions will be used in the CBF theory as described in the following.

In the QHA or SHA theories, a one phonon state $|{}^{q}_{j}\rangle$ is the product of a normal coordinate $Q_j(\boldsymbol{q})$ and the ground state. Thus

$$\left|\begin{matrix}\boldsymbol{q}\\ j\end{matrix}\right\rangle = Q_j(\boldsymbol{q})\,|0\rangle/\langle 0|\,|Q_j(\boldsymbol{q})|^2\,|0\rangle\,. \tag{4.16}$$

The normal coordinate is constructed as the three-dimensional analog of the definition (3.4). In a matrix approach, the energy of a one-phonon state is the expectation value of the hamiltonian with respect to the eigenfunction of a one-phonon state. One can now define the phonon energy $\nu_j(\boldsymbol{q})$ as the difference between this energy and the ground-state energy:

$$\nu_j(\boldsymbol{q}) = \left\langle\begin{matrix}\boldsymbol{q}\\ j\end{matrix}\right|\mathscr{H}\left|\begin{matrix}\boldsymbol{q}\\ j\end{matrix}\right\rangle - \mathscr{E}_0\,. \tag{4.17}$$

In the harmonic theories, (4.17) can be manipulated to yield the phonon energies as the roots of G, providing one uses H in QHA and $\mathscr{H}$ in SHA.

The most obvious generalization of (4.16) is the Ansatz that the one-phonon state in the CBF theory should be identified with

$$\left|\begin{matrix}\boldsymbol{q}\\ j\end{matrix}\right\rangle = Q_j(\boldsymbol{q})\,|\Psi_0\rangle/\langle\Psi_0|\,|Q_j(\boldsymbol{q})|^2\,|\Psi_0\rangle\,. \tag{4.18}$$

Then, if the phonon energy is defined by (4.17), one finds that the $\nu_j(\boldsymbol{q})$ are the roots of the inverse of either of two equivalent matrices whose elements are

$$\langle\Psi_0|\,u_\alpha(i)\,u_\beta(j)\,|\Psi_0\rangle/\langle\Psi_0|\Psi_0\rangle\,, \tag{4.19a}$$

or

$$\boldsymbol{G}^{-1}(ij) + \tfrac{1}{2}\lambda^2 \sum \boldsymbol{G}^{-1}(i1)\cdot\frac{\langle 0|\,\boldsymbol{\nabla}(1)\,\boldsymbol{\nabla}(2)\,\Psi_J^2\,|0\rangle}{\langle\Psi_0|\Psi_0\rangle}\cdot\boldsymbol{G}^{-1}(2j)\,. \tag{4.19b}$$

The result (4.19a) is especially interesting for it says that the phonon energies are to be identified with the inverse eigenvalues of the displacement correlation function. This is probably the best definition one could make in a time independent formalism, since one can readily recognize that the one-phonon Green's function is nearly identical with the rhs of (4.19a) if Ψ_0 is replaced by the true ground-state wavefunction and the appropriate time dependence is given to the $\boldsymbol{u}(i)$ operators.

The CBF theory at this level can be used for obtaining the ground-state energy and a spectrum of non-interacting phonons. As will be seen in subsection 5.1, the value for $\mathscr{E}_0$ is lowered from the Nosanow result by approximately 5 cal/mole. This improvement is about 12% of the kinetic energy and originates largely from the effect discussed in subsection 3.1.

The lowest-order CBF theory yields sound velocities which are in close agreement with the results of De Wette et al. (1967), but the agreement does not hold throughout the whole Brillouin zone. The force-constant matrix used by De Wette et al. is identical to the first term on the rhs of (4.15) except that the average value would be taken with respect to the NCG rather than the CG wavefunction. This and the addition of the second term on the rhs of (4.15) are found to make little difference. Since the $\omega_j(\boldsymbol{q})$ are

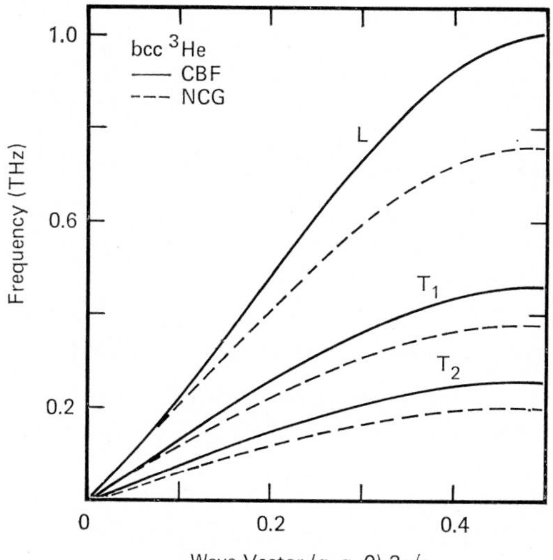

Fig. 7. Lowest-order phonon dispersion curves in bcc ^{3}He at 21.5 cc/mole as calculated from two Jastrow-cluster theories. The solid curves are the CBF results from Koehler (1967) and the dashed curves, according to the theory of Nosanow and Werthamer (1965), are obtained from a Jastrow-NCG wavefunction and omit the $\langle 0|\nabla\nabla f|0\rangle$ term.

determined essentially from the square-root of Φ, possible differences in its numerical value are further reduced.

Thus, the roots of G in the CBF formulation yield very nearly the same phonon spectrum as obtained by De Wette et al. However, the first term in (4.19b) is identically the inverse of the roots of G while the second term provides a correction which vanishes identically at the zone center and increases the phonon energy elsewhere up to about 20% at the zone boundary. This is illustrated in fig. 7, where dispersion curves along the (110) direction for bcc ^{3}He at 21.5 cc/mole are shown. This behavior could have been anticipated on physical grounds. The difference between ω and ν obviously is due to the Jastrow function, which is designed to prevent hard-core overlap. Thus, the force constants associated with the motion of nearest neighbors directly at each other, which is characteristic of a longitudinal zone boundary phonon in the bcc structure, should be stiffened. The effect of the short-range correlations on the phonon frequencies will be seen again in subsection 4.5.

Anharmonic effects are introduced into the CBF theory by an extension of the Ansatz used to define the one-phonon states. One can reason in the following way: an n-phonon state in the SHA is the product of the ground-state eigenfunction and a polynomial of order n in the $Q_j(\boldsymbol{q})$. The polynomials can be completely determined from the single requirement that the states be orthonormal, or equivalently, that the ground-state averages of the polynomials be orthonormal. This requirement is therefore sufficient for the definition of a complete set of functions which can be obtained without any explicit reference to a model harmonic hamiltonian and used as a basis set in perturbation calculations. Unfortunately, this particular set is inadequate. Because of the singular nature of the potential, the matrix elements do not exist. However, they do exist for a closely related set – products of Ψ_0 and polynomials orthogonalized with respect to Ψ_0^2. In fact, the lowest two members of the set have already been used to obtain expressions for $\mathscr{E}_0$ and $\nu_j(\boldsymbol{q})$. A theory based on this line of reasoning has also been developed by Gillessen and Biem (1971).

The philosophy described above is straightforward, but its algebraic implementation is not and one is forced to make several approximations in order to obtain expressions which are computationally tractable. The construction of the exact polynomials would require the diagonalization of very large matrices. (There are $9N^2$ three-phonon states of crystal momentum zero.) This is not a problem in SHA, because there the ground-state average of products of $Q_j(\boldsymbol{q})$ involves only δ-functions and $\omega_j(\boldsymbol{q})$ and terms involving different j, $\boldsymbol{q}$ always factor conveniently. In the CBF theory, terms involving averages of gradients of Ψ_J also appear and couple different j, $\boldsymbol{q}$ values. These should be small and in most cases can be neglected. Eventually, after some algebraic manipulation which will not be repeated here, one can arrive at a nearly orthonormal set which is the product of the SHA eigenfunctions and Ψ_0.

Using this set, one can work out matrix elements of $\mathscr{H}$. If one is to use the cluster expansion to evaluate the matrix elements (as was done by Koehler and Werthamer), some care is needed in order to apply the expansion consistently.

There is still another feature of the analysis which requires careful handling. The matrix approach is most suitable for time-independent perturbation theory. In that case, one obtains expressions like (3.32)–(3.34) with all quantities evaluated only at $\Omega = \omega_j(\boldsymbol{q})$. Particularly in extremely anharmonic substances like solid helium, one is interested in possible structure in the phonon spectral function and hence requires a time-dependent theory. Arguments for the use of time-dependent expressions were given by Koehler and Werthamer (1972) and Gillessen and Biem (1971). These were based on drawing a formal analogy between the matrix elements of $\mathscr{H}$ in the CBF basis set and a non-singular hamiltonian in the SHA basis set. A more satisfying approach was later pointed out by Koehler (1974), but will not be discussed here.

One can apply the usual Green's function treatment in a perturbation theory based upon a harmonic hamiltonian, because the bare hamiltonian and the perturbation can be expressed in a set of field-theoretic operators. This establishes a characteristic relationship between certain matrix elements, for example, between $\langle {}^{\boldsymbol{q}}_{j} | \mathscr{H} | 12 \rangle$ and $\langle 0 | \mathscr{H} | {}^{\boldsymbol{q}}_{j} 12 \rangle$. These relationships do not necessarily hold in a treatment based on matrix elements obtained in an arbitrary basis set. In the CBF theory, it was found that the proper relationships between matrix elements existed to a good approximation, hence the differences could be considered a higher-order perturbation and ignored. It was then found that the equations of subsection 3.3 could be employed with two modifications: 1) The third derivative of $v(ij)$ is replaced by the third derivative of

$$\tilde{v}(ij) = v_{\text{eff}}(ij) - \langle 0 | v_{\text{eff}}(ij) | 0 \rangle f(ij), \tag{4.20}$$

where the cluster expansion has been made in order to obtain this expression. 2) The $\omega_j(\boldsymbol{q})$ which are in energy denominators are replaced by the $\nu_j(\boldsymbol{q})$. The $\omega_j(\boldsymbol{q})$ which are associated with non-diagonal matrix elements remain the roots of G.

The anharmonic expressions so obtained are those whose numerical content will be discussed in section 5.

4.4. *t*-Matrix approaches

Several authors have applied *t*-matrix methods, which are familiar from nuclear physics theory, to the quantum solid problem. Since these methods were devised to cope with the hard-core problem, they are appropriate to either case. Application of this method to the calculation of the ground-state energy of quantum crystals has been made by Iwamoto and Namaizawa (1966), Guyer (1969a, b), Ebner and Sung (1971), and Østgaard (1971). Both the ground-state energy and anharmonic phonon properties have been calculated by Horner (1970a, b) and Glyde and Khanna (1971, 1972a, b). Each of the above authors used a somewhat independent theoretical development.

In a later, more formal theoretical treatment, Iwamoto and Namaizawa (1971) generalized their previous developments. A t-matrix approach to lattice dynamics was derived by Namaizawa (1972), who obtained an expression that is equivalent to a dynamical matrix and showed that this expression led to long-wavelength excitations which had the character of acoustic phonons. No numerical work has yet been done with this theory and its formal extension to include anharmonic effects has not been made.

The interrelations between the various t-matrix theories (including his own) are discussed at length by Brandow (1972) in another purely theoretical work. Because of the availability of this comparison, we will not discuss the relative merits of the different t-matrix approaches, but will present a simplified treatment which most closely follows the spirit of the derivations of Glyde and Khanna, and of Guyer. A further discussion of the derivation of Guyer is found in Guyer (1969b), and an alternative variational cluster-expansion derivation has been devised by Mullin (1971).

The theories which are classified here as t-matrix methods are those which attempt to derive an effective potential by focussing attention on the hard-core interaction between individual pairs of particles. Not all of these theories were termed t-matrix theories in their original development and not all of them are formally analogous to the t-matrix theories of nuclear physics. Hence, the term 't-matrix theory' is used somewhat loosely here and the derivation to follow will be one which is appropriate primarily in the context of quantum crystals.

In this context, E_0 and $|0\rangle$ are the ground-state energy and eigenfunction of the harmonic hamiltonian (2.3), and $\mathscr{E}_0$ and Ψ_0 are the ground-state energy and eigenfunction of the true hamiltonian (2.2). If we consider (2.3) as the unperturbed hamiltonian, the perturbation is $V(\text{crystal}) - V(\text{harmonic}) = \frac{1}{2}\sum_{i \neq j} v_p(ij)$, where

$$v_p(ij) = v(ij) - \boldsymbol{u}(ij)\cdot\boldsymbol{\Phi}(ij)\cdot\boldsymbol{u}(ij). \tag{4.21}$$

The shift in the ground-state energy from turning on the perturbation is given by the well-known level-shift expression:

$$\mathscr{E}_0 - E_0 = \langle 0|\, \tfrac{1}{2}\sum_{i \neq j} v_p(ij)\,|\Psi_0\rangle / \langle 0\,|\,\Psi_0\rangle. \tag{4.22}$$

The t-matrix for the pair (ij) is now defined as

$$\langle 0|\, t\,(ij)\,|0\rangle = \langle 0|\, v_{\mathrm{p}}\,(ij)\,|\Psi_0\rangle \tag{4.23}$$

and is quite analogous to the effective potential used in the theory of Bernardes and Primakoff (1960).

Thus we see that the fundamental idea of this method is to construct an operator – the t-matrix – which acts on the unperturbed ground-state wavefunction to produce a function that may be used in (4.22) in place of the true potential acting on the true ground-state wavefunction. Thus the t-matrix method can be viewed as a formal technique for defining a softened, effective potential. This potential is then used in place of the true hard-core potential, allowing one to work with a convenient set of basis functions such as phonon states or plane-wave states.

If Ψ_0 is expanded in terms of the unperturbed basis functions, the coefficients in the expansion (which involve matrix elements of the hard-core terms in V) are divergent. Nevertheless, a formal expression for this expansion can be obtained from the application of perturbation theory. Then the terms in this perturbation expansion can be arranged in such a way that, when one evaluates the expectation value of $v_{\mathrm{p}}\,(ij)$, the set of diagrams which account for the hard-core interaction between i and j are summed. This is the start of a perturbation theory derivation of the t-matrix.

However, this summation can be achieved in effect by a simpler, more intuitive approach. Suppose that one starts out with a perfectly harmonic crystal described by the hamiltonian (2.3). Next, the harmonic potential connecting the atoms i and j could be replaced by the true interatomic potential. The hamiltonian would now become

$$\mathrm{H}'\,(ij) = \mathrm{H} + v_{\mathrm{p}}\,(ij)\,. \tag{4.24}$$

Since the major effect of turning on $v\,(ij)$ is to introduce a short-range repulsion between i and j, a good approximation to the ground state eigenfunction of (4.24) should be

$$\Psi_0'\,(ij) = f\,(ij)\,|0\rangle\,, \tag{4.25}$$

where $f\,(ij)$ can be determined variationally because $\Psi_0'\,(ij)$ should satisfy the Schrödinger equation

$$\mathrm{H}'\,(ij)\,\Psi_0'\,(ij) = E_0'\,(ij)\,\Psi_0'\,(ij)\,. \tag{4.26}$$

The first-order expression for the energy shift is then

$$\mathscr{E}_0 - E_0 = \tfrac{1}{2}\sum \langle 0|\, v^t_{\text{eff}}(ij)\, |0\rangle \equiv \tfrac{1}{2}\sum \langle 0|\, t(ij)\, |0\rangle \tag{4.27a}$$

$$= \tfrac{1}{2}\sum \Delta E(ij), \tag{4.27b}$$

where the effective potential appropriate to the t-matrix theory is denoted by

$$v^t_{\text{eff}}(ij) = f(ij)\, v_{\text{p}}(ij) \tag{4.28}$$

and $f(ij)$ is normalized so that that $\langle 0|\, f(ij)\, |0\rangle = 1$. The quantity $\Delta E(ij)$ can be identified as the total energy shift in the hamiltonian (4.24) if $v(ij)$ is considered as a perturbation to H. It should be noted that $f(ij)$, as determined from (4.25), is a computationally convenient way to approximate the true ground-state eigenfunction of (4.24). The latter is what should really enter the theory.

The lowest-order theory of the ground-state energy is now specified provided one has a prescription for obtaining the model harmonic hamiltonian H. One way is for one to replace $v(ij)$ by $v^t_{\text{eff}}(ij)$ in all of the expressions in subsection 3.2. These expressions, together with the derivation of v^t_{eff} given in this section, form a self-consistent set of equations which can be solved iteratively to give the force-constants in H. Simultaneously, v^t_{eff} and all the other quantities of interest are obtained. This is the prescription that was followed by Glyde and Khanna.

The above procedure determines the ground-state energy to first order. The force constants in H can be assumed to provide a first-order determination of the phonon spectrum, but this has not yet been shown to follow directly from a derivation of the elementary excitation spectrum. Perhaps the work of Namaizawa (1972) will provide a starting point for this derivation.

One can then make an Ansatz that the anharmonic corrections to the first-order quantities are determined in a similar way – that is, one substitutes $v^t_{\text{eff}}(ij)$ for $v(ij)$ in all of the expressions in subsection 3.3. Although this Ansatz has been used in numerical calculations, it has not been rigorously justified. (In fact, it is not rigorously correct.) Nevertheless, it should represent a reasonably good approximation, and the anharmonic calculations on solid helium which start from the t-matrix approach are valid attempts to obtain something more from what is, in fact, a theory for the computation of the ground-state energy. The results of such calculations will be described in subsections 5.1, 5.2.

4.5. Fully consistent theories

A third modern, theoretical approach to the lattice dynamics of the quantum crystals (or of ordinary crystals at high temperatures) has been developed by Horner (1967, 1971b and 1972a). This will be called a fully consistent theory because renormalized phonon propagators are used throughout. Another fully consistent theory is that of Choquard (1967); however, this theory has never been computationally implemented except in an approximate form which reduces to the SHA with anharmonic corrections. It is not at all clear whether the second-order theory of Choquard can in fact be computationally implemented in the near future and, if it were, whether the implementation would avoid the hard-core problem.

The advantage of the theory of Horner is that the pair function is introduced at an early stage and forms an integral part of all expressions, so the hard-core is automatically treated on the same footing as any other aspect of the problem. Since Horner's chapter in volume 1 is devoted to the hard-core problem, only certain highlights of his theory will be discussed here especially those that present an illuminating contrast to other theoretical treatments.

The derivation of Horner uses the established technique of propagator renormalization according to the method of De Dominicis and Martin (1964). This technique was also applied in work by Beck and Meier (1971). Thus the essential innovative feature of Horner's theory is not the derivation itself, but rather, the way he organizes the formalism so as to focus on certain key quantities which can be approximated on physical grounds. An outline of the derivation follows.

A time-dependent force term $\sum U_\alpha(i,t)\, r_\alpha(i,t)$ is added to (2.2) to obtain a time-dependent hamiltonian, which will be denoted by $\mathscr{H}(t)$ in this subsection. A generalized partition function is then

$$Z = \mathrm{tr}\left\{ \mathrm{T}_\tau \exp\left[-\mathrm{i} \int_0^{-\mathrm{i}\beta} \mathscr{H}(t)\, \mathrm{d}t \right] \right\}, \tag{4.29}$$

where T_τ denotes time ordering along the imaginary axis and $\beta = 1/k_\mathrm{B}T$. A cumulant expansion of the free energy functional $\beta^{-1} \ln Z$ is obtained by defining n-point functions as the nth derivative of $\ln Z$ with respect to the $U_\alpha(i,t)$. Of particular importance are the one-point functions

$$d_\alpha(i,t) = -\mathrm{i}\langle r_\alpha(i,t)\rangle_U, \tag{4.30}$$

which equal $R_\alpha(i)$ if $\boldsymbol{U}$ is identically zero and the two-point functions

$$d_{\alpha\beta}(ij, tt') = -\langle \mathrm{T}_\tau r_\alpha(i, t)\, r_\beta(j, t')\rangle_U + \langle r_\alpha(i, t)\rangle_U \langle r_\beta(j, t')\rangle_U, \quad (4.31)$$

which are the phonon propagators. The average of an operator $O(t')$ is defined in the usual way as

$$\langle O(t')\rangle_U = \mathrm{tr}\left\{\mathrm{T}_\tau O(t') \exp\left[-\mathrm{i}\int_0^{-\mathrm{i}\beta} \mathscr{H}(t)\,\mathrm{d}t\right]\right\}/Z \quad (4.32)$$

and the subscript U is used as a reminder of the presence of the external forces $U_\alpha(i, t)$.

The pair function (or the equal-time correlation function for a pair of particles) plays a key role in this theory. One of the innovative features of the theory, which is quite important in its computational implementation, is a method for obtaining a reliable working approximation to this function based upon a sound theoretical derivation which separates out a short-range and a harmonic part. By definition, the pair function is

$$g_U(ij, t) = \langle \delta[\boldsymbol{r}(i, t) - \boldsymbol{r}(j, t) - \boldsymbol{r}(ij)]\rangle_U. \quad (4.33)$$

Substituting Fourier transforms of the delta functions, one obtains

$$g_U(ij, t) = (2\pi)^{-6} \int \mathrm{d}\boldsymbol{k}\,\mathrm{d}\boldsymbol{k}' \langle \mathrm{T}_\tau \exp\{-\mathrm{i}\boldsymbol{k}\cdot[\boldsymbol{r}(i, t) - \boldsymbol{r}(i)] + \mathrm{i}\boldsymbol{k}'\cdot[\boldsymbol{r}(j, t) - \boldsymbol{r}(j)]\}\rangle_U. \quad (4.34)$$

The quantity in the exponent can be expressed in terms of the n-point functions to obtain

$$\begin{aligned} g_U(ij, t) = (2\pi)^{-6} \int \mathrm{d}\boldsymbol{k}\,\mathrm{d}\boldsymbol{k}' &\times \exp(-\mathrm{i}\boldsymbol{k}\cdot[\mathrm{i}\boldsymbol{d}(i, t) - \boldsymbol{r}(i)] + \mathrm{i}\boldsymbol{k}'\cdot[\mathrm{i}\boldsymbol{d}(j, t) - \boldsymbol{r}(j)]) \\ &\times \exp(-\tfrac{1}{2}\boldsymbol{k}\cdot\boldsymbol{d}(ii, tt)\cdot\boldsymbol{k} + \boldsymbol{k}\cdot\boldsymbol{d}(ij, tt)\cdot\boldsymbol{k}' - \tfrac{1}{2}\boldsymbol{k}'\cdot\boldsymbol{d}(jj, tt)\cdot\boldsymbol{k}') \\ &\times \left\{\exp\left(\frac{1}{3!}\boldsymbol{kkk}\cdot\boldsymbol{d}(iii, ttt) - \tfrac{1}{2}\boldsymbol{kkk}'\cdot\boldsymbol{d}(iij, ttt) + \cdots\right) \times \cdots\right\}. \end{aligned} \quad (4.35)$$

This result is not obvious; however, one can verify the correctness of at least the first few terms by expanding the exponent on the right-hand side of (4.34), performing the indicated averaging and reassembling the results into the form of the right-hand side of (4.35).

The term in curly brackets can be moved in front of the integral sign by replacing all of its $\boldsymbol{k}$ and $\boldsymbol{k}'$ by $\nabla(i)$ and $\nabla(j)$ respectively. The quantity remaining inside the integral is then a quadratic in $\boldsymbol{k}$ and $\boldsymbol{k}'$ and the integrals can be performed exactly. At this point, one can assume that $g_U(ij, t)$ depends only on $\boldsymbol{r}(ij)$, not on $\boldsymbol{r}(i)+\boldsymbol{r}(j)$, and that the harmonic and short-range parts factorize, then

$$g_U(ij, t) = \exp\{\varphi[\nabla(ij)]\}\, g_{\mathrm{h}}(ij, t) \tag{4.36}$$

is obtained, where $\varphi[\nabla(ij)]$ is some function of the gradient operator with respect to $\boldsymbol{r}(ij)$ and

$$g_{\mathrm{h}}(ij, t) = [|\boldsymbol{\Lambda}(ij, t)|\, \pi^3]^{-1/2} \exp\{-\boldsymbol{u}(ij, t)\cdot[\boldsymbol{\Lambda}(ij, t)]^{-1}\cdot \boldsymbol{u}(ij, t)\}, \tag{4.37}$$

where $\boldsymbol{u}(ij, t)$ is defined in a manner similar to the time-independent $u(ij)$ introduced in subsection 1.2, but with

$$\boldsymbol{R}(ij, t) = \mathrm{i}[\boldsymbol{d}(i, t) - \boldsymbol{d}(j, t)]. \tag{4.38}$$

The quantity $g_{\mathrm{h}}(ij, t)$ is a time-dependent generalization of the harmonic pair function which has been given in (3.28). An important point is that

$$\boldsymbol{\Lambda}(ij, t) = -\tfrac{1}{2}[\boldsymbol{d}(ii, tt) - \boldsymbol{d}(ij, tt) - \boldsymbol{d}(ji, tt) + \boldsymbol{d}(ji, tt)] \tag{4.39}$$

is obtained from the actual phonon propagators. In the absence of external forces, the two-point functions on the right-hand side of (4.39) are no longer time-dependent and $g_{\mathrm{h}}(ij, t)$ becomes identical with (3.28). The short-range correlation function $f(ij, t)$ is now defined by

$$f(ij, t)\, g_{\mathrm{h}}(ij, t) = \exp\{\varphi[\nabla(ij)]\}\, g_{\mathrm{h}}(ij, t). \tag{4.40}$$

The fact that all of the dependence of $g_U(ij, t)$ on one- and two-point functions has been put into $g_{\mathrm{h}}(ij, t)$ places three important restrictions on $f(ij, t)$:

$$\int \mathrm{d}\boldsymbol{r}(ij, t)\, f(ij, t)\, g_{\mathrm{h}}(ij, t) = 1, \tag{4.41a}$$

$$\int \mathrm{d}\boldsymbol{r}(ij, t)\, \boldsymbol{u}(ij, t)\, f(ij, t)\, g_{\mathrm{h}}(ij, t) = 0 \tag{4.41b}$$

and

$$\int \mathrm{d}\boldsymbol{r}(ij, t)\, \boldsymbol{u}(ij, t)\, \boldsymbol{u}(ij, t)\, f(ij, t)\, g_{\mathrm{h}}(ij, t) = \tfrac{1}{2}\boldsymbol{\Lambda}(ij, t). \tag{4.41c}$$

Each of these three consistency relationships also hold with $f(ij, t)$ replaced by unity (with the trivial assumption that $g_h(ij, t)$ is normalized). The relationships impose conditions on the lowest moments of $f(ij, t)$ which prohibit the short-range correlations from altering the average distance between a pair of particles or the mean-square width of their distribution.

It is easily shown that (4.41a) and (4.41c) can be combined to give $\langle \nabla_\alpha(ij) \nabla_\beta(ij) f(ij, t)\rangle = 0$. If this requirement were inserted into the CBF theory, the term leading to the troublesome difference between ω and v would be removed. While it is clear from the form of the CBF theory that this removal would be aesthetically appealing, the argument of Horner indicates more – it is necessary for an internally consistent separation of $f(ij, t)$ and $g_h(ij, t)$. This indication is confirmed by recent work of Werthamer (1973), which showed that the consistency relationships are satisfied if a variationally optimized Jastrow function is used in the CBF theory.

As will be seen, it is important to retain the time-dependence in $g_U(ij, t)$ in order to obtain expressions for anharmonic effects. However, numerical evaluation of these expressions ultimately involves matrix elements of the derivatives of the potential with respect to a static pair function $g(ij) = f(ij) \times g_h(ij)$. One can make the hypothesis that the two most important characteristics of the short-range part of the static pair function are proper behavior at small $r(ij)$ to prevent hard-core overlap and satisfaction of the consistency requirements. This physical reasoning leads to a remarkably simple, approximate form for $f(ij)$. It is first taken to be the product of a spherically-symmetric function $f_s(ij)$ and a quadratic polynomial in $r(ij)$. It is not possible to satisfy the transverse parts of the consistency requirements with this form, but this should not be important as the hard-core overlap is a longitudinal effect.

The functional form of $f_s(ij)$ has to be determined most carefully in the region of hard-core overlap. A method of deriving f_s which focuses attention on this region is described in the following. The wavefunction $\Psi_0(r)$ describing s-wave scattering in the potential is the solution of

$$\left[\frac{d^2}{dr^2} + \frac{2}{r}\frac{d}{dr} - \frac{1}{\lambda^2} v(r)\right] \Psi_0(r) = 0, \tag{4.42}$$

with $\Psi_0(0) = 0$. Then a function $f_0(r)$ is defined by

$$\begin{aligned} f_0(r) &= \Psi_0^2(r), \quad r < r_0, \\ &= \Psi_0^2(r_0), \quad r > r_0, \end{aligned} \tag{4.43}$$

where r_0 is the first maximum in $\Psi_0(r)$. (The functional form of $f_0(r)$ beyond r_0 is unimportant.) Finally, $f_s(ij)$ is taken to be

$$f_s(ij) = f_0\left[a_0(ij) + a_1(ij)\,u(ij) + a_2(ij)\,u(ij)^2\right]. \tag{4.44}$$

The constants a_0, a_1 and a_2 are adjusted to satisfy (4.41a)–(4.41c) as nearly as possible. The density dependence arises entirely from the self-consistency requirements modifying the coefficients in the polynomials since f_0 is independent of density.

A graph of $g_s(ij)$ as obtained from (4.44) for three nearest neighbors in bcc ^{4}He is shown in fig. 8. The steep rise in the short-range part occurs at essentially the same place for the first two shells. Thus, in the bcc structure with large zero-point motion, the first two shells behave somewhat as one super shell with fourteen nearest neighbors. This stabilizes the bcc structure with respect to the fcc or hcp phase with twelve neighbors. By the third shell, the departure from the gaussian is negligible although the short range part is still needed to cut off the potential in the tail of the gaussian.

By taking the average value of the double commutator of $\mathscr{H}(t)$ with respect to $r_\alpha(i, t)$, the equation of motion of the one-point function is found to be

$$\hbar^2\partial^2 \boldsymbol{d}(i, t)/\partial t^2 = \mathrm{i}\lambda^2\left[\boldsymbol{K}(i, t) + \boldsymbol{U}(i, t)\right], \tag{4.45}$$

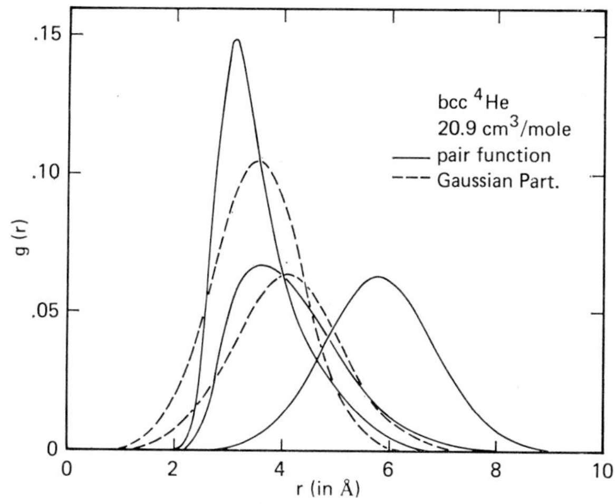

Fig. 8. The pair function for the first three shells of neighbors in bcc ^{4}He at 20.9 cc/mole as determined by Horner (1972a) is shown by the solid lines. The dashed lines give the gaussian part alone. For the third shell, the difference between the full pair function and the gaussian part cannot be seen on this plot.

where $\boldsymbol{K}(i, t)$, the internal force on particle i, is given by

$$\boldsymbol{K}(i, t) = \sum_{j \neq i} \iint \mathrm{d}\boldsymbol{r}(i)\, \mathrm{d}\boldsymbol{r}(j)\, g_U(ij, t)\, \boldsymbol{\nabla}(j)\, v(ij). \tag{4.46}$$

Differentiation of (4.45) with respect to $U_\beta(j, t')$ while considering the $d_\alpha(i, t)$ rather than the $U_\alpha(i, t)$ as independent variables, gives the equation of motion of the phonon propagator as

$$\hbar^2 \partial^2 d_{\alpha\beta}(ij, tt')/\partial t^2$$
$$= -\lambda^2 \sum \int_0^{-\mathrm{i}\beta} \mathrm{d}\tau\, M_{\alpha\gamma}(il, t\tau)\, d_{\gamma\beta}(lj, \tau t') + \mathrm{i}\lambda^2\, \delta(ij)\, \delta_{\alpha\beta}\, \delta(t - t'). \tag{4.47}$$

The quantity

$$M_{\alpha\beta}(ij, tt') = -\mathrm{i}\delta K_\alpha(i, t)/\delta_\beta(j, t') \tag{4.48}$$

is the phonon self energy and plays the role of a generalized force-constant matrix. It is to be interpreted as the change in the average force on particle i when the average position of particle j has been changed by the external force.

It is clear from (4.46) and (4.48) that $\boldsymbol{M}(ij, tt')$ is determined from the dependence of $g_U(ij, t)$ on $d(j, t')$. A detailed analysis of $\boldsymbol{M}$ is made by Horner (1971b). He finds that, when g_U is separated into a short-range and a harmonic part as in (4.40), three contributions to $\boldsymbol{M}$ can be distinguished:

a) An instantaneous contribution

$$\boldsymbol{M}^{(1)}(ij, tt')$$
$$= -\delta(t - t') \int \mathrm{d}\boldsymbol{r}(ij)\, g_{\mathrm{h}}(ij, t)\, \boldsymbol{\nabla}(ij)\, [f(ij, t)\, \boldsymbol{\nabla}(ij)\, v(ij)], \tag{4.49}$$

which comes from the explicit dependence of $g_{\mathrm{h}}(ij, t)$ on the average interparticle spacing $\boldsymbol{R}(ij, t)$. In the limit $f \to 1$, this expression reduces to the $\langle \boldsymbol{\nabla\nabla} V \rangle$ term familiar from the SHA theory.

b) A dispersive part $\boldsymbol{M}^{(2)}(ij, tt')$ which arises from the dependence of $g_{\mathrm{h}}(ij, t)$ on $\boldsymbol{\Lambda}(ij, t)$. The full term is quite complicated because in the limit $f \to 1$ it has to contain all of the anharmonic corrections of the SCH theory. An approximation analogous to retaining only three-phonon terms is then made. The result is that the cubic force constants are now given by

$$\Phi(123) = \tfrac{1}{2} \sum_{i \neq j} \mathrm{d}\boldsymbol{r}(ij)\, \boldsymbol{\nabla}(1)\, \boldsymbol{\nabla}(2)\, [f(ij)\, \boldsymbol{\nabla}(3)\, v(ij)] \tag{4.50}$$

instead of (3.35), and the full phonon propagators, expressed in terms of a frequency dependent spectral function, link the two three-phonon vertices in (3.34). As in (a), (4.50) reduces to the SHA form if $f \to 1$; however, because of the use of renormalized propagators, the $\boldsymbol{M}^{(2)}$ contribution does not, except in the additional limit of small anharmonicity.

c) A term which arises from the functional dependence of the short-range function $f(ij, t)$. This term does not have an analogue in the SHA theory. It can be further divided into a dependence of f on $\boldsymbol{R}(ij, t)$ and on $\boldsymbol{\Lambda}(ij, t)$. An argument is made that it is consistent with the approximations made in (b) to ignore the latter dependence. An adiabatic approximation is then made in which it is assumed that the response time of the short-range function is much faster than the phonon frequencies. The whole term then gives an instantaneous contribution

$$M^{(3)}_{\alpha\beta}(ij, tt) = \delta(t - t') \sum_{k \neq i} \int \mathrm{d}\boldsymbol{r}(il)\, g_{\mathrm{h}}(il) \frac{\delta f(il)}{\delta R_\beta(il)} \nabla_\alpha(ij)\, v(il), \qquad (4.51)$$

which can be added to the force-constant analog (4.49). An expression for the total instantaneous contribution which can be decomposed into (4.49) and (4.51) has been obtained by Meissner (1968a, b) from the ω^3 sum rule.

Thus we see that the framework provided in subsections 3.2, 3.3, which was originally associated with the QHA, provides a useful structure on which to build the computational apparatus for the considerably different, fully consistent theory. In section 5, all of the contributions to $\boldsymbol{M}(ij, tt')$ will be found to play an important role in the numerical predictions of the theory, and the method of constructing $f_s(ij)$ will be seen to be important in obtaining the overall correct density dependence.

5. *Numerical results and comparison with experiment*

5.1. Ground state energy

The first quantitative numerical calculations of the properties of the quantum crystals were efforts to obtain the volume dependence of the ground-state energy–that is, the cohesive energy at absolute zero. These calculations used a Lennard–Jones potential and their results were compared with sometimes not very reliable experimental data.

By now, however, more sophisticated theories and more powerful computational techniques have been developed. These, combined with the current availability of accurate experimental data, give us a broader perspective on the ground-state energy calculations. It is now clear that these calculations can be used to serve three purposes.

One purpose, obviously, is the first principles evaluation of the ground-state energy of the quantum crystals. Then one uses the most reliable form of He–He interaction and attempts to reproduce the experimental results of, for example, Dugdale and Franck (1964), Edwards and Pandorf (1965), (1966), Pandorf and Edwards (1968), Sample and Swenson (1967), Ahlers (1970), and Gardner et al. (1972).

Alternatively, one can use any of the various available theories to study the properties of a model quantum solid in which the interaction is known. (The well studied Lennard–Jones quantum solid with its analytically simple potential is the obvious choice.) The appropriate data are then the computer experimental results obtained in the Monte Carlo (MC) calculations of Hansen and Levesque (1968), Hansen (1969, 1970, 1971), and Hansen and Pollock (1972). Here, the motivation is to test a theory of quantum solids against a system in which the potential is known.

Finally, one can use the most reliable computational technique available together with a variety of model interatomic potentials. The comparative agreement between theory and experiment is then a guide to the selection of the best model potential. There is obviously a good deal of overlap between these approaches, but pursuit of all three lines of investigation is necessary if we wish to achieve the goal of discovering the best theory and the best potential.

Since the MC calculations themselves are probably the most reliable method of obtaining the ground-state energy from a given form of pair potential, the results of these calculations will form the basis of much of the discussions of this subsection. Therefore, a few preliminary remarks on the method are essential to provide the proper orientation.

We are not concerned here with the techniques of this method. Such details may be found in the papers cited above and references contained in these papers. For the purposes of this discussion, the MC technique can be viewed simply as a method for obtaining the pair function from a many-body wavefunction. The method is statistical and the resulting pair function is subject to random errors. The average error is determined by the amount of computer time one wishes to expend. With computer runs of reasonable length, the uncertainty in the evaluation of the total energy is about 0.2 K. Since different theories and different potentials give results which can differ from each other by several degrees, this is certainly an acceptable statistical error.

Another source of error of a technical nature is the number of particles used in the integration process. Here again, there is a trade-off between accuracy and computer time requirements. It has been established that the error is negligible with the size of systems used to obtain the results which will be quoted here.

Since we are treating the MC results as essentially correct in this subsection, it is well to introduce an element of caution concerning a possible source of error of a non-technical nature. The MC calculations to date (with a single exception which will be noted later) can be considered to have done the Nosanow calculation exactly. That is, they have used a Jastrow–NCG wavefunction, but have performed the many-body integrations exactly rather than approximately by means of a cluster expansion. This allows for a greater freedom in the choice of Jastrow factors as one is no longer restricted to forms for which the cluster expansion is known to converge. The form

$$f(r) = \exp[-2C/r^5] \tag{5.1}$$

was used, because $f(r)^{1/2}$ is the solution of the two-body Schrödinger equation for the Lennard–Jones potential at short distance with $C=\frac{2}{5}\sqrt{2}\lambda$. The quantity C was actually used as a variational parameter, but its optimum value did not differ from this by very much even for other forms of the potential. Thus (5.1) should seem to have the correct short-range behavior. However, it is known that the cluster expansion does not converge for this form and so it is not suitable for the cluster expansion approximation.

The Jastrow–NCG calculation is variational and, as such, is capable of yielding the correct ground-state energy providing the variational wavefunction has sufficient flexibility. The additional flexibility introduced by the MC procedure, which lifts the constraint of being suitable for the cluster expansion from the wavefunction, enables one to use (5.1) rather than the original Nosanow form. It has been shown by Hansen and Levesque (1968) that this lowers the ground-state energy by about 3.5 K.

Even if (5.1) is the optimal or nearly optimal form of Jastrow function, there is still obviously one remaining constraint: the use of a wavefunction of the form (4.2). Could the energy be lowered significantly by using a different variational wavefunction? This question is open, but it furnishes an attractive area for future investigation in view of some recent results which will be summarized below.

The most obvious possibility for improving the variational wavefunction would be to use a CG rather than a NCG wavefunction for the harmonic part. This was investigated by Hansen and Pollock (1972) who used a rather restricted form of CG in which the components of the G matrix connected each atom with its nearest and second nearest neighbor with equal strength. The resulting wavefunction only had two variable parameters. This calculation gave a negligible improvement in energy–a significant contrast to the 4.0 K difference between the results of Nosanow (1966) and Koehler (1967). This suggests either that the Jastrow function contains all of the necessary correlation or that a more general form of CG should be used.

The above problem can probably be resolved with a sufficient amount of effort; however, emphasis has recently been placed on another aspect by Bhattacharyya and Woo (1972), and Woo (1972), although their treatment was for the liquid rather than the solid. There is a discussion in these works and references contained therein about the correspondence between Jastrow-function calculations and diagrammatic perturbation theory. The essential point is that the optimum Jastrow function sums all diagrams up to a certain order exactly and partially sums a class of higher-order diagrams. It is shown that the optimal inclusion of three particle factors in the wavefunction will sum exactly to the next higher order (as well as partially summing a larger class of still higher-order terms). In anharmonic lattice calculations, the next highest term is the cubic term. As will be seen shortly, various calculations obtain a contribution from this term of approximately 1 K. Therefore it is possible that such additional terms will make an appreciable contribution to the ground-state energy and a calculation to at least estimate their magnitude is clearly called for.

The dependence of the ground-state energy calculations on the form of the interatomic potential has been investigated by several authors. In particular, two sets of MC calculations have been reported. In one set, Hansen and Pollock (1972) explored the differences between the usual Lennard–Jones potential LJ1, a Lennard–Jones potential LJ2 with $\sigma = 2.62$ Å, the potential of Bruch and McGee (1970), and that of Beck (1968) for fcc ^{3}He and ^{4}He over a density range of approximately 9 to 19 cc/mole. The results are plotted here in fig. 9. The differences between theory and experiment are plotted in cases where this will simplify the interpretation of the plots. The MC results have been smoothed somewhat, but some irregularities, which are probably due to statistical errors, remain. It is clear that only the Beck and LJ2 potentials are suitable over the entire density range.

Hansen and Pollock also tabulate values for the density dependence of the compressibility and pressure vs. molar volume. The comparison of these with experiment is a more sensitive test of the density dependence of the theory than is the direct comparison of the ground-state energy in fig. 9.

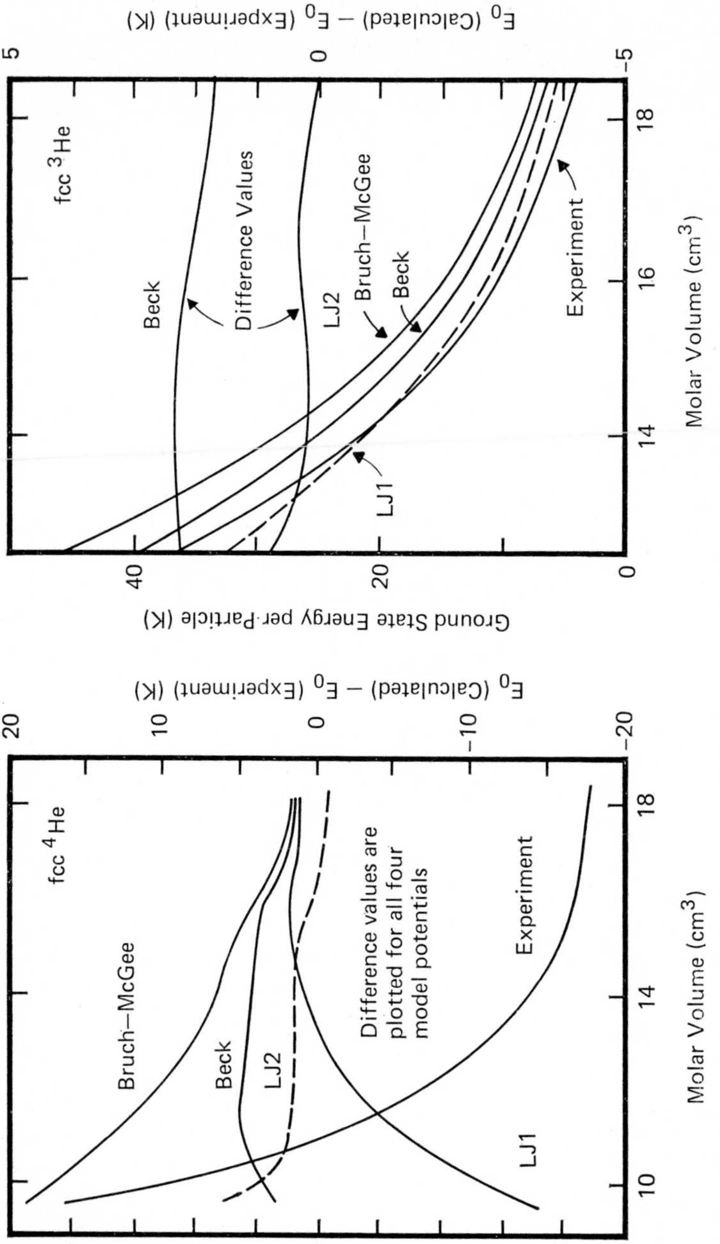

Fig. 9. The results of the Monte Carlo calculations of the ground-state energy of fcc ^{4}He and fcc ^{3}He by Hansen and Pollock (1972) for various model potentials, as described in the text, are contrasted with experimental results. For ^{4}He, the difference between the calculated values and the experimental results of Dugdale and Frank (1964) is shown, and the experimental values are also plotted directly. For ^{3}He, the calculated results for three potentials and the experimental results for the hcp phase deduced from Straty and Adams (1968) are shown; in addition, the difference values are plotted for the Beck and LJ2 potentials. The LJ2 values are too close to experiment to be easily distinguished on the direct plot. The difference values in both figures have been somewhat smoothed by hand.

The final conclusion one is led to by all the MC results is: the Beck potential gives the best over all agreement with experiment. This conclusion was also reached by Glyde (1971), who compared the LJ1, the Beck and the potential of Murrell and Shaw (1968). The analytic expression for the Beck potential is

$$v(r) = \varepsilon \left\{ A' \, e^{-\alpha r} \, e^{-\beta r^6} - \frac{D}{(r^2 + a^2)^3} \left[1 + \frac{2.709 + 3a^2}{r^2 + a^2} \right] \right\}, \tag{5.2}$$

with $\varepsilon = 10.371$ K, $A' = 44.62 \times 10^4$, $\alpha = 4.390$ Å^{-1}, $D = 972.5$, $\beta = 3.746 \times 10^{-4}$ Å^{-6}, and $a = 0.675$ Å. The comparison of the shape of this potential with the LJ1 potential is made in fig. 2a (see page 11). The primary differences between the two are the slightly larger hard-core radius of the Beck potential, its less steeply rising repulsive part and the occurrence of its minimum at a slightly larger value of r.

In the other set of MC calculations, Hansen (1971) obtained the density dependence of ^{4}He for the LJ1, LJ2 and Bruch–McGee potentials as well as for a 9–6 Lennard–Jones potential over a density range of about 17 to 22 cc/mole. Unfortunately, the Beck potential was not included in this study. The LJ2 and the Bruch–McGee potentials gave the best density dependence; the LJ2 was the closest to experiment and was everywhere slightly too low. Extrapolating the comparative behavior of the LJ2 and the Beck potentials from fig. 9, one would expect that the Beck potential would give the best agreement with experiment in this density range also. The 9–6 potential, which had also been used by Brueckner and Thieberger (1969) in order to improve the agreement between their theory and experiment, gave a bad density dependence and a ground-state energy which was much too low. Finally, the LJ1 potential also had a bad density dependence and the energies were about 1.5 K too high.

There were two important lessons to be learned from the MC studies: first, it is important to use the right potential in order to obtain the correct density dependence. This has been a problem in several quantum crystal calculations. Second, one should no longer hope to obtain agreement with experiment from calculations using the LJ1 potential.

Other calculations comparing different potentials have also been made, but these are not as revealing as the MC results. In the comparisons made by Ebner and Sung (1971), different numerical techniques used in their t-matrix method produced almost as much variation in results as did the choice of potential. The numerical effects will be mentioned again later. They obtained a ground-state energy with the potential of Yntema and Schneider (1950) which was about 6 K above their LJ1 results. This either rules the

Yntema–Schneider potential out or exposes these calculations to serious doubt. A variety of potentials were also studied by Glyde and Khanna (1972a), who used a cluster expansion and the Jastrow–CG wavefunction. Since this method is known to give too high a value for the ground-state energy and an incorrect density dependence, nothing definitive can be learned about the other potentials from this study. However, the relative results should be reasonably reliable, and the whole set could be normalized by adjusting, for example, the LJ1 results to agree with the MC calculations.

The results of various calculations using the Jastrow-cluster method for bcc ^{3}He with the LJ1 potential are shown in fig. 10 together with the MC results of Hansen (1970), which are the proper data for comparison. For

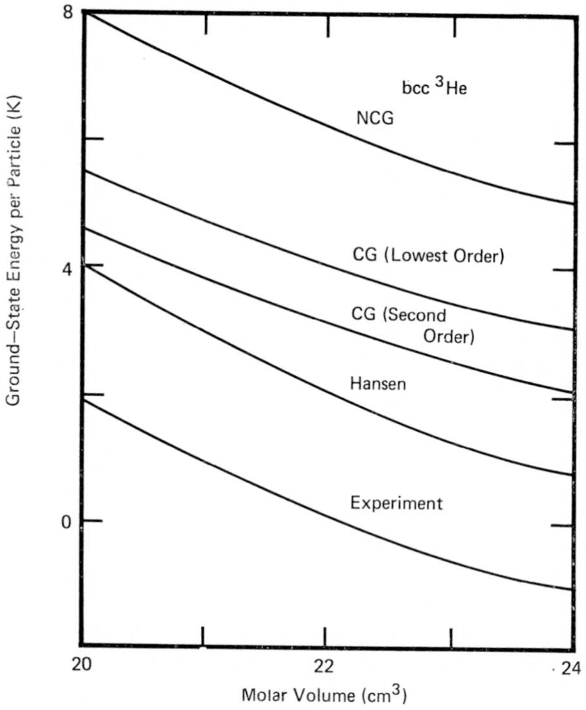

Fig. 10. Theoretical volume dependence of the ground-state energy per particle for bcc ^{3}He from various calculations using the Jastrow-NCG or CG wavefunction. The top three curves use the cluster expansion. The NCG curve is the result of the Nosanow (1966) method. The two CG curves are results of the CBF approach in the lowest-order and with cubic anharmonic corrections. The above should be compared with the Monte Carlo calculations of Hansen (1970). All of the calculations used the Lennard–Jones LJ1 potential. The experimental results of Pandorf and Edwards (1968) are also shown for reference.

reference, the experimental ground-state energy as determined by Pandorf and Edwards (1968) is also shown. There are several features of the graph which are worthy of comment: None of the energies obtained from the cluster expansion calculations have the correct density dependence. They neither agree with the MC nor with the experimental results. An important result, which was first noted by Koehler (1967), is the lowering in energy with the Jastrow–CG as opposed to the Jastrow–NCG wavefunction.

In the calculation of Koehler and Werthamer (1972) using a Jastrow–CG plus cubic anharmonic corrections, the corrections improved the energy by about one degree, but produced very little effect on the density dependence. It is possible that an improvement of similar magnitude could be obtained from perturbative corrections to the MC calculations, in which case the results from the Beck potential would be in even better agreement with experiment.

The work of Hetherington et al. (1967), which included three-body corrections to the ground state energy, is in quite close agreement with the Jastrow–NCG results and is not shown in this figure. Another indication, that the cluster expansion itself is not responsible for the disagreement between the three highest lying curves in fig. 10 and the 'experimental' MC results, was reported by Hansen and Levesque (1968). They performed a direct MC evaluation of the ground-state energy using the Nosanow wavefunction and their results were in essential agreement with the cluster expansion results. It would therefore appear that it is essential to use a wavefunction for which the cluster expansion is invalid, if one wishes to obtain a low enough value for the ground-state energy in the Jastrow-variational approach.

The results of the various t-matrix calculations for the volume dependence of the ground-state energy of bcc ^{3}He are shown in fig. 11. The calculations of Horner (1970b), Guyer (1969a), and Ebner and Sung (1971) all start from a single particle picture and use the LJ1 potential. The MC results of Hansen (1970) are shown for comparison. The spread in the results of the three calculations can be accounted for, at least in part, by differences in numerical approximations used in obtaining the final equation for the pair function. These technical details have not been discussed here, but some intercomparison can be found in Brandow (1972). In addition, an exploration of various approximations is made by Ebner and Sung and the curve shown here is the one they feel is their best. The fact that it lies below the MC result does not invalidate their numerical work, because the results of a t-matrix calculation are not an upper bound.

The two curves of Glyde and Khanna (1972a) are obtained with the Beck potential. The upper curve starts from the single particle picture and the

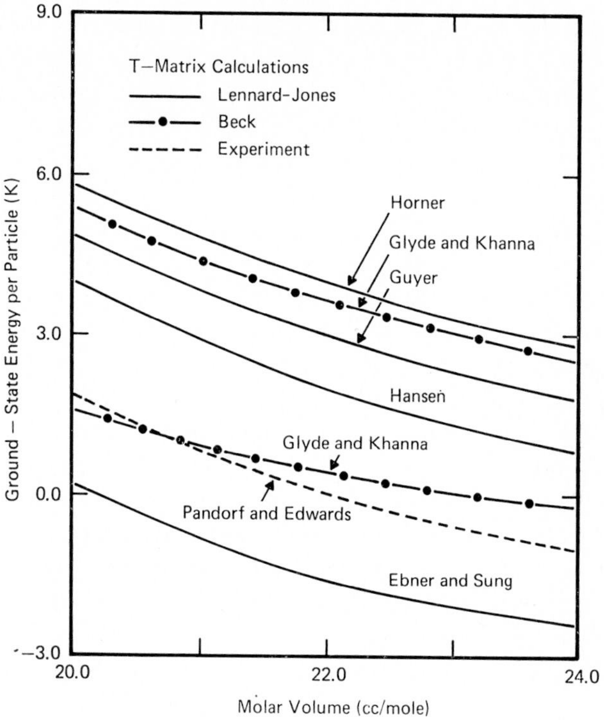

Fig. 11. Volume dependence of the ground-state energy of bcc ^{3}He from various *t*-matrix calculations together with the Monte Carlo results of Hansen (1970) and the experimental results of Pandorf and Edwards (1968). The solid and dot-dash curves are from calculations with the LJ1 and Beck potentials respectively. The four upper curves are *t*-matrix calculations which start from the single-particle picture, and the lower curve of Glyde and Khanna (1972a) is a *t*-matrix calculation which starts from the collective picture. Other relevant details are given in the text.

lower curve from the collective picture; the difference is similar to that found in the comparison of the Jastrow–NCG-cluster and the Jastrow–CG-cluster calculations. Each curve shown uses the same pair function for all (ij); a lowering of about $\frac{1}{2}$ K was found when a separate pair function was obtained for each shell of neighbors. Note that the density dependence of these results does not agree very well with the experimental data of Pandorf and Edwards (1968), even though the Beck potential was used.

The results of Østgaard (1971) are not shown in this figure. He used the Yntema–Schneider and the Bruch–McGee potentials and a comparison with the depicted results would not be meaningful. Both potentials gave results which were too high and had the wrong density dependence for bcc ^{3}He.

In general, the papers cited in this subsection contain more numerical results than were presented here, where the effort has been to show the general trend of the calculations. Each of the *t*-matrix calculations differs somewhat in numerical details and an effort to explore all of the theories from a common numerical approach would be useful.

5.2. Phonon dispersion curves

The first calculations of phonon dispersion curves for the quantum crystals with self-consistent theories were actually performed before any experimental data was available. Since these theories were the first that predicted real values for the phonon frequencies throughout the Brillouin zone, it was very important that inelastic neutron scattering experiments be performed in order to determine whether real, physical phonons actually existed in the quantum solids. Such experiments were impossible to perform with solid ^{3}He because of its large capture cross-section for thermal neutrons; the experiments were very difficult for solid ^{4}He because of the cryogenic environment, crystal growing problems, a small coherent neutron scattering cross section, and a large Debye–Waller factor.

Nevertheless, three groups responded to the challenge and inelastic neutron scattering experiments were performed on hcp ^{4}He at 21.1 cc/mole by the Brookhaven group (Minkiewicz et al. 1968), and on hcp ^{4}He at 16.0 cc/mole by the Iowa State group (Reese et al. 1971). Preliminary results from the Brookhaven experiments were reported by Lipschultz et al. (1967) and from the Iowa State experiments by Brun et al. (1968). In the third independent experiment, Bitter et al. (1967) studied polycrystalline hcp ^{4}He at 20.9 cc/mole.

These experiments established the sine qua non of the lattice dynamics of quantum crystals: there were indeed phonons in solid helium. This was gratifying, but not surprising, to followers of the self-consistent approach to lattice dynamics. The experiments also demonstrated that there was considerable broadening or lifetime effects associated with some of the more energetic phonon modes. This showed that it was absolutely essential to include anharmonicity in lattice dynamics calculations for the quantum crystals even at 0 K, thus stimulating the development of theories capable of treating anharmonicity and hard-core effects simultaneously.

The phonon dispersion curves obtained in the Iowa State experiments are shown in fig. 12 and the Brookhaven results are displayed in fig. 13. The solid lines in both figures are the theoretical results of Gillis et al. (1968). The analysis of the experimental data in terms of a conventional force-

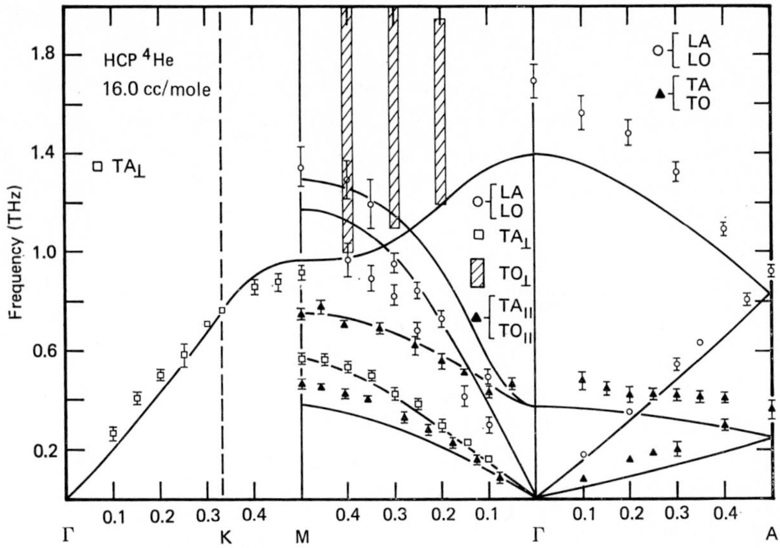

Fig. 12. Theoretical phonon dispersion curves for hcp ^{4}He at 16.0 cc/mole obtained by Gillis et al. (1968) together with the experimental results of Reese et al. (1971). The $TA_{\|}$ and $TO_{\|}$ branches along ΓM were obtained by scaling the results of Minkiewicz et al. (1968) as described in the text. The shaded areas are broad, ill-defined, anomalous groups.

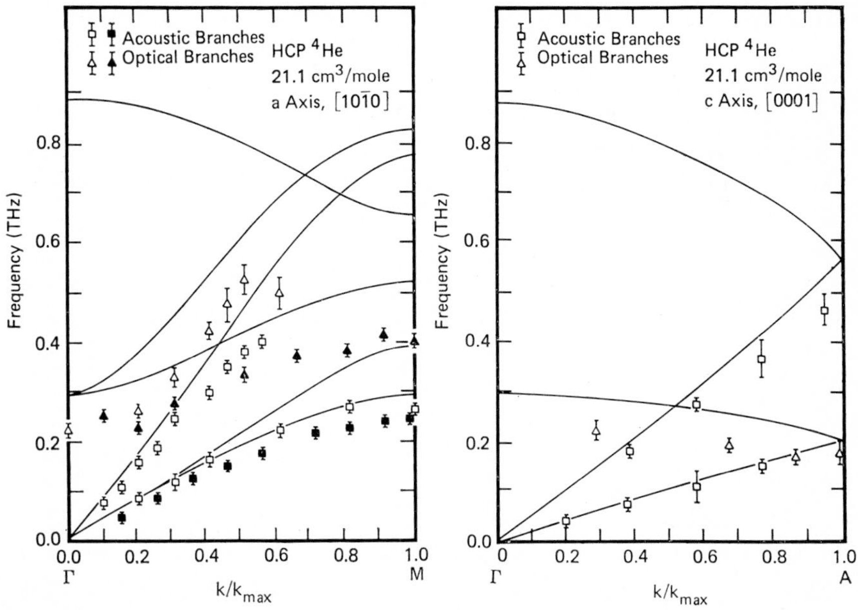

Fig. 13. Theoretical phonon dispersion curves for hcp ^{4}He along the *a* and *c* axes at 21.1 cc/mole obtained by Gillis et al. (1968) together with the experimental results of Minkiewicz et al. (1968).

constant fit was also made, but this treatment is not relevant here and its description may be found in the experimental papers.

On the whole, the agreement between theory and experiment could be considered satisfactory, but the need for more refined theoretical treatments was clearly established. The lowest-order CBF treatment led to results that were, on the whole, within about 20% of experiment and there were no adjustable parameters in the calculations. The same could be said for calculations based on the single particle picture. As discussed in subsection 4.3, this treatment yields frequencies which are almost identical with the lowest order CBF results for acoustic modes and are about 20% lower for optic modes. Both are in striking contrast to the QHA treatment which, as has been noted previously, predicts imaginary frequencies throughout the entire Brillouin zone.

The major disagreement between theory and experiment at each density was the incorrect degree of anisotropy in the theoretical curves; the agreement is quite good along some branches, but other theoretical branches are either too high or too low. A comparison of the results at the two different densities shows an overall incorrect density dependence for the theory. The density dependence of the experimental dispersion curves was remarkably simple: each phonon energy at one density was related to its energy at the other density by a single multiplicative constant. This implies that the Grüneisen parameter is approximately the same for all modes. The frequency scaling was used to obtain some of the points shown in fig. 12.

It is, of course, outside the bounds of the lowest-order CBF theory to evaluate either phonon widths or the resulting energy shifts. The width of the LA and LO phonons in the (001) direction, as obtained in the Iowa State work, is shown in fig. 14. In some cases, the magnitude of the associated damping rate is such that the excitation only lasts for about two periods of oscillation and is therefore not very well defined. Strong indications that certain lines were not only broad, but also non-symmetric were reported. Since, in addition, these lines were found at what seemed to be too high an energy, they are shown cross-hatched in fig. 12. There is further evidence of heavy damping in this branch: it was not found at all in the Brookhaven experiments. There were indications of anomalous intensity in certain lines. This and the asymmetry also cannot be obtained from the lowest-order theory.

By the time the next inelastic neutron scattering experiments were performed, the theory had advanced and anharmonic calculations had become more common. However, certain unexpected results of the experiments forced the theory to advance even further. The second set of experiments were performed at Brookhaven on bcc ^{4}He at 21.0 cc/mole by Osgood et al. (1972) and on fcc ^{4}He at 11.7 cc/mole at Iowa State by Traylor et al. (1971). The results which may be interpreted conventionally as anharmonically broadened phonons will be discussed in this subsection: the unexpected results will be treated in subsections 5.6 and 5.7.

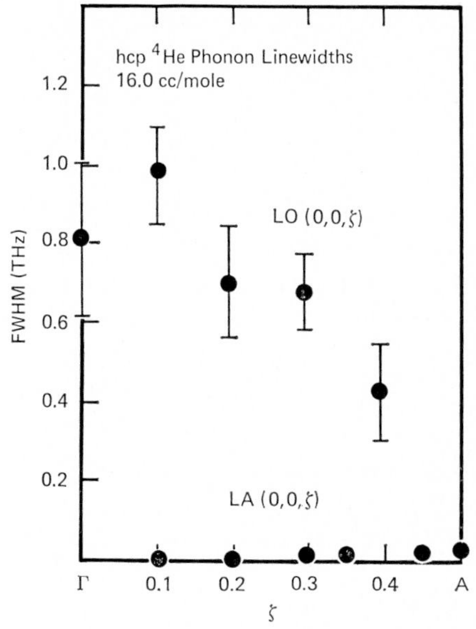

Fig. 14. Experimental full width at half-maximum (fwhm) of longitudinal phonon groups along (001) (the direction parallel to the c axis) from Reese et al. (1971). The zone boundary is at $\zeta = 0.5$.

The experiments on bcc ^{4}He are complicated by cryogenic considerations. That phase exists in a region which is only 0.60 atm high by 0.050 K wide at the most in a p–T diagram, and it is difficult to maintain a specimen in this phase for the length of time required to perform an inelastic neutron scattering experiment. However, once this problem is solved, both the data analysis and the computational aspect of the theory are considerably simplified by the cubic geometry. The geometrical simplifications also occur in the fcc experiments. Since cubic anharmonic calculations of phonon spectral functions have not yet been reported for hcp materials, the experiments in cubic helium were essential to test the anharmonic effects predicted by various theories.

The bcc results have been more readily available and there are more published comparisons between theory and these measurements. Therefore, we will concentrate mainly on this comparison. The results of the theoretical calculation of the anharmonic phonon spectra of bcc ^{4}He at 21.0 cc/mole by each of the three methods discussed in section 4 are shown in figs. 15–17 together with the experimental results. However, before these figures are discussed, some aspects of the interpretation of the experimental data and the computed results will be reviewed for background.

The experiment basically measures how many neutrons of a given wave-vector $\boldsymbol{q}$ (really of $\boldsymbol{q}+\boldsymbol{Q}$, where $\boldsymbol{Q}$ is a reciprocal lattice vector) are scattered by the crystal with an energy loss of $\hbar\Omega$. Thus the response of the system to a probe of frequency Ω and wave-vector $\boldsymbol{q}$ is measured. The precise determination of the response is complicated by various experimental considerations. There are inevitable effects from background and imprecise instrumental resolution. In addition, enough neutrons have to be counted at each q, Ω point so the counting rate is statistically meaningful. This is why scattering intensity is so important. Some experimental neutron groups are shown in fig. 18. After collecting such data, the experimenter must

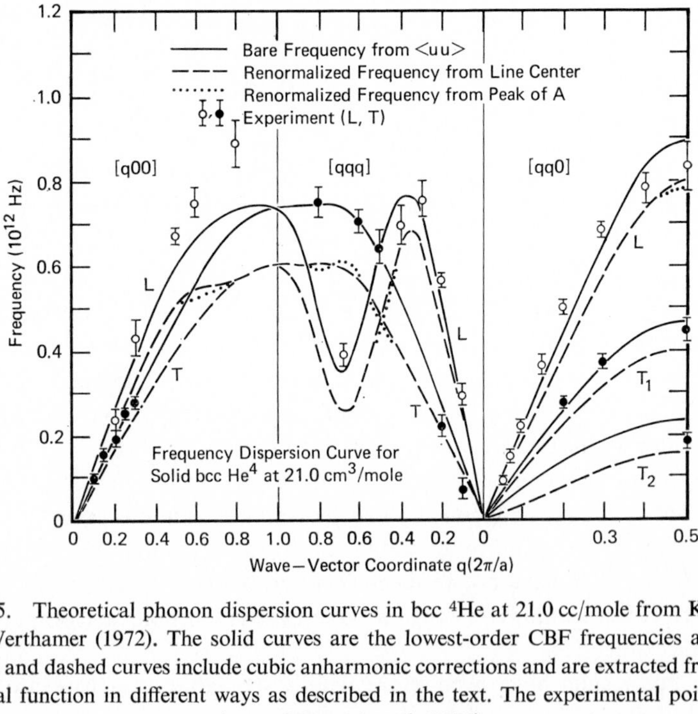

Fig. 15. Theoretical phonon dispersion curves in bcc ^{4}He at 21.0 cc/mole from Koehler and Werthamer (1972). The solid curves are the lowest-order CBF frequencies and the dotted and dashed curves include cubic anharmonic corrections and are extracted from the spectral function in different ways as described in the text. The experimental points are those of Osgood et al. (1972).

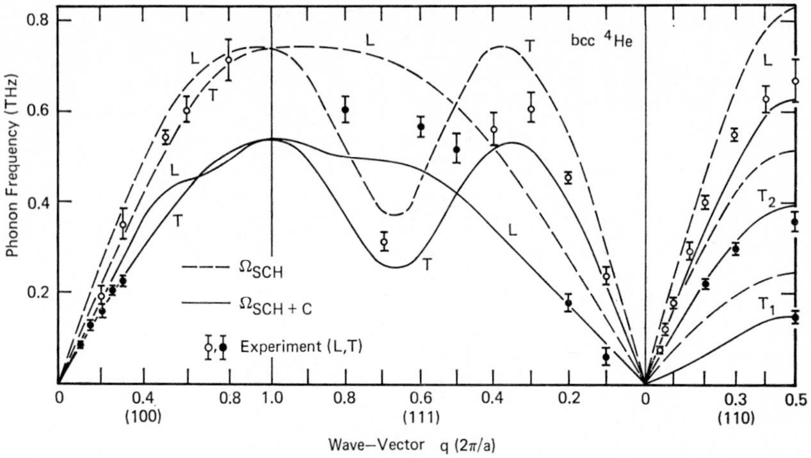

Fig. 16. Theoretical phonon dispersion curves for bcc ^{4}He after Glyde and Khanna (1972b). The *t*-matrix effective potential method is used, as described in the text. The lowest-order frequencies are given by the dashed curves and the frequencies obtained after the addition of cubic anharmonic corrections are given by the solid lines. The experimental points are those of Osgood et al. (1972).

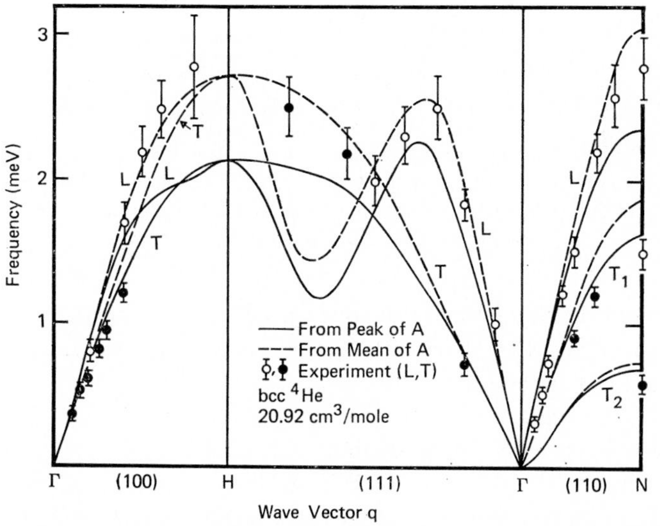

Fig. 17. Theoretical phonon dispersion curves for bcc ^{4}He at 20.92 cc/mole from Horner (1972a). The precise meaning of what is indicated here as the mean of *A* may be found in the reference. The experimental points are those of Osgood et al. (1972).

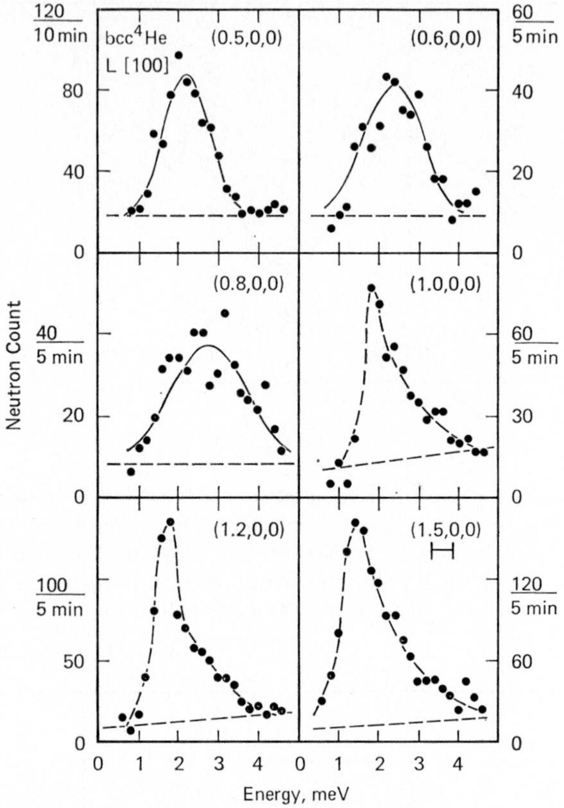

Fig. 18. Phonon profiles for the L(100) branch from Osgood et al. (1972), where the value of the reduced momentum transfer Q/a^* is indicated. The solid lines are gaussian fits to the data and the straight dashed lines are estimates of the background. The instrumental resolution is indicated in the (1.5, 0, 0) figure.

subtract out the background and cope with other experimental uncertainties in order to extract the numerical values that will be assigned to the frequency and width of the phonon.

The theoretician, on the other hand, calculates the response of the system by evaluating the frequency dependent spectral function $A(\Omega)$ defined in subsection 3.3. The results of such a calculation for the quantum crystals are exhibited in fig. 19. Here, the spectral functions for bcc ^{3}He at $q=(0.4, 0.4, 0)2\pi/a$ as obtained by Koehler and Werthamer (1972) are shown for all three branches together with $\Delta(\Omega)$ and $\Gamma(\Omega)$, the frequency dependent contributions to the phonon self-energy.

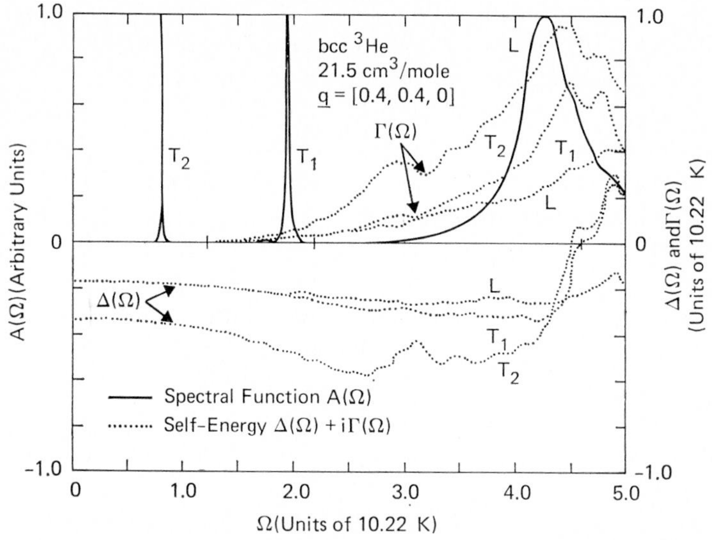

Fig. 19. The solid lines show the theoretical phonon spectral functions for the wavevector $q = (0.4, 0.4, 0)\ 2\pi/a$ in bcc ^{3}He at 21.5 cc/mole according to the calculation of Koehler and Werthamer (1972) with the CBF theory. The contributions $\Delta(\Omega)$ and $\Gamma(\Omega)$ to the phonon self-energy are indicated by the dotted lines. The short vertical lines show the positions of the bare phonon energies. Note that the T_2 line, although quite narrow, is shifted downward by about 30% of its bare frequency.

These results are quite typical. In units of ε, as used in this plot, the maximum phonon energy is about 5ε. Phonons with energies less than about 1.5ε are found to be quite narrow and their width is less than the minimum that can be experimentally resolved. Phonons with energies of about half of the maximum are beginning to broaden, but are fairly symmetrical in shape. As the energies increase from this, the lines become broader and more asymmetric. This general behavior is found in all of the theories. Since the various theories differ somewhat in their evaluation of the quantities which are used in the anharmonic expressions of subsection 3.3, one would expect that the predictions of the different theories would show the most pronounced variation in the region where the anharmonic effects are the greatest – the higher energy phonons. This indeed is the case.

There are several values for the phonon frequency that can be extracted from the theory. First of all, there is the bare or unrenormalized frequency. This quantity only exists in the perturbative theories. It is not what one would choose to compare with experiment, but the amount by which this frequency is renormalized is a measure of the strength of the perturbation and is also some measure of whether there is likely to be a significant difference between a fully consistent and a perturbative theory.

The renormalized frequency is the quantity that should be compared with experiment and there are several ways in which it can be evaluated. The simplest approach, the one that is followed in most of the older anharmonic calculations, is to take the change in energy and the phonon width to be $\Delta(\omega_b)$ and $\Gamma(\omega_b)$, respectively. Then $\omega_r = \omega_b + \Delta(\omega_b)$ and $\Gamma_r = \Gamma(\omega_b)$ where, for convenience in this discussion, ω_r and ω_b are used for the renormalized and bare phonon energies with $\boldsymbol{q}, j$ indices omitted. Similarly, Γ_r is used for the width of the renormalized phonon. This is the result that would be obtained from time-independent perturbation theory. It is computationally the simplest because one need only evaluate the self-energy at one frequency and it is a very good approximation if Δ and Γ are small and frequency independent.

When Δ and Γ are large and strongly frequency dependent, there is more information than can be contained in the two quantities ω_r and Γ_r. Then, for a direct comparison between theory and experiment, one should evaluate the spectral function, convolute it with the appropriate instrumental resolution function and compare the resulting curve with the experimental data adjusted for background. This would be an awkward and tedious procedure to follow for an entire set of dispersion curves, and might be additionally inconvenient if the instrumental data were not available to the theoretician.

It is therefore very useful to present both theoretical and experimental results in terms of a set of quantities ω_r and Γ_r. Three possibilities for assigning a value to ω_r are: (a) from the peak of $A(\Omega)$, (b) from the mean of $A(\Omega)$, and (c) from the center of the two half-maxima. Similarly, Γ_r can be evaluated (a) as the value of Γ at the peak of $A(\Omega)$, (b) from the width at half-maximum of $A(\Omega)$, or (c) as the weighted mean or mean-square deviation of the frequency from ω_r. Each of the above prescriptions may have some advantage when used to obtain a purely theoretical quantity for use in, for example, higher order expressions. However, the frequency as determined from (b) or (c) is most likely to agree with the experimental assignment and the width as obtained from (b) should agree with the experimental width (adjusted for resolution).

The effects of choosing alternative definitions for ω_r and Γ_r have been explored by Koehler and Werthamer (1972). The results are shown in fig. 15. These authors used the CBF method with anharmonic corrections as described in subsection 4.3. The LJ1 potential and the cluster expansion were used in these calculations, so that order of magnitude agreement with experiment would be fortuitous. However, it can be seen that neither of the computed curves could be scaled to achieve a good overall fit to experiment. Three sets of dispersion curves are presented, one is the unrenormalized frequencies obtained from the roots of the pair-correlation function and the other two are renormalized frequencies obtained from the spectral function $A(\Omega)$ according to methods (a) and (c) described above. The agreement between these two methods shows that the lines were not too asymmetric. In the case of bcc ^{3}He, which is not shown here, a greater disparity between the predictions of the two methods was found.

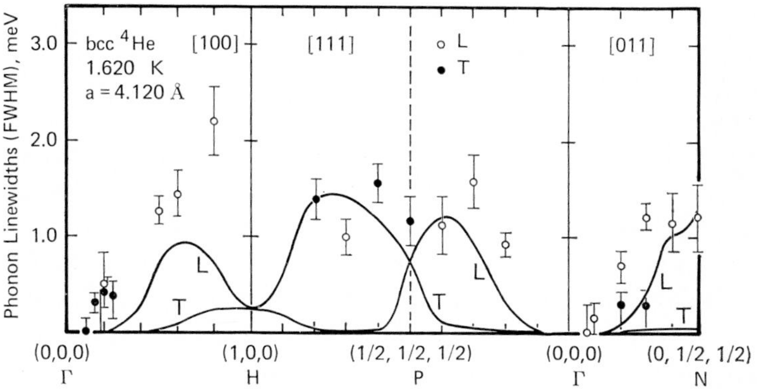

Fig. 20. Experimental full width at half-maximum (fwhm) from Osgood et al. (1972) for bcc ^{4}He at a lattice constant of $a = 4.120$ Å and temperature $T = 1.620$ K. The solid lines are the theoretical results of Koehler and Werthamer (1972) for the CBF theory at 21.0 cc/mole ($a = 4.116$ Å for the LJ1 potential) and 0 K. The slight difference in a and T should produce a negligible effect.

In this figure, the experimental results tend to lie between the unrenormalized and the renormalized frequencies except near the zone boundary in the (100) direction where the best fit is provided by ω_b. The phonon widths computed by method (b) agreed reasonably well with experiment as is shown in fig. 20.

The results of the t-matrix approach of Glyde and Khanna (1972b) are shown compared with experiment in fig. 16. In this calculation, the potential in the lattice dynamics expressions of section 3 was simply replaced everywhere by an effective potential, the t-matrix derived in subsection 4.4. This approach is not completely sound theoretically, but it is at least a reasonable method to try. The Beck potential was used in this calculation. The agreement with experiment is similar to that achieved by Koehler and Werthamer and nearly the same comments apply. The Glyde and Khanna linewidths were about half those obtained by Koehler and Werthamer [except along (100) where they were approximately equal] and agree less well with experiment.

It is interesting to note that a first-order calculation of Glyde (1970) yields a better agreement with experiment than either of the second-order calculations discussed above. This calculation used the Beck potential and a Jastrow–CBF approach. The procedure of subsection 4.3 was not followed. Rather, the method was similar to the effective potential method used later by Glyde and Khanna (1972b): the true potential was replaced by the effective potential of (4.14) in all lattice dynamics expressions. This procedure is without rigorous theoretical justification.

These first-order frequencies are those that would follow from (4.15) but with $\langle 0| \nabla\nabla\Psi_J^2 |0\rangle$ set equal to zero. Thus they correspond to the lowest set of curves in fig. 7 (page 43). They should agree with the lowest-order frequencies of fig. 15 for small wave-vectors and lie about 20% lower at the zone boundary. They, in fact, were found to lie somewhere between the first and second-order results of Koehler and Werthamer and to agree remarkably well with experiment with the exception of the longitudinal (100) branch near the zone boundary. Of course, this agreement cannot be taken too seriously since the lowest-order phonons are undamped. The second-order results of this calculation are shifted downward from these and therefore do not agree well with experiment.

The results of calculations based on the fully consistent theory described in subsection 4.5 are shown in fig. 17, which is taken from Horner (1972a). The Beck potential was used for these calculations. It is clear that these dispersion curves are in closer overall agreement with experiment than any which have been discussed previously. In view of the other results, it is particularly noteworthy that the longitudinal (100) and all of the other branches are simultaneously fitted with reasonable accuracy. This is probably due primarily to the use of renormalized phonons throughout the calculation and to a lesser extent to the use of a pair-function which fulfills the consistency conditions. The correct scale for all of the phonons is likely due to a combination of the latter point, to the choice of interatomic potential and to the use of the short-range contribution (4.51) to the phonon self-energy. It is pointed out that this contribution lowers the average energies by about 25% from the previous work of Horner (1970c). Although it is not shown here, the fully consistent theory also produces dispersion curves in excellent agreement with the fcc data of Traylor et al. (1971).

Another feature of this calculation that is ascribed to the use of renormalized phonons is the appearance of secondary structures (new peaks) on the high frequency side of the spectral function for phonons near the zone boundary. These are not seen in any other calculation. This will probably remain an open issue because these peaks would likely be hidden from experimental detection by other effects.

There are some technical aspects of the calculations based on the fully consistent theory which are described in Horner (1972a). These are concerned with a method of determining the spectral function which differs somewhat from the usual approach, with the definition of the renormalized phonon energies, and with the achievement of full consistency. These details are important in the numerical implementation of the theory, but will not be discussed further here.

Additional specialized results from the various theories of the lattice dynamics of the quantum crystals will be presented in the remainder of this section and a critical assessment of the theories will be made in section 7.

5.3. Velocity of sound and elastic constants

A good overview of the current status of the determination of the sound velocity and elastic constants in the quantum crystals has been given in the review by Trickey et al. (1972a). They have especially emphasized problems associated with the interpretation of experimental data, extraction of the elastic constants, and determination of the elastic θ_D. Here, we will treat only a few topics selected to provide a test of the theories of section 4. In particular, none of the experiments will be discussed in any detail.

In contrast to the phonon dispersion curves, the sound velocities involve only a few independent quantities which, in a harmonic model, are obtained from various well defined combinations of the force constants. However, the experiments to measure sound velocities are generally more accurate and require less elaborate apparatus than inelastic neutron scattering experiments, even though as pointed out by Wanner (1971), there are difficulties in the interpretation of sound velocity experiments in solid helium. Hence, the sound velocities are another experimentally independent lattice dynamics quantity whose calculation not only provides a general test of theory, but is especially useful for checking its density dependence.

The first calculations of sound velocities in the quantum crystals to use any of the modern theories were those of Nosanow and Werthamer (1965) for bcc ^3He and hcp ^4He. These used force constants which were the average of the second derivative of the effective potential in the Jastrow–NCG-cluster theory. A similar calculation for bcc ^{3}He alone was made by De Wette et al. (1967) using essentially the same theory but with the constants in the ground-state wavefunction adjusted to minimize the ground-state energy when three-body terms were included in the cluster expansion. Both calculations used the LJ1 potential. The most extensive experimental data available for comparison at the time was that of Vignos and Fairbank (1966). Even though this was for polycrystalline He and individual sound velocities could not be singled out, it was clear that the theory probably gave an incorrect density dependence. The correctness of this early indication of the theoretical density dependence problem has already been seen in subsection 5.2. This particular experiment had an additional importance: it was the one in which the bcc phase of ^{4}He was discovered.

In the calculations of Gillis et al. (1968) for hcp ^{4}He and of Glyde (1971), and Koehler and Werthamer (1972) for bcc ^{3}He an incorrect density dependence was also found. The work of Gillis et al. used the lowest-order CBF theory and the LJ1 potential. That of Glyde used the Beck potential and the CBF type of theory described in subsection 5.2 in which the Jastrow effective potential is substituted for the true interatomic potential in all lattice dynamics expressions.

Koehler and Werthamer used the CBF theory with anharmonic corrections, the cluster expansion, and the LJ1 potential. In addition, they performed a check on the overall internal consistency of the calculations by computing the bulk modulus in two ways: first, from the volume derivatives of the ground-state energy, and second, from the elastic constants obtained from their sound velocities. As discussed in Götze and Michel (1968), Goldman et al. (1970), and Werthamer (1970b), the two determinations of the bulk modulus should agree. In fact, an inconsistency of about 30% was found which was ascribed to the neglect of certain diagrams and to the ad hoc combination of short and long-range correlations in the Jastrow–CG wavefunction.

The general trend of all the above calculations was toward an insufficient variation of sound velocity with density. It was probably this that prevented some random combination of theory and potential from giving the correct behavior! Finally, the fully consistent calculations of Horner (1972a) yielded a good density dependence for the longitudinal branches and satisfactory overall behavior. The theoretical dependence for ^{3}He is shown in fig. 21 where the results of experiments on single crystal specimens at 21.6 cc/mole by Greywall (1971) and 24.0 cc/mole by Wanner (1971) are also shown. The primary reason for the general success of this calculation is probably the use of the consistency relations for the pair function.

The only sound velocities for which the theoretical fit is disappointing are those belonging to the two lowest lying transverse branches. However, the $T_2(110)$ branch especially poses singular problems both experimentally,

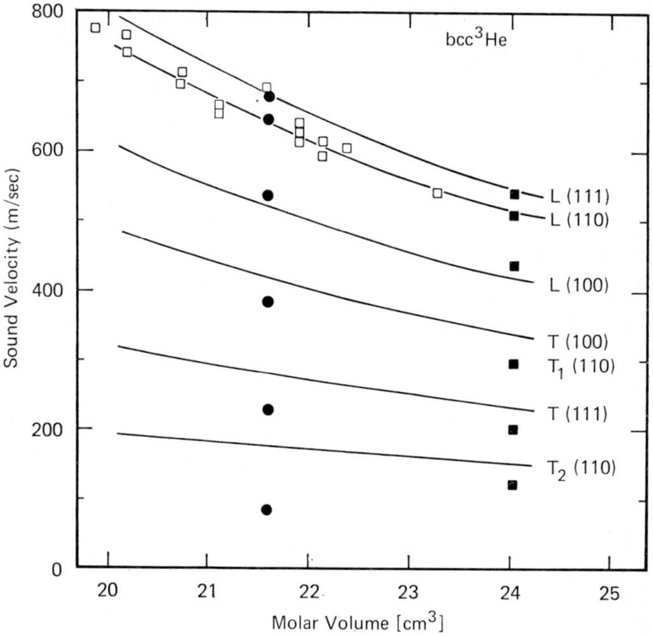

Fig. 21. Theoretical density dependence of the velocity of sound in bcc ^{3}He after Horner (1972a). Experimental results on oriented single crystals of Greywall (1971) at 21.6 cc/mole are shown by the solid dots and of Wanner (1971) at 24.0 cc/mole by the solid squares. The open squares indicate the measurements of Vignos and Fairbank (1966) on non-oriented specimens.

as reviewed by Trickey et al. (1972a), and theoretically, as will be discussed in subsection 5.5. In fact, this velocity has not yet been directly observed experimentally. Two nearly equal elastic constants, c_{11} and c_{12}, are observed directly and the $T_2(110)$ sound velocity, whose square is proportional to $c_{11} - c_{12}$, is inferred. However, Werthamer (1972c) has shown that direct experimental determination of this velocity by Brillouin scattering should be feasible. Such an observation would provide a key piece of data for comparison with theory.

5.4. Specific heat anomaly and upward dispersion

The topic of the low-temperature specific heat anomaly in bcc ^{3}He has been introduced in subsection 2.4 and a lattice dynamics explanation, based on upward dispersion in a low-lying phonon branch, was given. We have seen in subsection 5.3 that the sound velocity in the T_2 (110) branch is quite low; Horner (1970c) noted this and the fact that his calculations predicted upward dispersion in this branch. He then computed the low-temperature specific heat for a model harmonic solid in which the force constants were adjusted to provide a phonon spectrum which agreed with the values assigned to his renormalized frequencies.

The results of a similar calculation based on the improved phonon frequencies of Horner (1972a) are shown as the solid lines in fig. 5a (see page 18). It is clear that the theoretical curves contain a specific heat anomaly, although the quantitative agreement with experiment is not really satisfactory. This is not too alarming because of the known problems associated with the T_2 (110) branch. However, the recent experimental results of Castles et al. (1972), which are shown in fig. 5b, indicate a much more severe anomaly than had been previously suspected. It is very unlikely that any future lattice dynamics calculation of a similar nature will be able to explain an anomaly of this magnitude, especially since it showed no sign of leveling off in the experiment.

Nevertheless, the question of upward dispersion in the T_2 (110) branch is still an interesting one, even if it is not the explanation of the low-temperature specific heat anomaly. First of all, as indicated by the theoretical curves of fig. 5a, it can definitely affect the specific heat below about $\frac{1}{2}$ K. Second, it is a point of some theoretical controversy because not all calculations predict upward dispersion. This latter point will be treated in more detail in subsection 5.5.

5.5. Numerical experimentation

We have seen that there is a significant disagreement between various calculations for the sound velocity of the T_2 branch along (110) and for the question of whether or not this branch has upward dispersion. In fact, in an earlier calculation of Glyde and Cowley (1970) for bcc ^{3}He, the entire renormalized phonon branch was found to be imaginary. The reason for the sensitive nature of the calculated properties of this branch will be discussed in this subsection.

From fig. 19 (page 71) we note that, as measured by the quantity $\Delta(\Omega)$, there is an unusually large amount of anharmonicity in this branch: the line is renormalized downward by about 30%. This is because it is a 'soft' branch and the atomic motions in this mode are along a direction in which a bcc crystal has a tendency to be unstable. Because of this instability, the frequencies are unusually low and the vibrational motion is large, which increases the anharmonic interactions. The other case where anharmonic effects are large is that of longitudinal phonons at the zone boundary. Here, the atomic motion causes nearest-neighbors to move directly toward one another so that hard-core anharmonicity is maximized.

In a case where anharmonicity is large, the structure of the perturbative formulas makes the results sensitive to the magnitude of the three-phonon vertex. This, in turn, is strongly influenced by the details of the calculation, in particular by the approximations used to determine the pair function and by the precise definition of the three-phonon vertex. The sensitivity comes from the fact that the perturbative corrections are proportional to the square of the three-phonon vertex. In contrast, the phonon frequencies are determined essentially from the square root of the renormalized force constants. Thus one could expect that any reasonable theory of the renormalized force constants will give results that are, for the most part, within 30% of experiment but that various theories will give considerably different predictions in special situations where anharmonicity is quite important.

In order to make a direct assessment of effects caused by small changes in the three-phonon vertex, Koehler and Werthamer (1972) performed a series of numerical experiments. In this work, the renormalized phonon energies for a few points in $\boldsymbol{q}$-space around the origin were obtained as a function of a scaling parameter α which was used to multiply Δ and Γ while all other quantities remained fixed. This is equivalent to multiplying the three-phonon matrix element by $\sqrt{\alpha}$.

The variation in the three sound velocities with α along (110) is shown in fig. 22. For a range of values which change the matrix element from about -10% to $+20\%$, the T_2 sound velocity changes by a factor of three while the L and T_1 velocities hardly vary. A slight additional increase in α causes the T_2 velocity to go through zero and to become imaginary – that is, the crystal becomes unstable against the related distortion. Thus the apparent anisotropy in the sound velocities will vary markedly with the amount of anharmonicity. In the calculation of Glyde and Cowley (1970), a Jastrow–NCG rather than a Jastrow–CG was used to obtain the matrix elements.

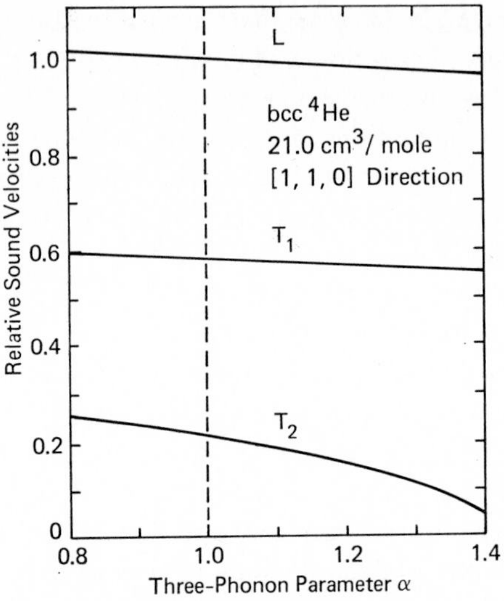

Fig. 22. Velocity of sound in bcc ^{4}He at 21.0 cc/mole in the (110) direction, scaled relative to the L velocity at $\alpha = 1$, after Koehler and Werthamer (1972). The square of the three-phonon vertex is multiplied by α.

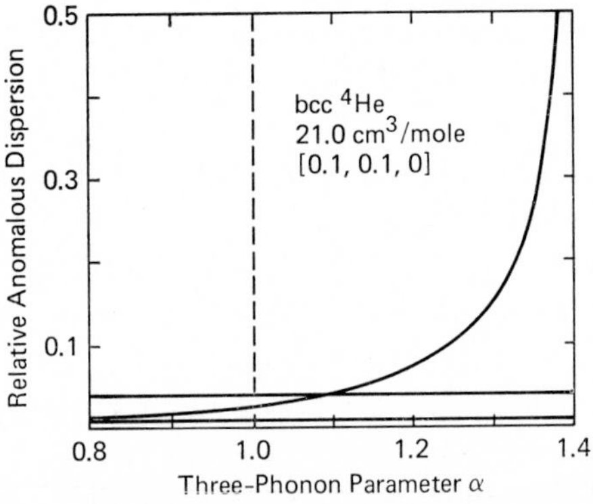

Fig. 23. Relative anomalous dispersion of phonons in bcc ^{4}He as a function of α which multiplies the square of the three-phonon vertex, after Koehler and Werthamer (1972). The quantity δ is a measure of the upward dispersion and is defined in the text.

This approach does not change the force constant matrix very much, but it increases the magnitude of the anharmonic vertices enough to overdamp the entire branch.

The dependence of upward dispersion of the branch on α was also investigated. These results are shown in fig. 23, where the dispersion is measured in terms of a quantity

$$\delta \equiv [\omega(2\boldsymbol{q})/2\omega(\boldsymbol{q})] - 1, \qquad \boldsymbol{q} = (0.1, 0.1, 0)\,\pi/a. \tag{5.3}$$

There is a very slight upward dispersion for $\alpha \lesssim 1$, but it increases dramatically for additional increases in the anharmonicity.

We see that the properties of the soft $T_2(110)$ branch are difficult to calculate accurately, just as they are difficult to measure experimentally. Thus the disagreement about them between various theories is not surprising. A few additional remarks on the significance of the above will be made in section 7.

5.6. Anomalous line shapes and intensities

An alternative title for this subsection would be 'One- and two-phonon interference effects' because these provide the most convincing current theoretical explanation of the experimental anomalies. However, the theoretical interpretation is more likely to change than the experimental results, so the title we have chosen is the more durable one. The experimental results of Osgood et al. (1972) on bcc ^{4}He will be emphasized here although similar anomalies were found by Traylor et al. (1971). There were also indications of scattering irregularities in the earlier experiments on hcp ^{4}He; however, these will not be discussed here since the precision of the experiments was less and their analysis would be complicated by the geometry.

There were two anomalous effects. The first is illustrated by the experimental data of Osgood et al. which is shown in fig. 18 (page 70). As compared to typical line profiles for less anharmonic substances, these are quite broad and, in some instances, asymmetrical. (These are not even typical lines for the helium experiment: they were selected to illustrate the anomaly and the majority of lines are considerably narrower.) However, such effects do not constitute the anomalies. The broadness is certainly not unexpected in such an anharmonic substance and many anharmonic calculations of phonon line profiles exhibit asymmetry near the zone boundary. The anomaly is that lines which are exactly equivalent on the basis of symmetry have experimental line shapes which are not identical. Examples of this are the (0.5, 0, 0), (1.5, 0, 0) and (0.8, 0, 0), (1.2, 0, 0) equivalent pairs which are shown in fig. 18. This anomaly seems to violate the most fundamental symmetry requirement of a crystal lattice.

The second anomaly concerns an unexpectedly high scattering amplitude for events in which the magnitude of the momentum exchange was $\boldsymbol{Q} \approx 1.6a^*$.

The anomalous scattering was nearly isotropic and occured for momentum exchanges outside the first Brillouin zone. [The zone boundary in (100) is $\boldsymbol{q}=(1,0,0)\,a^*$ and $a^*=2\pi/a$.] Some details of the theory of inelastic neutron scattering are necessary to further clarify the meaning of the intensity anomaly and to provide the background for the explanation of both anomalies. These details will be discussed briefly in the following.

Heretofore, we have followed a statement made in subsection 3.3 and have compared experimental line profiles to the phonon spectral function. In reality, the spectral function plays an important role, but other mechanisms are present. The differential scattering cross-section for neutron scattering is well known (see, for example March et al. 1967) to be proportional to the Fourier transform $S(\boldsymbol{Q},\Omega)$ of the 'density–density' correlation function. This quantity is given by

$$S(\boldsymbol{Q},\Omega)=(1/2\pi)\int_{-\infty}^{\infty}\mathrm{d}t\,\mathrm{e}^{\mathrm{i}\Omega t}\sum_j \mathrm{e}^{-\mathrm{i}\boldsymbol{Q}\cdot\boldsymbol{R}(ij)} \times\langle\exp[-\mathrm{i}\boldsymbol{Q}\cdot\boldsymbol{u}(i,t)]\exp[i\boldsymbol{Q}\cdot\boldsymbol{u}(j,t)]\rangle, \quad (5.4)$$

where the brackets denote thermal average.

In the case of a purely harmonic crystal, (5.4) can be cast into a form suitable for lattice dynamics calculations in a fairly straightforward way. The results of such a harmonic analysis form the basis of most of our intuitive viewpoints of the interpretation of inelastic neutron scattering data.

In the presence of anharmonicity, a more sophisticated analysis is necessary. The first such general treatment was performed by Ambegaokar et al. (1965), and later developments by Werthamer (1970b), and Beck and Meier (1972) were directly aimed at the quantum crystals. These authors showed that (5.4) could be rewritten as

$$S(\boldsymbol{Q},\Omega)=(2\pi)^{-1}\,\mathrm{e}^{-2W(\boldsymbol{Q})}\int_{-\infty}^{\infty}\mathrm{d}t\,\mathrm{e}^{\mathrm{i}\Omega t}\sum_i \mathrm{e}^{-\mathrm{i}\boldsymbol{Q}\cdot\boldsymbol{R}(ij)} \times|\langle[\mathrm{e}^{\mathrm{i}\boldsymbol{Q}\cdot\boldsymbol{u}(i,t)}-1]\,[\mathrm{e}^{-\mathrm{i}\boldsymbol{Q}\cdot\boldsymbol{u}(j,t)}-1]|\rangle_{\mathrm{L}}|^2, \quad (5.5)$$

where $\langle\rangle_{\mathrm{L}}$ denotes a cumulant (i.e., linked cluster) expansion of the enclosed quantity and

$$\mathrm{e}^{-2W(\boldsymbol{Q})}\equiv|\langle\mathrm{e}^{\mathrm{i}\boldsymbol{Q}\cdot\boldsymbol{u}(i)}\rangle_{\mathrm{L}}|^2 \quad (5.6)$$

is called the Debye–Waller factor.

For a harmonic crystal, the following holds: a) The Debye–Waller factor is a CG function of $\boldsymbol{Q}$, in which W reduces to $\frac{1}{6}\boldsymbol{Q}^2\langle \boldsymbol{u}^2(i)\rangle$ if the crystal is also cubic. b) The cumulant expansion of $\langle\rangle_L$ in (5.5) can be expressed as a series of terms: (elastic scattering$+S_1(\boldsymbol{Q},\Omega)+$multiphonon background). The elastic scattering term is unimportant here. The one phonon portion at $T=0$ is given by

$$S_1(\boldsymbol{Q},\Omega)=\mathrm{e}^{-2W(\boldsymbol{Q})}\sum_{j,\boldsymbol{q}}\frac{\hbar}{2mN\omega_j(\boldsymbol{q})}\left[\boldsymbol{Q}\cdot\boldsymbol{e}\begin{pmatrix}\boldsymbol{q}\\ j\end{pmatrix}\right]^2 \times\delta[\Omega-\omega_j(\boldsymbol{Q})]\,\Delta(\boldsymbol{Q}-\boldsymbol{q}), \quad (5.7)$$

where Δ is defined immediately below (3.36). As a function of Ω, S contributes a sharp peak in the scattering at those Ω values corresponding to the energy of any phonon of wavevector $\boldsymbol{Q}$ for which $\boldsymbol{Q}\cdot\boldsymbol{e}\binom{\boldsymbol{Q}}{j}\neq 0$. This term obviously comes from the excitation of a single phonon of wavevector $\boldsymbol{Q}$ by the neutron. The multiphonon background arises from excitation of two or more phonons The contribution from these terms is slowly varying with Ω, because the conservation of crystal momentum is not as restrictive.

In the presence of anharmonicity, the Debye–Waller factor is modified, but should still be well represented by a CG in $\boldsymbol{Q}$, and the $\delta[\Omega-\omega_j(\boldsymbol{Q})]$ in (5.7) broadens and turns into what is essentially the phonon spectral function. However, even in the presence of anharmonicity, the one-phonon scattering function obeys the important ACB sum rule

$$(2\pi)^{-1}\int_0^\infty \mathrm{d}\Omega\,\Omega S_1(\boldsymbol{Q},\Omega)=\mathrm{e}^{-2W}\,Q^2/2m, \quad (5.8)$$

which was derived in Ambegaokar et al. (1965). Since the total scattering obeys the sum rule

$$(2\pi)^{-1}\int_0^\infty \mathrm{d}\Omega\,\Omega S(\boldsymbol{Q},\Omega)=Q^2/2m \quad (5.9)$$

of Placzek (1952), (5.8) states that single-phonon scattering exhausts a fraction of the total scattering equal to the Debye–Waller factor. In (5.9), m is the mass of the atom and this sum rule shows that the average energy loss of the neutron is equal to the energy of an atom with momentum $\boldsymbol{Q}$.

The intensity anomaly simply means that scattering in the neighborhood of $\boldsymbol{Q}=1.6a^*$ was more intense than would be expected on the basis of the ACB sum rule. This is illustrated in fig. 24 where the line profiles for the (1.5, 0, 0) and (0.5, 0, 0) pair are shown after the experimental background has been subtracted out and the intensities adjusted for the Debye-Waller factor. After these adjustments, the lines should be identical; they clearly are not.

An alternative way of visualizing the intensity anomaly was taken by Werthamer (1972b) who used the experimental data and the ACB sum rule

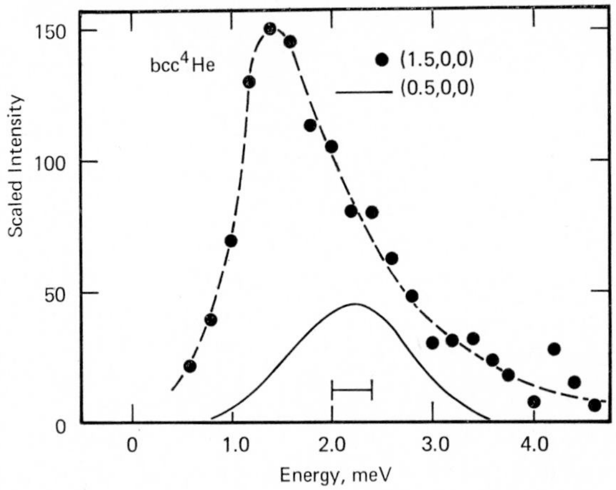

Fig. 24. Adjusted experimental line profiles for two equivalent L phonons from Osgood et al. (1972). The background has been subtracted out and the intensities adjusted for the Debye–Waller factor. The instrumental resolution is indicated.

to compute an experimental Debye–Waller factor as a function of $\boldsymbol{Q}$. This is shown in fig. 25 where the dashed line indicates the expected result for gaussian behavior. One of the purposes of this paper was to show the similarity between the scattering data for the solid, which is shown as points, and the liquid, which is shown as the solid curve. The resemblance is close enough so the solid curve forms a good guide to the eye in assessing the general trend of the points. The implications of this resemblance have not yet been adequately explained and will not be pursued further here.

Fig. 25 can, however, be interpreted as an oscillation in the Debye–Waller factor with an amplitude of about two, in which its value is first less and then larger than the expected value. A cumulant expansion in which W is expressed as a power series in $\boldsymbol{Q}$ can be found in, for example, Ambegaokar et al. (1965). This expansion is not necessary, however, if one realizes that (5.6) involves only the ground-state average of a rather simple quantity and that reliable expressions for the ground-state wavefunction of solid helium are available. This approach was taken by Sears and Khanna (1972), McMahan

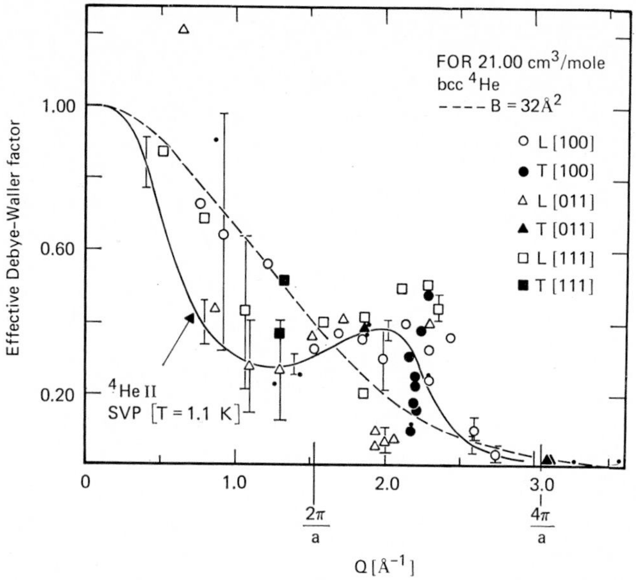

Fig. 25. The effective Debye–Waller factor obtained by Werthamer (1972b) as the normalized first moment of the one-phonon line profiles measured experimentally in bcc ^{4}He at 21.0 cc/mole by Osgood et al. (1972). The solid line shows the comparable results of Cowley and Woods (1971) for superfluid ^{4}He at saturated vapor pressure SVP. The dashed line indicates the gaussian behavior expected in the solid for a harmonic crystal.

and Guyer (1972) and Horner (1972b). These treatments unanimously concluded that any deviations from the gaussian behavior should be small, and that it would be virtually impossible to fit the solid curve of fig. 25 on the basis of such a model.

Various clues to the explanation of both anomalies can be found in the papers cited in this subsection, especially that of Werthamer. However, all of the pieces of a theoretical interpretation leading to a first principles calculation of both anomalies were first assembled by Horner (1972b, c). The interpretation was based on the more complete properties of (5.5) and of the ACB sum rule: in the presence of anharmonicity, the terms in the expansion of $\langle\rangle_L$ are not independent, rather there are interference terms, in particular, between the one-phonon and each n-phonon contribution to the multiphonon background. The ACB sum rule holds not only for the one-phonon term $S_1(\boldsymbol{Q}, \Omega)$, but also for S_1 plus any one-phonon, n-phonon interference term. This means that the interference terms give a zero contribution to the sum rule. These properties had been known previously, but had not been applied numerically to the interpretation of inelastic neutron scattering data in solid helium.

The inclusion of the interference terms modifies (5.7) so that

$$S_1(\boldsymbol{Q}, \Omega) = \mathrm{e}^{-2W(\boldsymbol{Q})} \sum \Delta(\boldsymbol{Q} - \boldsymbol{q}) \times \operatorname{Im}\left(G_{jj}(\boldsymbol{q}, \Omega)\left\{\left[\boldsymbol{Q} \cdot \boldsymbol{e}\begin{pmatrix}\boldsymbol{q}\\ j\end{pmatrix}\right]^2 + L_{jj}(\boldsymbol{q}, \boldsymbol{Q}, \Omega)\right\}\right), \tag{5.10}$$

where G is the one-phonon Green's function of (3.37) and $\boldsymbol{L}_{jj}(\boldsymbol{q}, \boldsymbol{Q}, \Omega)$ is a complex quantity which is proportional to $\boldsymbol{Q}^3$ for small $\boldsymbol{Q}$. If $\boldsymbol{L}$ is omitted, S_1 has the shape of the spectral function; its inclusion produces two main effects: 1) $\boldsymbol{Q}$ is involved in such a way that the periodicity in reciprocal space is destroyed. 2) A portion of the dispersive real part of $\boldsymbol{G}$ is mixed with the absorptive imaginary part. Since $\boldsymbol{L}$ is expected to have a fairly smooth frequency dependence, the major obvious effect of this will be an alteration in the shape of the line and a shift in the maximum to some other point within the linewidth. This will account for the anomalous dependence of the line profile on $\boldsymbol{Q}$. These observations were also made by Werthamer (1972b).

The observed anomalous intensity can arise from an unobvious consequence of effect 2) described above. When cubic anharmonicity is included, the spectral function is not only broadened from a δ-function spike, but also acquires a high-frequency tail – a fairly structureless component which extends up to twice the maximum frequency. This is especially obvious in the profile of the L mode shown in fig. 19. If higher order anharmonicities are included, the tail will extend to higher frequency. The tail should be included in the ACB sum rule, but in general it will not emerge above the background and will be subtracted off in the analysis of the experimental data. Only the main peak is observed experimentally. The situation is made even worse, however, because the mixing of the real and imaginary parts of $\boldsymbol{G}$ redistributes the intensity found in the tail in such a way as to either enhance or diminish the main peak, depending on the position of $\boldsymbol{Q}$ in reciprocal space. This explains the general trend of the points shown in fig. 25.

The above ideas have been computationally implemented, and the results, as obtained by Horner (1972b), are shown in fig. 26 for the equivalent points (1.5, 0, 0) and (0.5, 0, 0). The phonon spectral functions $S_1(\boldsymbol{Q}, \Omega)$, analogous to those shown in fig. 18 (page 70), are given by the dashed curves; they are identical for each member of the pair. The sum of the one, two-phonon interference terms $S_{\text{int}}(\boldsymbol{Q}, \Omega)$ is shown by the dot-dash line. These involve

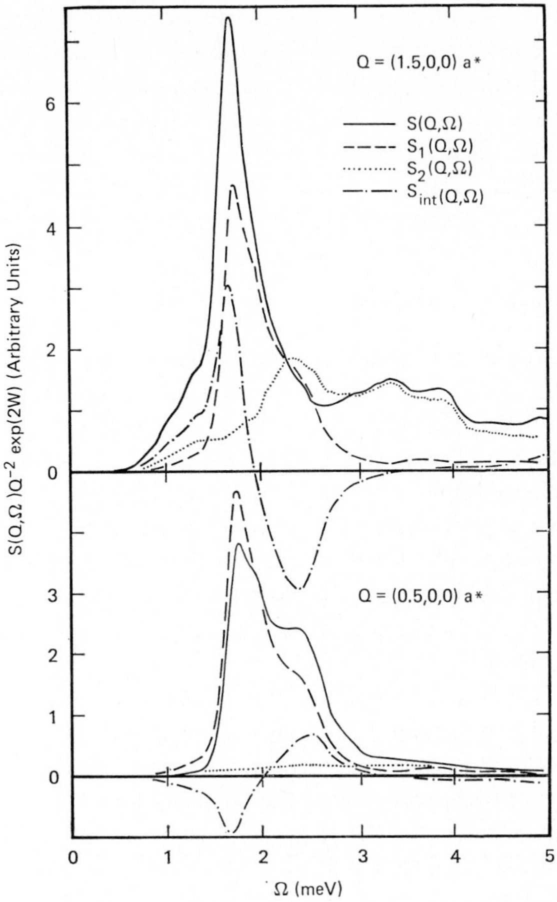

Fig. 26. The scattering function $S(\boldsymbol{Q}, \Omega)$ in bcc ^{4}He as obtained by Horner (1972b) for two scattering vectors $\boldsymbol{Q} = (0.5, 0, 0)\ 2\pi/a$ and $\boldsymbol{Q} = (1.5, 0, 0)\ 2\pi/a$, which are equivalent in reciprocal space, is shown by the solid curves. The separate contributions are: the one-phonon spectral function $S_1(\boldsymbol{Q}, \Omega)$ (dashed), the one, two-phonon interference terms $S_{\text{int}}(\boldsymbol{Q}, \Omega)$ (dot-dash), and the multiphonon background (dotted).

the three-phonon vertex and should be the leading interference terms. It is apparent to the eye that their integrated contribution to the ACB sum rule will be approximately zero and their frequency dependent contribution has an opposite sign. The sum of the lowest-order contributions to the multiphonon background $S_2(\boldsymbol{Q}, \Omega)$ is illustrated by the dotted curves, and the final calculated scattering functions $S(\boldsymbol{Q}, \Omega)$ are given by the solid curves.

Because of experimental uncertainties and unknown modifications caused by omitted theoretical terms, it is difficult to make a meaningful comparison between the calculated $S(\boldsymbol{Q}, \Omega)$ curves of fig. 26 and the experimental data shown in in fig. 18. Nevertheless, such a comparison is shown in Horner (1972c) and there is a satisfactory overall agreement on resolvable details. One can conclude, therefore, that interference effects provide a convincing explanation of the observed scattering anomalies.

5.7. Single-particle excitations

It is intuitively obvious that single-particle-like excitations should occur in high-momentum transfer inelastic neutron scattering. These should be similar to a collision between a free atom and a neutron in which the energy transferred to the atom would be $\boldsymbol{Q}^2/2m$. In a solid, one would expect a dispersion relationship of this form, but with a linewidth. This process has been observed experimentally by Kitchens et al. (1972) in solid bcc ^{4}He for momentum transfers $\Omega \approx 3\text{Å}^{-1}$. It was the first observation of such a dispersion relationship in a solid by neutron scattering. Helium is a particularly favorable substance because of its low Debye–Waller factor and binding energy per atom.

Single-particle scattering is quite important from a theoretical point of view in liquid helium and a brief discussion of this topic together with appropriate references can be found in Kitchens et al. (1972). This paper also compared the neutron groups scattered from the solid and from the liquid. A strong resemblance was found, which provides more evidence for the observation made in subsection 5.6 that a similarity between the two phases exists.

From a phonon point of view, the single-particle scattering must be viewed as a superposition of multiphonon processes, and its theory should be contained in (5.5). A theoretical evaluation of $S(\boldsymbol{Q}, \Omega)$ in the high-$\boldsymbol{Q}$ regime has been made by Horner (1972d). The calculation was made as follows: one and two-phonon processes and their interference terms were calculated directly, as described in the previous subsection. The contribution from all higher-order multiphonon processes was estimated from the appropriate expression for a harmonic crystal, but with renormalized rather than harmonic frequencies used. The calculation yielded two peaks for each $\boldsymbol{Q}$ value, which are shown as the two solid lines in fig. 27. One is periodic in reciprocal space and is the one-phonon peak. The other starts off at low $\boldsymbol{Q}$ as a broad maximum in the multiphonon background, which can be seen in fig. 26 in

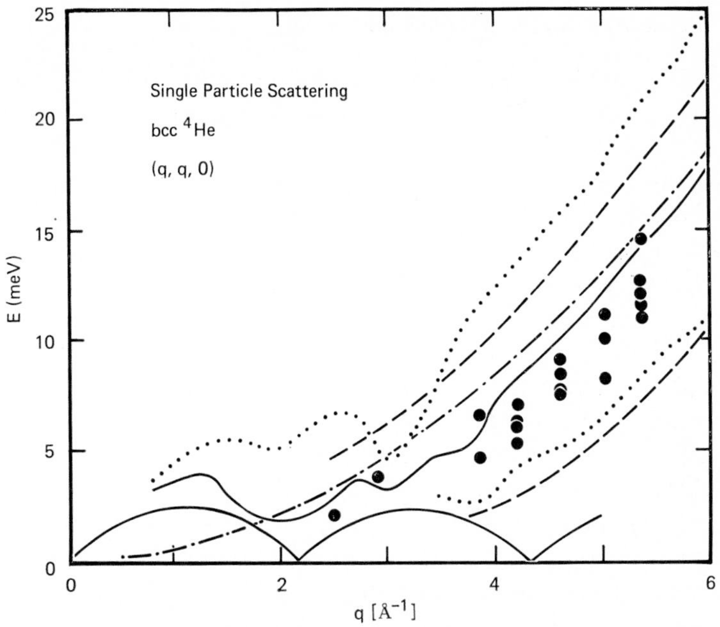

Fig. 27. Single-particle scattering from solid bcc ^{4}He after Horner (1972d). The solid lines are his theoretical results for maxima in $S(\boldsymbol{Q}, \Omega)$ and the dotted lines are theoretical half-maxima. The experimental results of Kitchens et al. (1972) are indicated by the points and approximate experimental half-maxima are given by the dashed curves. The free recoil energy is the dot-dash line.

the background of $S(1.5, 0, 0)$, and then turns into the single-particle peak. The half-maximum of the latter is shown by the dotted lines.

The experimental points are also shown in fig. 27, and the approximate half-maximum of the experimental intensities is indicated by the dashed curves. The linewidths are consistent with a picture in which the lifetime of the excitation is determined by collision with a nearest neighbor. The scattering was quite isotropic, which again is indicative of a liquid-like behavior. In fact, the experiments were along several directions and some points from polycrystalline hcp ^{4}He are even included; however, the differences are not distinguished here. The free recoil energy $\boldsymbol{Q}^2/2m$ is shown by the dot-dash line.

Here again, the agreement between theory and experiment can be considered quite satisfactory, although the apparent resemblance between the solid and the liquid remains unexplained.

5.8. Raman scattering in solid helium

Raman scattering experiments are another source of lattice dynamics information about the quantum crystals. The results are complementary to those of inelastic neutron scattering. The only one-phonon property that can be measured by Raman scattering is the line profile for the $q \approx 0$ TO optic mode in hcp helium; however, the experiments have a high accuracy and can be performed in ^{3}He, which is inaccessible to neutron scattering. Two-phonon processes are observable for any crystal structure. They provide information about the joint density of states and, in particular, about the location of critical points.

The theory of light scattering from solid helium has been worked out by Werthamer (1969b) and calculations based on this theory were performed by Werthamer et al. (1971). The coupling between light and phonons is through point dipoles induced by the electric field of the light. Since the polarizability of the helium atom is small, the Raman scattering efficiency is expected to be rather small, but observable with laser sources.

Raman scattering experiments were carried out by Slusher and Surko (1971), and the results are shown as the solid lines in fig. 28 for bcc ^{3}He, hcp ^{3}He and hcp ^{4}He. The sharp peaks in the hcp solids are for the TO optic mode. The theoretical results of Werthamer et al. for the two-phonon scattering are shown by the dashed lines and the theoretical location of the TO mode is indicated by the arrows. The TO frequencies were obtained from the lowest order CBF theory, so there is no theoretical linewidth available and the renormalised frequency would be expected to be lower. In fact, it would probably fall below the experiment. Although the experiments were performed with single crystals, the theoretical results for the two-phonon scattering are averaged over direction. The experiments do not show the structure predicted by the theory, are more intense, and extend to higher frequency. All of these results, especially the latter, indicate that more than two-phonon processes are important or that two-phonon processes have to be viewed as more than a simple convolution of two single-phonon processes.

The direct two-phonon response of an anharmonic lattice has been considered by Werthamer (1972a). Although the results of this study have implications for the transport properties and for the possibility of two-phonon bound states, they will not be discussed in further detail here. Nevertheless, such considerations should be incorporated into further theoretical analyses of Raman experiments.

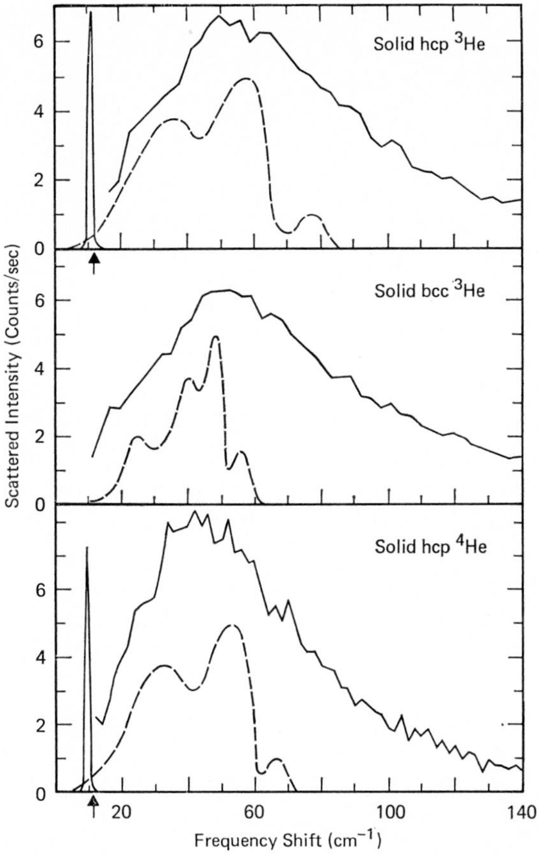

Fig. 28. Raman spectra of solid He. The solid lines are the experimental results of Slusher and Surko (1971) and the dashed lines are the theoretical values of Werthamer et al. (1971) for two-phonon scattering. The sharp spikes and the arrows indicate, respectively, the experimental and theoretical determination of the $q \approx 0$, TO optic mode for the hcp crystals.

6. Related work

6.1. Introduction

The main emphasis in this chapter has been on the development of the capability to perform reliable anharmonic lattice dynamics calculations for the quantum crystals. The featured theoretical approaches have been those which not only contain anharmonicity, but have also been computationally implemented. However, there are other theories which provide an interesting alternative viewpoint or suggest a possible path for future development. Some of these will be reviewed in this section.

The topics to be treated in subsections 6.3 and 6.4 are quite broad and have an extensive background in classical lattice dynamics. Complete referencing, even to all the literature most immediately concerned with quantum crystals, would be unwieldy: the papers cited should be considered as source references.

6.2. Bubble diagrams and high-density helium

These are actually two separate topics, but they have been linked in such a way that it is convenient to treat both in a single subsection.

A group of terms, whose significance was first discussed by Götze and Michel (1968) and later by Goldman et al. (1970) and Werthamer (1970b),

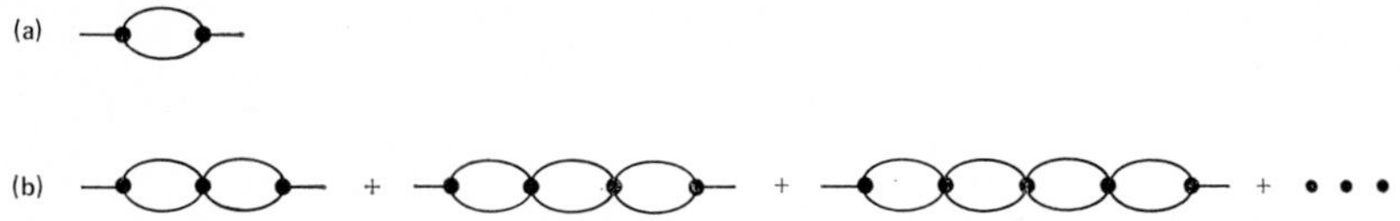

Fig. 29. Anharmonic contributions to the phonon self-energy. (a) The usual cubic anharmonic term. (b) Higher-order bubble diagrams.

has been omitted from all of the anharmonic calculations discussed in section 5. The usual cubic anharmonic term in shown diagramatically in fig. 29a and the related, additional terms, which represent multiple interactions of the two intermediate phonons via the four-phonon vertex, are shown in fig. 29b. All of the terms in this figure (the bubble diagrams) may be summed and the net effect has been found in practice to be equivalent to a decrease in the magnitude of the cubic anharmonic term. Frequencies which are calculated with the inclusion of the bubble diagrams are, in a sense which is described by Goldman et al., the lowest-order self-consistent frequencies. Therefore, this will be termed the LSC theory.

The above has been applied to helium in a specialized context which was first treated by Morley and Kliewer (1969): at high densities, hard-core effects should diminish in importance and the SHA treatment, with no explicit accounting for the hard-core, might be sufficient. These authors performed extensive lattice dynamics calculations in hcp ^{3}He and ^{4}He using the lowest order SHA theory. The Debye temperatures came out too high, which indicates that their phonon frequencies were too high, and with the wrong density dependence, which could be from the use of the LJ1 potential. Chell et al. (1970) later showed that cubic anharmonic corrections were substantial in fcc helium in the same density range, and finally, Goldman et al. (1970) showed that these corrections were overestimated unless one included the contributions from all the bubble diagrams.

In another calculation with the LSC theory, Chell (1970) evaluated the compressibility of fcc ^{3}He and ^{4}He over a density range of 12 to 18 cc/mole. The magnitude of the compressibility was in good agreement with experiment, but the density dependence was not as good as obtained in the t-matrix calculation of Horner (1970b). However, the LJ1 potential was used in all the calculations, and in view of the discussion of subsection 5.1, this is unlikely to be valid at high densities.

The significance of all the work described above is currently somewhat uncertain. First of all, the treatment of solid helium using the SHA with anharmonic corrections or the LCS theory even at densities as high as 12 cc/mole is questionable. The fully consistent calculations of Horner (1972a) agree with the experimental data on fcc ^{4}He at 11.7 cc/mole better than any of the SHA based calculations. It is probable that the four-phonon vertices in fig. 29b are considerably smaller in the fully consistent theory, since the average value of the fourth derivative of the potential is calculated with the true pair function rather than a gaussian pair function. Thus, even though these terms are not present in Horner's calculations, they (as well as other omitted terms) may be considerably smaller than terms omitted in the SHA calculations. This line of reasoning is substantiated by calculations on fcc ^{4}He at 11.5 cc/mole by Horner (1971a).

Second, in situations where their contribution is significant, the case for the inclusion of the bubble diagrams only, and not other perturbative terms which may be as large and of opposite sign, is not clear. As was mentioned in subsection 5.3, the elastic constants, obtained from the variation of the lowest-order SHA free energy with respect to lattice distortions, will agree with those obtained from the $q \to 0$ limit of the LSC phonon energies. However, the best theoretical value one could assign to the compressibility is that obtained from the volume dependence of the free energy calculated with the anharmonic SHA theory, and this is the value one would like to agree with the limit of the phonon energies. This agreement could be achieved by simply multiplying the three-phonon vertex by an adjustable constant in the spirit of the work described in subsection 5.5. This should be considered as an empirical adjustment to account for omitted diagrams.

A calculation of the compressibility of ^{3}He from 12 to 18 cc/mole was made by Chell (1971) using the anharmonic SHA free energy. A density dependence superior to his previous work was obtained, but the Beck potential was used in this calculation and the two can not really be compared.

In addition to the empirical approach suggested above, more theoretical and computational work could be performed to extend the work described in this subsection. The importance of the bubble diagrams in a theory which includes hard-core effects has not yet been evaluated, and additionally, as has been discussed by Werthamer (1972a), the four-phonon vertex will be involved in the computation of other properties of the crystal.

6.3. Transport properties and phonon interactions

Since energy in insulating crystals is carried by phonons, the thermal transport properties of perfect crystals without structural defects will be governed by interactions between phonons. The traditional theoretical approach to such properties involves a phonon-Boltzmann transport equation which was first introduced by Peierls (1929). Recently, alternative approaches based on the direct calculation of the energy current autocorrelation function using linear response theory have been investigated by a number of authors, for example, by Ranninger (1969) and Niklasson (1970). The first principles evaluation of transport properties by either of these methods poses quite a formadible computational problem. However, the leading contribution to phonon scattering comes from the three-phonon vertex. Julian (1965) has derived an expression for thermal conductivity in fcc crystals based on an approximate treatment of contributions from this interaction term. Benin (1968) has shown that, in anharmonic substances such as helium or even neon, it is important to use a SPA theory to evaluate the cubic force constants which enter into the three-phonon vertex. This conclusion would be expected to hold for a more exact theory.

The time is now ripe for additional evaluation of transport properties in the quantum crystals. First of all, there are very good experimental measurements of these properties; references to this work may be found in Trickey et al. (1972a). Next, the theory of the anharmonic lattice dynamics in quantum crystals now appears to be in good shape. Finally, Werthamer and Chui (1972a, b) have obtained an expression for the transport relaxation time, appropriate to a crystal of arbitrary structure, whose explicit numerical evaluation involves only computations which are very similar to those already used in obtaining the cubic anharmonic contributions to the phonon self-energy. These could be performed with existing computer programs.

A more exotic transport phenomenon is second sound, which arises from a sound-like motion (i.e., density fluctuations) in the gas of phonons. Here again the quantum crystals are unique: the first experimental observation of second sound in solids was that of Ackerman et al. (1966) in solid ^{4}He. A detailed discussion of this experiment and other aspects of second sound in solids has been given by Ackerman and Guyer (1968). See also ch. 4.

6.4. Defects

In addition to the intriguing aspect of vacancy waves in quantum crystals, which has been mentioned in subsection 2.4, the properties of more ordinary, static defects are also of interest. The problem of a point mass impurity caused by isotopic substitution is well known and adequately treated in classical lattice dynamics. However, the scattering of phonons, as deduced from the thermal resistivity measurements of Berman et al. (1965) and Bertman et al. (1966), appears to be substantially greater than is expected on the basis of the classical theory. This problem has been investigated by Klemens (1968), Jones (1970) and Varma (1971): the last two were based on the SHA. Of these, the work of Jones starts with the SHA frequencies and eigenvectors for the perfect crystal and determines those for the impure crystal perturbatively. The work of Varma uses a variational approach throughout; this is more in the spirit of the SHA and leads to more mathematically satisfying expressions.

A few results of Varma's are: (a) The force constants around the defect are altered significantly up to at least the third neighbor. This is in contrast to the classical theory where a mass defect would not lead to a force constant defect. (b) The lattice is not much distorted around the defect. Thus the force constant change does not come from a change in interparticle spacing, but from zero-point energy and averaging effects. (c) The force constant changes cause the scattering enhancement. This effect would be entirely missed in a classical calculation. (d) The expression for the frequency spectrum of the impure lattice resembles the classical expression except for a modification which has the appearance of a frequency-dependent mass.

A more general approach to this problem was taken by Nelson and Hartmann (1972), who used a quantum-mechanical Green's function theory. Their work substantiated the conclusions of Varma and they were able to draw an interesting general conclusion about changes in the crystal properties from mass defects: changes which depend linearly on the scattering amplitude, such as specific heat, are largely cancelled by the force constant renormalization, while those that depend on even powers, such as therma resistivity, are enhanced.

Many other defect properties are of most concern in the exchange problem and will not be considered here.

6.5. Miscellaneous theories

Trickey et al. (1972b, 1973) have applied point transform theory to the quantum crystal problem. In this method, a coordinate transformation is made which removes the hard core, but at the expense of introducing a momentum-dependent potential. They noticed that the density matrices associated with the transformation are all harmonic in the SHA theory, and so the transformed hamiltonian should be tractable. The theory was developed, and dispersion curves were calculated from an approximate version. The phonon energies were about 40% higher than were obtained in a typical calculation discussed in section 5. Since the theory does not contain anharmonic effects at this stage, it cannot compete with those described in section 4, but it is an interesting alternative approach.

Noolandi and Van Kranendonk (1972) have used the coherent state formalism of Glauber (1963) to derive a theory of phonons in quantum crystals. This approach provides a natural and interesting way to view phonons as the superposition of a low amplitude, but coherent, motion of the atoms in a quantum crystal on their large amplitude, random zero-point motion. They introduce short-range correlations by means of a Jastrow function and derive equations for the phonon energies which are similar to the lowest-order CBF results; however, their interpretation of the expressions is different, as is discussed in the paper. This theory also has not been extended to include interactions among phonons.

Some of the theoretical development traced in section 4 was concerned with obtaining suitable expressions for the three-phonon vertex to be used in the anharmonic expressions of subsection 3.3. Jäckle and Kerr (1970) have established a relationship between the low-frequency and temperature behavior of the imaginary part of the phonon self-energy and effective vertices which are related to higher-order elastic constants. The three-phonon vertex is obtained from the third-order elastic constants, which are experimentally obtainable in principle. If such measurements could actually be performed, another check on the predictions of various theories would be available.

Other quantum-mechanical developments of lattice dynamics have been made by Meissner (1967), Plakida and Siklós (1969), and Takeno (1970). These all avoid the starting assumption of small atomic displacements from equilibrium and reduce to the SHA at a certain level of approximation.

7. Conclusion and perspective

Compared to the situation of ten years ago, the leading theoretical and experimental problems of the lattice dynamics of quantum crystals can now be considered mostly solved. This does not imply there is no more work to be performed in the field, but merely that the existence of strongly interacting phonons in the solids has been conclusively demonstrated experimentally and the "elementary" theory is now in quite good shape. However, the elementary theory of the lattice dynamics of quantum crystals, in the sense of being the minimal first-principles theory which agrees reasonably well with experiment, is not a particularly simple theory. The classical theory of lattice dynamics, although quite adequate to treat almost all other materials at low temperatures, cannot even be used as a starting point for quantum crystals. Rather one must use from the outset a theory which includes some method for treating the hard-core problem, uses phonons which are at least partially renormalized and includes effects from dispersive anharmonicity.

An abbreviated derivation of three such theories was given in subsections 4.3–4.5. The results of the numerical evaluation of these to obtain theoretical, anharmonic phonon spectra of ^{4}He for various densities and crystal structures were presented in subsection 5.2. The results of all the theories could be considered satisfactory, although those from the fully consistent theory of Horner were in the best agreement with experiment.

This is not accidental; Horner's approach contains two features which are wholly or partially lacking in other calculations. These are the consistency conditions on the pair function and the use of renormalized phonons in obtaining quantities such as the Λ matrices in the harmonic pair function. The full implications of the latter feature are somewhat difficult to assess because it is a detail whose effect tends to become obscured by the computational process. The best clue to its importance is Horner's success in fitting dispersion curves for all branches simultaneously. This is an area in which a good bit more numerical exploration could be performed.

The consistency conditions are easier to visualize and to apply. In the Jastrow–CBF theory, conditions (4.41a)–(4.41c) not only improve the appearance of the theory, but were recently shown by Werthamer to be a consequence of the use of a variationally-optimal Jastrow function. A condition similar to (4.41c) can be found in the procedure of Glyde and Khanna, but (4.41b), whose content is simply that the average position of the particles is where they are supposed to be, is lacking. This condition should be crucial for the proper density dependence. A similar constraint was imposed empirically in the t-matrix theory of Ebner and Sung, but they had nothing like (4.41c). The CBF and t-matrix approaches each have something to recommend them and the exploration of the consequences of adding the consistency relations to these theories is clearly called for.

The consistency relations can be used to provide an ad hoc adjustment to the harmonic pair function in the pure SHA theory so that matrix elements of hard-core potentials can be evaluated and used in its expressions. This empirical approach is more modest than the fully consistent theory, but could prove useful for less anharmonic systems than solid helium: obvious examples are solid hydrogen and the rare gas solids at high temperature. All of the theoretical and computational machinery which has been developed for solid helium will undoubtedly be applied to solid hydrogen, since research into the properties of this interesting substance should increase considerably in the near future. Discussion of finite temperature effects has been avoided in this chapter, but they are contained in Horner's formalism.

The ground-state energy calculations, espectially by the Monte Carlo method, are now quite reliable. This permits the attempt to find the optimum of the available semi-empirical pair potentials for helium, even though the effect of perturbative corrections to the Monte Carlo results has yet to be assessed. Helium, of course, is still a likely candidate for an ab initio evaluation of its interatomic potential.

A remaining relatively unexplored area in the lattice dynamics of quantum crystals is the hcp phase. The inelastic neutron scattering experiments for this phase were not performed with the same precision as those for the cubic phases. A quantitative search for the anomalies discussed in subsection 5.6 should prove rewarding, since evidence for these has been found in the existing experiments. On the theoretical side, anharmonic calculations for this phase should be performed. Here, a theoretical prediction of line profiles and anomalies could point the way for experiments. Still another reason for the intensive exploration of the hcp phase is the very wide density range over which it exists. This poses a challenge to the density dependence of the theory and the interatomic potential.

It is unfortunate that ^{3}He is not a good subject for neutron scattering experiments, although crude experiments with very high flux reactors may be possible. Nevertheless, it may be possible to obtain a reliable theoretical picture of its lattice dynamics. The current success of the best theories is such that the entirety of a spectrum which fits a few points determined from sound velocity and Raman scattering experiments could be accepted with some confidence.

Another quantity which could possibly be obtained from light scattering experiments is the measure of upward dispersion in the $T_2(110)$ branch δ, as defined in (5.3). As was shown in subsection 5.5, both the sound velocity for this branch and δ are very sensitive to the details of the theory and its computational implementation; thus their accurate experimental determination would provide the theorist with a unique aid for fine tuning a calculation.

We now have a good feeling for the effect of anharmonicity on the entire phonon spectrum of the quantum crystals. The implications of this knowledge for some of the topics discussed in section 6 should be explored. The near future should see progress in the study of the implications of alternative theoretical viewpoints, of the defect problem, of the effect of higher-order perturbation terms, of phonon–phonon interactions and of transport properties.

The possibility of calculating transport properties puts the quantum solids theorist in an unexpected position. Not too long ago, we were in an era in which it was not clear if there even was a lattice dynamics of solid helium. Let us review the current situation: the Beck potential appears to be a good He–He interatomic potential; even better forms will probably be forthcoming, and three-body effects do not seem to be important. The ground-state energy calculations for all three phases are satisfactory. The one-phonon properties, even anomalous ones caused by multiphonon interference, are in good agreement with experiment for the cubic phases. Presumably this could be extended to the hcp phase. And now, there is a possibility of direct evaluation of transport properties in all three phases to complement already existing experimental data.

What are the prospects for the future? Several reasons why the special properties of solid helium should make it a particularly simple system for theoretical study were given in subsection 1.1. These are still valid, and we have developed the tools with which to exploit them. Possibly, we are now on the verge of understanding the lattice dynamics properties of solid helium from first principles better than those of any other substance.

Acknowledgements

I wish to thank several people who have aided me in one way or another in the preparation of this chapter. Some of the aid was by personal consultation or advice, other help was by sending material or helping to track down references. The individuals, in alphabetical order, are: H. Horner, T. Kitchens, V. Minkiewicz, S. K. Sinha, S. B. Trickey, and N. R. Werthamer.

In addition, I wish to thank in advance anyone who sends me comments, criticism or advice on any feature of this chapter. In particular, I have tried to be quite careful in the referencing and would appreciate having any errors found there called to my attention.

References

ACKERMAN, C.C., B. BERTMAN, H.A. FAIRBANK and R.A. GUYER (1966), Phys. Rev. Lett. **16**, 789.

ACKERMAN, C.C. and R.A. GUYER (1968), Ann. Phys. (N.Y.) **50**, 128.

AHLERS, G. (1970), Phys. Rev. **A2**, 1505.

AMBEGAOKAR, V., J.M.CONWAY and G. BAYM (1965), *Inelastic Scattering of Neutrons by Anharmonic Crystals*, In: WALLIS, R.F., ed., Lattice Dynamics, (Pergamon, London).

BARKER, J.A. and D. HENDERSON (1971), Accounts Chem. Res. **4**, 303.

BECK, D.E. (1968), Mol. Phys. **14**, 311.

BECK, H. and P.F. MEIER (1971), Z. Phys. **247**, 189.

BECK, H. and P.F. MEIER (1972), Phys. Kondens. Materie **14**, 336.

BENIN, D.B. (1968), Phys. Rev. Lett. **20**, 1352.

BERMAN, R., C.L. BOUNDS and S.J. ROGERS (1965), Proc. Roy. Soc. **A289**, 66.

BERNARDES, N. (1958), Phys. Rev. **112**, 1534.

BERNARDES, N. (1959), Nuovo Cimento **11**, 628.

BERNARDES, N. (1960a), Phys. Rev. **120**, 807.

BERNARDES, N. (1960b), Phys. Rev. **120**, 1927.

BERNARDES, N. and H. PRIMAKOFF (1960), Phys. Rev. **119**, 968.

BERTMAN, B., H.A. FAIRBANK, R.A. GUYER and C.W. WHITE (1966), Phys. Rev. **142**, 79.

BHATTACHARYYA, A. and C.W. WOO (1972), Phys. Rev. Lett. **28**, 1320.

BITTER, M., W. GISSLER and T. SPRINGER, (1967), Phys. Status Solidi **23**, K155.

BORN, M. (1951), *Göttingen Akademie Festschrift*, (Springer-Verlag, Berlin), pp. 1–16. This paper has been translated as Bell Laboratories Tr. 70-14.

BRANDOW, B.H. (1972), Ann. Phys. (N.Y.) **74**, 112.

BRENIG, W. (1963), Z. Phys. **171**, 60.

BRUCH, L.W. and I.J. MCGEE (1970), J. Chem. Phys. **52**, 5884.

BRUECKNER, K.A. and J. FROHBERG (1965), Progr. Theoret. Phys. (Kyoto) Suppl., 383.

BRUECKNER, K.A. and R. THIEBERGER (1969), Phys. Rev. **178**, 362.

BRUN, T.O., S.K. SINHA, C.A. SWENSON and C.R. TILFORN (1968), *Lattice Dynamics of hcp^{4}He by Inelastic Neutron Scattering*, In: Neutron and Inelastic Scattering VI, (International Atomic Energy Agency, Vienna).

CASTLES, S.H., W.P. KIRK and E.D. ADAMS (1972), *Specific Heat of Solid ^3He*, In: Proc. 13th Intern. Conf. Low-Temp. Phys., (to be published).

CHELL, G.G. (1970), J. Phys. C.: Solid St. Phys. **3**, 1861.

CHELL, G.G., V.V. GOLDMAN, M.L. KLEIN and G.K. HORTON (1970), Phys. Rev. **B2**, 560.

CHELL, G.G. (1971), J. Phys. C: Solid Solid St. Phys. **4**, L168.

CHOQUARD, P. (1967), *The Anharmonic Crystal*, (W.A. Benjamin, New York).

COWLEY, R.A. and A.D.B. WOODS (1971), Can. J. Phys. **49**, 177.

DE BOER, J. (1957), *Quantum Effects and Exchange Effects on the Thermodynamic Properties of Liquid Helium*, In: Gorter, C.J., ed., Progress in Low-Temperature Physics, Vol. 2, (North Holland, Amsterdam) pp. 1–58. References to earlier papers may be found in this reference.

DE BOER, J. and R.J. LUNBECK (1948), Physica 14, 318.

DE DOMINICIS, C. and P.C. MARTIN (1964), J. Math. Phys. **5**, 14.

DE WETTE, F.W., and B.R.A. NIJBOER (1965), Phys. Lett. **18**, 19.

DE WETTE, F.W., L.H. NOSANOW and N.R. WERTHAMER (1967), Phys. Rev. **162**, 824.

DE WETTE, F.W. and N.R. WERTHAMER (1969), Phys. Rev. **184**, 209.

DOMB, C. and J.S. DUGDALE (1957), *Solid Helium*, in: Gorter, C.J., ed., Progress in Low Temperature Physics, Vol. 2, (North Holland, Amsterdam) pp. 338–367.

DOMB, C. and L. SALTER (1952), Phil. Mag. **43**, 1083.

DUGDALE, J.S. and J.P. FRANCK (1964), Phil. Trans. R. Soc. **257**, 1.

DUGDALE, J.S. (1965), *Solid Helium and its Melting Curve*, in: Van Itterbeek, A., ed., Physics of High Pressures and the Condensed Phase (North Holland, Amsterdam) pp. 382–425.

EBNER, C. and C.C. SUNG (1971), Phys. Rev. **A4**, 269.

EDWARDS, D.O. and R.C. PANDORF (1965), Phys. Rev. **140**, A816.

EDWARDS, D.O. and R.C. PANDORF (1966), Phys. Rev. **144**, 143.

FEENBERG, E. (1969), *Theory of Quantum Fluids* (Academic, New York).

FREDKIN, D.R. and N.R. WERTHAMER (1965), Phys. Rev. **138**, A1527.

FROHBERG, J.H. (1967), *Correlation Effects in Solid Helium Three*, Thesis, University of California (San Diego), (unpublished).

GARDNER, W.R., J.K. HOFFER and N.E. PHILLIPS (1972), Unpublished.

GARWIN, R.L. and A. LANDESMAN (1965), Physics **2**, 107.

GILLESSEN, P. and W. BIEM (1971), Z. Phys. **242**, 250.

GILLIS, N.S., T.R. KOEHLER and N.R. WERTHAMER (1968), Phys. Rev. **175**, 1110.

GILLIS, N.S. and N.R. WERTHAMER (1968), Phys. Rev. **167**, 607.

GLAUBER, R.J. (1963), Phys. Rev. **131**, 2766.

GLYDE, H.R. (1970), J. Low Temp. Phys. **3**, 559.

GLYDE, H.R. and R.A. COWLEY (1970), Solid State Comm. **8**, 923.

GLYDE, H.R. (1971), Can. J. Phys. **49**, 761.

GLYDE, H.R. and F.C. KHANNA (1971), Can. J. Phys. **49**, 2997.

GLYDE, H.R. and F.C. KHANNA (1972a), Can. J. Phys. **50**, 1143.

GLYDE, H.R. and F.C. KHANNA (1972b), Can. J. Phys. **50**, 1152.

GOLDMAN, V.V., G.K. HORTON and M.L. KLEIN (1970), Phys. Rev. Lett. **24**, 1424.

GÖTZE, W. and K.H. MICHEL (1968), Z. Phys. **217**, 170.

GREYWALL, D.S. (1971), Phys. Rev. **A3**, 2106.

GUYER, R.A. (1969a), Solid State Comm. **7**, 315.

GUYER, R.A. (1969b), *The Physics of Quantum Crystals*, in: Seitz, F. and D. Turnbull, eds., Solid State Physics, Vol. 23, (Academic Press, New York) pp. 413–499.

GUYER, R.A. (1970), Phys. Rev. Lett. **24**, 810.

GUYER, R.A., R.C. RICHARDSON and L.I. ZANE (1971), Rev. Mod. Phys. **43**, 532.

GUYER, R.A. (1972a), J. Low Temp. Phys. **6**, 251.

GUYER, R.A. (1972b), J. Low Temp. Phys. **8**, 427.

HANSEN, J.P. and D. LEVESQUE (1968), Phys. Rev. **165**, 293.

HANSEN, J.P. (1969), Phys. Lett. **30A**, 214.

HANSEN, J.P. (1970), J. Phys. (Paris) **31**, Suppl. C3, 67.

HANSEN. J.P. (1971), Phys. Lett. **34A**, 25.

HANSEN, J.P. and E.L. POLLOCK (1972), Phys. Rev. **A5**, 2651.

HENRIKSEN, P.N., M.F. PANCZYK, S.B. TRICKEY and E.D. ADAMS (1969), Phys. Rev. Lett. **23**, 518.

HETHERINGTON, J.H., W.J. MULLIN and L.H. NOSASOW (1967), Phys. Rev. **154**, 175.

HETHERINGTON, J.H. (1968), Phys. Rev. **176**, 231.

HOOTON, D.J. (1955a), Phil. Mag. **46**, 422, 433.

HOOTON, D.J. (1955b), Z. Phys. **142**, 42.

HORNER, H. (1967), Z. Phys. **205**, 72.

HORNER, H. (1970a), Phys. Rev. **A1**, 1712.

HORNER, H. (1970b), Phys. Rev. **A1**, 1722.

HORNER, H. (1970c), Phys. Rev. Lett. **25**, 147.

HORNER, H. (1971a), Solid State Comm. **9**, 79.

HORNER, H. (1971b), Z. Phys. **242**, 432.

HORNER, H. (1972a), J. Low Temp. Phys. **8**, 511.

HORNER, H. (1972b), Phys. Rev. Lett. **29**, 556.

HORNER, H. (1972c), *Quantum Crystals: Theory of the Phonon Spectrum*, in: Proc. 13th Intern. Conf. Low Temp. Phys., (to be published).

HORNER, H. (1972d), *Multiphonon and Single Particle Excitations in Quantum Crystals*, in: Proc. 13th Intern. Conf. Low Temp. Phys., (to be published).

IWAMOTO, F. and H. NAMAIZAWA (1966), Prog. Theoret. Phys. Suppl. **37–38**, 234.

IWAMOTO, F. and H. NAMAIZAWA (1971), Prog. Theoret. Phys. **45**, 682.

JACKSON, H.W. and E. FEENBERG (1961), Ann. Phys. (N.Y.) **15**, 266.

JÄCKLE, J. and K.W. KERR (1970), Phys. Rev. Lett. **24**, 1101.

JONES, H.D. (1970), Phys. Rev. **A1**, 71.

JULIAN, C.L. (1965), Phys. Rev. **137**, A128.

KERR, W.C. and A. SJÖLANDER (1970), Phys. Rev. **B1**, 2723.

KITCHENS, T.A., G. SHIRANE, V.J. MINKIEWICZ and E.B. OSGOOD (1972), Phys. Rev. Lett. **29**, 552.

KITTEL, C. (1963), *Quantum Theory of Solids* (Wiley, New York).

KLEMENS, P.G. (1968), Phys. Rev. **169**, 229.

KOEHLER, T.R. (1965), Phys. Rev. **139**, A1097.

KOEHLER, T.R. (1966a), Phys. Rev. **141**, 281.

KOEHLER, T.R. (1966b), Phys. Rev. Lett. **17**, 89.

KOEHLER, T.R. (1967), Phys. Rev. Lett. **18**, 654.

KOEHLER, T.R. (1968), Phys. Rev. **165**, 942.

KOEHLER, T.R. and N.P. WERTHAMER (1971), Phys. Rev. **A3**, 2074.

KOEHLER, T.R. (1972), *Computational Aspects of Anharmonic Lattice Dynamics*, in: Herman,

F.H., N.W. Dalton and T.R. Koehler, eds., Computational Solid State Physics (Plenum, New York).
Koehler, T.R. and N.R. Werthamer (1972), Phys. Rev. **A5**, 2230.
Koehler, T.R. (1973a), *Introduction to Quantum Lattice Dynamics*, in: Califano, S., ed., Proc. of the Intern. School of Physics Enrico Fermi, Course 55 (Varenna, 1972), (to be published).
Koehler, T.R. (1974), (to be published).
Lipschultz, F.P., V.J. Minkiewicz, T.A. Kitchens and G. Shirane (1967), Phys. Rev. Lett. **19**, 1307.
London, F. (1954), Superfluids, Vol. II, (Wiley, New York).
March, N.H., W.H. Young and S. Sampanthar (1967), *The Many-Body Problem in Quantum Mechanics*, (Cambridge University Press, London).
Massey, W.E. and C.W. Woo (1968), Phys. Rev. **169**, 241.
McMahan, A.K. and R.A. Guyer (1972), *Single-Particle Density and Debye-Waller Factor for bcc ^4He*, in: Proc. 13th Intern. Conf. Low Temp. Phys., (to be published).
Meissner, G. (1967), Z. Phys. **205**, 249.
Meissner, G. (1968a), Phys. Rev. Lett. **21**, 435.
Meissner, G. (1968b), Phys. Lett. **27A**, 261.
Minkiewicz, V.J., T.A. Kitchens, F.P. Lipschultz, R. Nathans and G. Shirane (1968), Phys. Rev. **174**, 267.
Morely, G.L. and K.L. Kleiwer (1969), Phys. Rev. **180**, 245.
Mullin, W.J. (1964), Phys. Rev. **134**, A1249.
Mullin, W.J. (1968), Phys. Rev. **166**, 142.
Mullin, W.J. (1971), J. Low. Temp. Phys. **4**, 135.
Murrell, J.N. and G. Shaw (1968), Mol. Phys. **15**, 325.
Namaizawa, H. (1972), Prog. Theor. Phys. **48**, 709.
Nelson, R.D. and W.M. Hartmann (1972), Phys. Rev. Lett. **28**, 1261.
Niklasson, G. (1970), Ann. Phys. (N.Y.) **59**, 263.
Noolandi, J. and J. Van Kranendonk (1972), Can. J. Phys. **50**, 1815.
Nosanow, L.H. (1964), Phys. Rev. Lett. **13**, 270.
Nosanow, L.H. (1966), Phys. Rev. **146**, 120.
Nosanow, L.H. and G.L. Shaw (1962), Phys. Rev. **128**, 546.
Nosanow, L.H. and N.R. Werthamer (1965), Phys. Rev. Lett. **15**, 618.
Osgood, E.B., V.J. Minkiewicz, T.A. Kitchens and G. Shirane (1972), Phys. Rev. **A5**, 1537.
Østgaard, E. (1971), J. Low Temp. Phys. **5**, 237.
Pandorf, R.C. and D.O. Edwards (1968), Phys. Rev. **169**, 222.
Peierls, R. (1929), Ann. Physik **3**, 1055.
Placzek, G. (1952), Phys. Rev. **86**, 377.
Plakida, N.M. and T. Siklós (1969), Phys. Stat. Sol. **33**, 103.
Pluvinage, P. (1950), Ann. Phys. **5**, 145.
Ranninger, J. (1969), J. Phys. C: Solid St. Phys. **2**, 640.
Reese, R.A., S.K. Sinha, T.O. Brun and C.R. Tilford (1971), Phys. Rev. **A3**, 1688.
Rosenwald, D. (1967), Phys. Rev. **154**, 160.
Sample, H.H. and C.A. Swenson (1967), Phys. Rev. **158**, 188.
Saunders, E.M. (1962), Phys. Rev. **126**, 1724.
Sears, V.F. and F.C. Khanna (1972), Phys. Rev. Lett. **29**, 549.

SIKLÓS, T. (1971), Acta Phys. Hung. **30**, 181.
SLUSHER, R.E. and C.M. SURKO (1971), Phys. Rev. Lett. **27**, 1699.
STRATY, G.C. and E.D. ADAMS (1968), Phys. Rev. **169**, 232.
TAKENO, S. (1970), Progr. Theoret. Phys. Suppl. **45**, 137.
TRAYLOR, J.G., C. STASSIS, R.A. REESE and S.K. SINHA (1971), in: Inelastic Scattering of Neutrons, Vol. I, (I.A.E.A., Vienna). (to be published).
TRICKEY, S.B. (1968), Phys. Rev. **166**, 177.
TRICKEY, S.B., W.P. KIRK and E.D. ADAMS (1972a), Rev. Mod. Phys. **44**, 668.
TRICKEY, S.B., N.M. WITRIOL and G.L. MORLEY (1972b), Solid State Comm. **11**, 139.
TRICKEY, S.B., N.M. WITRIOL and G.L. MORLEY (1973), Phys. Rev. **A7**, 1662.
VAN KAMPEN, N.G. (1961), Physica **27**, 783.
VARMA, C.M. (1970), Phys. Rev. Lett. **24**, 203.
VARMA, C.M. (1971), Phys. Rev. **A4**, 313.
VIGNOS, J.H. and H.A. FAIRBANK (1966), Phys. Rev. **147**, 185.
WANNER, R. (1971), Phys. Rev. **A3**, 448.
WERTHAMER, N.R. (1969a), Am. J. Phys. **37**, 763.
WERTHAMER, N.R. (1969b), Phys. Rev. **185**, 348.
WERTHAMER, N.R. (1970a), Phys. Rev. **B1**, 572.
WERTHAMER, N.R. (1970b), Phys. Rev. **A2**, 2050.
WERTHAMER, N.R., R.L. GRAY and T.R. KOEHLER (1971), Phys. Rev. **B4**, 1324.
WERTHAMER, N.R. (1972a), Phys. Rev. **B5**, 285.
WERTHAMER, N.R. (1972b), Phys. Rev. Lett. **28**, 1102.
WERTHAMER, N.R. (1972c), Phys. Rev. **B6**, 4075.
WERTHAMER, N.R. and S.T. CHUI (1972a), Solid. State Comm. **10**, 843.
WERTHAMER, N.R. and S.T. CHUI (1972b), Phys. Lett. **41A**, 157.
WERTHAMER, N.R. (1973), Phys. Rev. **A7**, 254.
WILKS, J. (1967), *The Properties of Liquid and Solid Helium* (Oxford University Press, London) pp. 560–664.
WOO, C.W. (1972), Phys. Rev. Lett. **28**, 1442.
YNTEMA, J.L. and W.G. SCHNEIDER (1950), J. Chem. Phys. **18**, 646.
ZUCKER, I.J. (1961), Proc. Phys. Soc. **77**, 889.

CHAPTER 2

Lattice Dynamics of Ferroelectricity

N.S. GILLIS*

Sandia Laboratories
Albuquerque, New Mexico 87115
USA

* *Present address: Physics Department, Colorado State University, Ft. Collins, Colorado 80521, USA*

Dynamical Properties of Solids, edited by G.K. Horton and A.A. Maradudin

Contents

1. Introduction

It has become increasingly clear since the advent of the self-consistent renormalization techniques in anharmonic lattice dynamics that a re-examination of some of the conventional ideas associated with the lattice dynamics of ferroelectricity may be in order. Until recently, the application of these self-consistent techniques to the ferroelectric problem would have been impossible because of the computational difficulties involved. However, in view of the experience gained through the detailed calculations which have been carried out on the rare gas solids in the past few years, it is now possible to treat the ferroelectric problem within the framework of self-consistent lattice dynamics. It is to this task that we address ourselves in the present chapter.

Ferroelectric crystals have in the past been grouped into one or the other of two categories – displacive or order–disorder. Experience now tells us that few, if any, ferroelectric crystals fall unequivocally into either of these classifications – most real systems probably reside somewhere between the two extremes. In spite of this, the lattice dynamical approach to ferroelectricity is primarily concerned with the microscopic description of *displacive* ferroelectrics, i.e., ferroelectrics in which the macroscopic ionic displacements in the low-temperature ordered phase may be unambiguously associated with the symmetry of an anomalously temperature dependent optic mode of the high-temperature paraelectric phase. This definition of a displacive ferroelectric does not, unfortunately, allow us to escape entirely from the specter of order–disorder phenomena – indeed, even in the case where the phonon character of the transition may manifest itself quite strongly, the existence of an underlying order–disorder mechanism cannot be entirely discounted. Having admitted this possibility, we will perforce confine ourselves to a description of displacive ferroelectric phase transitions as a purely phonon dominated phenomenon. Our approach in this chapter can best be described as that of examining the consequences of carrying out a systematic study of displacive ferroelectricity in which phonons are assumed at the outset to play a significant role.

The application of conventional anharmonic perturbation techniques to the treatment of ferroelectricity is fraught with problems, the primary difficulty being that the harmonic approximation represents an unstable state of equilibrium for the crystal. Thus, a perturbation expansion employing a harmonic basis cannot in principle be carried out. A similar situation, of course, holds for the quantum crystals of solid helium and solid molecular hydrogen – in both of these systems the harmonic approximation does not exist. Thus, it would seem that the self-consistent phonon techniques, which work so well in the treatment of the quantum crystal problem, should be ideally suited to the study of ferroelectricity. Silverman (1964) was the first to suggest the possibility of a self-consistent calculation within the context of the displacive ferroelectric problem. Later, Boccara and Sarma (1965) and Doniach (1965) presented variational formulations for the treatment of lattice structural transformations, but did not present any actual results.

There exist in the literature several excellent expositions of the lattice dynamics of ferroelectricity employing conventional anharmonic perturbation theory. Of particular interest to the reader desiring a general overview of the subject are the works of Cowley (1965), Maradudin (1967), Kwok and Miller (1966), and Cochran (1969).

2. *The soft mode concept*

A feature which characterizes almost all ferroelectric transitions is the Curie–Weiss law temperature dependence of the static dielectric constant as one approaches the transition from above. The intimate relation between this anomolous temperature dependence and a strongly temperature dependent zone center transverse optic mode of the paraelectric phase was first pointed out by Cochran (1960) and Anderson (1960). Cochran and Anderson had proposed that in crystals of the displacive ferroelectric type a long-wavelength cancellation occurred between the long-range dipolar interaction and the short-range interaction such that a group of optic modes at zone center would be purely imaginary in the harmonic approximation. They then assumed that anharmonic interactions would provide a renormalization of the phonon frequencies such that above a certain temperature the paraelectric phase would be stabilized. The idea which is of critical importance here is that for a crystal which undergoes a lattice structural transformation from a high-temperature paraelectric phase to a low-temperature ordered ferroelectric phase, the harmonic approximation represents an unstable state of equilibrium and the crystal will be characterized by imaginary harmonic frequencies for a group of optic modes of long wavelength. The most striking experimental verification of the existence of soft mode behavior was first made by Cowley (1962). Cowley employed the technique of inelastic neutron diffraction to measure the phonon dispersion curves in $SrTiO_3$ over a wide range of temperature. The original Cowley data are reproduced in fig. 1 together with the static dielectric constant measurements of Mitsui and Westphal (1961). The most arresting feature of the data is the fact that the

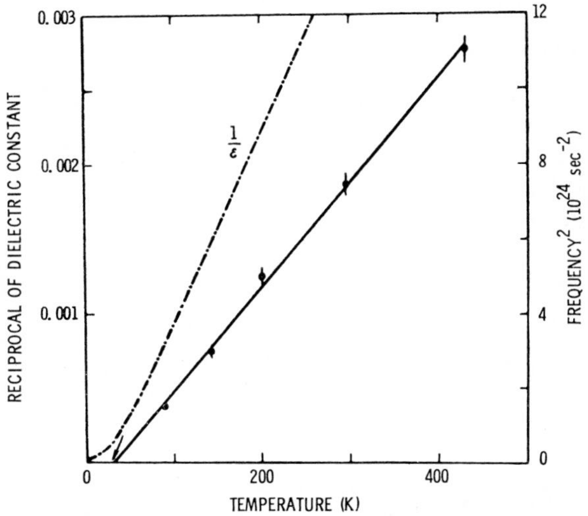

Fig. 1. Temperature dependence of the lowest transverse optic mode frequency squared in $SrTiO_3$ (Cowley 1962). Also plotted is the inverse dielectric constant as a function of temperature (Mitsui and Westphal 1961).

linear temperature dependence of the zone center frequency squared extends over a temperature interval of almost 400 K, reflecting a similar temperature dependence in the inverse dielectric constant ε_0^{-1}. That the temperature dependence of ε_0^{-1} and $\omega_{TO}^2(q=0)$ should be similar follows from the Lyddane–Sachs–Teller relation (Lyddane et al. 1941) which, for diatomic cubic crystals, reads

$$\varepsilon_0/\varepsilon_\infty = \omega_{LO}^2(q=0)/\omega_{TO}^2(q=0). \tag{1}$$

Assuming the high-frequency dielectric constant ε_∞ and the zone center longitudinal optic mode frequency to be relatively temperature independent, we see that the temperature dependence of ω_{TO}^2 mirrors the temperature dependence of ε_0^{-1}. This qualitative argument is highly oversimplified, of course, since the Lyddane–Sachs–Teller relationship is rigorously true only in the harmonic approximation.

As illustrated in fig. 2, soft mode behavior similar to that which is observed in $SrTiO_3$ has also been observed in $KTaO_3$ (Shirane et al. 1967), another crystal of the perovskite structure. It is to be noted that both $SrTiO_3$ and $KTaO_3$ are *paraelectric* at all temperatures, i.e., no structural transformation related to the soft mode behavior at zone center occurs at any temperature.

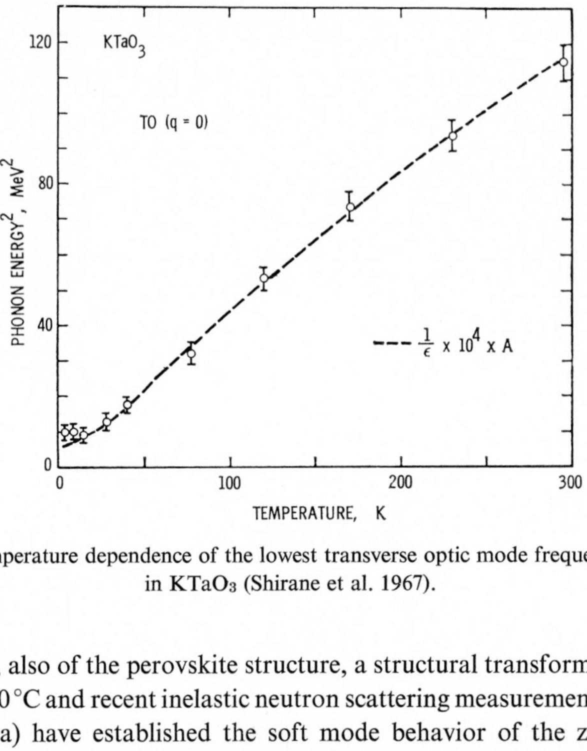

Fig. 2. Temperature dependence of the lowest transverse optic mode frequency squared in $KTaO_3$ (Shirane et al. 1967).

In $PbTiO_3$, also of the perovskite structure, a structural transformation does occur at 490 °C and recent inelastic neutron scattering measurements (Shirane et al. 1970a) have established the soft mode behavior of the zone center transverse optic frequency in the paraelectric phase. The neutron data are reproduced in fig. 3. $PbTiO_3$ is probably the best example of a displacive ferroelectric from the point of view of the ionic displacements of the low-temperature phase corresponding to the symmetry of the soft mode of the paraelectric phase. $BaTiO_3$, long thought to be the classic example of displacive ferroelectricity, has now reached the status of uncertainty. The extreme anisotropy of the forces, the highly overdamped soft modes, and the possibility of order–disorder mechanisms at work place this perovskite in a category by itself (Shirane et al. 1970b, Harada et al. 1971).

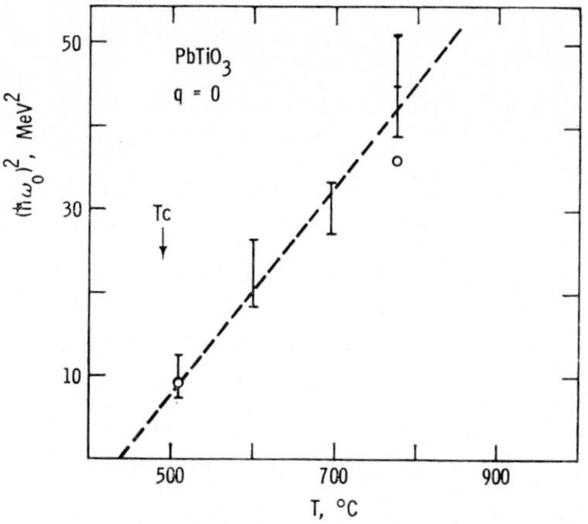

Fig. 3. Temperature dependence of the lowest transverse optic mode frequency squared in $PbTiO_3$ above the transition (Shirane et al. 1970a).

The idea of the soft mode is of such fundamental importance to our later discussion that it is of interest to pursue the concept in somewhat more detail by showing how soft mode behavior can arise out of a simple model of interacting phonons. Although no new results will be obtained at this stage, this simple calculation will serve to illustrate some of the points discussed above. We consider a system of interacting excitations of optic phonon character, described by the hamiltonian ($\hbar = 1$)

$$H = \sum_q \left(-\frac{1}{2M} \frac{\partial^2}{\partial Q_q \partial Q_{-q}} + \tfrac{1}{2} M \Omega_q^2 Q_q Q_{-q} \right) + (\varphi/N) \sum_{q,q',q''} Q_q Q_{-q+q''} Q_{q'} Q_{-q'-q''} . \quad (2)$$

In the absence of the quartic interaction φ this hamiltonian would describe a set of non-interacting optical phonons of wave-vector q and energy Ω_q. M has the significance of a reduced effective mass of the fictitious lattice. In the presence of the interaction, the equation of motion of the normal mode coordinate $Q_q(t)$ is easily written down as

$$-M \partial^2 Q_q(t)/\partial t^2 = M \Omega_q^2 Q_q(t) + (4\varphi/N) \sum_{q',q''} Q_{q'}(t)\, Q_{-q'+q''}(t)\, Q_{q-q''}(t) . \quad (3)$$

Instead of working directly with (3), it is convenient at this point to introduce equations for the thermal averages $\langle Q_q(t) \rangle$ and $\langle [Q_q(t)\, Q_{q'}(t')]_+ \rangle$, defined as

$$\langle Q_q(t)\rangle \equiv \mathrm{tr}\,\{\mathrm{e}^{-\beta H}[SQ_q(t)]_+\}/\mathrm{tr}\,\{\mathrm{e}^{-\beta H}S\},$$
$$\langle [Q_q(t)\,Q_{q'}(t')]_+\rangle \equiv \mathrm{tr}\,\{\mathrm{e}^{-\beta H}[SQ_q(t)\,Q_{q'}(t')]_+\}/\mathrm{tr}\,\{\mathrm{e}^{-\beta H}S\}, \tag{4}$$

where

$$S \equiv \left[\exp\left(-\mathrm{i}\int_0^{-\mathrm{i}\beta} \mathrm{d}t \sum_q F_{-q}(t)\,Q_q(t)\right)\right]_+ .$$

We have introduced a time-dependent external field $F_q(t)$ which couples linearly to the normal mode coordinate Q_q. All operators are now defined in the imaginary time interval $[0, -\mathrm{i}\beta]$, where $\beta \equiv (k_B T)^{-1}$. The symbol $[\cdots]_+$ denotes the time-ordering operation in this interval. The operator S plays the part of a time evolution operator in the interaction picture. At this point and henceforth we will be employing the functional derivative Green's function technique for dealing with thermal averages of products of phonon operators. This technique has been reviewed in great detail recently by Kwok (1967) within the context of lattice dynamics and we refer the reader to this extensive work for more details.

We define the one-phonon Green's function within the context of the present example as

$$D_q(t, t') \equiv \delta\langle Q_q(t)\rangle/\delta F_q(t')$$
$$= -\mathrm{i}\{\langle [Q_q(t)\,Q_{-q}(t')]_+\rangle - \langle Q_q(t)\rangle\langle Q_{-q}(t')\rangle\}. \tag{5}$$

The equations satisfied by $\langle Q_q(t)\rangle$ and $D_q(t, t')$ follow in a straightforward manner from (3) and the definitions (4) and (5). Indeed, we find

$$\left[-M\frac{\partial^2}{\partial t^2} - M\Omega_q^2\right]\langle Q_q(t)\rangle$$
$$= F_q(t) + (4\varphi/N)\sum_{q', q''}\langle [Q_{q'}(t)\,Q_{-q'+q''}(t)\,Q_{q-q''}(t)]_+\rangle, \tag{6}$$

and

$$\left[-M\frac{\partial^2}{\partial t^2} - M\Omega_q^2\right]D_q(tt') = \delta(t-t')$$
$$-(4\mathrm{i}\varphi/N)\sum_{q', q''}\{\langle [Q_{q'}(t)\,Q_{-q'+q''}(t)\,Q_{q-q''}(t)\,Q_{-q}(t')]_+\rangle$$
$$-\langle [Q_{q'}(t)\,Q_{-q'+q''}(t)\,Q_{q-q''}(t)]_+\rangle\langle Q_{-q'}(t')\rangle\}. \tag{7}$$

There are, of course, similar equations of motion for thermal averages of products of three of more Q's. Indeed, an infinite hierarchy of such equations exists. Typically, the equations are solved by a truncation procedure in which thermal averages of three or more Q's are expressed approximately in terms of $\langle Q \rangle$ and the one-phonon Green's function D. We will in fact show at a later stage how one can solve (6) and (7) self-consistently. At this point, however, we wish to recover only the lowest order results of the conventional perturbation theory. To this end we observe that the interaction terms on the right-hand side of (6) and (7) are proportional to φ. Thus, if in some sense φ is small, we can in lowest order evaluate averages of three or more Q's employing the hamiltonian (2) with $\varphi = 0$. But it is well known that for thermal averages with respect to a harmonic hamiltonian the *cumulant* or *linked average* of three or more normal mode operators vanishes identically (Kubo 1962). For the problem at hand, the vanishing of cumulants of order three or greater is equivalent to the statement

$$\delta^n \langle Q_q(t) \rangle / \delta F_{q_1}(t_1) \cdots \delta F_{q_n}(t_n) = 0\,, \quad n > 1 \tag{8}$$

and is exact if (2) is harmonic in form. For $n=2$, (8) yields

$$\begin{aligned}\langle [Q_q(t)\, Q_{q_1}(t_1)\, Q_{q_2}(t_2)]_+ \rangle &= \langle Q_q(t) \rangle \langle [Q_{q_1}(t_1)\, Q_{q_2}(t_2)]_+ \rangle \\ &+ \langle Q_{q_1}(t_1) \rangle \langle [Q_q(t)\, Q_{q_2}(t_2)]_+ \rangle + \langle Q_{q_2}(t_2) \rangle \langle [Q_q(t)\, Q_{q_1}(t_1)]_+ \rangle \\ &- 2 \langle Q_q(t) \rangle \langle Q_{q_1}(t_1) \rangle \langle Q_{q_2}(t_2) \rangle . \end{aligned} \tag{9}$$

A similar, but somewhat lengthier expression holds for $n=3$. We are now in a position to express the interaction terms in (6) and (7) in terms of the quantities $\langle Q \rangle$ and D alone. In retrospect, we might note that these terms could have initially been expressed in terms of $\langle Q \rangle$, D and functional derivatives of D. Thus, the vanishing of cumulants of third order or higher may be restated as the vanishing of functional derivatives of the one-phonon Green's function, as is obvious from (8). Starting from (8) as a lowest order approximation, an iteration scheme could be set up which would reproduce the standard anharmonic perturbation expansion (Kwok 1967).

With these rather lengthy preliminaries out of the way we now rewrite (6) and (7) using the approximation (8).

$$\begin{aligned}\left[- M \frac{\partial^2}{\partial t^2} - M\Omega_q^2 \right] \langle Q_q(t) \rangle &= F_q(t) \\ &+ (4\varphi/N) \Big[3 \langle Q_q(t) \rangle \sum_{q'} \langle Q_{q'}(t)\, Q_{-q'}(t) \rangle_0 \\ &- 2 \sum_{q', q''} \langle Q_{q'}(t) \rangle \langle Q_{-q'+q''}(t) \rangle \langle Q_{q-q''}(t) \rangle \Big], \end{aligned} \tag{10}$$

$$\left[-M\frac{\partial^2}{\partial t^2} - M\Omega_q^2\right] D_q(t,t')$$
$$= \delta(t-t') + (12\varphi/N)\sum_{q'} \langle Q_{q'}(t)\, Q_{-q'}(t)\rangle_0\, D_q(t,t'). \quad (11)$$

We have placed a subscript zero on the averages on the right-hand sides of (10) and (11) to remind us that these are harmonic averages, i.e., averages with respect to (2) with $\varphi = 0$. We might note that terms of the form $\langle [Q_q(t)\, Q_{q'}(t')]_+\rangle_0$ with $q \neq -q'$ do not appear since these are identically zero in the harmonic approximation. Allowing $F_q(t) \to 0$, terms of the form $\langle Q_q(t)\rangle$ and $\langle Q_q(t)\, Q_{-q}(t)\rangle$ become time-independent. We further assume that the only non-zero $\langle Q_q\rangle$ is $\langle Q_0\rangle$. Eq. (10) then yields the following equation for $\langle Q_0\rangle$:

$$[M\Omega_0^2 + (4\varphi/N)\langle Q_0\rangle^2 + (12\varphi/N)\sum_{q'} \langle Q_{q'} Q_{-q'}\rangle_0]\,\langle Q_0\rangle = 0. \quad (12)$$

It is obvious from (12) that in addition to the usual solution $\langle Q_0\rangle = 0$, there exists the possibility of a 'displaced' solution, given by

$$\langle Q_0\rangle^2/N = -(1/4\varphi)\,[M\Omega_0^2 + (12\varphi/N)\sum_{q'} \langle Q_{q'} Q_{-q'}\rangle_0]. \quad (13)$$

Such a solution will in general be possible if $\Omega_0^2 < 0$ and $\varphi > 0$. In the presence of anharmonic effects, the resonances exhibited by the one-phonon Green's function no longer appear at the frequencies $\pm\Omega_q$ but at new frequencies $\pm\bar{\Omega}_q$ which may be easily obtained from (11). For $q = 0$ we have,

$$M\bar{\Omega}_0^2 = \begin{cases} M\Omega_0^2 + (12\varphi/N)\sum_{q'} \langle Q_{q'} Q_{-q'}\rangle_0, & \langle Q_0\rangle = 0, \\ (8\varphi/N)\langle Q_0\rangle^2, & \langle Q_0\rangle \neq 0. \end{cases} \quad (14)$$

Since the thermal fluctuations of the normal modes monotonically increase with temperature, it is clear that $\Omega_0^2 < 0$ implies that $\bar{\Omega}_0^2$ will vanish at a temperature defined by

$$M\Omega_0^2 + (12\varphi/N)\sum_{q'} \langle Q_{q'} Q_{-q'}\rangle_0 = 0, \quad (15)$$

and will be positive both above and below this temperature. Thus, we see that in this simple model of interacting phonons a displacive transition occurs, defined by the appearance of a non-zero 'order parameter' $\langle Q_0\rangle$ of long wavelength. The transition is continuous, with the transition temperature being defined by the simultaneous vanishing of $\langle Q_0\rangle$ and $\bar{\Omega}_0^2$. The vanishing of $\bar{\Omega}_0^2$ reflects an anomolous behavior in the inverse static susceptibility. Indeed, we can use (10) to easily evaluate the static susceptibility $\delta\langle Q_0\rangle/\delta F_0$, where F_0 is a static external field of long wavelength. Thus,

$$(\delta\langle Q_0\rangle/\delta F_0)_{\langle Q_0\rangle=0} = 1/M\bar{\Omega}_0^2,$$

and we see that the vanishing of $\bar{\Omega}_0^2$ as the transition is approached from above implies that the susceptibility becomes infinite.

It is not difficult to give some physical interpretation to the parameters which appear in the hamiltonian (2). In insulating crystals it is usual to separate the interaction potential into a part arising from the short-range forces together with a part arising from the long-range dipolar interaction. Assuming that the anharmonic effects are dominated by the short-range part of the interaction, then one can think of φ as arising from the short-range potential only, with the Coulombic interaction treated harmonically. The unrenormalized frequencies Ω_a^2 will then contain contributions from both the harmonic short range and the harmonic dipolar interaction and we can assume that $\Omega_q^2<0$ for a group of modes near zone center because of an over-cancellation between short range and dipolar forces. If the component φ of the quartic interaction is taken to be positive definite, then it is possible for (15) to be satisfied at some temperature T_c and we can think of the system as undergoing a displacive transition at this temperature. Although the arguments up to this point are intuitively appealing, certain difficulties inherent to this approach become obvious upon a little reflection. Since the Ω_q near zone center are imaginary, the long-wavelength thermal averages which appear in (12)–(15) do not in principle exist. Thus, in order to proceed further we must assume that the imaginary harmonic modes constitute a negligible fraction of the total, so that one would be justified in neglecting them altogether in normal mode sums. Once this is done, the thermal average $\langle Q_q Q_{-q}\rangle$ for the harmonically stable modes may be evaluated as (reduced temperature units are used)

$$\langle Q_q Q_{-q}\rangle_0 = (1/2M\Omega_q)\coth(\Omega_q/2T).$$

Eqs. (13)–(15) may now be rewritten as

$$\langle Q_0\rangle^2/N = -(1/4\varphi)\left[M\Omega_0^2 + (6\varphi/MN)\sum_{q'}{}'(1/\Omega_{q'})\coth(\Omega_{q'}/2T)\right], \qquad (13')$$

$$M\bar{\Omega}_0^2 = \begin{cases} M\Omega_0^2 + (6\varphi/MN)\sum_{q'}{}'(1/\Omega_{q'})\coth(\Omega_{q'}/2T), & \langle Q_0\rangle = 0 \\ (8\varphi/N)\langle Q_0\rangle^2, & \langle Q_0\rangle \neq 0 \end{cases} \qquad (14')$$

$$M\Omega_0^2 + (6\varphi/MN)\sum_{q'}{}' (1/\Omega_{q'}) \coth(\Omega_{q'}/2T_c) = 0 . \tag{15'}$$

The primed summations in the above equations are meant to indicate that we must neglect that portion of phase space subtended by the imaginary harmonic modes. We can pursue this approach even further. If the energies of all the harmonically stable modes are much less than the thermal energy $k_B T$, then one can make a high-temperature expansion in (13′)–(15′), obtaining

$$\begin{aligned} T_c^{-1} &= -(1/M\Omega_0^2)\left((12\varphi/MN)\sum_{q'}{}' 1/\Omega_{q'}^2\right), \\ \langle Q_0\rangle^2 &\propto (T_c - T), \qquad T < T_c, \\ \bar{\Omega}_0^2 &\propto |T - T_c| . \end{aligned} \tag{16}$$

Results similar to these have been obtained previously in one form or the other by Anderson, Cochran, Cowley, Silverman, and others.

It would appear on the face of it that the model considered here reproduces most of the qualitative features of the soft mode behavior observed in many ferroelectric crystals. The model predicts a classical second order phase transition and can be extended to encompass first order transitions by including sixth order anharmonicity, allowing the quartic contribution to be negative. With the possible exception of $SrTiO_3$ (Riste et al. 1971, Müller and Berlinger 1971), classical behavior is the rule rather than the exception for the majority of displacive ferroelectric transitions – critical phenomena associated with order parameter fluctuations are not in general observed. The model is unrealistic in the sense that it consisted of interacting optic phonons only, whereas in a real lattice modes of acoustic character are necessarily present also. However, for the system of phonons interacting via quartic anharmonicity only, the results are not drastically changed by the introduction of acoustic modes – we need only interpret q as a composite index $q\lambda$. In the normal mode sums such as appear in (13′)–(15′), one must then sum over all modes, acoustic as well as optic. Having neglected the soft modes altogether in the normal mode sums, however, the major contribution to the renormalization of the zone center optic frequency will now arise from the acoustic modes, since the energies of such modes are generally less than the energies of the optic modes.

The approximations which were made in arriving at the results (13′)–(15′) and (16) are difficult to justify in general, so that one might conclude that the good qualitative agreement between the model results and observed soft mode behavior in actual ferroelectrics may to a certain extent be fortuitous. The first indication that something might be amiss arises from the experimental fact that in the incipient ferroelectrics $SrTiO_3$ and $KTaO_3$ the linear temperature dependence of the zone center squared frequency extends into the very low temperature regime – indeed, it extends to much lower temperatures than would justify an expansion of the thermal population factors in powers of Ω/T such as was done in obtaining (16). The implication is that agreement with experiment would require an implicit temperature dependence to the frequencies Ω_q, which of course is impossible if they represent bare harmonic modes. From the purely formal point of view, the process of excluding a portion of phase space in the normal mode sums is arbitrary and unsystematic, depending critically on a knowledge of the unrenormalized state of the crystal – which, of course, has little meaning since it represents an unstable state of the lattice. The escape from this latter difficulty is straightforward, though difficult, in practice. One should, at all points of the calculation, deal with the physical (i.e., renormalized) phonons only. This was first pointed out by Silverman (1964) and is implicit in the work of Maradudin (1967) and Kwok and Miller (1966). For the model which we have considered above we can easily illustrate how such a self-consistent calculation can be carried out. Again, we start with the approximation (8) but no longer restrict the thermal averages to harmonic averages. Thus, (10) and (11) remain formally the same, but with the subscripts zero removed from the thermal averages on the right-hand side of the equations. This is essentially the *linear anharmonic approximation* of Kwok and Miller, but without their further simplification to harmonic averages. A similar approximation has been employed by Ambegaokar et al. (1965) in evaluating the inelastic neutron scattering cross section in crystals. Thus, with this approximation, (10) and (11) represent two coupled equations for the order parameter $\langle Q_0 \rangle$ and the one-phonon Green's function and are to be solved self-consistently. Thermal averages such as $\langle Q_q Q_{-q} \rangle$ will be well-defined for all q and can be evaluated as

$$\langle Q_q Q_{-q} \rangle = (1/2M\bar{\Omega}_q) \coth(\bar{\Omega}_q/2T),$$

where $\bar{\Omega}_q$ now represents a renormalized frequency rather than the frequency of the corresponding harmonic mode. The phonon energies $\bar{\Omega}_q$ and the order parameter $\langle Q_0 \rangle$ are then obtained as the solutions to a set of coupled nonlinear integral equations. We will not pursue the solution of these equations within the context of the pedagogical model that we have been considering. Rather, we will demonstrate somewhat later employing a more realistic model of a ferroelectric crystal how equations of this type can in fact be solved without an inordinate amount of labor.

3. *Order parameter description of the ferroelectric crystal*

Central to the description of structural transitions in crystal lattices is the concept of the order parameter as originally introduced by Landau (1937). When used to describe lattice structural transformations, the order parameter denotes the degree by which the equilibrium ionic configuration of the less symmetrical (ordered) phase deviates from the ionic configuration of the more symmetrical (disordered) phase. In the disordered phase the order parameter is identically zero, whereas it takes on a non-zero value in the ordered phase, with the transition between the two phases being either continuous (2nd order) or discontinuous (1st order). It is obvious, however, that regardless of whether the transition is continuous or discontinuous, the *symmetry* of the lattice always changes discontinuously at the transition. We saw in the previous section how in a model of interacting phonons an order parameter arose quite naturally as a non-zero thermal expectation value of an optic phonon normal mode coordinate of long wavelength. In a real lattice, a non-zero value for a long-wavelength optic mode order parameter would represent a relative displacement of the component sublattices from their equilibrium positions in the disordered phase. In the most general description of the crystal lattice there will be associated with each normal mode a microscopic order parameter equal to the thermal expectation value of the corresponding mode coordinate (Kwok and Miller 1966). As the crystal undergoes a transition to the lower symmetry phase, the long-wavelength optic modes gives rise to macroscopic polarizations, whereas the acoustic modes of long wavelength manifest themselves as macroscopic strains.

The discussion in this section will be concerned with the lattice dynamical description of a three-dimensional crystal which is assumed to undergo a structural transformation from a high-temperature paraelectric phase to a low-temperature phase of lower symmetry. The symmetry of the paraelectric phase will be such as to disallow the phenomenon of pyroelectricity, whereas the ordered low-temperature phase must belong to one of those symmetry groups which consists of a single axis together with planes of symmetry which pass through the axis, so that pyroelectricity is allowed in this phase. The conventional approach to the lattice dynamics of ferroelectricity starts from an expansion of the crystal potential in powers of the displacements of the ions from their equilibrium positions in the paraelectric phase. One can then introduce a normal mode transformation which diagonalizes the harmonic part of the hamiltonian. Since the techniques that we will be employing are non-perturbative in nature, however, we will not be concerned with an expansion of the type just mentioned. Furthermore, no normal mode transformation will be made at this point–rather, we will work in the direct lattice space of the crystal.

Under the adiabatic hypothesis it is well known that the crystal potential may be expressed in terms of an effective interaction potential which depends only on the instantaneous position vectors of all the ions. This is a considerable simplification, since it removes the electronic degrees of freedom completely. Even so, the interaction potential in insulators is quite complicated and is not in general expressible as a sum of pairwise interactions. This difficulty will be of little consequence initially, since we are primarily interested at this point in merely establishing the requisite formalism for treating the lattice dynamics of the ferroelectric crystal. However, in the following section where we carry out an actual model calculation we will find it necessary to parameterize the interaction potential in order to proceed further.

We assume that the true crystal hamiltonian has the form

$$H = -\sum_{\alpha lk} \frac{1}{2m_k} \frac{\partial^2}{\partial x_\alpha^2 \binom{l}{k}} + \Phi\left(\boldsymbol{x}\begin{pmatrix} l_1 \\ k_1 \end{pmatrix}, \boldsymbol{x}\begin{pmatrix} l_2 \\ k_2 \end{pmatrix}, \cdots, \boldsymbol{x}\begin{pmatrix} l_N \\ k_N \end{pmatrix}\right), \tag{17}$$

where $x_\alpha\binom{l}{k}$ represents the α cartesian component of the instantaneous position vector of an ion of type k and mass m_k in the lattice cell l. The interaction potential, Φ, is local but otherwise arbitrary. The position vector $\boldsymbol{x}\binom{l}{k}$ may be further decomposed as

$$\boldsymbol{x}\begin{pmatrix} l \\ k \end{pmatrix} = \boldsymbol{x}^0\begin{pmatrix} l \\ k \end{pmatrix} + \boldsymbol{u}\begin{pmatrix} l \\ k \end{pmatrix}, \tag{18}$$

where $\boldsymbol{x}^0\binom{l}{k}$ is a lattice vector of some arbitrary reference structure and $\boldsymbol{u}\binom{l}{k}$ is the dynamic displacement operator associated with ion (l, k), referred to this structure. Deviations of the true crystal structure from the assumed structure of the reference phase will be marked by the appearance of a non-zero value for the thermal average of $\boldsymbol{u}\binom{l}{k}$. At a later point, when we choose the reference structure to be that of the paraelectric phase, it will be convenient to decompose this thermal expectation value in the following manner,

$$\left\langle u_\alpha\begin{pmatrix} l \\ k \end{pmatrix}\right\rangle = \eta_\alpha\begin{pmatrix} l \\ k \end{pmatrix} + \sum_\beta \varepsilon_{\alpha\beta} x_\beta^0\begin{pmatrix} l \\ k \end{pmatrix}. \tag{19}$$

Here $\boldsymbol{\eta}\binom{l}{k}$ denotes the displacement of the ion (l, k) from its equilibrium position in the paraelectric phase and $\varepsilon_{\alpha\beta}$ represents the symmetric strain tensor associated with a homogeneous deformation of the paraelectric unit cell.

The equations of motion satisfied by the thermal averages of products of displacement operators are easily written down. These equations, when truncated in the proper fashion, will yield a self-consistent set of equations for the order parameters and the one-phonon Green's function. The derivation of such equations has been discussed in detail by Horner (1967) and others. Hence, we review only those equations which suffice to establish the notation. In general, one is interested in the equations satisfied by the imaginary time n-point correlation functions, defined as

$$d_{\alpha_1 \cdots \alpha_n}\begin{pmatrix} l_1 \cdots l_n \\ k_1 \cdots k_n \end{pmatrix}; t_1 \cdots t_n\Big) = \mathrm{i}\,\frac{\delta^n}{\delta J_{\alpha_1}\binom{l_1}{k_1}t_1\big)\cdots \delta J_{\alpha_n}\binom{l_n}{k_n}t_n\big)} \ln Z \tag{20}$$

in terms of the generating functional

$$Z \equiv \mathrm{tr}\,[\mathrm{e}^{-\beta H} S],$$

where

$$S = \left[\exp\left(-\mathrm{i}\int_0^{-\mathrm{i}\beta} \mathrm{d}t \sum_{lk\alpha} J_\alpha\begin{pmatrix} l \\ k \end{pmatrix} t\Big)\, x_\alpha\begin{pmatrix} l \\ k \end{pmatrix} t\Big)\right)\right]_+$$

and we have introduced in the usual manner an external time-dependent field $J_\alpha(\substack{l\\k}t)$. Except where confusion might result, we will in what follows always employ the summation convention for repeated indices (including integration over the imaginary time interval $[0, -\mathrm{i}\beta]$ for repeated time variables). The fourfold set of indices $(\alpha_1, l_1, k_1, t_1)$ will sometimes be denoted by 1, $(\alpha_2, l_2, k_2, t_2)$ by 2, etc. Our primary interest will be in the equations satisfied by the one-point function, which is related to the order parameters, and the two-point function, which is the phonon propagator. Employing (20) for $n=1$ and 2, the one- and two-point functions may be written down explicitly as

$$d(1) = \left\langle \left[S x_{\alpha_1}\begin{pmatrix} l_1 \\ k_1 \end{pmatrix} t_1\Big) \right]_+ \right\rangle / \langle S \rangle,$$

$$d(1,2) = -\mathrm{i}\left\{ \left\langle \left[S x_{\alpha_1}\begin{pmatrix} l_1 \\ k_1 \end{pmatrix} t_1\Big)\, x_{\alpha_2}\begin{pmatrix} l_2 \\ k_2 \end{pmatrix} t_2\Big) \right]_+ \right\rangle / \langle S \rangle - d(1)\, d(2) \right\}. \tag{21}$$

The equations satisfied by these functions are then found employing the usual methods. The one-point function satisfies

$$D(1\bar{1})\, d(\bar{1}) = J(1) + K(1), \tag{22}$$

where

$$D(12) = -\, m_{k_1}\, \delta_{\alpha_1\alpha_2}\, \delta_{l_1 l_2}\, \delta_{k_1 k_2}\, \partial^2 \delta(t_1 - t_2)/\partial t_1^2 ,$$

and

$$K(1') = \frac{\partial}{\partial x_{\alpha_{1'}}\left(\begin{smallmatrix} l_{1'} \\ k_{1'} \end{smallmatrix}\, t_{1'}\right)} \times \left\langle \left[S\Phi\left(x_{\alpha_1}\begin{pmatrix} l_1 \\ k_1 \end{pmatrix} t_1 \right), x_{\alpha_2}\begin{pmatrix} l_2 \\ k_2 \end{pmatrix} t_2 \right), \cdots, x_{\alpha_N}\begin{pmatrix} l_N \\ k_N \end{pmatrix} t_1 \right) \right) \right]_+ \right\rangle / \langle S \rangle . \tag{23}$$

A functional differentiation of (22) then yields the equation for the phonon propagator,

$$[D(1\bar{1}) - M(1\bar{1})]\, d(\bar{1}1') = \delta(1 - 1'), \tag{24}$$

where the phonon self energy M is defined by the relation

$$M(11') = [\delta K(1)/\delta J(\bar{1})]\, d^{-1}(\bar{1}1') = \delta K(1)/\delta d(1') . \tag{25}$$

It is possible to reduce eq. (23) to a form which will point the way to various non-perturbative approximation schemes (Horner 1967). Using Taylor's theorem, we can re-express $K(1)$ formally exact as

$$K(1') = \langle S \rangle^{-1} \left\langle \left[S \exp\left\{ \left(x_{\bar{\alpha}}\begin{pmatrix} \bar{l} \\ \bar{k} \end{pmatrix} t_1 \right) - x^0_{\bar{\alpha}}\begin{pmatrix} \bar{l} \\ \bar{k} \end{pmatrix} \right) \frac{\partial}{\partial x^0_{\bar{\alpha}}\left(\begin{smallmatrix} \bar{l} \\ \bar{k} \end{smallmatrix}\right)} \right\} \right]_+ \right\rangle \times \frac{\partial}{\partial x^0_{\alpha_{1'}}\left(\begin{smallmatrix} l_{1'} \\ k_{1'} \end{smallmatrix}\right)} \Phi\left(x^0_{\alpha_1}\begin{pmatrix} l_1 \\ k_1 \end{pmatrix}, \cdots, x^0_{\alpha_N}\begin{pmatrix} l_N \\ k_N \end{pmatrix} \right) .$$

A further reduction is possible if we introduce a cumulant expansion for the exponential operator in the above expression. Thus, we finally obtain

$$K(1') = \int_0^{-i\beta} dt_2\, dt_3 \cdots dt_N\, \delta(t_{1'} - t_2)\, \delta(t_{1'} - t_3) \cdots \delta(t_{1'} - t_N) \times \exp\left\{ \left[d_{\bar{\alpha}_1}\begin{pmatrix} \bar{l}_1 \\ \bar{k}_1 \end{pmatrix} t_{1'} \right) - x^0_{\bar{\alpha}_1}\begin{pmatrix} \bar{l}_1 \\ \bar{k}_1 \end{pmatrix} \right] \frac{\partial}{\partial x^0_{\bar{\alpha}_1}\left(\begin{smallmatrix} l_1 \\ k_1 \end{smallmatrix}\right)} + \sum_{n=2}^{\infty} (\mathrm{i}^{n-1}/n!) \times d_{\bar{\alpha}_1 \cdots \bar{\alpha}_n}\begin{pmatrix} \bar{l}_1 \cdots \bar{l}_n \\ \bar{k}_1 \cdots \bar{k}_n \end{pmatrix} ; t_{1'} \cdots t_n \right) \frac{\partial^n}{\partial x^0_{\bar{\alpha}_1}\left(\begin{smallmatrix} l_1 \\ k_1 \end{smallmatrix}\right) \cdots \partial x^0_{\bar{\alpha}_n}\left(\begin{smallmatrix} l_n \\ k_n \end{smallmatrix}\right)} \right\} \frac{\partial}{\partial x^0_{\alpha_{1'}}\left(\begin{smallmatrix} l_{1'} \\ k_{1'} \end{smallmatrix}\right)} \Phi . \tag{26}$$

In section 2 we examined a simple model of soft mode behavior and there discussed briefly the linear anharmonic approximation as employed by Kwok and Miller (1966) and Ambegaokar et al. (1965). The validity of the linear anharmonic approximation rested on the assumption that cumulants of order greater than two are small. This will, of course, be the case if the collective excitations in the crystal can be approximated by a spectrum of undamped phonons. In any case, the assumption permits us to establish a low order approximation for $K(1)$ by assuming that correlations between three or more phonons may be neglected in lowest order. Thus, in (26) we neglect cumulants of third and higher order. Further, we allow the time-dependent external field $J(t)$ to vanish. The one-point function $d(1)$ will then be independent of time and the propagator $d(12)$ will depend only on the time difference t_1-t_2. From (22) and (26) we then obtain the relation

$$K(1)=0=\partial\tilde{\Phi}/\partial d_{\alpha_1}\begin{pmatrix}l_1\\k_1\end{pmatrix}, \tag{27}$$

where

$$\tilde{\Phi}=\exp\left(\tfrac{1}{2}\mathrm{i}d_{\bar{\alpha}_1\bar{\alpha}_2}\begin{pmatrix}\bar{l}_1\,\bar{l}_2\\\bar{k}_1\bar{k}_2\end{pmatrix}\frac{\partial^2}{\partial d_{\bar{\alpha}_1}\left(\begin{smallmatrix}\bar{l}_1\\\bar{k}_1\end{smallmatrix}\right)\partial d_{\bar{\alpha}_2}\left(\begin{smallmatrix}\bar{l}_2\\\bar{k}_2\end{smallmatrix}\right)}\right)$$
$$\times\,\Phi\left(d_{\alpha_1}\begin{pmatrix}l_1\\k_1\end{pmatrix}, d_{\alpha_2}\begin{pmatrix}l_2\\k_2\end{pmatrix}, \cdots, d_{\alpha_N}\begin{pmatrix}l_N\\k_N\end{pmatrix}\right).$$

Eq. (27) represents one of the equations of the lowest order self-consistent phonon approximation. An additional equation may be obtained by evaluating the equilibrium phonon propagator using the prescription (25). At this level of approximation the functional differentiation is carried out neglecting the implicit dependence of $d(12)$ on $d(1)$. Thus,

$$M(1,2)=\delta(t_1-t_2)\frac{\partial^2\tilde{\Phi}}{\partial d_{\alpha_1}\left(\begin{smallmatrix}l_1\\k_1\end{smallmatrix}\right)\partial d_{\alpha_2}\left(\begin{smallmatrix}l_2\\k_2\end{smallmatrix}\right)}. \tag{28}$$

Eqs. (24), (27), and (28) represent a coupled set of equations for the order parameter $d(1)$ and the equilibrium phonon propagator $d(1,2)$. The significance of this set of equations is threefold. Firstly, they represent a set of equations for the self-consistent determination of renormalized quantities – no assumption is made concerning the unrenormalized state of the crystal and, hence, the difficulties associated with the harmonic approximation in the treatment of the ferroelectric crystal can be avoided. Secondly, the equations may be derived independently from a variational formulation. This provides an upper bound on the free energy of the crystal and assures that the renormalized state represents a stable state of equilibrium. We will examine this aspect in more detail later. Finally, the result (28) is physically appealing from the point of view that it effectively replaces the bare harmonic force constants $\nabla\nabla\Phi$ by their thermally averaged values $\langle\nabla\nabla\Phi\rangle$. The implication is that even if the bare force matrix is not positive definite, at high enough temperatures the thermal fluctuations will renormalize this matrix in such a way that the effective force matrix *will* be positive definite. This is exactly the prescription that is needed for treating the ferroelectric problem realistically.

At this point we can easily make contact with the discussion in section 2. Neglecting strains, we use (12.19) to express the one-point function in the form

$$d_\alpha\begin{pmatrix} l \\ k \end{pmatrix} = x_\alpha^0\begin{pmatrix} l \\ k \end{pmatrix} + \eta_\alpha\begin{pmatrix} l \\ k \end{pmatrix}$$

with the lattice vectors $x_\alpha^0\binom{l}{k}$ of the reference lattice chosen to have the symmetry of the paraelectric phase. We can now recover a generalized form of (12) through a direct expansion of (27). Neglecting terms involving third derivatives of Φ (which is consistent with neglecting the strain), we have

$$\Phi^{(2)}(12)\,\eta(2) + \tfrac{1}{2}\mathrm{i}\Phi^{(4)}(1234)\,d(23)\,\eta(4) + \tfrac{1}{6}\Phi^{(4)}(1234)\,\eta(2)\,\eta(3)\,\eta(4) + \cdots = 0, \tag{29}$$

where

$$\Phi^{(n)}(12\cdots n) = \delta(t_1 - t_2)\,\delta(t_1 - t_3)\cdots\delta(t_1 - t_n)\left(\frac{\partial^n\Phi}{\partial d(1)\,\partial d(2)\cdots\partial d(n)}\right)_0,$$

and the subscript zero indicates that the derivatives are to be evaluated at the equilibrium configuration of the paraelectric structure. Expansion of (28) yields an equation analogous to (14):

$$M(12) = \Phi^{(2)}(12) + \tfrac{1}{2}\mathrm{i}\Phi^{(4)}(1234)\,d(34) + \tfrac{1}{2}\Phi^{(4)}(1234)\,\eta(3)\,\eta(4) + \cdots. \tag{30}$$

Eqs. (29) and (30) represent generalizations of (12) and (14), which were obtained within the context of a model of optic phonons interacting via quartic anharmonicity alone. When combined with (25), (29) and (30) provide a closed set of equations for the determination of the order parameters $\eta(1)$ and the phonon propagator $d(12)$. We emphasize that $d(12)$ represents a renormalized propagator, not a harmonic propagator such as was used in obtaining (12) and (14). This is of considerable importance since $\Phi^{(2)}(12)$ will not, in general, be positive definite for the ferroelectric crystal and would, when diagonalized in a normal mode representation, yield a set of imaginary frequencies.

An expansion of the type employed in obtaining (29) and (30) is convenient if one does not have a well-defined functional form for the interaction potential, as is usually the case in insulating crystals of the ferroelectric type. One proceeds by parameterizing the coefficients $\Phi^{(n)}(12\cdots n)$, keeping as many terms as are necessary in the expansion. The determination of $\eta(1)$ and $d(12)$ is still self-consistent, of course. The expressions (27)–(28), though more general, can be solved self-consistently without an undue amount of labor if one has a functional form for the potential at one's disposal.

The solution of the dynamical equations (24), (27), and (28) does not provide us with all the information necessary for treating the structural transformation problem self-consistently. A complete treatment requires a knowledge of the free energy appropriate to the level of approximation represented by (27) and (28). This points to the utility of the variational approach, which uses as its starting point a trial free energy functional. However, as demonstrated by Horner (1967) and Götze and Michel (1968), one can, within the framework of the Green's function formalism, deduce the free energy functional consistent with a given approximation to $K(1)$. To this end we note that the generating functional defined in (20) is, in the limit $J \to 0$, proportional to the free energy of the system. In general, the functional Z will be an explicit function of the field J. By means of a Legendre transformation we may construct a functional $\mathscr{F}$ which is a function of both the one- and two-point functions and satisfies

$$\delta\mathscr{F}/\delta d(1) = -\,\mathrm{i}K(1)\,. \tag{31}$$

Indeed, the expression

$$\mathscr{F} = \ln Z + \mathrm{i}d(1)\,J(1) - \tfrac{1}{2}\mathrm{i}d(1)\,D(12)\,d(2) \tag{32}$$

satisfies (31). For a given approximate $K(1)$, we construct an $\mathscr{F}$ consistent with this approximation by integrating $K(1)$ with respect to $d(1)$. For the approximation (27) the integration can be carried out, although one must remember not to neglect the implicit dependence of $d(12)$ on $d(1)$. In the $J \to 0$ limit, one then obtains

$$\ln Z = \mathscr{F} = -\,\tfrac{1}{2}\mathrm{tr}\ln d^{-1}(12) - \tfrac{1}{2}M(12)\,d(12) - \mathrm{i}\tilde{\Phi}\,, \tag{32}$$

where $\mathrm{tr}\ln d^{-1}(12)$ is an operational definition such that $\delta\ \mathrm{tr}\ln d^{-1}(12) = d(12)\,\delta d^{-1}(12)$. One easily sees that with $\tilde{\Phi}$ and $M(12)$ defined by (27) and (28) respectively, the relation (31) is satisfied by (32). Eq. (32) has been obtained by Horner using a functional derivative technique and by Götze and Michel employing diagrammatics. For all practical purposes, however, it is more straightforward to employ a variational approach of the type which will be discussed in the next section.

4. *Variational treatment of a model ferroelectric*

As we pointed out previously, a variational approach to the treatment of ferroelectric crystals is of particular interest from the point of view that it provides a bound on the free energy and at the same time assures that the model crystal occupies a stable state of equilibrium. This last is of particular importance if, as in the present case, the harmonic approximation does not exist. The idea of approaching the displacive ferroelectric problem from the point of view of a variational treatment first appeared in two independent works by Doniach (1965) and Boccara and Sarma (1965). These authors, although outlining the necessary formalism for treating the structural transformation problem variationally, did not carry out any actual calculations. The first detailed calculations on a model system employing a variational technique were first carried out by Gillis and Koehler (1971, 1972a), who determined self-consistently the frequency spectrum of a model crystal exhibiting a displacive transition from a high-temperature NaCl structure phase to a low-temperature distorted rhombohedral phase. The idea which underlies all of the variational approaches is simply that if the low-lying collective excitation spectrum of the crystal is well described by phonons, then one can introduce a trial harmonic hamiltonian to describe the dynamics of these excitations, with the parameters in the hamiltonian determined variationally. Such a procedure gives rise to a renormalized spectrum of undamped phonons.

One of the simplest structures capable of exhibiting a ferroelectric transition accompanied by soft mode behavior at zone center is the NaCl structure. This structure may deform continuously into one of two polar phases–either into a tetragonal structure or into a rhombohedral structure of trigonal symmetry. In the former case the macroscopic polarization is directed along one of the cartesian axes, whereas in the latter case the polarization will be directed along a body diagonal of the cubic cell. The occurrence of ferroelectric phenomena in crystals of the NaCl structure is exemplified by the IV–VI semiconducting compounds of SnTe, GeTe, and $Sn_xGe_{1-x}Te$, which exhibit ferroelectric behavior associated with a zone center phonon instability. SnTe, an incipient ferroelectric, exhibits soft mode behavior at zone center (Pawley et al. 1966) but does not undergo a structural transformation, whereas GeTe transforms from a high-temperature NaCl structure phase to a distorted rhombohedral phase at about 700 K (Goldak et al. 1966). The solid solutions of SnTe and GeTe undergo a similar transformation, with the transition temperature varying linearly with the concentration of Sn (Bierly et al. 1963). A survey of the ferroelectric properties of diatomic crystals of the NaCl structure has been given by Cochran (1967) and the reader is referred to this review for more details.

The simplicity of the crystal structure of the IV–VI compounds is more than offset by the complexity of the interatomic forces. However, by employing a model of mixed ionic and covalent bonding, a reasonably satisfactory description of the soft mode behavior in the paraelectric SnTe has been carried out using self-consistent phonon techniques (Gillis 1969). A much more crucial test of such a calculation would be the description of the actual transition in a material such as GeTe. Unfortunately, this is a much more difficult task and has not as yet been carried out employing a realistic model for the interatomic forces. The main thrust of the discussion in this section will be directed toward a theoretical examination of a transition of the type which occurs in GeTe. We do not, of course, pretend that the simple model of the interatomic forces which we will employ mirrors at all accurately the true interactions in this material. Rather, we will be concerned with some very qualitative features of the transition which will be essentially model independent. The conclusions which we reach will thus apply not only to the transition in GeTe, but to transitions in other displacive ferroelectrics as well.

We could begin our discussion by working directly with eq. (27) and (28). However, it will be more instructive to derive the equivalent of these equations variationally within the context of the model that we are considering. The model consists of an NaCl lattice of anions and cations of unequal masses interacting via long range Coulomb forces plus a short range interaction extending to nearest neighbors only. In order to simplify our considerations as much as possible we agree at the outset to treat the Coulomb interaction harmonically–this will not alter our qualitative conclusions. Furthermore, since we do not have a well-defined functional form for the short range contribution to the interatomic forces, we will introduce the short-range interaction as a parameterized expansion up to fourth order in the displacements about the paraelectric structure. This will provide us with as much flexibility as we will need in specifying the model. Indeed, one can easily convince oneself that the introduction of higher order anharmonicity in lowest order, such as is contained in (27)–(28), will not alter our qualitative considerations to any extent.

The true hamiltonian of the lattice is assumed to be of the form (17). We approximate the short range contribution to the interaction potential by the following parameterized nearest neighbor interaction

$$V_{\rm SR} = V_{\rm SR}^{(0)} + V_{\rm SR}^{(1)}$$
$$+ \tfrac{1}{2}\sum [\varphi_\ell^{(2)} u_1^2 + \varphi_t^{(2)}(u_2^2 + u_3^2)] + \sum [\varphi_\ell^{(3)} u_1^3 + \varphi_t^{(3)} u_1 (u_2^2 + u_3^2)]$$
$$+ \sum [\varphi_{11}^{(4)} u_1^4 + \varphi_{22}^{(4)}(u_2^4 + u_3^4) + \varphi_{12}^{(4)} u_1^2 (u_2^2 + u_3^2) + \varphi_{23}^{(4)} u_2^2 u_3^2], \quad (33)$$

while the Coulombic contribution to the interaction has the form

$$V_{\rm C} = V_{\rm C}^{(0)} + V_{\rm C}^{(1)} + \tfrac{1}{2} \sum_{\substack{ll',kk',\\ \alpha\beta}} u_\alpha \binom{l}{k} C_{\alpha\beta} \binom{l\ l'}{k\ k'} u_\beta \binom{l'}{k'}. \quad (34)$$

In the above $V_{\rm SR}^{(0)}$ and $V_{\rm C}^{(0)}$ denote the static contributions to the interaction. The linear terms $V_{\rm SR}^{(1)}$ and $V_{\rm C}^{(1)}$ do not by themselves vanish; rather $V_{\rm SR}^{(1)} + V_{\rm C}^{(1)} = 0$ if the reference lattice (i.e., the NaCl structure) represents an extremum of the potential energy. In eq. (33) u_α is used to symbolically denote the α cartesian component of the relative displacement between nearest neighbor A and B ions, i.e.,

$$u_\alpha = u_\alpha \binom{l}{\rm A} - u_\alpha \binom{l'}{\rm B}, \quad (35)$$

where l and l' are such that $x_\alpha^0 \binom{l}{\rm A} - x_\alpha^0 \binom{l'}{\rm B}$ is one of the six nearest neighbor vectors of the NaCl structure. The summation in (33) implies a sum over all unit cells together with a permutation over the octahedral environment of nearest neighbor ion pairs. The force constants depend, of course, on the nearest neighbor pair considered – however, any $\varphi^{(n)}$ of order n may be obtained from a reference $\varphi^{(n)}$ of the same order by means of an appropriate symmetry operation. Finally, $C_{\alpha\beta} \binom{l\ l'}{k\ k'}$ represents the Coulombic contribution to the harmonic dynamical matrix, the properties of which are well known (Kellerman 1940).

In order to allow for the possibility of a structural transformation occurring between the paraelectric phase and an ordered ferroelectric phase, we introduce a set of order parameters associated with (1) the relative displacement of the two sublattices of the NaCl phase and (2) the homogeneous deformation of the unit cell. This is accomplished by making the replacement

$$u_\alpha \binom{l}{k} \to u_\alpha \binom{l}{k} + \eta_\alpha + \sum_\beta \varepsilon_{\alpha\beta} x^0 \binom{l}{k} \quad (36)$$

in (33) and (34). $\boldsymbol{\eta}$ is chosen independent of cell indices and hence will denote the rigid relative displacements of the A and B sublattices. As such $\boldsymbol{\eta}$ may be identified as an order parameter associated with the optic modes at zone center. The strain tensor $\varepsilon_{\alpha\beta}$ is symmetric and describes a homogeneous deformation of the paraelectric unit cell associated with acoustic modes of long wavelength.

The underlying assumption of the present approach is that the dynamics of the collective excitations should be well-described by a trial harmonic hamiltonian H_t, which we write in the form

$$H_t = -\sum_{\alpha lk} \frac{1}{2m_k} \frac{\partial^2}{\partial u_\alpha^2 \binom{l}{k}} + \frac{1}{2} \sum_{\substack{\alpha\beta, ll', \\ kk'}} u_\alpha \begin{pmatrix} l \\ k \end{pmatrix} C_{\alpha\beta} \begin{pmatrix} l & l' \\ k & k' \end{pmatrix} u_\beta \begin{pmatrix} l' \\ k' \end{pmatrix}$$

$$+ \frac{1}{2} \sum_{\substack{\alpha\beta, ll', \\ kk'}} u_\alpha \begin{pmatrix} l \\ k \end{pmatrix} \tilde{\varphi}_{\alpha\beta} \begin{pmatrix} l & l' \\ k & k' \end{pmatrix} u_\beta \begin{pmatrix} l' \\ k' \end{pmatrix}. \tag{37}$$

The summation in the last term of (37) is assumed to extend only over nearest neighbor configurations and the force constants $\tilde{\varphi}$ denote renormalized nearest neighbor force constants which are to be determined variationally. The exact expression for the free energy per unit cell,

$$F = -(N\beta)^{-1} \ln \operatorname{tr}(\mathrm{e}^{-\beta H}), \tag{38}$$

may be expressed as a cumulant expansion in powers of $H - H_t$. The lowest order term in such an expansion yields

$$F_t = F_0 + \langle H - H_t \rangle / N, \tag{39}$$

where

$$F_0 = -(N\beta)^{-1} \ln \operatorname{tr}(\mathrm{e}^{-\beta H_t})$$

and the thermal average is with respect to the canonical density matrix

$$\rho_t = \mathrm{e}^{-\beta H_t} / \operatorname{tr}(\mathrm{e}^{-\beta H_t}). \tag{40}$$

Higher order terms may be included in the cumulant expansion of the free energy. A variational treatment including higher order terms would introduce phonon damping. In this more general case the trial force constants must include a frequency dependence. Hence, one can no longer deal with a trial hamiltonian – rather, one must introduce a trial *action*. Such a generalization of the variational approach has been discussed in detail by Werthamer (1970a, b).

We can easily carry out an evaluation of the free energy in the approximation (39). Using (33)–(37) in eq. (38), a straightforward, but tedious, calculation yields for the free energy per unit cell the following expression

$$
\begin{aligned}
F = F_0 &+ 3(\varphi_\ell^{(2)} - \tilde{\varphi}_\ell)\langle u_1^2\rangle + 6(\varphi_t^{(2)} - \tilde{\varphi}_t)\langle u_2^2\rangle \\
&+ 6[3\varphi_{11}^{(4)}\langle u_1^2\rangle^2 + (6\varphi_{22}^{(4)} + \varphi_{23}^{(4)})\langle u_2^2\rangle^2 + 2\varphi_{12}^{(4)}\langle u_1^2\rangle\langle u_2^2\rangle] \\
&+ [\varphi_\ell^{(2)} + 2\varphi_t^{(2)} - (2\pi/3r_0)(Z^*)^2 + 4(3\varphi_{11}^{(4)} + \varphi_{12}^{(4)})\langle u_1^2\rangle \\
&+ 4(6\varphi_{22}^{(4)} + \varphi_{12}^{(4)} + \varphi_{23}^{(4)})\langle u_2^2\rangle](\eta_1^2 + \eta_2^2 + \eta_3^2) \\
&+ 2(\varphi_{11}^{(4)} + 2\varphi_{22}^{(4)})(\eta_1^4 + \eta_2^4 + \eta_3^4) \\
&+ 2(\varphi_{23}^{(4)} + 2\varphi_{12}^{(4)})(\eta_1^2\eta_2^2 + \eta_1^2\eta_3^2 + \eta_2^2\eta_3^2) \\
&+ 2(3\varphi_\ell^{(3)}\langle u_1^2\rangle + 2\varphi_t^{(3)}\langle u_2^2\rangle)(\varepsilon_{11} + \varepsilon_{22} + \varepsilon_{33}) + E_{11}(\varepsilon_{11}^2 + \varepsilon_{22}^2 + \varepsilon_{33}^2) \\
&+ 2E_{12}[\varepsilon_{11}\varepsilon_{22} + \varepsilon_{11}\varepsilon_{33} + \varepsilon_{22}\varepsilon_{33} + 2(\varepsilon_{12}^2 + \varepsilon_{13}^2 + \varepsilon_{23}^2)] \\
&+ 4(3\varphi_{11}^{(4)}\langle u_1^2\rangle + \varphi_{12}^{(4)}\langle u_2^2\rangle)(\varepsilon_{11}^2 + \varepsilon_{22}^2 + \varepsilon_{33}^2) \\
&+ 4(6\varphi_{22}^{(4)}\langle u_2^2\rangle + \varphi_{12}^{(4)}\langle u_1^2\rangle + \varphi_{23}^{(4)}\langle u_2^2\rangle)(\varepsilon_{12}^2 + \varepsilon_{13}^2 + \varepsilon_{23}^2) \\
&+ 6\varphi_\ell^{(3)}(\varepsilon_{11}\eta_1^2 + \varepsilon_{22}\eta_2^2 + \varepsilon_{33}\eta_3^2) \\
&+ 2\varphi_t^{(3)}[\varepsilon_{11}(\eta_2^2 + \eta_3^2) + \varepsilon_{22}(\eta_1^2 + \eta_3^2) + \varepsilon_{33}(\eta_1^2 + \eta_2^2) \\
&+ 4(\varepsilon_{12}\eta_1\eta_2 + \varepsilon_{23}\eta_2\eta_3 + \varepsilon_{13}\eta_1\eta_3)],
\end{aligned} \tag{41}
$$

and we have neglected terms of order ε^3. In the above expression, E_{11} and E_{12} denote the two independent elastic constants for the NaCl structure, calculated in the harmonic approximation. Z^* is the effective charge associated with the ions and r_0 is the nearest neighbor separation (in a.u.) for the NaCl structure. All lengths are in units of $r_0 a_B$ and the free energy is in Ry. Finally, u_1 and u_2 are defined by (12.35) and the thermal averages are with respect to the density matrix (40).

The renormalized force constants $\tilde{\varphi}_\ell$ and $\tilde{\varphi}_t$, together with the order parameters $\varepsilon_{\alpha\beta}$ and η_α, are to be determined self-consistently from a minimization of the free energy (41); i.e., we must solve the set of equations

$$
\partial F/\partial\tilde{\varphi}_\ell = 0, \quad \partial F/\partial\tilde{\varphi}_t = 0, \quad \partial F/\partial\varepsilon_{\alpha\beta} = 0, \quad \partial F/\partial\eta_\alpha = 0. \tag{42}
$$

The simultaneous solution of eq. (42) is, in fact possible. However, before we proceed in that direction some comments are in order concerning the form of the free energy functional (41). Eq. (41) was obtained directly from the approximation (39). We could as well have started from the expression (32), expanding all quantities in powers of the order parameters–the end result would have been the same. The important point to note is that (41) resembles, in its explicit dependence on $\varepsilon_{\alpha\beta}$ and η_α, a conventional Landau free energy expansion in powers of the order parameters (Landau and Lifshitz

1958). Alternatively, if we identify η_α with a macroscopic polarization, then (41) is formally identical with a conventional Devonshire expansion, consistent with cubic symmetry, of the free energy in powers of the macroscopic strains and polarizations (Devonshire 1954). There is, of course, an important difference between the expression (41) and a conventional Devonshire expression. Because of the self-consistency conditions (42), the free energy (41) contains an additional implicit dependence on the order parameters through the thermal average $\langle u_\alpha^2 \rangle$ and through the quantity F_0. This is to be contrasted with the usual Devonshire expansion, where the coefficients are treated phenomenologically and are not related self-consistently to the microscopic order parameters. Even in the conventional microscopic derivations of the Devonshire free energy expansion (Cowley 1965, Kwok and Miller 1966), the coefficients in the expansion are not related self-consistently to $\varepsilon_{\alpha\beta}$ and η_α for the simple reason that the thermal average $\langle u_\alpha^2 \rangle$ is evaluated using a harmonic basis. Let us note that setting $\varepsilon_{\alpha\beta}=0$ in (41) formally yields a Landau expansion up to fourth order in the optic mode order parameter. Within the context of a conventional theory, such an expression would predict a classical second order transition. This follows from the fact that the coefficient of $\eta_1^2+\eta_2^2+\eta_3^2$ is proportional to the zone center optic mode frequency squared and will be negative below a certain temperature T_c and positive above [cf. eq. (16)], with the transition taking place continuously. We shall see below that the results one obtains when the problem is treated self-consistently are decidedly different.

We proceed with the solution of (42) by making one further assumption which will simplify our labors considerably. We make the not unreasonable assumption that the only non-zero components of the anharmonic interaction are the longitudinal components $\varphi_\ell^{(3)}$ and $\varphi_{11}^{(4)}$, which we choose to be negative definite and positive definite, respectively. This choice will, as we shall see, favor a rhombohedral distortion accompanied by uniform expansion with temperature. The self-consistent equations (42) take the form

$$\begin{aligned}
\tilde{\varphi}_\ell &= \varphi_\ell^{(2)} + 12\varphi_{11}^{(4)}\langle u_1^2\rangle + 4\varphi_{11}^{(4)}(\eta_1^2+\eta_2^2+\eta_3^2) \\
&\qquad + 2\varphi_\ell^{(3)}(\varepsilon_{11}+\varepsilon_{22}+\varepsilon_{33}) + 4\varphi_{11}^{(4)}(\varepsilon_{11}^2+\varepsilon_{22}^2+\varepsilon_{33}^2), \\
\tilde{\varphi}_t &= \varphi_t^{(2)}, \\
&3\varphi_\ell^{(3)}\langle u_1^2\rangle + (E_{11} + 12\varphi_{11}^{(4)}\langle u_1^2\rangle\,\varepsilon_{\alpha\alpha} + E_{12}(\varepsilon_{\beta\beta}+\varepsilon_{\gamma\gamma}) + 3\varphi_\ell^{(3)}\eta_\alpha^2 = 0, \\
&\qquad \alpha \neq \beta \neq \gamma, \\
&E_{12}\varepsilon_{\alpha\beta} = 0, \quad \alpha \neq \beta, \\
&\eta_\alpha\{[\varphi_\ell^{(2)} + 2\varphi_t^{(2)} - (2\pi/3r_0)(Z^*)^2 + 12\varphi_{11}^{(4)}\langle u_1^2\rangle] \\
&\qquad + 4\varphi_{11}^{(4)}\eta_\alpha^2 + 6\varphi_\ell^{(3)}\varepsilon_{\alpha\alpha}\} = 0.
\end{aligned} \tag{43}$$

In examining the solutions to the above set of equations, two cases are to be distinguished–the paraelectric case with $\boldsymbol{\eta}=0$ and the ordered ferroelectric case with a non-zero value of $\boldsymbol{\eta}$. For the paraelectric solution,

$$\varepsilon_{11}=\varepsilon_{22}=\varepsilon_{33}=\varepsilon=-\,3\varphi_\ell^{(3)}\langle u_1^2\rangle/(\varphi_\ell^{(2)}+2\varphi_t^{(2)}+12\varphi_{11}^{(4)}\langle u_1^2\rangle), \tag{44}$$

whereas for the ordered solution,

$$\begin{aligned}\eta_1^2=\eta_2^2=\eta_3^2&=\tfrac{1}{3}\eta^2\\&=(1/3\Delta)\{-\,18\langle u_1^2\rangle(\varphi_\ell^{(3)})^2+(\varphi_\ell^{(2)}+2\varphi_t^{(2)}+12\varphi_{11}^{(4)}\langle u_1^2\rangle)\\&\qquad\times[\varphi_\ell^{(2)}+2\varphi_t^{(2)}-(2\pi/3r_0)(Z^*)^2+12\varphi_{11}^{(4)}\langle u_1^2\rangle]\},\end{aligned}$$

and

$$\begin{aligned}\varepsilon_{11}=\varepsilon_{22}=\varepsilon_{33}=\varepsilon&=(1/\Delta)\{-\,\varphi_\ell^{(3)}[\varphi_\ell^{(2)}+2\varphi_t^{(2)}\\&\quad-(2\pi/3r_0)(Z^*)^2+12\varphi_{11}^{(4)}\langle u_1^2\rangle]+4\varphi_{11}^{(4)}\varphi_l^{(3)}\langle u_1^2\rangle\},\end{aligned}$$

where

$$\Delta\equiv6(\varphi_\ell^{(3)})^2-\tfrac{4}{3}\varphi_{11}^{(4)}(\varphi_\ell^{(2)}+2\varphi_t^{(2)}+12\varphi_{11}^{(4)}\langle u_1^2\rangle). \tag{45}$$

The renormalized nearest neighbor force constants are then given in terms of η, ε and $\langle u_1^2\rangle$ as

$$\begin{aligned}\tilde{\varphi}_\ell&=\varphi_\ell^{(2)}+12\varphi_{11}^{(4)}\langle u_1^2\rangle+4\varphi_{11}^{(4)}\eta^2+6\varphi_\ell^{(3)}\varepsilon+12\varphi_{11}^{(4)}\varepsilon^2,\\\tilde{\varphi}_t&=\varphi_t^{(2)}.\end{aligned} \tag{46}$$

We can introduce a set of units such that the long-wavelength properties are independent of the reduced mass M_R of the ions as well as independent of the parameters of the dipolar interaction. Squared frequencies ω^2 will be expressed in units of $M_R^{-1}[4\pi(Z^*e)^2/2r_0^3]$ and force constants $\varphi^{(n)}$ in units of $r_0^{2-n}[4\pi(Z^*e)^2/2r_0^3]$. With this choice of units the zone center TO mode frequency squared is given by

$$\begin{aligned}\omega_{TO}^2(\Gamma)=2[\varphi_\ell^{(2)}+2\varphi_t^{(2)}-\tfrac{1}{6}+12\varphi_{11}^{(4)}\langle u_1^2\rangle\\+4\varphi_{11}^{(4)}\eta^2+6\varphi_\ell^{(3)}\varepsilon+12\varphi_{11}^{(4)}\varepsilon^2],\end{aligned} \tag{47}$$

and the splitting between the LO and TO modes at zone center is normalized to unity, i.e.,

$$\omega_{LO}^2(\Gamma)-\omega_{TO}^2(\Gamma)=1.$$

Because of the stability criterion $V_{SR}^{(1)}+V_C^{(1)}=0$, the tangential component of the harmonic short range force can be eliminated in terms of the dipolar energy per particle,

$$\varphi_t^{(2)} = \tfrac{1}{3} V_C^{(0)}/2N .$$

Thus, we are left with essentially three parameters at our disposal: $\varphi_\ell^{(2)}$, $\varphi_\ell^{(3)}$, and $\varphi_{11}^{(4)}$. The simulation of soft mode behavior at zone center then requires that $\varphi_\ell^{(2)}$ be chosen such that the harmonic value of $\omega_{TO}^2(\Gamma)$ is negative.

The correlation function $\langle u_1^2 \rangle$ represents a non-linear, single-valued function of $\tilde{\varphi}_\ell$ at each temperature. If we diagonalize the trial hamiltonian (37) to obtain a set of renormalized frequencies and eigenvectors, then $\langle u_1^2 \rangle$ may be decomposed in a normal mode representation

$$\langle u_1^2 \rangle = (1/2N) \sum_{q\lambda} \omega^{-1}(q\lambda) \coth \tfrac{1}{2}\beta\omega(q\lambda) \{ M_A^{-1} (\varepsilon_1^A\ q\lambda))^2 + M_B^{-1} (\varepsilon_1^B(q\lambda))^2 - 2(M_A M_B)^{-1/2}\, \varepsilon_1^A(q\lambda)\, \varepsilon_1^B(q\lambda) \cos q_1 \} , \quad (48)$$

where $\omega(q\lambda)$ and $\varepsilon_\alpha^k(q\lambda)$ are the renormalized frequency and eigenvector associated with mode $(q\lambda)$. Eq. (48) permits us to plot a set of temperature parameterized curves of $\langle u_1^2 \rangle$ vs $\tilde{\varphi}_\ell$ – curves which will be independent of the parameters $\varphi_\ell^{(2)}$, $\varphi_\ell^{(3)}$, and $\varphi_{11}^{(4)}$. On the other hand, eqs. (44)–(46) provide an additional relation between $\langle u_1^2 \rangle$ and $\tilde{\varphi}_\ell$ – indeed, $\tilde{\varphi}_\ell$ will be expressible as a simple non-linear function of $\langle u_1^2 \rangle$, independent of explicit dependence on temperature, but dependent on the parameters $\varphi_\ell^{(2)}$, $\varphi_\ell^{(3)}$, and $\varphi_{11}^{(4)}$. The self-consistent solutions for $\langle u_1^2 \rangle$ (or $\tilde{\varphi}_\ell$) will then be given as the intersections of two families of curves on a $\langle u_1^2 \rangle$ vs $\tilde{\varphi}_\ell$ plot, one family of curves parameterized by temperature, the other family being parameterized by the force constants $\varphi_\ell^{(2)}$, $\varphi_\ell^{(3)}$, and $\varphi_{11}^{(4)}$. In practice, one proceeds by locating the approximate roots graphically and then iterates the self-consistent equations numerically to obtain the desired degree of accuracy.

Gillis and Koehler (1972a) considered in detail the solution of (44)–(46) and (48) in the special case where the coupling to the strain was neglected ($\varphi_\ell^{(3)}=0$; $\varepsilon=0$). This work, which we review briefly now, demonstrated that the paraelectric phase solutions described quite adequately many of the qualitative features of the frequency spectrum such as is observed experimentally in incipient ferroelectrics such as $SrTiO_3$, $KTaO_3$, and SnTe. Reproduced in fig. 4 are plots of the renormalized zone center TO mode frequency squared vs temperature for four different choices of the parameters $\varphi_\ell^{(2)}$ and $\varphi_{11}^{(4)}$ –these plots clearly illustrate the wide variety of behavior obtainable in this simple model. Cases (A)–(C) give the impression of a vanishing mode frequency at zero temperature, whereas (D) suggests that the frequency vanishes at finite temperature. The conditions under which the self-consistent

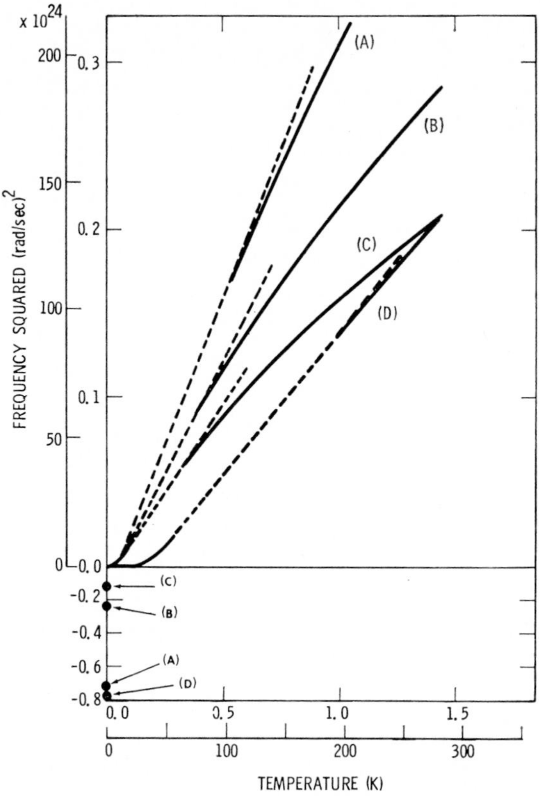

Fig. 4. Temperature dependence of the renormalized transverse optic mode frequency squared for four different sets of the model parameters $\varphi_{\ell}^{(2)}$ and $\varphi_{11}^{(4)}$. The values taken by the unrenormalized squared frequencies are indicated on the negative ordinate. Dashed portions of the curves denote the linear regions of the plots. The inner temperature and frequency scales are the reduced units discussed in text.

equations admit a zero solution for the zone center TO mode frequency will be discussed below. It should be pointed out that in cases (A)–(C) the linear region (denoted by dashed lines) extends to lower temperatures than one would expect from a direct expansion of the population factor coth $(\hbar\omega/k_B T)$ for $(\hbar\omega/k_B T) \ll 1$. The point is that by treating all modes self-consistently, the density of modes with energies less than $k_B T$ is weighted more heavily at low temperatures than if the contribution from the optic branches of long wavelength had been neglected, as in conventional approaches. If we refer back to fig. (1), we see that experimentally the linear temperature dependence of ω_{TO}^2 in $SrTiO_3$ extends almost to $T=0$. Similar behavior is observed in $KTaO_3$. As was pointed out in section 2, the extension of the linear temperature dependence of ω_{TO}^2 into the low-temperature regime cannot be adequately explained on the basis of conventional approaches.

By considering the ordered phase solutions and comparing the free energies of the undistorted and distorted structures, it can be verified that a transition to an ordered phase at a temperature T_c always takes place with a discontinuous change in the optic mode order parameter. Of considerable interest is the fact that there exists a limiting temperature T_0 such that in the temperature interval $0 \leqslant T \leqslant T_0$ two ordered phase solutions exist – one stable and one unstable – whereas above T_0 no ordered solutions exist. On the other hand, the paraelectric solution exists in an interval $T_0' < T < \infty$, with $T_0' < T_c < T_0$. The principle features of the ordered and paraelectric solutions for the case of zero strain are best illustrated by plotting the qualitative behavior of the free energy as a function of η in the manner shown in fig. 5. It is clear that the paraelectric solution is metastable with respect to the stable ordered solution in the interval $T_0' \leqslant T < T_c$, with the opposite being true for $T_c < T < T_0$. Thus, T_0' is the supercooling temperature of the paraelectric phase. In general, the transition is first order and occurs at a temperature T_c less than the limiting temperature T_0 (superheating temperature) above which no ordered solutions exist. We can compare these results with what one would expect from a conventional Devonshire expansion up to fourth order in the macroscopic polarizations. The dotted plot in fig. 5 represents the conventional result. The Devonshire phenomenological theory would predict that a second order transition would occur at the temperature T_0' at which the paraelectric solution becomes unstable. Thus, we see that for the crystal stabilized by quartic anharmonicity alone, the conventional approach yields a second order transition, whereas a self-consistent treatment yields a first order transition always.

It is to be expected that the effect of the coupling of the strain field to the optic mode order parameter will only increase the first order character of the transition. We can confirm this speculation by considering the details of the general case in which the coupling between ε and η is included. Eqs. (44)–(46) provide us with the necessary relations for expressing $\tilde{\varphi}_\ell$ as a function of $\langle u_1^2 \rangle$ in the general case. For definiteness, we choose the values of the parameters $\varphi_\ell^{(2)}$ and $\varphi_{11}^{(4)}$ to be those appropriate to case (B) of fig. 2. We then examine the effect of the strain coupling by introducing non-zero values for the cubic force constant $\varphi_\ell^{(3)}$. Fig. 6 illustrates the graphical solution in the general case where both ε and η can take on non-zero values. From the simultaneous

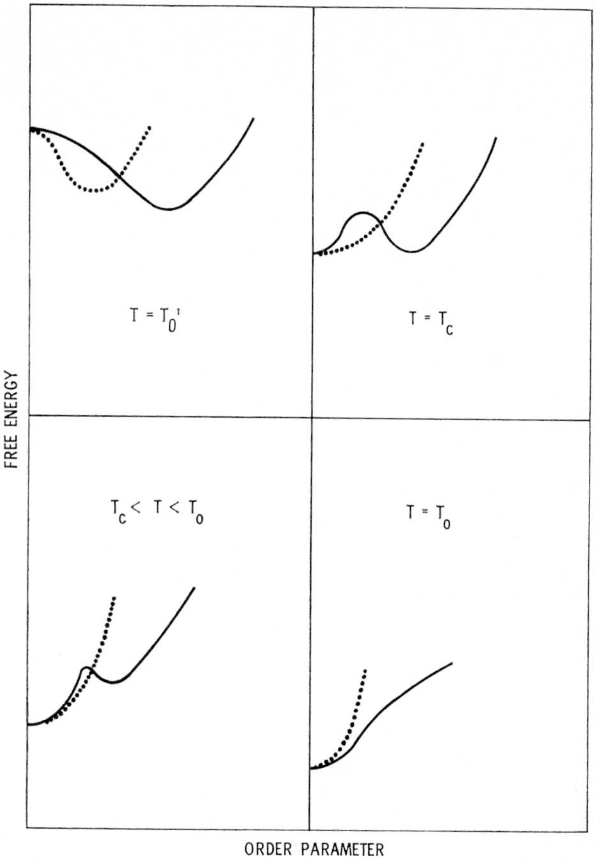

Fig. 5. Qualitative behavior of the free energy as a function of order parameter. Solid curve is the model calculation considered in the text. Dotted curve is the conventional Landau result.

solution of (44)–(46) one obtains the curves labeled (a)–(c) and (a′)–(c′) for the paraelectric and ordered states, respectively. The six curves labeled with temperatures ranging from 0 K to 112 K are the temperature parameterized curves obtained from the evaluation of (48). The intersection of these curves with the curves labeled (a)–(c) and (a′)–(c′) yield the self-consistent paraelectric and ordered solutions for different values of the cubic anharmonicity.

In evaluating $\langle u_1^2 \rangle$ using (48) a finite mesh in wave-vector space was employed. This yielded temperature parameterized curves having the general properties that $\mathrm{d}\langle u_1^2 \rangle / \mathrm{d}_\ell \tilde{\varphi} < 0$ and $\mathrm{d}^2 \langle u_1^2 \rangle / \mathrm{d}\tilde{\varphi}_\ell^2 > 0$ for $\tilde{\varphi}_\ell$ in the interval $[\tilde{\varphi}_{\min}, \infty]$, $\tilde{\varphi}_{\min}$ being the value of $\tilde{\varphi}_\ell$ for which $\omega_{\mathrm{TO}}^2(\Gamma)$ vanishes. Although it

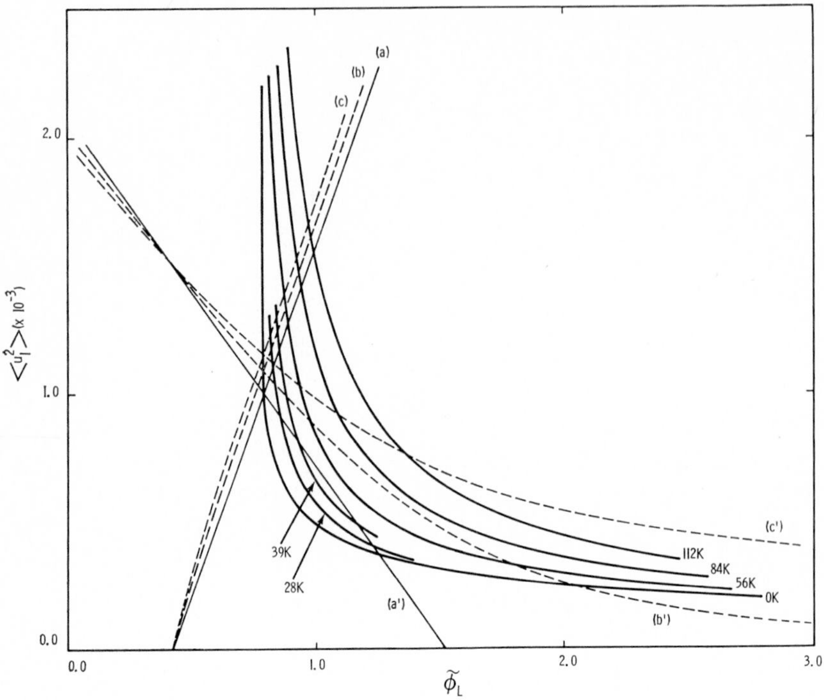

Fig. 6. Graphical solution of the coupled self-consistent equations for three values of $\varphi_\ell^{(3)}$, keeping $\varphi_\ell^{(2)}$ and $\varphi_{11}^{(4)}$ constant.

would appear that $\langle u_1^2 \rangle \to \infty$ as $\tilde{\varphi}_\ell \to \varphi_{\min}$, this effect is an artifact of the finite crystal approximation. If one takes the infinite crystal limit ($N \to \infty$), $\langle u_1^2 \rangle$ rigorously approaches a finite value as $\tilde{\varphi}_\ell \to \tilde{\varphi}_{\min}$. Indeed, the curves of $\langle u_1^2 \rangle$ vs $\tilde{\varphi}_\ell$ in fig. 6 would, if continued to smaller values of $\tilde{\varphi}_\ell$, intersect the line $\tilde{\varphi}_\ell = \tilde{\varphi}_{\min}$ with a slope of $-\infty$. Taking the infinite crystal limit does not alter the first order character of the transition. However, whether or not the TO mode frequency associated with the paraelectric phase vanishes at a finite temperature depends to a large extent on whether or not the $N \to \infty$ limit has been taken. Indeed, for the finite crystal case, the supercooling temperature is always negative and the paraelectric solution is at least metastable at all temperatures. However, for the infinite crystal case it is possible to have either a positive or negative supercooling temperature, depending on the limiting value of $\langle u_1^2 \rangle$ ($T=0$) as $\tilde{\varphi}_\ell \to \tilde{\varphi}_{\min}$. If the supercooling temperature is positive, then the paraelectric frequency vanishes at T_0'. The transition to the distorted phase is still first order, of course, and occurs before the supercooling temperature is ever reached. By decreasing sufficiently the mesh size used in the evaluation of the reciprocal space sums, it was ascertained that the paraelectric solutions found in Gillis and Koehler (1972) existed at all temperatures. For the cases considered there the effective supercooling temperatures were negative.

The intersection of the straight lines (a) and (a′) with the temperature parameterized curves yields the paraelectric and ordered solutions, respectively, for case (B) of fig. 4. Keeping the parameters $\varphi_{\ell}^{(2)}$ and $\varphi_{11}^{(4)}$ the same, a small increment of cubic anharmonicity $\varphi_{\ell}^{(3)}$ is introduced, resulting in the dashed curves (b) and (c) (in the order of increasing $|\varphi_{\ell}^{(3)}|$) for the paraelectric phase and the curves (b′) and (c′) for the ordered phase. As in the case where the strain was neglected, there is one paraelectric solution for $T_0'<T<\infty$ together with two ordered solutions for $0<T<T_0$. We see from fig. 6 that T_0 may be identified as the temperature at which a primed curve becomes tangent to one of the temperature curves. The most striking feature of fig. 6 is the fact that the introduction of a small component of cubic anharmonicity has a small effect on the paraelectric solution as might be expected, but a relatively large effect on the ordered solutions. We can illustrate this point even more vividly by means of a plot of the free energy vs temperature both in the presence and in the absence of cubic anharmonicity. In fig. 7 we have plotted the free energies appropriate to the paraelectric solutions (a) and (b) and the ordered solutions (a′) and (b′). The upper solid curve and the upper dashed curve correspond to the paraelectric solutions (a) and (b) of fig. 6. It is clear that the introduction of a small amount of cubic anharmonicity in linear order has little effect on the free energy of the paraelectric phase. The lower solid and lower dashed curves of fig. 7 correspond to the solutions (a′) and (b′) of fig. 6 – these curves terminate at two limiting temperatures T_0(a′) and T_0(b′) denoted by the solid dots in the plot. It can be clearly seen from the figure that the effect on the ordered phase free energy of introducing a non-zero $\varphi_{\ell}^{(3)}$ is quite large when compared to the change in the paraelectric free energy. Another important feature revealed in the plot is the fact that the introduction of strain coupling increases both the limiting temperature T_0 and the transition temperature T_c. Thus, in the presence of strain the crystal undergoes a first order transition at a temperature T_c which is higher than the corresponding transition temperature in the absence of strain–this was already anticipated. Furthermore, the discontinuity at the transition in quantities such as the entropy and the optic mode order parameter is enhanced by the introduction of strain. We have not demonstrated this explicitly here, but detailed calculations do in fact bear this out.

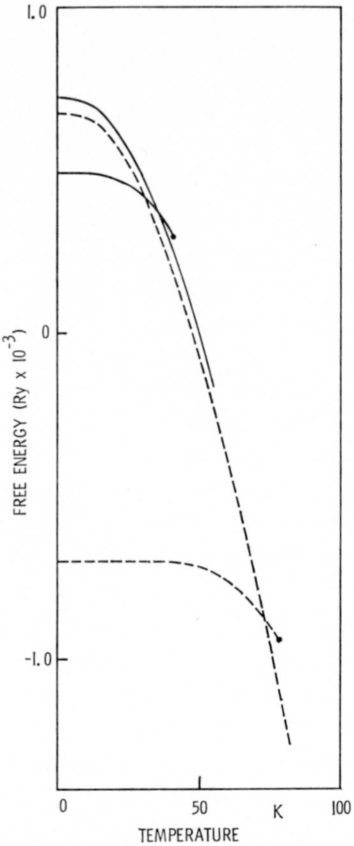

Fig. 7. Free energies vs temperature of the ferroelectric and paraelectric phases: in the absence of linear cubic anharmonicity (solid line) and in the presence of linear cubic anharmonicity (dashed line).

It is appropriate at this point to re-examine the main thrust of the discussion presented in this section. We examined in detail a model crystal stabilized by quartic anharmonicity alone, the goal being to carry out a systematic study of the relation between soft mode behavior and structural transitions in a model NaCl structure crystal. The calculation represented an improvement over previous more conventional approaches to the displacive ferroelectric problem. In spite of this, the model is unrealistic in several aspects when applied to the discussion of a transition such as occurs in GeTe. The most obvious inadequacy is the fact that the model of the interatomic forces is relatively primitive. In a material such as GeTe both covalent and ionic forces are known to be present, with all forces relatively long range in character. Furthermore, the non-stoichiometry of as-grown crystals of GeTe causes the material to be a degenerate semiconductor and it is not known how the presence of free carriers directly affects the transition. It is clear, however, that a simple rigid ion model with nearest neighbor short-range forces only cannot hope to duplicate this complexity. One can overcome this difficulty somewhat if one has enough parameters at one's disposal. However, we found that in order to simplify the calculation as much as possible it was necessary to confine ourselves to a purely longitudinal force matrix. This favored a relative displacement of sublattices consistent with the rhombohedral distortion observed in GeTe. In addition, however, it restricted the strain deformation to a uniform expansion only, whereas we know that in GeTe a strain deformation characterized by $\varepsilon_{12}=\varepsilon_{13}=\varepsilon_{23}$ occurs in addition to the uniform expansion. This additional strain corresponds to a change in the unit cell angle. This failing in the model could be easily remedied by introducing non-zero tangential components of the cubic force matrix. Such a calculation would be straightforward but, until a better understanding of the interactions in insulators and semiconductors is possible, probably not worthwhile. Thus, the question of why GeTe undergoes a ferroelectric-like transition while the alkali halides do not, cannot be definitively answered at the present time. Progress is being made in this direction, however, with the recent advent of microscopic lattice dynamical theories (Keating 1968, Pick et al. 1970, Gillis 1970, Sham 1969, 1972).

In spite of the inadequacy of the force model, the model calculation of this section was carried out with the hope that certain qualitative features would emerge which would be essentially model independent. To a certain extent this hope was rewarded. It was demonstrated that many of the qualitative features associated with soft mode behavior in real paraelectric materials were well described within the context of the self-consistent model. A more stringent test, however, resulted from the description of the transition region. With the parameters of the short-range interaction chosen such that a transition to a distorted phase was energetically favored, a self-consistent treatment of a model NaCl crystal yielded a first order transition always. This last is essentially a model independent result, i.e., we would have reached the same conclusion concerning the order of the transition if we had treated the perovskite structure with a realistic model of the interatomic forces. One can also convince oneself that this conclusion will not be altered by the inclusion of higher order even anharmonicity in lowest order, such as is contained in (28). The question still remains, then, as to how one can adequately describe a ferroelectric transition which is close to second order, such as occurs in GeTe or, for example, in $SrTiO_3$ at 110 K. It is reasonable to assume that true second order behavior, including the effects of order parameter fluctuations in the critical region, cannot be obtained in any finite perturbation expansion – self-consistent or otherwise. Of course, we saw earlier that the conventional techniques, starting from a harmonic approximation, yielded classical second order behavior; yet, this result can only be viewed as fortuitous because of the unsystematic approximations which were made. In the last section we will see that by making certain assumptions about the long-range nature of the interaction, one can obtain a second order transition within the context of a self-consistent treatment.

Before concluding this section it should be pointed out that the approximations which have been employed are essentially low-temperature approximations. It is well known that within the context of ordinary anharmonic perturbation theory, the cubic anharmonic term to second order is comparable in magnitude to the quartic term to first order – this is especially true at high temperatures. It would seem that even in a self-consistent treatment a similar term should also enter in lowest order. That this is in fact the case will be discussed in the following section. The discussion there will set the stage for extending the calculations to higher temperatures, which is, of course, necessary if one is to treat a material such as GeTe realistically, where the transition takes place at 700 K.

5. *One-phonon response function*

One of the most useful experimental probes of the dynamical aspects of lattice structural transformations is the technique of inelastic neutron diffraction. In those crystals where the relevant neutron cross sections are favorable, this technique is capable of mapping out the complete phonon dispersion curves as a function of wave-vector and temperature. Thus, in ferroelectrics where soft phonon mode behavior is an integral feature of the structural transformation, the inelastic neutron technique provides an important tool for determining the temperature dependence and symmetry of the soft mode both above and below the transition. A good example is the work of Shirane et al. (1970a) on $PbTiO_3$, not to mention extensive work on a host of other soft mode materials by both the Brookhaven and Chalk River groups. To a lesser extent, light scattering provides an experimental probe of ferroelectric crystals. Unfortunately, first order Raman scattering is confined to the study of zone center modes and to crystals whose symmetry is such that the relevant phonons are Raman active. If the modes of interest are not Raman active, then activity must be induced by effectively reducing the crystal symmetry through the application of small externally applied fields. The most serious drawback of first order Raman scattering, however, is the restriction to zone center. In principle, second order Raman spectroscopy provides a probe of phonons throughout the zone, although in most cases a previous knowledge of the complete dispersion curves (usually from neutron data) is necessary in order to unambiguously interpret the spectra.

Whether one is probing the ferroelectric crystal by light or by neutrons, the quantity that one is invariably interested in from the theoretical point of view is the scattering cross section as a function of momentum transfer and energy. For the case of inelastic neutron scattering, this quantity is proportional to the Fourier transform $S(q\omega)$ of the density–density correlation function,

$$S(q\omega) = \int \mathrm{d}^3 r \int \mathrm{d}t \exp\left[\mathrm{i}\omega(t-t') - \mathrm{i}\boldsymbol{q}\cdot(\boldsymbol{r}-\boldsymbol{r}')\right] \langle \rho(\boldsymbol{r}t)\, \rho(\boldsymbol{r}'t')\rangle . \quad (49)$$

In a typical neutron diffraction experiment, the momentum transfer $\boldsymbol{q}$ is fixed and the differential cross section plotted as a function of the energy transfer ω. The positions of the resonances in the scattering cross section then yield the energies of the physical phonons. The work by Ambegaokar et al. (1965) showed that if one expresses the density operator $\rho(\boldsymbol{r}t)$ in terms of the ionic displacements and subsequently performs a cumulant expansion with respect to the phonon coordinates, then one can formally separate out the part of (49) which is rapidly varying in time (and, hence, peaked in ω). Werthamer (1970b) has recently expressed this rapidly varying one-phonon peak in closed form in terms of functional derivatives of a general free energy functional. In our notation, the free energy functional corresponds to the function $\mathscr{F}$ introduced in (32). Werthamer has shown that the true one-phonon propagator, extracted from (49), is formally given by

$$M(12) = \mathrm{i}\delta^2 \mathscr{F} / \delta d(1)\, \delta d(2), \quad (50)$$

in agreement with (25) and (31). As was noted previously, the importance of this result stems from the fact that it provides a definite prescription for evaluating the one-phonon response consistent with a given approximation for $\mathscr{F}$. In section 3 we indicated that the results of the lowest order self-consistent phonon approximation could be obtained from the approximate free energy (32). However, in obtaining the phonon propagator via eq. (25), the implicit dependence of $d(12)$ on $d(1)$ was neglected–it was then pointed out that such an approximation was equivalent to the variational treatment outlined in the last section. It was first demonstrated by Götze and Michel (1968) that the approximation which yields (28) as the phonon propagator is *not* consistent in the field-theoretic sense established by Baym (1962)–that, in fact, the functional derivative must in principle be carried out including the implicit dependence of $d(12)$ on $d(1)$. A direct result of the inconsistency inherent in the approximation (28) is the fact that the elastic constants obtained from a direct differentiation of the free energy (32) are not equal to the elastic constants obtained from the long-wavelength expansion of (28). The point, of course, is that the equilibrium propagator (28) is not the true one-phonon response that would be observed, for example, in a neutron scattering experiment. For the approximate free energy (41), the $q=0$ one-phonon optic mode response differs from the expression (47). It is thus of considerable interest to calculate this response function within the context of the model considered in the last section.

As in section 3 we start with the exact expression (26) for $K(1)$ and then establish the approximation by neglecting all cumulants of third or higher order. The one-phonon response is given, as before, by the prescription (25), but now we must remember to include the implicit dependence of $d(12)$ on $d(1)$. Carrying out the appropriate functional differentiations yields the formal expression

$$M(12) = M_0(12) + \tfrac{1}{2}\mathrm{i}\tilde{\Phi}^{(3)}(1\bar{2}\bar{3})\,Q(\bar{2}\bar{3}2) \tag{51}$$

for the one-phonon response. The three-point function $Q(123) \equiv \delta d(12)/\delta d(1)$ satisfies the integral equation

$$Q(123) = d_0(1\bar{2})\,\tilde{\Phi}^{(3)}(\bar{2}\bar{3}3)\,d_0(\bar{3}2) + \tfrac{1}{2}\mathrm{i}d_0(1\bar{2})\,\tilde{\Phi}^{(4)}(\bar{2}\bar{3}\bar{4}\bar{5})\,d_0(\bar{3}2)\,Q(\bar{4}\bar{5}3). \tag{52}$$

Eqs. (51) and (52) have been obtained in one form or the other by Horner (1967), Götze and Michel (1968) and Werthamer (1970a, b). The quantities $M_0(12)$ and $d_0(12)$ denote the equilibrium self-energy and propagator appropriate to the approximation (28). $\tilde{\Phi}^{(n)}(12\cdots n)$ is defined similarly to (29a) with Φ replaced by $\tilde{\Phi}$. The lowest order evaluation of $Q(123)$ yields a correction to $M_0(12)$ which formally resembles the second order cubic anharmonic correction of ordinary perturbation theory, but with the important difference that the propagators which appear in this correction are renormalized propagators. Furthermore, $\tilde{\Phi}^{(3)}$ appears instead of $\Phi^{(3)}$. For the simple model considered in the last section, we can easily evaluate the lowest order correction to $M_0(12)$. Indeed, for the zone center transverse optic mode of the paraelectric phase, the one-phonon response frequency Ω_{TO} is obtained as the solution to the equation

$$\Omega_{\mathrm{TO}}^2 = \omega_{\mathrm{TO}}^2 - \tfrac{2}{3}(\varphi_\ell^{(3)})^2 N^{-1} \sum_{q,\lambda_2,\lambda_3} F(\Omega_{\mathrm{TO}}; q, \lambda_2, \lambda_3) \times \sum_{\alpha=1}^{3} \sin^2 q_\alpha [\varepsilon_\alpha^{\mathrm{A}}(q\lambda_2)\, \varepsilon_\alpha^{\mathrm{B}}(q\lambda_3) - \varepsilon_\alpha^{\mathrm{A}}(q\lambda_3)\, \varepsilon_\alpha^{\mathrm{B}}(q\lambda_2)]^2, \quad (53)$$

where

$$F(\Omega; q, \lambda_2, \lambda_3) = \omega_2^{-1} \coth \tfrac{1}{2}\beta\omega_2 \left(\frac{1}{\omega_3^2 - (\Omega + \omega_2)^2} + \frac{1}{\omega_3^2 - (\Omega - \omega_2)^2} \right) + \omega_3^{-1} \coth \tfrac{1}{2}\beta\omega_3 \left(\frac{1}{\omega_2^2 - (\Omega + \omega_3)^2} + \frac{1}{\omega_2^2 + (\Omega - \omega_3)^2} \right),$$

and ω_1 and ω_2 refer to the renormalized frequencies $\omega(q\lambda_2)$ and $\omega(q\lambda_3)$. In the above, ω_{TO}^2 is given by (47) and the renormalized frequencies and eigenvectors are obtained from the diagonalization of (37). $\varphi_\ell^{(3)}$ is the cubic force constant introduced in the last section. Since $F(0; q, \lambda_2, \lambda_3)$ is positive definite, it is clear that one can force a zero solution for the one-phonon response frequency through an appropriate choice of $\varphi_\ell^{(3)}$. This result is not confined to the low-order expression (53). One can easily convince oneself that $\Omega_{\mathrm{TO}}=0$ is a possible solution of the more general equations (51) and (52), although this result depends critically on the specification of the interaction potential.

In the last section we found the result that the self-consistent zone center TO mode frequency ω_{TO} did not vanish at the temperature T_c at which the crystal underwent a structural transformation. However, as the foregoing discussion has demonstrated, the frequency ω_{TO} characterizes the equilibrium phonon propagator and is not the true one-phonon response frequency Ω_{TO}. The question remains as to whether the vanishing of Ω_{TO} signals a classical second order transition. Unfortunately, the answer is not clear-cut. The free energy functional from which the response was derived is identical to that which was considered in the last section, and on the basis of this free energy the transition remains first order. In this case the vanishing of Ω_{TO} would merely signify the approach to the supercooling temperature. On the other hand, if we were to construct a better approximation to the free energy by including the true collective modes (as defined by the one-phonon response function), the transition might in fact be second order on the basis of this new free energy. It is clear that much remains to be done in order to unravel the details of the transition. However, in spite of the lingering uncertainty concerning the order of the transition in this model, we expect the fully self-consistent treatment to provide an improvement over the approximations of the last section, at least at high temperatures. Actual calculations are difficult, although Goldman et al. (1970) have succeeded in carrying out numerical calculations of the one-phonon response in the rare gas solids.

We have not as yet touched on the question or phonon damping. The lowest order results presented in sections 3 and 4 yielded an equilibrium phonon spectrum which was undamped. On the other hand, the fully self-consistent theory of the present section introduced damping via an initial phonon decaying into two thermal phonons. Since the intermediate state phonons are themselves undamped, this approximation is valid only in the 'collisionless' regime $\omega\tau \gg 1$, where τ is an average collision time for the thermal phonons. It is clear, however, that as the soft mode decreases in magmagnitude, one will eventually enter the hydrodynamic regime $\omega\tau \ll 1$ and in this regime the decay of the soft mode must be treated in an approximation in which the intermediate state phonons are damped. Such approximations have been considered recently by Cowley (1970).

6. *Mean field theory*

Up to this point the treatment of the ferroelectric crystal has been aimed at a description of the frequency spectrum employing self-consistent lattice dynamics. In this approach the excitation spectrum of the crystal is viewed as a collection of dynamically coupled normal modes of phonon-like character. The self-consistent feature arises from the fact that in an actual crystal lattice each atom feels not the bare potential of the remaining atoms, as in the harmonic approximation, but rather an effective potential which incorporates in some manner an average over the mean positions of all the particles, each of which is treated equivalently. This physically appealing picture manifests itself through the appearance in lowest order of effective force constants $\langle \nabla\nabla\Phi \rangle$ which replace the bare force constants $\nabla\nabla\Phi$ familiar from harmonic theory. As applied to the displacive ferroelectric problem, an intrinsic feature of this approach is the fact that as far as the harmonic correlations are concerned, the long-range dipolar forces are treated on an equal footing with the short-range interactions. In contrast to this, there is a somewhat different approach to the ferroelectric problem which treats the two classes of interactions separately. This is the so-called mean field theory approach, which borrows much in its spirit from the molecular field theories of magnetism. Lines (1969a, b) has recently developed a statistical theory of displacive ferroelectrics which employs classical statistics in conjunction with the mean field approximation. Because of the long-range character of the dipolar forces, one can treat this contribution to the interaction in an effective field approximation. Once this is done, and classical statistics introduced, a semi-phenomenological theory can be constructed with few enough adjustable parameters as to be overdetermined by experiment, thus providing a consistency check on the theory. In a somewhat different vein, Onodera (1970, 1971) has treated a system of interacting classical quartic oscillators in a mean field approximation, with some exact results being obtained for temperatures greater than the Curie temperature. Of considerable interest also is the work of Pytte and Feder (1969), and Pytte (1972a). These authors treat the phase transitions which occur in the perovskite ferroelectrics employing a model hamiltonian including quartic anharmonicity. Their approach is similar in several aspects to the model calculation presented in section 4, with the exception that the temperature dependence of the correlation functions and the order parameters are determined by treating the correlations between different cells in a mean field approximation. This latter approximation can give rise to a classical second order transition, and it is this aspect of the mean field theory that we would like to examine in more detail.

We can best illustrate some of these ideas by returning once again to the pedagogical model of section 2. As was pointed out in the discussion of that model, the bare frequencies Ω_q contain contributions from both the harmonic dipolar *and* the harmonic short range interactions–hence, the possibility exists of a group of frequencies Ω_q of long wavelength being imaginary. One can, however, take the alternative approach of interpreting the bare frequencies as arising only from the short-range interaction (in which case $\Omega_q^2 > 0$ for all q). The long-range Coulombic interaction, which enters via a term of the form

$$-\tfrac{1}{2}\sum_q C(q)\, Q_q Q_{-q}$$

can then be treated in an effective field approximation.

We can examine in more detail the content of the mean field approximation by returning to the model hamiltonian (2), replacing the squared frequency Ω_q^2 by $\Omega^2 - C(q)/M$, where Ω is a constant frequency associated with the short-range interaction and $C(q)$ is the force matrix of the dipolar interaction. The equations which determine the order parameter and the renormalized optic mode $\bar{\Omega}_0$ are identical to (13) and (14) with Ω_0^2 replaced by

$\Omega^2 - C(0)/M$ and the subscript zero removed from the thermal averages; i.e.,

$$\langle Q_0\rangle^2/N = -[M\Omega^2 - C(0) + 12\varphi\Delta]/4\varphi, \tag{54}$$

$$\begin{aligned} M\bar{\Omega}_0^2 &= M\Omega^2 - C(0) + 12\varphi\Delta, \quad &\langle Q_0\rangle = 0, \\ &= 8\varphi\langle Q_0\rangle^2/N, &\langle Q_0\rangle \neq 0, \end{aligned} \tag{55}$$

where

$$\Delta \equiv \sum_q \langle Q_q Q_{-q}\rangle/N \tag{56}$$

and

$$\begin{aligned} M\bar{\Omega}_q^2 &= M\Omega^2 - C(q) + 12\varphi\Delta + 12\varphi\langle Q_0\rangle^2/N \\ &= M\bar{\Omega}_0^2 + C(0) - C(q). \end{aligned} \tag{57}$$

Up to this point no assumption has been made concerning the nature of the dipolar interaction. Indeed, the equations (54)–(57) are identical to those that would be obtained in the usual self-consistent phonon approximation with the harmonic force matrix given by $M\Omega_q^2 = M\Omega^2 - C(q)$. In order to obtain the mean field counterparts of (54)–(57) one must characterize the long-range behavior of the dipolar interaction. Specifically, one assumes that this interaction is infinitely long range and infinitely weak. Thus, for the dipolar interaction between ions located at lattice sites R_i and R_j one makes the Ansatz

$$C(R_i - R_j) = C/N, \quad N \to \infty,$$

or

$$C(q) = \delta_{q0} C. \tag{58}$$

The result of this Ansatz is to effectively introduce a symmetry breaking field of the form $-\delta_{q0}C(q)\langle Q_q\rangle$ into the hamiltonian.

Employing (58) in conjunction with (56) and (57), the equilibrium correlation function Δ may be evaluated simply as

$$\Delta = (1/2M\tilde{\Omega})\coth(\tilde{\Omega}/2T), \tag{59}$$

where $\tilde{\Omega}^2 = \bar{\Omega}_0^2 + C/M$ and terms $O(1/N)$ have been neglected. Eqs. (54), (55) and (59) constitute the coupled set of equations for $\bar{\Omega}_0^2$ and $\langle Q_0\rangle^2$ in the mean field approximation.

It is to be noted that the difference between the mean field approximation and the usual self-consistent phonon approximation is the way in which Δ

is evaluated. The mean field evaluation employs a flat frequency spectrum with a discontinuity at $q=0$, whereas in the self-consistent phonon approximation the sum in (56) is carried out exactly. In the large $\bar{\Omega}_0^2$ regime the behavior of the correlation function is similar in both approximations. However, for small values of $\bar{\Omega}_0^2$, the two approximations yield a vastly different behavior for Δ. Indeed, in the self-consistent phonon approximation $\mathrm{d}\Delta/\mathrm{d}\bar{\Omega}_0^2 \to -\infty$ as $\bar{\Omega}_0^2 \to 0$, whereas the mean field approximation yields a finite negative value for this derivative in the same limit. This difference in the small $\bar{\Omega}_0$ behavior of Δ in the two approximations is intimately connected with the order of the phase transition which can occur in this model. The self-consistent phonon treatment may lead to a first order transition or no transition, whereas the mean field approximation may give rise to a first- or second-order transition or no transition depending on the magnitudes of the model parameters. The detailed features of the mean field and self-consistent phonon approximations have been discussed in detail by Gillis and Koehler (1972b) and Pytte (1972b).

Pytte (1972b) has suggested that the difference in the order of the transition in the two approximations arises solely from the long-wavelength fluctuations in the transition region; that in the self-consistent phonon treatment the fluctuations become so large as to violate the Ginzburg criterion (Ginzburg 1960) in the transition region, whereas the mean field evaluation of the correlation functions cuts off these fluctuations before they become too large. Unfortunately, a true assessment of the size of the order parameter fluctuations can only be made after a realistic theory for the transition region is achieved. Recent numerical estimates seem to indicate that the Ginzburg criterion is not violated in the transition region; that, in fact, the first order character of the transition is due more to the restricted form of the variational wave-function rather than the magnitude of the critical fluctuations.

The mean field approximation is physically appealing from the point of view that one would expect a dichotomy to exist between the short-range and long-range interactions, at least as far as the approximations to be used in treating them are concerned. Furthermore, a second order transition and vanishing mode frequency are intimately tied to the symmetry breaking character of the effective field. This leads to a term in the equilibrium effective hamiltonian which is linear in the order parameter, whereas no such term can appear in the true crystal hamiltonian (17). Unfortunately, there remains a disturbing ambiguity in the mean field approach, since from the microscopic viewpoint there appears to be no clear-cut prescription for determining which part of the long range interaction is to be treated as an effective field. Lines (1970) has shown that treating the entire dipolar interaction in a mean field approximation leads to inconsistencies–that in fact there exist correlation effects between different cells involving the dipolar interaction. Thus, part of the dipolar contribution must be treated on the same footing as the short-range interaction, the remaining part being introduced as an effective field.

Some concluding remarks are perhaps in order at this point. In previous sections we have seen that a lattice dynamical treatment of ferroelectricity provided a satisfactory description of many of the properties of real paraelectric materials such as SnTe, $KTaO_3$, and $SrTiO_3$. However, the description of the transition region in materials exhibiting classical second order structural transformations was less than adequate. We found in the present section that a numerically exact evaluation of the correlation function (56) led to a first order transition always, whereas an approximate evaluation of the type used in obtaining eq. (59) could lead to a classical second order transition. Although the results of the mean field approach are gratifying in the sense that a classical second order transition can be obtained, the approximation of replacing the wave-vector dependent frequency spectrum by a flat averaged spectrum is difficult to justify in general. Furthermore, the mean field treatment can give rise to *both* first- and second-order transitions. Thus, since one does not start from a well-defined model of the interatomic forces in the mean field approach, it is difficult to determine when the theory is applicable and when it is not. Hence, a major problem remaining is that of being better able to judge the applicability of the two types of approximations for a realistic treatment of actual ferroelectric transitions. This will form a basis for answering the other remaining important question, i.e., why, for two crystals of the same lattice structure, is one ferroelectric and the other not? The answer to this latter question is, as we remarked earlier, intimately tied to a realistic description of the interatomic forces in insulators.

Acknowledgement

This work was supported by the U.S. Atomic Energy Commission.

References

Ambegaokar, V., Conway, J.M., and Baym, G. (1965), Inelastic Scattering of Neutrons by Anharmonic Crystals. *In*: *Lattice dynamics*, Wallis, R.F., ed. (Pergamon), 261–270.

ANDERSON, P.W. (1960), *in*: *Fizika Dielektrikov*, Skanayi, G.I., ed. (Akad. Nauk SSSR, Fiz. Inst. im P.N. Lebedeva, Moscow).
BAYM, G. (1962), Phys. Rev. **127**, 1391.
BIERLY, J.N., MULDAWER, L. and BECKMAN, O. (1963), Acta Met. **11**, 447.
BOCCARA, N. and SARMA, G. (1965), Physics **1**, 219.
COCHRAN, W. (1960), Advan. Phys. **9**, 387.
COCHRAN, W. (1967), Lattice Dynamics of Diatomic Crystals. *In*: *Ferroelectricity*, Weller, E.F., ed. (Elsevier, Amsterdam), 62–71.
COCHRAN, W. (1969), Advan. Phys. **18**, 157.
COWLEY, R.A. (1962), Phys. Rev. Letters **9**, 159.
COWLEY, R.A. (1965), Phil. Mag. **11**, 673.
COWLEY, R.A. (1970), J. Phys. Soc. Japan **28**, Suppl., 239.
DEVONSHIRE, A.F. (1954), Advan. Phys. **3**, 85.
DONIACH, S. (1965), A Variational Approach to the Anharmonic Lattice Problem (with an Application to the Theory of Ferroelectric Transitions). *In*: *Lattice dynamics*, Wallis, R.F., ed. (Pergamon) 305–312.
GILLIS, N.S. (1969), Phys. Rev. Letters **22**, 1251.
GILLIS, N.S. (1970), Phys. Rev. B **1**, 1872.
GILLIS, N.S. and KOEHLER, T.R. (1971), Phys. Rev. B **4**, 3971.
GILLIS, N.S. and KOEHLER, T.R. (1972a), Phys. Rev. B **5**, 1925.
GILLIS, N.S. and KOEHLER, T.R. (1972b), Phys. Rev. Letters **29**, 369.
GINZBURG, V.L. (1960), Sov. Physics Solid State **2**, 1824.
GOLDAK, J., BARRETT, C.S., INNES, D., and YOUDELIS, W. (1966), J. Chem. Phys. **44**, 3323.
GOLDMAN, V.V., HORTON, G.K. and KLEIN, M.L. (1970), Phys. Rev. Letters **24**, 1424.
GÖTZE, W. and MICHEL, K.H. (1968), Z. Physik **217**, 170.
HARADA, J., AXE, J.D. and SHIRANE, G. (1971), Phys. Rev. B **4**, 155.
HORNER, H. (1967), Z. Physik **205**, 72.
KEATING, P.N. (1968), Phys. Rev. **175**, 1171.
KELLERMAN, E.W. (1940), Phil. Trans. Roy. Soc. London **238**, 513.
KUBO, R. (1962), J. Phys. Soc. Japan **17**, 1100.
KWOK, P.C. (1967), Solid State Physics **20**, 213.
KWOK, P.C. and MILLER, P.B. (1966), Phys. Rev. **151**, 387.
LANDAU, L.D. (1937), Zhurnal eksperimental'noi i teoreticheskoi fiziki **7**, 627. Translation in: *Collected papers of L.D. Landau* (Pergamon, 1965) 209.
LANDAU, L.D. and LIFSHITZ, E.M. (1958), Statistical Physics (Addison-Wesley), Ch. 14.
LINES, M.E. (1969a), Phys. Rev. **177**, 797.
LINES, M.E. (1969b), Phys. Rev. **117**, 812.
LINES, M.E. (1970), Phys. Rev. B **2**, 690.
LYDDANE, R.H., SACHS, R.G. and TELLER, E. (1941), Phys. Rev. **59**, 673.
MARADUDIN, A.A. (1967), Ferroelectricity and Lattice Anharmonicity. *In*: *Ferroelectricity*, Weller, E.F., ed. (Elsevier, Amsterdam, 1967) 72–100.
MITSUI, T. and WESTPHAL, W.B. (1961), Phys. Rev. **124**, 1354.
MÜLLER, K.A. and BERLINGER, W. (1971), Phys. Rev. Letters **26**, 13.
ONODERA, Y. (1970), Prog. Theor. Phys. **44**, 1477.
ONODERA, Y. (1971), Progr. Theor. Phys. **45**, 986.
PAWLEY, G.S., COCHRAN, W., COWLEY, R.A., and DOLLING, G. (1966), Phys. Rev. Letters **17**, 753.

Pick, R.M., Cohen, M.H. and Martin, R.M. (1970), Phys. Rev. B **1**, 910.
Pytte, E. and Feder, J. (1969), Phys. Rev. **187**, 1077.
Pytte, E. (1972a), Phys. Rev. B **5**, 3758.
Pytte, E. (1972b), Phys. Rev. Letters **28**, 895.
Riste, T., Samuelson, E.J., Otnes, K., and Feder, J. (1971), Solid State Commun. **9**, 1455.
Sham, L.J. (1969), Phys. Rev. **188**, 1431.
Sham, L.J. (1972), Phys. Rev. B **6**, 3581; *ibid.* **6**, 3584.
Shirane, G., Nathans, R. and Minkiewicz, V.J. (1967), Phys. Rev. **157**, 396.
Shirane, G., Axe, J.D., Harada, J., and Remeika, J.P. (1970a), Phys. Rev. B **2**, 155.
Shirane, G., Axe, J.D., Harada, J., and Linz, A. (1970b), Phys. Rev. B **2**, 3651.
Silverman, B.D. (1964), Phys. Rev. **135**, A1596.
Werthamer, N.R. (1970a), Phys. Rev. B **1**, 572.
Werthamer, N.R. (1970b), Phys. Rev. B **2**, 2050.

CHAPTER 3

Lattice Dynamics of Molecular Solids

O. SCHNEPP and N. JACOBI

Department of Chemistry
University of Southern California
Los Angeles, California 90007
USA

Dynamical Properties of Solids, edited by G.K. Horton and A.A. Maradudin

Contents

1. Introduction

Molecular solids are composed of units of tightly bound atoms. This molecular unit retains its identity in the solid and is identified by its structure which is very close to, if not identical with that in the gas phase. The distances between atoms in the same molecule are considerably smaller than those between atoms on different molecules. The above properties are based on the fact that the intermolecular binding energy is in most cases much smaller (by an order of magnitude) than the interatomic or intramolecular binding energies. As a result, the internal molecular vibrations have considerably higher frequencies (typically 1000 cm^{-1}) than the external or lattice modes, which typically have frequencies of the order of 100 cm^{-1} or less. In view of this difference, the two classes of motions are separable to a good approximation. It is then justified to discuss the lattice vibrations separately and to assume the molecule to move as a rigid body.

The motions of the molecular units in a lattice are of two types: translatory displacements of the centers of mass which are common to all solids and have been treated extensively, and orientational or librational displacements with the centers of mass remaining stationary. The latter type of motion is characteristic of molecular solids or ionic crystals containing large and tightly bound units. The lattice dynamical treatment of librations is relatively less developed and will be emphasized in the present chapter.

The importance of lattice motions in molecular solids and their relevance to the determination of molecular structure by X-ray diffraction was recognized early by Cruickshank (1958). This author made, in fact, attempts to deduce the frequencies of lattice vibrations from X-ray data. This application is still of great interest (Pawley 1967, Schomaker and Trueblood 1968) and more detailed work remains to be done.

In recent years, interest in the lattice vibrations of molecular solids has centered on the elucidation of intermolecular potential functions. A specific pair potential can be tested by calculation of observable frequencies using appropriate lattice dynamics. Dows (1962) was the first to attempt a calculation of lattice mode frequencies from such an assumed potential. He was concerned with solid ethylene and used a pair potential consisting of a sum over the repulsions between the hydrogen atoms on neighboring molecules.

The total number of external degrees of freedom in a molecular solid (including translations and librations) is $6NZ$ ($5NZ$ for linear molecules), where N is the number of unit cells and Z the number of molecules or sites in the unit cell. Of these, as always, three modes have zero frequency.

Because of the low frequencies of the lattice vibrations of molecular solids, experimental difficulties prevented their measurement until relatively recent years when the development of modern instrumentation in both Raman and far infrared spectroscopy stimulated activity in this area. These optical techniques are restricted to the study of lattice modes at the zone center ($\boldsymbol{q}=0$). Such vibrations are a very small fraction of all $6NZ$ modes of the solid, but it is possible to make definitive assignments of the observed lines because of the symmetry selection rules which apply at $\boldsymbol{q}=0$). Early investigators measured low-frequency Raman spectra before the advent of the laser. Kastler and Rousset (1941) investigated solid naphthalene and Fruehling (1950) solid benzene. The first far infrared studies of lattice vibrations of molecular solids were carried out by Gebbie's group who used interferometric techniques. Anderson et al. (1964), and Walmsley and Anderson (1964) (also Anderson and Walmsley 1964) studied the far infrared spectra of the hydrogen halides (HCl, HBr), the halogens (Cl_2, Br_2, I_2) and carbon dioxide (CO_2) solids.

Inelastic neutron scattering is a most powerful tool for the study of lattice dynamics. In particular, coherent scattering from single crystals allows, in principle, the measurement of all modes of the solid as a function of $\boldsymbol{q}$, the wave vector in the Brillouin zone. An extensive investigation of this type has recently been reported (Dolling and Powell 1970) for a molecular solid, hexamethylenetetramine. It is to be expected that our knowledge of intermolecular potentials will be greatly enriched by such studies. Incoherent scattering studies are also profitable inasmuch as they measure the total density of states as a function of frequency. This distribution frequently exhibits prominent peaks which do not necessarily coincide with $\boldsymbol{q}=0$ modes and therefore provide additional observables for comparison with theory.

The lattice vibrations of molecular solids received brief attention in reviews dealing with the infrared spectra of these solids (Dows 1963, 1965, 1966). The short review by Schnepp (1969) followed by a more detailed review (Schnepp and Jacobi 1972) covered the area in some depth, including infrared and Raman intensities. Venkataraman and Sahni (1970) reviewed the lattice dynamics of complex crystals and covered much subject matter relevant also to molecular solids.

Section 2 is concerned with the potential models which have been proposed for lattice dynamical treatments of molecular solids. In section 3 the different forms of classical lattice dynamics treatments which have been applied to molecular solids are discussed. This section also includes detailed applications to a few selected systems and comparison with experimental measurements. In section 4 quantum lattice dynamics as pertinent to molecular solids is treated. Specifically, the treatment of librational motions is discussed and also the application of quantum treatments of translational motions to solid hydrogen is included.

2. *Potential models*

It is in some instances useful to carry through the calculation of the frequency spectrum in terms of the potential parameters or 'force constants' which can then be determined by fitting the theoretical results to experimental measurements. This procedure is only applicable to solids of high symmetry and preferably containing one molecule per primitive unit cell. In such a case, the number of independent force constants is limited. However, even then, such a calculation is limited to one or two neighbor shell interactions since every shell considered requires a new set of force constants. The above approach has been successfully applied to the solid of hexamethylenetetramine by Cochran and Pawley (1964) and more recently by Dolling and Powell (1970). This solid has a body-centered cubic structure with one molecule per unit cell.

In most cases, the number of independent force constants is too large relative to the number of observables (at least by optical techniques) to use phenomenological intermolecular force models as described above. It is then necessary to assume an explicit form of the potential function of the solid which contains a small number of parameters. The force constants can then be calculated by differentiation with respect to the displacements. This approach also has the advantage of providing insight into the physical content of the potential function.

It is generally assumed that the potential of the solid may be expressed as a sum of pair interactions:

$$\Phi = \tfrac{1}{2} \sum_{ll'} \sum_{kk'} v(lk, l'k'). \tag{1}$$

Here $v(lk, l'k')$ represents the contribution to the potential due to the interaction between the two molecules located at lk, $l'k'$ where l designates the unit cell and k the site. The neglect of three-body and higher terms is probably reasonable in most cases and has been discussed in the literature (Dymond and Alder 1968, Williams et al. 1967).

Two basic forms of the pair potential v have been used. The first is a sum of two terms, one a function of the distance R between centers of mass and the other a function of the orientations Ω, Ω' of the molecules:

$$v = v_1(R) + v_2(\Omega, \Omega'). \tag{2}$$

The distance-dependent term $v_1(R)$ is often written as a Lennard–Jones, 6–12 potential:

$$v_1(R) = 4\varepsilon[-(\sigma/R)^6 + (\sigma/R)^{12}], \tag{3}$$

although an exponential repulsive term has also been used (6-exponential). The orientation-dependent term $v_2(\Omega, \Omega')$ can be conveniently expanded in spherical harmonics. For electrically neutral molecular units, the first non-vanishing term in this expansion may be the dipole–dipole term or the quadrupole–quadrupole term, depending if the molecules are polar or not. Walmsley and Pople (1964) used such a potential for their treatment of solid CO_2. Their distance dependent term was as given in eq. (3) and v_2 was the quadrupole–quadrupole term as in eq. (4):

$$v_2(\Omega, \Omega') = \sum_{m=-2}^{2} c_m Y_{2m}(\Omega) Y_{2m}(\Omega'). \tag{4}$$

The second type of pair potential v consists of atom-atom interactions, summed over pairs of atoms on different molecules:

$$v = \tfrac{1}{2} \sum_{\kappa\kappa'} [-A/R_{\kappa\kappa'}^6 + B\exp(-CR_{\kappa\kappa'})]. \tag{5}$$

The index κ designates a particular atom in molecule (lk) and $R_{\kappa\kappa'}$ is the distance between two atoms, one on molecule (lk) and the other on molecule ($l'k'$). In eq. (5) the most usual form consisting of 6-exponential terms is given. This type of pair potential function was proposed by De Boer (1942) for H_2 molecules and was first applied to the lattice dynamics problem of solid ethylene by Dows (1962). Kitaigorodskii (1966) proposed sets of parameters for organic molecular solids and showed that it was possible to account for the structures of a large number of such crystals on the basis of H–H, C–H and C–C interaction terms. Williams (1967) determined another set of parameters by fitting a large number of crystal properties including structures, elastic constants and sublimation energies of nine aromatic hydrocarbons. In some instances, atom–atom sum pair potentials in terms of 6–12 interactions have been used for lattice dynamics applications (Kuan et al. 1970, Suzuki and Schnepp 1971). Such a potential is modeled after the 'diatomic potential' used by Sweet and Steele (1967) for the calculation of virial coefficients. The molecule is represented by two centers of interaction which do not necessarily have to coincide with atoms. The pair potential is then given by a sum over four terms, each being a function of the distance R_α between two such centers of interaction on different molecules:

$$v = \varepsilon \sum_{\alpha=1}^{4} [-(\sigma/R_\alpha)^6 + (\sigma/R_\alpha)^{12}]. \tag{6}$$

This potential model is illustrated in fig. 1. The distance between the centers of interaction, $2H$, has been used as adjustable parameter (Kuan et al. 1970, Suzuki and Schnepp 1971).

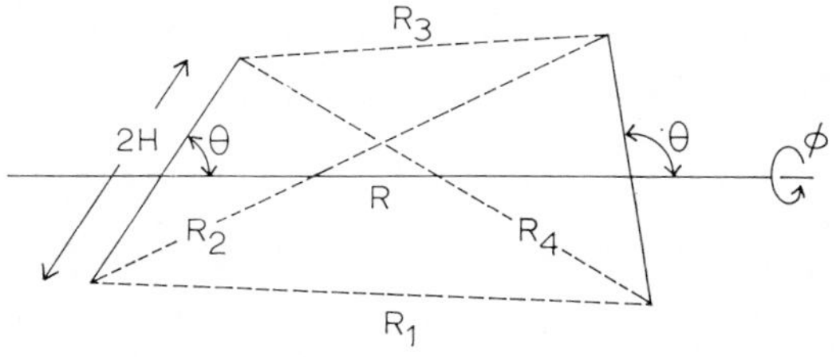

Fig. 1. The diatomic potential model (Suzuki and Schnepp 1971, fig. 1).

3. *Classical lattice dynamics*

3.1. General

As already discussed, the internal vibrations of the molecules making up the lattice will be assumed to be separable from the external or lattice vibrations. This separation is justifiable because of the considerably stronger intramolecular forces as compared to the intermolecular binding in a molecular solid. The intramolecular vibrations typically have frequencies of the order of 1000 cm^{-1} whereas lattice vibrations lie near 100 cm^{-1} or below. We shall then consider here the motions of the molecules assuming these to be rigid bodies. The special feature in the dynamics of molecular crystals is the occurrence of torsional motions or librations in addition to the usual translational displacements. These additional angular degrees of freedom are due to the non-spherical shapes of the molecules.

Extension of the conventional classical harmonic treatment of small vibrations to include angular degrees of freedom results in the following form of the kinetic energy T:

$$T = \tfrac{1}{2} \sum_{lk} \sum_{i=x,y,z} m_k \dot{u}_i^2(lk) + \tfrac{1}{2} \sum_{lk} \sum_{\alpha\beta} I_{\alpha\beta}(k)\, \dot{u}_\alpha(lk)\, \dot{u}_\beta(lk)\,. \tag{7}$$

As before, l designates the unit cell and k the site. The displacement $u_i(lk)$ is the ith component of the translational displacement of molecule (lk) with the summation over i extending over $i = x, y, z$. The first term in (7) obviously represents the kinetic energy of the center of mass motions as usual. The second term represents the kinetic energy of the solid due to the angular displacements $u_\alpha(lk)$. (Note that the Greek letters α, β designate angular displacement components while Latin letters i, j will be used for translational displacement components). $I_{\alpha\beta}(k)$ is the $\alpha\beta$-element of the moment of inertia tensor $\boldsymbol{I}$ of molecule of type k. In a space-fixed general coordinate system $\boldsymbol{I}(k)$ is not diagonal. However, for every molecular site k there exists a transformation $\boldsymbol{A}(k)$ which transforms the space-fixed coordinate frame into the local 'principal axes frame' for which $\boldsymbol{I}(k)$ is diagonal (Venkataraman and Sahni 1970), simplifying the second term of (7). In this principal axes frame we then obtain the kinetic energy of the system as shown in (7′) with superscripted symbols:

$$T = \tfrac{1}{2} \sum_{lk} \sum_{i} m_k [\dot{u}_i^{\mathrm{p}}(lk)]^2 + \tfrac{1}{2} \sum_{lk} \sum_{\alpha} I_\alpha^{\mathrm{p}}(k)\, [\dot{u}_\alpha^{\mathrm{p}}(lk)]^2\,. \tag{7′}$$

It can be shown (Venkataraman and Sahni 1970) that the $\boldsymbol{I}^{\mathrm{p}}$ and $\boldsymbol{I}$ are related as in eq. (8):

$$\boldsymbol{I}^{\mathrm{p}}(k) = \boldsymbol{A}(k)\, \boldsymbol{I}(k)\, \tilde{\boldsymbol{A}}(k)\,. \tag{8}$$

The potential energy is given by eq. (9):

$$\begin{aligned} \Phi = \Phi_0 + \tfrac{1}{2} \sum_{ll',kk'} \Bigg[& \sum_{ij} \Phi_{ij}(lk, l'k')\, u_i(lk)\, u_j(l'k') + \sum_{i\alpha} \Phi_{i\alpha}(lk, l'k') \\ & \times u_i(lk)\, u_\alpha(l'k') + \sum_{\alpha i} \Phi_{\alpha i}(lk, l'k')\, u_\alpha(lk)\, u_i(l'k') \\ & + \sum_{\alpha\beta} \Phi_{\alpha\beta}(lk, l'k')\, u_\alpha(lk)\, u_\beta(l'k') \Bigg]. \end{aligned} \tag{9}$$

The second term of eq. (9) contains the translational part of the potential (subscripts i, j) and the fifth or last term the librational part (subscripts

α, β). The third and fourth terms contain the translation–libration interactions. The potential energy can also be rewritten in terms of the displacement components in the principal axes frame and again the force constants $\phi^{\mathrm{P}}_{ij}(lk, l'k')$ can be related to the $\phi_{ij}(lk, l'k')$ by means of the transformation matrix $\boldsymbol{A}$, block by block [corresponding to the terms in eq. (9), Venkataraman and Sahni 1970]. This transformation of the force constant matrix as well as the analog for the moment of inertia tensor [eq. (8)] are valid and straightforward if the rotational displacement components u_α are infinitesimal rotations about the coordinate axes. For other choices, each case must be considered with care.

The equations of motion obtained in the classical lagrangian treatment are derived using (7) and (9) and they are given in eq. (10).

$$m_k \ddot{u}_i(lk) = -\sum_{l'k'} \left[\sum_j \Phi_{ij}(lk, l'k')\, u_j(l'k') + \sum_\beta \Phi_{i\beta}(lk, l'k')\, u_\beta(l'k') \right],$$

$$I_{\alpha\alpha}(k)\, \ddot{u}_\alpha(lk) = -\sum_{l'k'} \left[\sum_j \Phi_{\alpha j}(lk, l'k')\, u_j(l'k') + \sum_\beta \Phi_{\alpha\beta}(lk, l'k')\, u_\beta(l'k') \right] - \sum_{\beta \neq \alpha} I_{\alpha\beta}(k)\, \ddot{u}_\beta(lk). \tag{10}$$

As before, the subscripts i, j refer to translational and α, β to librational displacement components. We now assume the usual periodic solutions for $u_i(lk)$ or $u_\alpha(lk)$:

$$u_s(lk) = U_s(\boldsymbol{q}k) \exp\{\mathrm{i}[\boldsymbol{q}\cdot\boldsymbol{R}(lk) - \omega(\boldsymbol{q})\, t]\},$$

with s spanning all degrees of freedom, i.e. $s = i, j, \cdots, \alpha, \beta, \cdots$. The requirement of non-trivial solutions for the amplitudes U_s leads then to the secular equation from which the frequencies $\omega(\boldsymbol{q})$ are obtained:

$$|\boldsymbol{M}(\boldsymbol{q}) - \omega^2(\boldsymbol{q})\, \boldsymbol{m}| = 0, \tag{11}$$

where

$$M^{kk'}_{st}(\boldsymbol{q}) = \sum_{l'} \Phi_{st}(0k, l'k') \exp\{\mathrm{i}\boldsymbol{q}\cdot[\boldsymbol{R}(0k) - \boldsymbol{R}(l'k')]\}. \tag{12}$$

The elements of the matrix $\boldsymbol{M}(\boldsymbol{q})$ are designated by 4 indices, i.e. s, t designate the displacement components which may be translations or librations, and k, k' the molecular sites. The molecule at $(0k)$ is at a site k in a reference unit cell, designated by $l=0$. The matrix $\boldsymbol{m}$ is built up of 3×3 submatrices which are null matrices except those on the principal diagonal. There, two types appear, namely $\boldsymbol{m}_{ij}(kk) = \boldsymbol{m}_k \boldsymbol{e}$ with $\boldsymbol{e}$ being a 3×3 unit matrix and $\boldsymbol{m}_{\alpha\beta}(kk) = \boldsymbol{I}(k)$.

Generally speaking, the lattice dynamics of librational motions is far less developed and therefore less standardized than that for translational motions. The first full treatments are due to Cochran and Pawley (1964), and Pawley (1967). Treatments including librations for $\boldsymbol{q}=0$ only were, however, reported earlier, e.g. the matrix formulation due to Shimanouchi et al. (1961) and the treatment of solid CO_2 by Walmsley and Pople (1964). More recently, Schnepp and Ron (1969) have treated α-N_2 and Suzuki and Schnepp (1971) have carried out a full treatment of solid CO_2.

3.2. Libration as harmonic oscillator

The principal justification for using the methods of classical mechanics to calculate the excitation energies of an atomic solid is to be found in the basic result that the energy levels of a 3-dimensional harmonic oscillator in quantum mechanics can be derived from the classical oscillator frequencies. It is then simpler to use the lagrangian formulation to obtain these frequencies. The same situation does not obtain for angular oscillators.

The problem of an angular small displacement in one dimension (ϕ) with harmonic potential (in u_ϕ) can be solved quantum mechanically and the result is the same as for a one-dimensional linear harmonic oscillator. However, if two degrees of rotational freedom are allowed, (e.g. the spherical coordinates θ, ϕ) the corresponding Schrödinger equation has not been solved for a potential expansion to second order in the displacements, e.g. u_θ, u_ϕ. The difficulty is primarily caused by the lack of separability of the coordinates in the kinetic energy (laplacian). The quantum-mechanical problem has been solved for one cylindrically symmetric body (e.g. a linear molecule with degrees of freedom θ, ϕ) in a potential $v=K\sin^2\theta$ (Kohin 1960, Curl et al. 1968). This potential obviously reduces to being harmonic in one of the degrees of freedom, θ. The solutions are ellipsoidal polynominals and these, in turn, may best be expanded in associated Legendre polynomials or associated Laguerre polynomials for the low or high potential barrier limiting cases. These one-particle solutions are clearly not simple functions, but recently Raich (1972) has made use of them in a lattice dynamical calculation. Jacobi and Schnepp (1972) have also formulated a quantum-mechanical lattice dynamics theory for librations using a variational method. These treatments are most valuable since they alone permit an evaluation of the validity of the classical calculations.

Devonshire (1936) and later Sauer (1966) treated the quantum-mechanical problem of the angular motions of a linear molecule in an octahedral potential. Devonshire (1936) determined the energy levels in the limit of high potential barrier as given in eq. (13):

$$W \equiv E/B = -k + 2(n+1)(5k)^{1/2} - (\tfrac{3}{2}n^2 + 3n + \tfrac{11}{4}). \tag{13}$$

Here B is the rotational constant and W is therefore the energy in units of B. The dimensionless constant k is proportional to the potential well depth, also in the same units, and n is the quantum number. From (13) we obtain for the excitation energy ΔW from $n=0$ to $n=1$:

$$\Delta W = 2(5k)^{1/2} - \tfrac{9}{2}. \tag{14}$$

It can be concluded from the work of Devonshire (1936) and of Sauer (1966) that these limiting energy equations are valid for $k > 80$. We shall return to compare the excitation energy (14) to that obtained from a classical treatment involving a harmonic expansion of the Devonshire octahedral potential.

We now consider the classical treatment of the two-dimensional rigid rotor in spherical coordinates θ, ϕ, with the corresponding displacement coordinates u_θ, u_ϕ (Schnepp and Ron 1969). The kinetic energy is given by:

$$T = \tfrac{1}{2} \sum_{lk} (\dot{u}_\theta^2 + \sin^2\theta\, \dot{u}_\varphi^2). \tag{15}$$

The potential energy is assumed to be harmonic in the angular displacements and is written by analogy to eq. (9):

$$\Phi = \Phi_0 + \tfrac{1}{2}\Phi_{\theta\theta} u_\theta^2 + \tfrac{1}{2}\Phi_{\varphi\varphi} u_\varphi^2 + \Phi_{\theta\varphi} u_\theta u_\varphi. \tag{16}$$

On applying the lagrangian treatment it is found that the appearance of the variable coefficient $\sin^2\theta$ in T [eq. (15)] causes serious difficulty. It is usual to assume that the amplitude of the oscillation is small enough to justify expansion of $\sin^2\theta$ about the equilibrium position and retain only the lowest term, $\sin^2\theta_0$. This procedure amounts to a harmonic approximation for the kinetic energy. The accuracy of this approximation depends sensitively on the amplitude of the vibration since, in general, first order corrections occur. Estimates indicate that the root mean square librational amplitudes are of the order of 6° for solid CO_2 and N_2O and 18° for α-N_2 and α-CO (Cahill and Leroi 1969a, b, Goodings and Henkelman 1971). For solid naphthalene and anthracene the corresponding values are of the order of 1° (Suzuki et al. 1967). As a result, we expect first order corrections of the order of 10% for CO_2 and N_2O, 30% for α-N_2 and α-CO and 3% for naphthalene and anthracene. It is, therefore, not obvious that the infinitesimal displacement limit approximation is justified for at least the solids of the linear molecules considered here. On the other hand, if we retain the variable coefficient $\sin^2\theta$, the lagrangian problem becomes intractable.

Schnepp and Jacobi (1972) treated the Devonshire problem classically in the kinetic energy approximation described in the preceding paragraph with the potential expansion (16) applied to the octahedral Devonshire potential. They thus obtained the excitation energy as given below:

$$\Delta W = 2(5k)^{1/2}. \tag{17}$$

Comparison between eqs. (17) and (14) shows that the classical harmonic oscillator result does indeed approach the quantum-mechanical result in the limit of large k or high barrier (or low B). However, the value of k must be of the order of 1000 or greater for the additive term $\frac{9}{2}$ to be negligible. Schnepp and Jacobi (1972) showed that this condition is fulfilled for CO_2, N_2O, benzene, naphthalene, anthracene and the halogens (Cl_2, Br_2, I_2). On the other hand, values of k less than 50 are found for α-N_2, α-CO, acetylene, HCl and HBr. It may then be predicted from this discussion that the classical harmonic treatment will be good for the librations of the former group of molecular solids but its application to the latter group remains open to question. Again, a full quantum-mechanical lattice dynamics treatment is required to provide the answer. Such treatments will be presented in section 4.

The lattice dynamics treatments of molecular solids given in the literature mostly ignore the special problems associated with the librational motions and use the zero order classical treatment as described. The different treatments used, involving different choices of librational displacement coordinates will now be critically reviewed in subsection 3.3.

3.3. Classical treatments

3.3.1. Cartesian coordinate treatment

It is possible to formulate the lattice dynamics of a molecular solid by choosing the cartesian displacement coordinates of individual atoms as dynamical variables (Pawley 1967). In this case, all vibrational degrees of freedom of the system, both inter- and intra-molecular are included. It is then clearly necessary to include intramolecular as well as intermolecular interactions in the potential function Φ. For the intramolecular part, a force field derived from a molecular normal coordinate analysis is used with force constants determined by comparison with experimentally measured molecular frequencies. The intermolecular contribution to the potential is usually written as in eq. (1) with $v(lk, l'k')$ given by eq. (5).

As already pointed out, the interactions between atoms of the same molecule are much stronger than those between atoms on different molecules and as a result the frequency separation permits easy recognition of external or lattice modes. Here, librational and translational motions are not explicitly distinguished and their characterization is contingent on an analysis of the eigenvectors. The method has the advantage that interactions between internal and external motions can be included and their effect on the lattice vibrational frequencies can be studied quantitatively. This is found to be small (Taddei et al. 1972).

It is of interest to discuss one particular aspect of a lattice dynamics calculation based on a potential as given by eq. (5). It is easily seen that the displacements $r_{\kappa\kappa'}$ in the interatomic distances $R_{\kappa\kappa'}$ have non-linear dependence on the cartesian displacement coordinates of the atoms x_κ; furthermore, the $r_{\kappa\kappa'}$ are not independent displacement coordinates and they are, in fact, highly redundant. Therefore $\partial\Phi/\partial r_{\kappa\kappa'}$ evaluated at the equilibrium position does not vanish for all $\kappa\kappa'$. On the other hand, the atomic cartesian displacement coordinates $x_{\kappa i}$ (component i) are independent dynamical variables. In the cartesian coordinate treatment, the potential Φ is expanded to second order in the $x_{\kappa i}$ as in eq. (9) with the $x_{\kappa i}(lk)$ taking the place of the $u_i(lk)$ and only translational components appear ($i=x, y, z$). The force constants or second order coefficients $\Phi^{\mathrm{c}}_{ij}(\kappa\kappa')$ in this expansion are given by eq. (18), the superscript c denoting the cartesian displacement basis:

$$\Phi^{\mathrm{c}}_{ij}(\kappa\kappa') = (\partial^2\Phi/\partial x_{\kappa i}\partial x_{\kappa' j})_0$$

$$= \sum_{\mu\nu}\left(\frac{\partial^2\Phi}{\partial r_{\kappa\mu}\partial r_{\kappa'\nu}}\right)_0 \frac{\partial r_{\kappa\mu}}{\partial x_{\kappa i}}\frac{\partial r_{\kappa'\nu}}{\partial x_{\kappa' j}} + \sum_{\mu}\left(\frac{\partial\Phi}{\partial r_{\kappa\mu}}\right)_0 \frac{\partial^2 r_{\kappa\mu}}{\partial x_{\kappa i}\partial x_{\kappa' j}}. \tag{18}$$

The second term on the right-hand side of eq. (18) is often, but not always small. We shall return to discuss its importance below when we describe the 'matrix method' in which this term is neglected.

3.3.2. *Matrix treatment*

Shimanouchi et al. (1961) formulated the matrix treatment of lattice dynamics of molecular solids. This treatment is analogous to the *F–G* matrix method for the normal coordinate problem of molecular vibrations (Wilson et al. 1955). Harada and Shimanouchi (1966, 1967) applied the treatment to the $\boldsymbol{q}=0$ lattice motions of solid benzene and since then it has been used by several others authors (e.g. Bernstein 1970).

The secular equation takes here the form

$$|\boldsymbol{G}\boldsymbol{\Phi} - \boldsymbol{E}\lambda| = 0, \tag{19}$$

where $\boldsymbol{\Phi}$ is the potential energy or force constant matrix and $\boldsymbol{G}$ is the inverse of the kinetic energy matrix in the chosen displacement coordinates. $\boldsymbol{E}$ is the unit matrix of appropriate dimension, and $\lambda=4\pi^2c^2\nu^2$. For a periodic solid, the matrices $\boldsymbol{\Phi}$ and $\boldsymbol{G}$ can be transformed into semidiagonal form by making use of the translational symmetry. It is advantageous to use the cartesian displacements of the *atoms* as basis since $\boldsymbol{G}$ is then diagonal. The potential function is as given in eq. (5). We shall here briefly sketch the procedure and discuss the approximations intrinsic to the method. We refer the reader for the details of the calculation to the references cited.

The potential is written in terms of 'internal' coordinates or, explicitly atom–atom distances [see eq. (5)]. All these distances (including now those between atoms in the same molecule as well as those in different molecules) form a column vector $\boldsymbol{R}$. The harmonic force constant matrix in the corresponding displacements $\boldsymbol{r}$ is $\boldsymbol{\Phi}^{\mathrm{i}}$. Since it is desirable to use cartesian displacements as noted above, it is necessary to transform to this basis in which we designate the potential energy matrix $\boldsymbol{\Phi}^{\mathrm{c}}$ with corresponding column vector $\boldsymbol{x}$. We then obtain

$$\boldsymbol{\Phi} = \tfrac{1}{2}\boldsymbol{r}^{\dagger}\boldsymbol{\Phi}^{\mathrm{i}}\boldsymbol{r} = \tfrac{1}{2}\boldsymbol{x}^{\dagger}\boldsymbol{\Phi}^{\mathrm{c}}\boldsymbol{x}. \tag{20}$$

We then seek the transformation

$$\boldsymbol{r} = \boldsymbol{B}\boldsymbol{x} \tag{21}$$

to satisfy (20) and immediately obtain

$$\boldsymbol{\Phi}^{\mathrm{c}} = \boldsymbol{B}^{\dagger}\boldsymbol{\Phi}^{\mathrm{i}}\boldsymbol{B}. \tag{22}$$

In other words, we require a *linear* transformation $\boldsymbol{B}$ between the internal displacement coordinates $\boldsymbol{r}$ (usually atom–atom distance changes) and the atomic cartesian displacement coordinates $\boldsymbol{x}$. However, the exact relation between these coordinates is non-linear and an approximation must be made to satisfy (21) and to obtain $\boldsymbol{B}$. Shimanouchi et al. (1961) expanded the change in distance between atoms κ and κ', $r_{\kappa\kappa'}$ from its equilibrium value $R^0_{\kappa\kappa'}$ to first order only in the cartesian displacements of the atoms as given in (23).

$$r_{\kappa\kappa'} = R_{\kappa\kappa'} - R^0_{\kappa\kappa'} \cong (1/R^0_{\kappa\kappa'})\,[X^0_{\kappa\kappa'}(x_{\kappa'} - x_\kappa) + Y^0_{\kappa\kappa'}(y_{\kappa'} - y_\kappa) + Z^0_{\kappa\kappa'}(z_{\kappa'} - z_\kappa)]. \quad (23)$$

Here, $X^0_{\kappa\kappa'}$, $Y^0_{\kappa\kappa}$, $Z^0_{\kappa\kappa'}$ are the components of the interatomic equilibrium vector $\boldsymbol{R}^0_{\kappa\kappa'}$ and x_κ, y_κ, z_κ are the cartesian displacements of atom κ. Eq. (23) defines the linear transformation matrix $\boldsymbol{B}$ of (21) and (22).

In order to examine the approximation inherent in the assumption of linearity of the transformation between $\boldsymbol{r}$ and $\boldsymbol{x}$, we refer to eq. (18) where the exact $\Phi_{ij}(\kappa\kappa')$ element of $\boldsymbol{\Phi}^c$ is given. We then find that we can rewrite the first term on the right-hand side of (18) to conform with eq. (22), but the second term is not contained in (22). Thus we obtain

$$\Phi^c_{ij}(\kappa\kappa') = \sum_{\mu\nu} B^\dagger_{i\kappa\mu}\Phi^i_{\mu\nu}(\kappa\kappa')\,B_{j\nu\kappa'} + \sum_\mu \left(\frac{\partial\Phi}{\partial r_{\kappa\mu}}\right)_0 \frac{\partial^2 r_{\kappa\mu}}{\partial x_{\kappa i}\partial x_{\kappa' j}}. \quad (24)$$

The second term of (22) and of (24) vanishes only in the approximation of linear dependence of $\boldsymbol{r}$ on $\boldsymbol{x}$ [eq. (21)].

The magnitude of the second term in (24) relative to the first term is then decisive for the accuracy of the matrix formulation. Investigations have shown that this term contributes to the $\boldsymbol{q}=0$ or optic frequencies to varying degrees. For solid CO_2 it was found (Suzuki and Schnepp 1971) that the translational modes are changed by a few percent (mostly of the order of 1%). However, the librational modes are more sensitive and are affected by between 3% and 8%. For α-N_2 the error introduced by neglecting the second term is less than 2% for the translational modes but ranges from 25% to 44% for the librations. This large error is consistent with the considerable amplitudes of the librational modes of α-N_2 (Cahill and Leroi 1969a, b). In the case of benzene, a recent study has shown that the error is always less than 5% (Taddei et al. 1972).

It should be noted that in most matrix method treatments for the lattice dynamics of molecular solids, the parameters of the potential model are adjusted to fit experimental observables (frequencies, lattice energy). In such cases, the error introduced by the above approximation is, for all practical purposes, eliminated. The error may be of importance in cases where the same potential model is carried over from an interpretation of one class of physical properties to another, e.g. lattice dynamics and gas phase virial coefficients. It is also clear from the above discussion that the error will be great in every case involving low-frequency and large-amplitude librations (as in α-N_2). The reason for the small effect of the first derivative term in many cases is as follows. Both repulsive and attractive terms of the potential usually contribute significantly to the first derivative but these contributions have opposite signs and tend to offset each other. By comparison, for the second derivative the repulsive term contribution tends to dominate (Shimanouchi 1970).

Piseri and Zerbi (1968) extended the matrix method to include treatments for the entire Brillouin zone. They use translationally symmetrized displacement coordinates and consequently the transformation matrix $\boldsymbol{B}$ is also $\boldsymbol{q}$ dependent or

$$\boldsymbol{B}(\boldsymbol{q}k) = N^{-1/2} \sum_{l} \boldsymbol{B}(lk) \exp\{\mathrm{i}[\boldsymbol{q} \cdot \boldsymbol{R}(lk)]\}. \tag{25}$$

The secular equation is then of the usual form (eq. 19) except that $\boldsymbol{\Phi}^{\mathrm{i}}$ and $\boldsymbol{\Phi}^{\mathrm{c}}$ are $\boldsymbol{q}$-dependent.

3.3.3. Infinitesimal rotation coordinates

We shall now discuss methods aimed at the investigation of the librational motions of the molecule (assumed rigid) directly and explicitly. Displacement coordinates are chosen describing the librational degrees of freedom while keeping the center of mass of the molecule fixed. The normal coordinates will, however, in the general case be combinations of translational and librational displacements, since the potential expansion (9) contains such interaction terms. Only in solids which have centers of symmetry can translations be separated from librations at some special points in the Brillouin zone. Carbon dioxide, benzene and anthracene are examples of such structures.

We shall here discuss the treatment of the librational modes only in terms of a number of different choices of displacement coordinates, assuming separability from motions of the center of mass (translational modes). However, these treatments can always be expanded by including the translational displacements in the basis. Also, translation–libration interaction matrix elements must in general be calculated before the secular equation for the entire problem can be solved. These interaction terms will be discussed in sub-section 3.3.7.

The librational part of the kinetic energy of a molecular solid in terms of the infinitesimal rotation coordinates is given by the second term of eq. (7). The displacement coordinates are infinitesimal rotations about the x,y,z-coordinate axes. Such a basis has been used by several authors

(Cochran and Pawley 1964, Pawley 1967). As has been pointed out by Oliver and Walmsley (1968), the u_α are independent to first order only, and the kinetic energy ,as given by (7) is an approximation, similar to our discussion following (15). We shall here discuss the use of these coordinates in some detail only as applied to a linear molecule as an illustration of the pitfalls encountered in practice. Such a molecule has only two rotational degrees of freedom.

Consider a rotation by an angle α about the space-fixed x-axis followed by a rotation by β about the y-axis. A point in space can then be defined by r, α, β and the transformation to cartesian coordinates is given by

$$\begin{aligned} x &= r \cos\alpha \sin\beta\,, \\ y &= -r \sin\alpha\,, \\ z &= r \cos\alpha \cos\beta\,, \end{aligned} \tag{26}$$

and the square of the infinitesimal displacement is given by

$$\mathrm{d}s^2 = r^2\,\mathrm{d}u_\alpha^2 + r^2 \cos^2\alpha\,\mathrm{d}u_\beta^2 \tag{27}$$

resulting in the librational part of the kinetic energy expression for a solid:

$$T = \tfrac{1}{2} I \sum_{lk} [\dot{u}_\alpha^2(lk) + \cos^2\alpha(lk)\,\dot{u}_\beta^2(lk)]\,.$$

As before [eq. (15)] it is usual to expand the non-constant coefficient $\cos^2\alpha(lk)$ about the equilibrium value of α which is $\alpha = 0°$ in the 'principal axes' frame [(7′) et seq.]. Then we obtain, in fact, the form of the second term in (7′). Again, we have introduced the harmonic approximation into the kinetic energy which limits the treatment to small displacements, as does the corresponding approximation always used for the potential energy.

When using a potential $\Phi(R_{\kappa\kappa'})$ which is a function of atom–atom distances as in (5), the changes in these distances, $r_{\kappa\kappa'}$ have nonlinear dependence on the u_α as seen from the fact that the cartesian components have such nonlinear dependence [see (26)]. When developing Φ to second order in the u_α, proper care must be taken to include terms containing first derivatives of Φ with respect to the $R_{\kappa\kappa'}$ and second derivatives of the $r_{\kappa\kappa'}$ with respect to the u_α (Schnepp and Jacobi 1972, eqs. 2.66, 2.67). Cochran and Pawley (1964) and Pawley (1967) calculated the first derivatives of the potential analytically and the second derivative of Φ with respect to the u_α numerically, thus ensuring accuracy of their treatment.

3.3.4. *Direction cosine displacement coordinates*

Walmsley and Pople (1964) treated the lattice dynamics of solid CO_2 for

$\boldsymbol{q}=0$ only. In this problem, the librational motions are separable from the translations for a centro-symmetric solid (Pa3–T_h^6). These authors chose as librational displacement coordinates the changes in the direction cosines of the molecular axes in the crystal or space-fixed coordinate frame. If $\Lambda_j(lk)$ is the direction cosine for the symmetry axis of molecule (lk) (at site k in unit cell l) with respect to coordinate axis j (x, y, or z), then we call $\lambda_j(lk)$ the change of the direction cosine:

$$\Lambda_j(lk) = \Lambda_j^0(lk) + \lambda_j(lk), \quad j = x, y, z. \tag{28}$$

In the above equation the superscript 0 designates the equilibrium orientation. We note that CO_2 is a linear molecule which has only two degrees of rotational freedom, whereas three displacement coordinates have been used (λ_x, λ_y, λ_z). Thus we have introduced a redundancy. The redundancy constraint conditions are obtained from the requirement that the sum of the squares of the direction cosines must be unity both before and after displacement:

$$\sum_j [\Lambda_j^0(lk)]^2 = \sum_j [\Lambda_j^0(lk) + \lambda_j(lk)]^2 = 1. \tag{29}$$

Eq. (29) immediately yields the condition

$$\sum_j [2\Lambda_j^0(lk)\,\lambda_j(lk) + \lambda_j^2(lk)] = 0. \tag{30}$$

The displacement coordinates are symmetrized with respect to translation giving

$$\lambda_j(\boldsymbol{q}k) = N^{-1/2} \sum_l \lambda_j(lk) \exp\{\mathrm{i}[\boldsymbol{q}\cdot\boldsymbol{R}(lk)]\}. \tag{31}$$

Using the inverse of this transformation (31) in (30) and setting all $\lambda_j(\boldsymbol{q}k)$ to zero except those for $\boldsymbol{q}=0$ we obtain the redundancy conditions for the $\lambda_j(\boldsymbol{0}k)$ as in (32) remembering that $\Lambda_j^0(k)$ is independent of l:

$$\sum_j [2\Lambda_j^0(k)\,\lambda_j(\boldsymbol{0}k) + N^{-1/2}\lambda_j^2(\boldsymbol{0}k)] = 0. \tag{32}$$

For the particular example of solid CO_2 the molecular axes of the four sublattices are oriented parallel to the four body diagonals of the cube and the equilibrium direction cosines are as follows:

$$\begin{array}{llll} k=1 & \Lambda_x^0 = 1/\sqrt{3} & \Lambda_y^0 = 1/\sqrt{3} & \Lambda_z^0 = 1/\sqrt{3}, \\ k=2 & \Lambda_x^0 = 1/\sqrt{3} & \Lambda_y^0 = -1/\sqrt{3} & \Lambda_z^0 = -1/\sqrt{3}, \\ k=3 & \Lambda_x^0 = -1/\sqrt{3} & \Lambda_y^0 = 1/\sqrt{3} & \Lambda_z^0 = -1/\sqrt{3}, \\ k=4 & \Lambda_x^0 = -1/\sqrt{3} & \Lambda_y^0 = -1/\sqrt{3} & \Lambda_z^0 = 1/\sqrt{3}. \end{array} \tag{33}$$

Using the values of (33) in (32) we obtain the redundancy conditions for $\boldsymbol{q}=0$ using $l_1=\lambda_x(\mathbf{01})$, $m_1=\lambda_y(\mathbf{01})$, $n_1=\lambda_z(\mathbf{01})$, etc.

$$\begin{aligned}
&\tfrac{2}{3}\sqrt{3}\quad(l_1+m_1+n_1)+N^{-1/2}(l_1^2+m_1^2+n_1^2)=0\,,\\
&\tfrac{2}{3}\sqrt{3}\quad(l_2-m_2-n_2)+N^{-1/2}(l_2^2+m_2^2+n_2^2)=0\,,\\
&\tfrac{2}{3}\sqrt{3}(-l_3+m_3-n_3)+N^{-1/2}(l_3^2+m_3^2+n_3^2)=0\,,\\
&\tfrac{2}{3}\sqrt{3}(-l_4-m_4+n_4)+N^{-1/2}(l_4^2+m_4^2+n_4^2)=0\,.
\end{aligned}\tag{34}$$

Clearly, the redundant coordinates are $(l_1+m_1+n_1)$, $(l_2-m_2-n_2)$, $(-l_3+m_3-n_3)$, $(-l_4-m_4+n_4)$ which vanish to first order in the displacements. Since each molecule has one redundancy, and there are 4 sites in the unit cell, we obtain 4 redundancy conditions for $\boldsymbol{q}=0$.

The use of redundant coordinates requires extensive modification of the lattice dynamical calculation. It is, however, often worth the additional complication if their use facilitates the calculation. At points of high symmetry in the Brillouin zone, it is often useful to construct symmetry coordinates which belong to irreducible representations of the applicable group. This is done by using the Wigner projection operator (Wigner 1931) and for this purpose it is necessary to understand in full the results of the application of all symmetry operations to the displacement coordinates chosen. This is relatively simple for the direction cosine displacement coordinates and therein lies their principal advantage. These coordinates transform like axial vectors.

A procedure which takes into account the existence of redundancy in the basis set has been described by Wilson et al. (1955, pp. 171–3) for molecular vibration problems. Walmsley and Pople (1964) and Oliver and Walmsley (1968) have applied such a procedure to the lattice dynamics problem. We shall not describe the treatment further and refer the interested reader to the above references.

A different method for handling the redundancy encountered in the treatment of the librations of a linear molecule when using direction cosine displacement coordinates has been described by Coll et al. (1970). These authors use a local or principal system of coordinates such that the molecular axis is oriented at equilibrium parallel to the z-axis. Thus $\Lambda_x^0=0$, $\Lambda_y^0=0$, $\Lambda_z^0=1$, and $\Lambda_x=\lambda_x$, $\Lambda_y=\lambda_y$, $\Lambda=1+\lambda_z$. They then note the condition

$$\Lambda_x^2+\Lambda_y^2+\Lambda_z^2=1$$

and since small oscillations are assumed, and therefore Λ_x and Λ_y will be small, Λ_z can be expanded and written as follows:

$$\Lambda_z \cong 1 - \tfrac{1}{2}\Lambda_x^2 - \tfrac{1}{2}\Lambda_y^2 . \tag{35}$$

The angle-dependent part of the potential was assumed to be the quadrupole–quadrupole term of (4) and this was expanded to second order in the Λ_j's. Then, using (35) Λ_z was eliminated. The kinetic energy was also written by making use of (35) in the form

$$T = \tfrac{1}{2}I \sum_{lk} [\dot{\lambda}_x^2(lk) + \dot{\lambda}_y^2(lk)] .$$

As a result, the redundancy is completely eliminated at the start and λ_z is effectively set to zero which is the result of (35) since $\Lambda_z = 1$ or constant to first order in small displacements. Coll et al. (1970) did not carry out any full calculation using the method proposed by them.

3.3.5. Spherical displacement coordinates

Schnepp and Ron (1969) and Kuan et al. (1970) treated the lattice dynamics of solid α-N_2 using the usual spherical coordinates, θ, ϕ to describe the orientations of the molecular axes in a space-fixed crystal coordinate frame. The librational displacement coordinates were then the displacements in these angles. Suzuki and Schnepp (1971) applied a similar calculation to solid CO_2. The one-particle librational kinetic energy in these coordinates has already been discussed [eq. (15)]. The usual approximation was made and $\sin^2\theta(lk)$ was replaced by the equilibrium value $\sin^2\theta_0(lk)$. The potential was again of the form (1) with the pair potential $v(lk, l'k')$ a sum of atom–atom terms, each a function of the distance between the atoms $R_{\kappa\kappa'}$, with atoms κ, κ' on different molecules (lk and $l'k'$). The x-component $X_{\kappa\kappa'}$ of $R_{\kappa\kappa'}$ is given by

$$X_{\kappa\kappa'}(lk, l'k') = \tfrac{1}{2}a + u_x(lk) - u_x(l'k') + H \sin\theta(lk) \cos\varphi(lk) \\ - H \sin\theta(lk) \cos\varphi(l'k') . \tag{36}$$

In the crystal structure treated here (Pa3–T_h^6) the molecular centers of mass occupy face-centered cubic sites and the cubic cell parameter is a. The u_x are the translational displacements of the molecule as a rigid body. The half distance between atoms is designated H (fig. 1). This distance is used as one of the parameters of the intermolecular potential model and then $2H$ becomes the distance between the two 'centers of interaction' of the molecule. It is obvious from (36) that $X_{\kappa\kappa'}(lk, l'k')$ has non-linear dependence on θ, ϕ and therefore second derivatives of $X_{\kappa\kappa'}$ with respect to u_θ, u_ϕ do not vanish ($\theta = \theta_0 + u_\theta$, etc.).

The equations of motion are here

$$I\ddot{u}_\theta(lk) = -\sum_{l'k'}\left[\sum_\alpha \Phi_{\theta\alpha}(lk,l'k')\,u_\alpha(l'k') + \sum_j \Phi_{\theta j}(lk,l'k')\,u_j(l'k')\right],$$

$$I\sin^2\theta_0(lk)\,\ddot{u}_\varphi(lk) = -\sum_{l'k'}\left[\sum_\alpha \Phi_{\varphi\alpha}(lk,l'k')\,u_\alpha(l'k') + \sum_j \Phi_{\varphi j}(lk,l'k')\,u_j(l'k')\right]. \qquad (37)$$

As before, the index α runs over the librational degrees of freedom (here θ, ϕ) and $j = x, y, z$. These equations are analogous to (10). In (37) the factor $\sin^2\theta_0(lk)$ appears in the ϕ-equation and therefore will persist in the appropriate rows of the secular determinant, which loses its symmetric structure. This difficulty can be overcome by defining a new displacement coordinate u_ω:

$$u_\omega = u_\varphi \sin\theta_0 .$$

Alternatively, the secular determinant can be transformed by multiplying appropriate rows and dividing appropriate columns by $\sin\theta_0$.

As has already been pointed out, the understanding of the behavior of the displacement coordinates under symmetry operations is of great importance when symmetry coordinates are to be constructed. Schnepp and Ron (1969) therefore investigated the transformation properties of u_θ, u_ω under the operations of T_h^6. These transformations were found to be non-linear, but for the construction of symmetry coordinates the transformations to first order are sufficient. This is so since the symmetry coordinates must be valid for arbitrarily small displacements. These transformation properties of u_θ and u_ϕ have been summarized in table 2 of Schnepp and Ron (1969).

3.3.6. *Extended point mass model*

Rafizadeh and Yip (1970) have proposed a new formalism for the inclusion of librations in their lattice dynamical treatment of solid hexamethylene-tetramine (often abbreviated to hexamine). The potential is assumed to be a function of the 'net' molecular displacements $\boldsymbol{\Delta}(lk)$ only. The ith cartesian component of net displacement includes translational and librational motions and is defined as the sum of the center-of-mass translational displacement component $u_i(lk)$ and the displacement component due to an angular displacement $\boldsymbol{\theta} \times \boldsymbol{R}$. The molecule is labeled by (lk) as before. The defining relation for $\boldsymbol{\Delta}(lk)$ is given in (38):

$$\Delta_i(lk) = u_i(lk) + [\boldsymbol{\theta}(lk) \times \boldsymbol{R}(lk)]_i . \qquad (38)$$

The vector $\boldsymbol{R}(lk)$ is a characteristic feature of the model and its components are parameters of the potential model. It can be thought of as defining the 'effective size' of the molecule since it determines the position of a point mass relative to the molecular center of mass. The translational displacement $\boldsymbol{u}(lk)$ and the angular displacement $\boldsymbol{\theta}(lk)$ together produce then the net displacement $\boldsymbol{\Delta}(lk)$.

The potential is expanded to second order in terms of the $\Delta_i(lk)$ and it is then possible to express all force constants (translational, librational and interaction) in terms of the translational force constants and the components of the vectors $\boldsymbol{R}(lk)$, $\boldsymbol{R}(l'k')$. The total of 12 independent parameters compares with 21 independent force constants which appear in a 6×6 hermitian matrix. In actual fact, symmetry usually serves to reduce this number further in all models.

It appears that the extended point-mass treatment is useful inasmuch as it requires relations between the force constants and thereby the total number of parameters is reduced. All this assumes that the force constants are all independent parameters (except for symmetry relations). If, on the other hand, a pair potential function is specified and this contains a limited number of parameters only, and then all force constants can be derived from this function, then the number of independent parameters is only as the number of parameters of the potential function. In such a case, it is not yet clear if the treatment has advantages. It is evident, that this model does not emphasize the shape of the molecule. In the case of hexamine, which is close to being spherical, the shape is probably not a factor, but this may not always be the case. Also, the treatment is not immediately applicable to a solid of linear molecules since the resulting redundancy would have to be carefully considered.

3.3.7. Translation–libration interactions and solution of the lattice dynamics problem

In all lattice dynamics treatments which involve librational degrees of freedom as discussed in the preceding sections, interactions between these coordinates and translations must in general be considered. It has already been pointed out that interaction matrix elements only vanish at the zone center and at some special points on the zone boundary for centrosymmetric crystals. The first calculation of dispersion curves for a molecular solid throughout the Brillouin zone was carried out by Cochran and Pawley (1964) for hexamethylenetetramine (hexamine) and these authors discussed the properties of the interaction matrix elements. We designate an interaction force constant by $\phi_{j\alpha}$ where j refers to a translational displacement component and α to a libration. The corresponding dynamical matrix element $M_{j\alpha}^{\kappa\kappa'}$ is defined in eq. (12) in terms of the $\Phi_{j\alpha}(0k, l'k')$. In general, the elements are complex and the matrix is hermitian.

If the crystal has centro-symmetric structure, some simplification results. Referring to eq. (12) we assume that the reference molecule $(0k)$ is now located at a center of inversion for the whole solid and we consider the interaction between this molecule and two other molecules $(l'k')$, $(l''k')$ which are related by the operation of inversion. Then clearly,

$$\boldsymbol{R}(0k; l'k') = -\boldsymbol{R}(0k; l''k').$$

Considering a translation–translation matrix element $M_{ij}^{\kappa\kappa'}$, we note that translational displacements u_i are antisymmetric to inversion. As a result we have

$$\Phi_{ij}(0k; l'k') = \Phi_{ij}(0k; l''k'),$$

and the sum of these two terms in the summation over l' gives

$$2\Phi_{ij}(0k; l'k') \cos[\boldsymbol{q} \cdot \boldsymbol{R}(0k; l'k')].$$

Since there exists a partner related by the center of inversion for every molecule, we conclude that this part of the dynamic matrix is real.

Next, we consider libration–libration elements $\Phi_{\alpha\beta}^{\kappa\kappa'}$. We note that librational displacements u_α are symmetric with respect to inversion and we reach again the same conclusion as before, i.e. also this part of the dynamical matrix is real. However, we find that

$$\Phi_{j\alpha}(0k; l'k') = -\Phi_{j\alpha}(0k; l''k')$$

and therefore the sum of the corresponding two terms in (17.12) gives

$$2\mathrm{i}\Phi_{j\alpha}(0k; l'k') \sin[\boldsymbol{q} \cdot \boldsymbol{R}(0k; l'k')]$$

and the $M_{j\alpha}^{\kappa\kappa'}$ are all pure imaginary. It is also found that the following relations hold for the dynamical matrix elements

$$\begin{aligned} M_{ij}(\boldsymbol{q}kk') &= M_{ji}(\boldsymbol{q}k'k), \\ M_{\alpha\beta}(\boldsymbol{q}kk') &= M_{\beta\alpha}(\boldsymbol{q}k'k), \\ M_{j\alpha}(\boldsymbol{q}kk') &= -M_{\alpha j}(\boldsymbol{q}k'k), \end{aligned}$$

and the matrix is hermitian as expected and its roots are all real.

The dynamical matrix consists then of two square blocks – translation–translation and libration–libration – whose elements are all real. In addition, the two off-diagonal blocks – translation–libration interactions – are generally rectangular and their elements are purely imaginary. Such a matrix can be transformed into a real matrix of the same dimension (Cochran and Pawley 1964) by a transformation of coordinates which leaves all translational coordinates unchanged and transforms all librational coordinates $u_\alpha(lk)$ as follows:

$$\mathrm{i}u_\alpha(lk) = u_\xi(lk).$$

Solution of the resulting matrix gives real eigenvectors in terms of the u_j, u_ξ and resubstitution in terms of u_j, u_α results in complex eigenvectors such that the librational part is multiplied by i. The physical significance of this form is to be found in that the librational motions are out of phase with the translational motions by $\frac{1}{2}\pi$.

The symmetry of the crystal structure requires relations between matrix elements. Such symmetry relations have been discussed extensively by Cochran and Pawley (1964) for the case of hexamine, (Im3m–O_h^9 or body centered cubic structure), by Pawley (1967) for the naphthalene and anthracene structure ($P2_1/c$–C_{2h}^5) and by Schnepp and Ron (1969) for the α-N_2 and CO_2 structure (Pa3–T_h^6).

3.4. Applications and comparison with experiment

3.4.1. Solid α-nitrogen

Table 1 summarizes all available information concerning the $\boldsymbol{q}=0$ modes of α-N_2. Translational and librational modes are separable in this case since the solid may be assumed to be centro-symmetric (Pa3–T_h^6), although the exact structure has been reported to be somewhat distorted (Jordan 1964). However, all spectroscopic observations are compatible with the existence of a center of symmetry (Schnepp and Ron 1969).

The two infrared active translational mode frequencies were first reported by Anderson and Leroi (1966) and by Ron and Schnepp (1967). Both these groups studied solid films prepared by condensation of vapor on a cold window. Subsequently, St. Louis and Schnepp (1969) measured the far infrared absorption of solid samples prepared by cooling the liquid in a closed cell. The frequencies were not affected by the method of sample preparation but the lines were narrower when the solid was formed under

TABLE 1

Lattice vibrational frequencies and intensity ratios for α-N_2. (Frequencies are in units of cm^{-1} with half-intensity widths in parentheses). Translational modes [Calculated values are listed for two potential models: (I) Lennard–Jones potential plus quadrupole–quadrupole term (Ron and Schnepp 1967). Nearest neighbor interaction only; (II) Diatomic potential (Kuan et al. 1970) with 6–12 terms].

Lattice mode	Experimental	Calculated I	Calculated II
A_u	Inactive		47.5
E_u	Inactive		54.9
$T_u(Q_2)$	48.8(0.3)[a–c]	48	51.3
$T_u(Q_1)$	70 (6)[a–c]	71	75.7
Infrared intensity ratio $I(Q_1)/I(Q_2)$	1.0 ± 0.2[b]	2.3	1.1

Librational modes [Calculated values are listed for the quadrupole–quadrupole potential with two values for the molecular quadrupole moment (Anderson et al. 1970). Column I: Molecular quadrupole moment $\Theta = 1.26 \times 10^{-26}$ esu, 4 neighbor shells. Column II: $\Theta = 1.52 \times 10^{-26}$ esu or best gas phase value (Stogryn and Stogryn 1966)].

Lattice mode	Experimental	Calculated I	Calculated II
E_g	32(1.5)[d–g]	29.0	35.0
$T_g(Q_2)$	36.5(1.5)[d–g]	37.4	45.1
$T_g(Q_1)$	60(4)[f–g]	61.5	74.3
Raman intensity ratios			
$I(E_g):I(T_g, Q_2):I(T_g, Q_1)$	3.6:1.0:0[d–e]		
	2.8:1.0:0.1[f]	2.8:1.0:0.12	
	3.5:1.0:0.05[g]		

a. Anderson and Leroi (1966)
b. St. Louis and Schnepp (1969)
c. Ron and Schnepp (1967)
d. Cahill and Leroi (1969a)
e. Brith et al (1969)
f. Anderson et al. (1970)
g. Mathai and Allin (1971)

equilibrium conditions. In particular, the lower frequency line was found to be remarkably sharp (half-intensity width 0.3 cm^{-1} or less). The frequencies of these translational modes could be satisfactorily accounted for by a classical harmonic calculation (Ron and Schnepp 1967) using an intermolecular Lennard–Jones term with gas phase parameters and a quadrupole–quadrupole angle dependent term. Such a potential was used by Walmsley and Pople (1964) for solid carbon dioxide. The Lennard–Jones term is mostly decisive for the translational modes, the quadrupole–quadrupole term contributing only of the order of 10%. Another potential model ('diatomic potential') consisting essentially of atom–atom interactions was found to be equally successful (Kuan et al. 1970). It is therefore concluded that the frequencies of the translational modes of symmetry T_u are not very sensitive to the potential model.

The Raman spectrum of α-N_2 was first reported by Cahill and Leroi (1969a, b) and by Brith et al. (1969). Both these groups observed only two lines (at 31.5 cm^{-1} and at 35.8 cm^{-1}) as compared to group-theoretical prediction of three Raman active modes (E_g+2T_g). Subsequently, Anderson et al. (1970) reinvestigated the Raman spectrum and observed a very weak third line at 60 cm^{-1} of half intensity width 4 cm^{-1}. The intensity ratio as reported here between the 32 cm^{-1} and 36 cm^{-1} lines was 2.8 as compared to 3.6 for the earlier investigations. These authors prepared their solid sample by condensation from the vapor on a cold metal surface. Mathai and Allin (1971) confirmed the above observations using a sample obtained by freezing liquid. Here the observed intensity ratio (for the 32 cm^{-1} and 36 cm^{-1} lines) was, however, 3.5, or close to the value previously reported for the same sample preparation.

Anderson and coworkers (1970) assigned the new line at 60 cm^{-1} as the second T_g mode. They then found that they could account very well for the librational frequency pattern on the basis of a classical harmonic calculation with a quadrupole–quadrupole potential. However, the gas phase value of the molecular quadrupole moment gave frequencies which were too high by about 20%. As a result, the molecular quadrupole moment was adjusted to fit the experimental frequencies. In this way, a value of $\theta = 1.23\times10^{-26}$ esu or $\theta=1.26\times10^{-26}$ esu was found, depending on the extent of the lattice sum. These values compare to the accepted gas phase value of 1.52×10^{-26} esu. Anderson and coworkers also showed that the intensity ratios of the three fundamental Raman lines as observed by them agreed well with those calculated using the theory of Brith et al. (1969) and the librational eigenvectors given by Walmsley and Pople (1964); these eigenvectors are characteristic of the quadrupole–quadrupole potential but they are independent of the value of the quadrupole moment.

The fact that the molecular quadrupole moment had to be adjusted to fit the experimental frequencies requires the conclusion that the quadrupole–quadrupole term does not completely reproduce the anisotropic part of the intermolecular potential. However, the frequency pattern does provide evidence that this potential contains relevant information. It also must be remembered that the results of the classical harmonic lattice dynamics cannot be accepted without reservation for the librations of α-N_2, as discussed in subsection 3.2. This subject will be further discussed in section 4 dealing with quantum lattice dynamics treatments of librations.

As already mentioned above, Kuan et al. (1970) fitted the observed optical frequencies of α-N_2 and the lattice energy to a 3-parameter diatomic potential and Schnepp and Ron (1969) carried out a full lattice dynamical calculation throughout the Brillouin zone using this potential. However, the potential was fitted to an assignment of the librational frequencies which is now known to be incomplete.

The existence of soft modes in solid α-N_2 has been investigated theoretically by Raich and Etters (1971) in connection with the phase transition at 36 K (α-N_2 to β-N_2).

3.4.2. Solid carbon dioxide

Table 2 summarizes the available data for solid CO_2. The far infrared spectrum in the lattice mode region was reported first by Anderson and Walmsley (1964) at 77 K and later by Ron and Schnepp (1967) at 20 K. Helium temperature measurements were carried out by Kuan (1969) and 35 K measurements by Brown and King (1970). Of these workers, only Kuan prepared the solid sample from the vapor under equilibrium conditions. The results indicate that the frequencies of the two infrared active lattice modes are not very sensitive to temperature or to sample preparation. However, the line widths observed by Kuan were about half those reported by Brown and King. Kuan's line widths are given in table 2. Also, the measured intensity ratios are quite different and both results are given in the table.

The low-temperature Raman spectrum has been studied by Ito and Suzuki (1968) and by Cahill and Leroi (1969a, b). The latter authors studied the temperature dependence and found the frequencies to vary appreciably in the range 212 K–81 K. The frequencies reported by Cahill and Leroi (1969a, b) for 15 K agree well with those of Ito and Suzuki for liquid helium temperature. Anderson and Sun (1971) have also reported the Raman spectrum at 18 K.

As has been discussed in subsection 3.2, the classical harmonic approximation is expected to give good results for the librations of solid CO_2. This is also confirmed by comparison with the results of a quantum-mechanical lattice dynamics treatment (see section 4). It is therefore profitable to compare theoretical results obtained by assuming different potential models

TABLE 2

Lattice energy, lattice vibrational frequencies and intensity ratios for solid CO_2 [Frequencies are in units of cm^{-1} with half-intensity widths in parentheses. Experimental frequencies and intensity ratios are those for liquid helium temperature. Calculated values are listed for three potentials: (I) Lennard–Jones potential plus quadrupole–quadrupole term (Walmsley and Pople 1964, nearest neighbor interaction only; for librational frequencies: Jacobi and Schnepp 1972, 10 neighbor shells). (II) Diatomic potential with 6–12 terms (Suzuki and Schnepp 1971). (III) Empirical potential expansion (Donkersloot and Walmsley 1971)].

		Calculated		
	Experimental	I	II	III
Lattice energy (kcal/mole)	−6.58		−6.38	
Translational modes				
A_u	Inactive	94	109.4	
E_u	Inactive	77	116.9	
$T_u(Q_2)$	68.2[a–b](0.9)[a]	74	68.8	68
$T_u(Q_1)$	117.2[a–b](2.1)[a]	113	135.0	108
Infrared intensity ratio				
$I(Q_1)/I(Q_2)$	4.4[a] 1.5[b]	5.4	1.9	
Librational modes				
E_g	72(2)[c–e]	45.2	69.0	76
$T_g(Q_2)$	92(3)[c–e]	58.6	88.2	94
$T_g(Q_1)$	136(6)[c–e]	96.0	138.5	134
Raman intensity ratios				
$I(E_g):I(T_g, Q_2):I(T_g, Q_1)$	10:2.4:1[d] (at 88 K)	20:7:1[f]	5.3:1:1.6	

a. Kuan (1969)
b. Brown and King (1970)
c. Ito and Suzuki (1968)
d. Cahill and Leroi (1969a)
e. Anderson and Sun (1971)
f. Calculated using the eigenvectors of Walmsley and Pople (1964) and the intensity calculation of Brith et al. (1969). Note a misprint in Walmsley and Pople pointed out by Anderson et al. (1970). The eigenvectors are $0.42S_{15}+0.91S_{18}$ and $0.91S_{15}-0.42S_{18}$.

with experiment in order to evaluate the validity of these models. Table 2 includes the available theoretical results for the $\boldsymbol{q}=0$ modes. It is again seen here, as was the case for α-N_2, that the translational frequencies can be well reproduced from a gas phase Lennard–Jones potential (Walmsley and Pople 1964). Also the diatomic potential model gives a good fit. However, the experimental librational modes are substantially higher in frequency than predicted by a quadrupole–quadrupole potential. It should be noted here that Walmsley and Pople (1964) only took into account nearest neighbor interactions in their calculations. Anderson et al. (1970) pointed out that the lattice sums must be extended further since, in particular, the second neighbor shell interactions make appreciable contributions to the frequencies calculated from a quadrupole–quadrupole potential. The values given in the table are for an extended lattice sum to 10 neighbor shells.

As is seen from table 2, the diatomic potential model can be parametrized to give a good overall fit (Suzuki and Schnepp, 1971). Three parameters were used to fit 5 experimental frequencies, the lattice energy and zero uniform stress condition (equilibrium condition with respect to intermolecular distances). It has been shown (Kuan et al. 1970) that the Pa3-T_h^6 structure is at a minimum of potential energy with respect to the angular coordinates for the diatomic potential. The calculated intensity ratios, also listed in the table, are not in good agreement with experiment, although the general trends are reproduced.

Donkersloot and Walmsley (1971) used a more elaborate potential containing adjustable parameters and in addition the exponent of the distance between molecular centers of mass in the intermolecular repulsive term is adjusted (R^{-9} was found to be most satisfactory). The pair potential consists of three terms as below:

$$v = v_q + v_s - JR^{-6}.$$

Here v_q represents the quadrupole–quadrupole potential term, v_s is the 'steric interaction' and the third term is the attractive dispersion term. The steric interaction term (v_s) represents the short-range interactions expressed as an expansion in spherical harmonics, up to order 4; the first term is a zero-order term or it is a repulsive term in the distance (R^{-n}) without angle dependence; the second term is a zero order – second order term; the third term is second order – second order and the fourth term is zero order – fourth order. The parameters of the potential were determined by fitting the infrared and Raman frequencies (5 observables) and the lattice energy and the lattice constant, or a total of 7 observables. Effectively 5 parameters were available to fit to these and the results obtained are included in table 2.

Suzuki and Schnepp (1971) have carried out a complete lattice dynamical treatment of solid CO_2 throughout the Brillouin zone using the diatomic potential model calibrated as described above. Dispersion curves, density of state function and specific heat have been calculated. The calculated specific heat is in very good agreement with measurements. The group theory of the space group Pa3 was discussed for symmetry points and symmetry directions and it was shown that the calculations are in agreement with the predicted degrees of degeneracy and compatibility relations.

In fig. 2, the dispersion curves from the work of Suzuki and Schnepp are reproduced for the [111] direction. The calculations were carried out including translation–libration interactions as required, and also separately excluding these interactions. The curves for both cases are given in the figure. It is quite clear that the interactions have a profound effect. Examination of the eigenvectors confirms that the mixing between these modes is quite extensive.

It may be concluded that solid CO_2 is a system which promises to be very profitable for further work. In particular, neutron scattering investigations – both coherent and incoherent – would be of great value for detailed investigation and refinement of the intermolecular potential.

Walmsley (1968) applied the lattice dynamical calculation of elastic constants to solid CO_2 and compared his results to the incomplete experimental data available. Agreement was found to be very good. This author used in this calculation an intermolecular pair potential consisting of Lennard–Jones and quadrupole–quadrupole terms (Walmsley and Pople 1964). He concluded that the contribution of the angle-dependent part of the potential to the absolute values of the elastic constants is relatively small. On the other hand, this part of the potential determines the ratio between c_{12} and c_{44} which are equal if angle dependence is ignored.

3.4.3. Miscellaneous inorganic solids

A number of other inorganic solids have been investigated in greater or less detail. Among them are CO, N_2O, C_2N_2, the hydrogen halides and the halogen solids. These and other molecular solids have been reviewed by Schnepp and Jacobi (1972) and there the pertinent references may be found. The low-frequency Raman spectra of solid oxygen in two phases (α-O_2 and β-O_2) have been reported by Cahill and Leroi (1969a, b) and for α-O_2 by Mathai and Allin (1971) but no infrared absorptions in the lattice region have been found. Laufer and Leroi (1971) calculated the lattice modes of the two low-temperature phases of O_2 (α and β) using a 6–12 atom–atom diatomic potential and adding on a quadrupole–quadrupole term.

3.4.4. Hexamethylenetetramine

This is the organic solid for which the most extensive published experimental information is available at this time. Dolling and Powell (1970) measured the dispersion curves for several symmetry directions by coherent

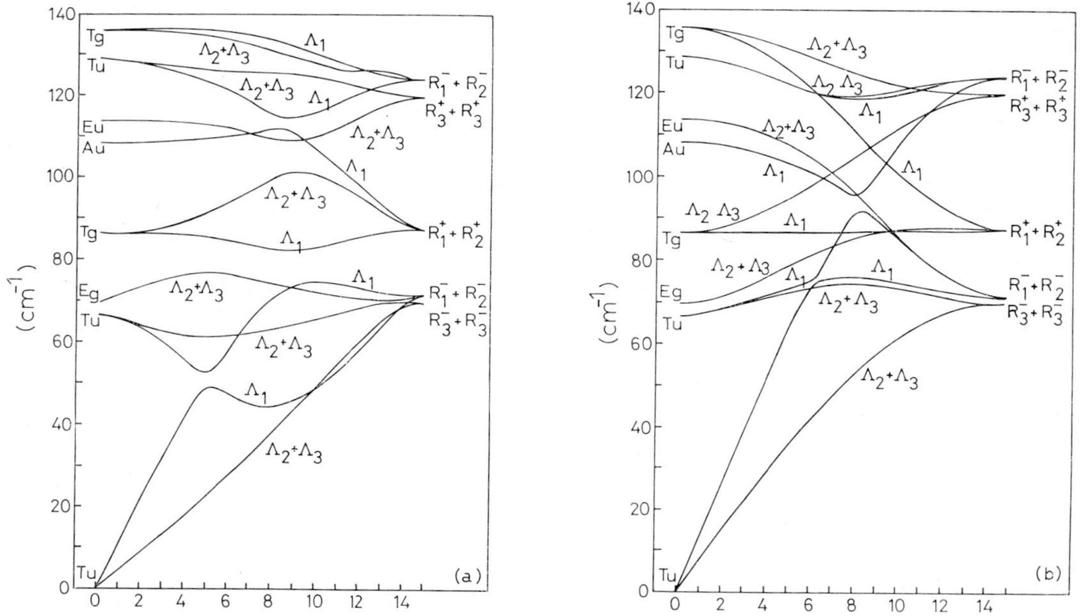

Fig. 2. Dispersion curves for the CO_2 crystal [111] direction. (a) Including translation–libration interactions, and (b) excluding interactions. Abscissa represents values of $\boldsymbol{q}$ between (000) and $(\pi/a, \pi/a, \pi/a,)$ divided arbitrarily into 15 parts (Suzuki and Schnepp 1971, fig. 2).

inelastic neutron scattering. They investigated the fully deuterated compound at 100 K and 298 K, since hydrogen has a large cross section for incoherent scattering. Sample dispersion curves are reproduced in fig. 3. The molecule has the empirical formula $(CH_2)_6N_4$ and has tetrahedral symmetry T_d. The crystal structure is body-centered cubic with one molecule per primitive until cell and the space group of the crystal is also tetrahedral ($I43m–T_d^3$).

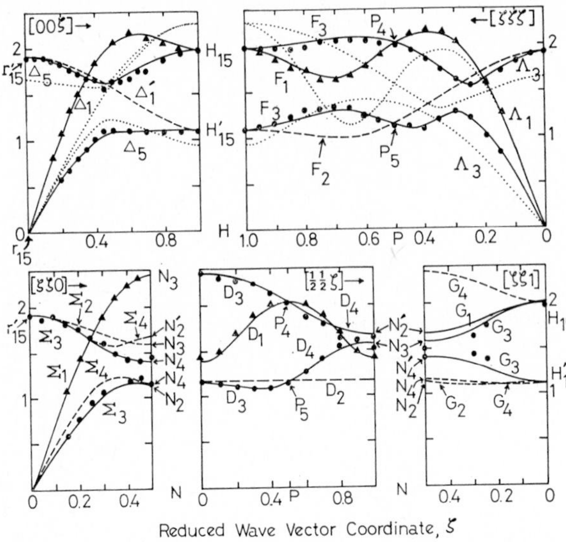

Fig. 3. Dispersion curves for directions of high symmetry in deutero-hexamethylene-tetramine at 100 K (Dolling and Powell 1970). The group theoretical labels are derived on the assumption of a centrosymmetric molecule (O_h^9 symmetry). The solid curves are a best least-squares fit to the results using a five-parameter force model. The dashed curves are also computed from this model, but represent branches not observed experimentally. The dotted curves are the best fit to the results using a four-parameter model involving only nearest neighbor interactions (Dolling and Powell 1970, fig. 2).

For purposes of calculations, it is generally assumed that the molecule has a center of symmetry (this is so if the nitrogen atoms are assumed to be indistinguishable from the carbon atoms). In this approximation the pertinent space group is O_h^9. One very significant result of this work was the correct assignment of the $\boldsymbol{q}=0$ librational mode at 63 cm^{-1}. Since the solid has one molecule per primitive unit cell, only one such optic mode ($\boldsymbol{q}=0$) is expected. However, a frequency of 40 cm^{-1} had been accepted for this mode since its assignment by Couture–Mathieu et al. (1951) and Cheutin and Mathieu (1956) on the basis of Raman measurements. Dolling and

Powell (1970) found that there is, in fact, a high peak in the density of states in the region of 40 cm^{-1} due to librational modes of $\boldsymbol{q} \neq 0$ and the Raman spectrum presumably reflects this peak; in any case, the $\boldsymbol{q}=0$ librational mode is not predicted to be Raman active on group theoretical grounds.

Cochran and Pawley (1964) chose this solid, because of its simple and symmetric structure for the first complete lattice dynamical treatment of a molecular crystal. These authors did not choose a specific functional form for their potential model but instead determined the independent force constants by fitting the calculation to observables, i.e. elastic constants and the librational optic mode frequency. Symmetry was used fully to reduce the number of independent parameters to four for nearest neighbor interactions. At the time, the number of measured observables was very restricted. Dolling and Powell (1970) used an approach similar to that of Cochran and Pawley (1964) to interpret their very large body of experimental results. They used six parameters to characterize each of the nearest neighbor and second-nearest neighbor force constants, a total of 12 parameters, and achieved a very good fit for the dispersion curves. Other models, using fewer parameters were somewhat less successful. Dolling and Powell also calculated the frequency distribution function for the hydrogen compound from an eight parameter model calibrated by fitting their deuterated molecule results. They compared the results of this calculation to the incoherent neutron scattering data of Buhrer et al. (1967). Agreement was generally poor. However, Becka (1962) had observed peaks in such measurements which agreed well with prominent peaks in the distribution function calculated by Dolling and Powell. These authors also calculated the heat capacity and found it to agree well with experiment up to about 60 K; above this temperature it was believed that the higher-frequency internal molecular vibrational modes make themselves felt. These modes were not included in the calculation which was based solely on lattice motions of molecular units assumed rigid. Moderate agreement with experimental elastic constants was achieved.

Rafizadeh and Yip (1970) used their 'extended point mass' method discussed in subsection 3.3 to treat the lattice dynamics of hexamethylenetetramine. They successfully compared their calculated results with the neutron scattering measurements of Dolling and Powell (1970) which were available to them prior to their full publication. Rafizadeh and Yip (1970) also calculated the frequency distribution function and succeeded to fit the experimental specific heat up to about 60 K. These authors also showed that they could obtain good agreement above 60 K by including the intramolecular (internal) modes. Further, they succeeded in fitting the inelastic incoherent neutron scattering results of Becka (1962). Rafizadeh and Yip also made the interesting observation that they could achieve quite a good, although not completely quantitative fit for the dispersion curves by using a potential model containing only four parameters calibrated by four observables, i.e. the three independent elastic constants and the correct librational frequency at $\boldsymbol{q}=0$.

3.4.5. Benzene

Table 3 summarizes the available information and present understanding of the lattice vibrations of solid benzene. The low-frequency Raman spectrum was described by Ito and Shigeoka (1966) and more recently Bonadeo et al. (1971) studied the Raman spectrum of a single oriented crystal at about 140 K and thereby obtained a complete assignment of the seven observed lines by means of polarization measurements. The far infrared spectrum was first reported by Harada and Shimanouchi (1967) at 80 K and at 140 K. They observed three of the six predicted infrared active lattice modes.

Harada and Shimanouchi (1966, 1967) carried out lattice dynamical calculations using the matrix method (see subsection 3.3). They first took into account H–H interactions only but the frequencies so calculated were too low. They then carried out a further calculation including both H–H and C–H repulsive interactions and were able to assign the observed frequencies on the basis of these theoretical results. The atom–atom potential interaction was represented by a repulsive exponential only for which some of the parameters were taken from previous workers and others were obtained by fitting to the Raman measurements available at the time. The observed and calculated frequencies are listed in table 3. Oliver and Walmsley (1969) treated the $\boldsymbol{q}=0$ librational lattice modes of benzene using direction cosine displacement coordinates (see subsection 3.3). They also treated the translational modes. These authors compared the results obtained from three different sets of potential parameters and concluded that those due to Williams (1967) were the most successful. The frequencies so obtained are listed in table 3. Good agreement with experiment was achieved and, in particular, agreement is nearly perfect for the translational modes. The treatment of Oliver and Walmsley does not make the approximation inherent in the matrix method, but on the other hand Harada and Shimanouchi (1967) took into account interactions between lattice and internal vibrational modes. It is therefore not possible to compare these two sets of results and

TABLE 3

Lattice vibrations of solid benzene (frequencies are in units of cm^{-1}).

Translational modes

Mode species (in point group D_{2h})	Observed	Calculated		
	140K[c]	138K[c]	138K[d]	138K[e]
A_u	Inactive	86	91	95
	Inactive	66	61	65
	Inactive	54	53	56
B_{1u}	85	79	82	86
	70	66	69	72
B_{2u}	94	86	96	99
		55	56	57
B_{3u}	94	87	93	98
		49	53	52

Librational modes

Mode species (in point group D_{2h})	Observed			Calculated		
	4K[a]	138K[a]	140K[b]	138K[c]	138K[d]	138K[e]
A_g	(100)	(90)	92	102	94	95
	86	79	79	80	76	75
	64	57	57	55	43	55
B_{1g}	136	126	128	131	134	128
	(86)	(79)	100	99	93	96
	69	61	57	65	48	60
B_{2g}	(100)	(90)	–	106	100	101
	100	90	90	102	87	93
	86	79	79	82	81	83
B_{3g}	136	126	128	128	131	127
	107	100	–	96	85	89
	(86)	(79)	61	81	61	66

a. Ito and Shigeoka (1966)
b. Bonadeo et al (1971)
c. Harada and Shimanouchi (1967)
d. Oliver and Walmsley (1969), potential parameters of Williams (1967)
e. Taddei et al (1972), potential parameters of Williams (1967)

to make a judgement concerning the effect of the approximation discussed. Bernstein (1970) carried out another calculation using the matrix method and on this basis made assignments which are in disagreement with previous authors.

Taddei et al. (1972) carried out extensive calculations with the aim to investigate quantitatively the effects of different potentials, interactions between internal and external modes and the approximation inherent in the matrix method, i.e. neglect of nonlinear dependence of the atom-atom distances on the cartesian coordinates of the atoms. They chose a basis set consisting of the cartesian displacements of molecular centers of mass and infinitesimal rotations about the principal molecular axes. For the internal modes a set of normal coordinates were used. These authors also pointed out that the crystal structure is accurately known at 138 K and therefore comparison between calculated and observed frequencies is only valid for measurements at that temperature. It was concluded that the best procedure is to interpolate experimental measurements obtained at various temperatures to determine the frequencies at 138 K. Harada and Shimanouchi (1967) measured the far infrared spectrum at 138 K and Ito and Shigeoka (1966) gave enough information on the Raman spectrum to make interpolation possible. Two sets of potential parameters were used and one of these (Williams 1967) was distinctly superior. This set of frequencies is given in table 3.

Taddei and coworkers concluded from their investigation that the coupling between internal and lattice modes affects the latter usually by 1–2 cm^{-1} and never by more than 3 cm^{-1}. Thus the rigid molecule approximation was shown to be well based. The studies conducted also showed that the linear term neglected in the calculation of force constants in the matrix formulation (or sometimes referred to as the "giant molecule" formulation) is of minor importance for benzene; the inclusion of this term lowered the calculated frequencies by up to 3 cm^{-1}.

Rush (1967) measured the inelastic incoherent neutron scattering from solid benzene and determined the phonon frequency distribution. Nakamura and Miyazawa (1969) carried out a complete Brillouin zone lattice dynamics calculation using the potential constants of Harada and Shimanouchi (1967), assuming the benzene molecule to be a non-vibrating rigid body. These authors first obtained agreement to better than 6% with Harada and Shimanouchi for the $\boldsymbol{q}=0$ modes. They then calculated the frequency distribution and were able to fit the experimental specific heat to better than 2% by taking into account the internal modes as well and making the appropriate correction for the difference between the calculated C_v and the measured C_p. Nakamura and Miyazawa further calculated $G(\nu)$ (or frequency distribution weighted by the squared H-amplitudes) to allow comparison with the measurements of Rush (1967). The highest peak in $G(\nu)$ at 90 cm^{-1}

was observed by Rush but the other calculated peaks at about 50 and 125 cm^{-1} appeared barely as shoulders in Rush's results.

Logan et al. (1970) measured the inelastic incoherent neutron scattering from a crystalline sample of benzene at temperatures in the range 77–270 K. They found qualitative agreement at low temperatures with the one-phonon neutron scattering cross section calculated from $G(\nu)$ of Nakamura and Miyazawa (1969).

Tarina (1967) reported inelastic incoherent neutron scattering results for solid benzene. No sharp features were observed at 77 K and only a broad peak at about 100 cm^{-1} was found.

3.4.6. Miscellaneous organic solids

A considerable number of organic solids have been investigated experimentally and theoretically. Naphthalene and anthracene have been studied extensively and Pawley (1967) carried out lattice dynamical calculations for these solids. Jacobi and Schnepp (1972) have reviewed the work for these and other organic molecular solids. These include acetylene, ethylene, substituted benzenes, pyrazine, methane and others. Recently Stenman (1971) measured the Raman spectrum of powdered naphthalene. Durig et al. (1971) investigated the far infrared and Raman spectra of solid methanol. Chihara et al. (1971) discussed soft librational modes in solid tetrachloro-p-benzoquinone (p-chloranil) in connection with a phase transition in this solid. Geddes and Bottger (1971) described the lattice vibrational spectra of urea.

4. *Quantum lattice dynamics*

4.1. General

Quantum lattice dynamics treatments have proven essential in the study of translational phonons of systems of light particles and for weak binding energies. This subject is reviewed in ch. 9 of vol. 1 and in ch. 1 of this volume, and we state the main result only. The classical secular equation derived in eqs. (11) and (12) is replaced by a similar quantum secular equation, where the force constants, the second derivatives of the potential with respect to equilibrium positions, are replaced by effective quantum force constants

$$\Phi_{ij}(lk, l'k') \rightarrow \left\langle \psi(lk)\,\psi(l'k') \left| \frac{\partial^2 \Phi}{\partial u_i(lk)\,\partial u_j(l'k')} \right| \psi(lk)\,\psi(l'k') \right\rangle \qquad (39)$$

obtained by averaging over suitable vibrational wavefunctions. The main task is to determine these vibrational wavefunctions and perform the lattice dynamics self-consistently. The common approach is to use harmonic oscillator like functions as variational wavefunctions and regard the parameters of those functions as variational parameters.

Molecular solids have, in addition, librational degrees of freedom, and as the properties of an angular oscillator are not as well-known and as well-established as those of a linear oscillator, the usual method cannot be trivially extended so as to include librational, as well as translational, modes. We present here, in some detail, a quantum-mechanical lattice dynamics formulation for molecular solids recently developed (Jacobi and Schnepp 1972), having in mind particularly its application to librational modes. Concerning these modes, there is a clear distinction between solid hydrogen, where the rotational spacing is much larger than the librational excitation, and the other molecular solids, where the opposite holds. This distinction is the reason that only solid hydrogen was treated quantum mechanically, and as J is a good quantum number, free rotor wavefunctions of definite J were used as a basis set (see below).

However, some other molecular solids exhibit low barriers to rotation and, as a result, large root-mean-square librational displacements from the equilibrium orientations. For example, the angular displacement in solid α-nitrogen is close to 20° (Goodings and Henkelman 1971), while in adamantane the librational amplitude is estimated to reach 30° (Dolling 1970). This leads to the conclusion that "fresh thinking is called for when large amplitude rotational motions are involved" (Venkataraman and Sahni 1970). In such cases the standard harmonic approximation is obviously inadequate and it is important to know whether anharmonicities can be treated as small perturbations or whether a completely new treatment is needed. We present such a treatment and compare it, for some cases, with the classical harmonic approximation.

Following the discussion above we separate internal from external vibrations, and treat here only the latter, so that the molecule is really assumed to be a rigid body. The vibrational degrees of freedom of a given molecule will be characterized by the 6 indices $\xi = (x, y, z, \theta, \phi, \chi)$, where the first three components are the translational degrees of freedom and the last three are the librational degrees of freedom. Only two of the last three components are present if linear molecules are considered. The hamiltonian of the system is

$$H = \sum_{lk} t(lk) + \tfrac{1}{2} \sum_{lk,\, l'k'} v(lk, l'k'), \tag{40}$$

where the kinetic and potential energy are one- and two-particle operators, respectively, whose particular forms become important in specific applications.

The next step is the construction of variational wavefunctions for the ground and excited states. The ground state wavefunction for a system of bosons is

$$\Psi_{\text{gs}} = \prod_{lk\xi} \psi_{\text{gs}}^{lk\xi}. \tag{41}$$

An excited state basis set is chosen, using the translational symmetry, in the form

$$\Psi_{\text{ex}}^{k\xi}(\boldsymbol{q}) = (1/\sqrt{N}) \sum_{l=1}^{N} \exp\{\mathrm{i}[\boldsymbol{q}\cdot\boldsymbol{R}(lk)]\}\, \Psi_{\text{ex}}^{lk\xi}, \tag{42}$$

where $\Psi_{\text{ex}}^{lk\xi}$ is the localized excited function

$$\Psi_{\text{ex}}^{lk\xi} = \psi_{\text{ex}}^{lk\xi} \prod_{l'k'\xi'}^{l'k'\xi' \neq lk\xi} \psi_{\text{gs}}^{l'k'\xi'}. \tag{43}$$

Such wavefunctions occur in exciton theory (Knox 1963) and were used for handling the libron problem of solid hydrogen (Mertens et al. 1968). The size of this basis set is $6Z$ ($5Z$ for linear molecules), which is the number of vibrational degrees of freedom per unit cell (Z being the number of sites in the primitive cell).

To obtain excitation energies we have to evaluate the expectation values of the hamiltonian in the ground and excited states described above. The ground state energy is

$$\begin{aligned} E_{\text{gs}} &= \langle \Psi_{\text{gs}} | H | \Psi_{\text{gs}} \rangle \\ &= \sum_{lk} \langle \psi_{\text{gs}}^{lk} | t(lk) | \psi_{\text{gs}}^{lk} \rangle + \tfrac{1}{2} \sum_{lk,\, l'k'} \langle \psi_{\text{gs}}^{lk} \psi_{\text{gs}}^{l'k'} | v(lk, l'k') | \psi_{\text{gs}}^{lk} \psi_{\text{gs}}^{l'k'} \rangle . \end{aligned} \tag{44}$$

The variational wavefunctions depend usually on one or more parameters, which are determined by varying E_{gs} with respect to them. The excited state wavefunction can be described by a linear combination of the excited state basis (42):

$$\Psi_{\text{ex}}(\boldsymbol{q}) = \sum_{k\xi} C_{k\xi}(\boldsymbol{q})\, \Psi_{\text{ex}}^{k\xi}(\boldsymbol{q}). \tag{45}$$

The coefficients are determined by applying the variational principle to the excited state, which gives the following secular equation

$$|\langle \Psi_{\text{ex}}^{k\xi}(\boldsymbol{q}) | H | \Psi_{\text{ex}}^{k'\xi'}(\boldsymbol{q}) \rangle - E_{\text{ex}}(\boldsymbol{q})\, \delta_{k'\xi'}^{k\xi}| = 0. \tag{46}$$

The evaluation of the matrix element of the hamiltonian (40) in the basis set given by (42) and (43) is straightforward but lengthy. While details of the derivation are given elsewhere (Jacobi and Schnepp 1972) the result is

$$\begin{aligned} H^{k\xi}_{k'\xi'}(\boldsymbol{q}) &= E_{\mathrm{gs}}\delta^{k\xi}_{k'\xi'} + (\langle\psi^{\xi}_{\mathrm{ex}}|\, t\,|\psi^{\xi}_{\mathrm{ex}}\rangle - \langle\psi_{\mathrm{gs}}|\, t\,|\psi_{\mathrm{gs}}\rangle)\,\delta^{k\xi}_{k'\xi'} \\ &\quad + \delta_{kk'}\sum_{l''k''}(\langle\psi^{lk\xi}_{\mathrm{ex}}\,\psi^{l''k''}_{\mathrm{gs}}|\, v(lk, l''k'')\,|\psi^{lk\xi'}_{\mathrm{ex}}\psi^{l''\xi''}_{\mathrm{gs}}\rangle \\ &\quad - \delta_{\xi\xi'}\langle\psi^{lk}_{\mathrm{gs}}\psi^{l''k''}_{\mathrm{gs}}|\, v(lk, l''k'')\,|\psi^{lk}_{\mathrm{gs}}\psi^{l''k''}_{\mathrm{gs}}\rangle) \\ &\quad + (1/N)\sum_{l,l'}\exp\{\mathrm{i}[\boldsymbol{q}\cdot(\boldsymbol{R}_{l'k'} - \boldsymbol{R}_{lk})]\}\,\langle\psi^{lk\xi}_{\mathrm{ex}}\,\psi^{l'k'}_{\mathrm{gs}}|\, v(lk, l'k')\,|\psi^{l'k'\xi'}_{\mathrm{ex}}\psi^{lk}_{\mathrm{gs}}\rangle . \end{aligned} \tag{47}$$

The first term can be absorbed into the eigenvalue, so that (46) can be modified to give the excitation energy directly. The second term, the kinetic energy excitation, contributes to the diagonal elements only. It gives the same, $\boldsymbol{q}$-independent contribution to all matrix elements, since the kinetic energy is a one-particle operator only. The secular equation can, therefore, be solved by diagonalizing the potential energy matrix only and adding the kinetic energy contribution later. The third term is the direct term, with the excitation located on the same particle, and appears on the principal and secondary diagonals only. The last term is the $\boldsymbol{q}$-dependent exchange term, describing excitations on different particles, and it appears everywhere in the secular matrix. The direct and exchange terms are very similar to the shift and splitting terms, respectively, in molecular exciton theory (Knox 1963).

The result (47) is quite general and can be applied to a complete lattice dynamics of a molecular solid. While in the next subsection we apply this formalism to librations, we consider now its applications to translational modes. The variational wavefunctions in this case are linear harmonic oscillator wavefunctions in displacements from equilibrium

$$\begin{aligned} \psi^{lk}_{\mathrm{gs}} &= (\alpha/\pi)^{3/4}\exp[-\tfrac{1}{2}\alpha(\boldsymbol{r}_{lk} - \boldsymbol{R}_{lk})^2], \\ \psi^{lki}_{\mathrm{ex}} &= (2\alpha)^{1/2}(\boldsymbol{r}_{lk} - \boldsymbol{R}_{lk})_i\,\psi^{lk}_{\mathrm{gs}} = (2/\alpha)^{1/2}\,\partial\psi^{lk}_{\mathrm{gs}}/\partial R_{lki}. \end{aligned} \tag{48}$$

The following identity, which is obtained by a double integration by parts, is very helpful in evaluating potential energy matrix elements

$$\langle u_{lki}\Psi_{\mathrm{gs}}|\, V\,|u_{l'k'i'}\Psi_{\mathrm{gs}}\rangle = \frac{\delta^{lki}_{l'k'i'}}{2\alpha}\langle\Psi_{\mathrm{gs}}|\, V\,|\Psi_{\mathrm{gs}}\rangle + \frac{1}{4\alpha^2}\frac{\partial^2}{\partial R_{lki}\,\partial R_{l'k'i'}}\langle\Psi_{\mathrm{gs}}|\, V\,|\Psi_{\mathrm{gs}}\rangle . \tag{49}$$

Using this identity, valid for linear harmonic oscillator functions only, to evaluate the direct and exchange terms in (47), they are reduced to

$$\frac{1}{2\alpha}\,\delta_{kk'}\sum_{l''k''}\frac{\partial^2\langle v(lk,l''k'')\rangle}{\partial R_{lki}\,\partial R_{lki'}}$$

$$+\frac{1}{2N\alpha}\sum_{l''l}\exp\{\mathrm{i}[\boldsymbol{q}\cdot(\boldsymbol{R}_{l''k'}-\boldsymbol{R}_{lk})]\}\frac{\partial^2\langle v(lk,l''k')\rangle}{\partial R_{lki}\,\partial R_{l''k'i'}}$$

$$=\frac{1}{2\alpha}\sum_{l''k''}(\delta_{k''k'}\exp\{\mathrm{i}[\boldsymbol{q}\cdot(\boldsymbol{R}_{l''k''}-\boldsymbol{R}_{lk})]\}-\delta_{kk'})\frac{\partial^2\langle v(lk,l''k'')\rangle}{\partial R_{lki}\,\partial R_{l''k''i'}}. \quad (50)$$

The kinetic energy excitation in (47) is cancelled (Jacobi and Schnepp 1972) by a correction term that is obtained in modifying the wavefunctions so that they become translationally invariant (Gartenhaus and Schwartz 1957). The resulting secular equation for the excitation energy becomes

$$|D^{ki}_{k'i'}(\boldsymbol{q})-\Delta E(\boldsymbol{q})\,\delta^{ki}_{k'i'}|=0, \quad (51)$$

where the dynamic matrix is given by (50). This result is the analog to that of conventional quantum lattice dynamics (Gillis et al. 1968).

It is to be noted that the eigenvalue is here linear in the lattice frequency rather than quadratic, as is the case in both the previous quantum theories and in the classical formulation.

Another, and perhaps more meaningful difference lies in that the variational parameter α is determined by minimizing the ground state energy (44) in the previous treatments and this value of α_{gs} is then used to calculate the excitations. In the present formalism, on the other hand, a $\boldsymbol{q}$-dependent excited state value of the variational parameter $\alpha_{ex}(\boldsymbol{q})$ is obtained from the application of the variational principle to the excited state. Since α is related to an effective force constant this seems quite natural for highly anharmonic crystals, where the potential is shallow and the excited state force constant may be quite different from the ground state force constant. However, this point requires further investigation.

4.2. Librations of linear molecules

We now apply the formalism to the librational modes of a crystal of structure Pa3 consisting of linear symmetric molecules. Examples of such structures are o-H_2, α-N_2, and CO_2, although for α-N_2 there is evidence for a slightly different structure, $P2_13$ (Jordan et al. 1964). As noted above, for structures with an inversion center the librations can be separated and treated independently of the translations at the Γ-point of the Brillouin zone ($\boldsymbol{q}=0$). The librational frequencies are sensitive to the anisotropic part of the intermolecular potential, and one of the purposes of this study is to obtain information about that part of the potential.

To evaluate the matrix elements in (46) and (47) we have to specify the potential and choose suitable variational wavefunctions. For axially symmetric molecules the pair potential can be expanded in spherical harmonics of the angles between the molecular axes and the intermolecular axis (Pople 1954):

$$v(1,2) = \sum_{l_1, l_2=0}^{\infty} \sum_{m}^{|m| \leqslant \min(l_1, l_2)} A_{l_1 l_2, m}(R)\, Y_{l_1 m}(\Omega_1)\, Y_{l_2 m}(\Omega_2), \tag{52}$$

where R is the distance between the centers of molecules 1 and 2 and $A_{l_1 l_2, m}(R)$ are radial functions specifying the various components. If the molecules possess a center of symmetry, only even values of l_1 and l_2 appear in the expansion. For spherical molecules v is a function of R only and the series reduces to the first term $A_{00,0}(R)$, the central part of the potential. Higher terms correspond to various interactions involving orientation forces. For example, terms in $l_1 = l_2 = 1$ represent dipole–dipole forces, terms in $l_1 = 1$, $l_2 = 2$ represent dipole–quadrupole forces, terms in $l_1 = l_2 = 2$ represent quadrupole–quadrupole forces, etc. Only the latter were considered in this study, and they are further characterized by

$$\tfrac{1}{6} A_{22,0} = \tfrac{1}{4} A_{22,1} = A_{22,2} = \Theta^2 / 5R^2, \tag{53}$$

where Θ is the molecular quadrupole moment.

The choice of the single-particle variational wavefunctions must be made according to the nature of the problem. Studies of molecular rotation in crystals that were initiated forty years ago (Pauling 1930) seem to indicate that the motion in solid hydrogen is rotational, while that in most other molecular solids can be classified as vibrational. There are a few intermediate cases, like solid methane, where the motion must be considered a combination of both. A criterion for the motion being vibrational is a high barrier between different potential wells, so that tunneling is unimportant, and energy levels of the same vibrational state, but of different symmetries, are practically degenerate. Thus, for solid hydrogen, one would use free rotor wavefunctions of suitable J, and, indeed, for o-H_2, by choosing

$$\psi_{gs} = Y_{1,0}, \quad \psi_{ex}^{\pm 1} = Y_{1,\pm 1} \tag{54}$$

our theory reduces to the treatment of the libron spectrum (Mertens et al. 1968).

Being interested mainly in the vibrational region, we next proceed to construct vibrational single-particle wavefunctions. Before that we note that very recently Raich (1972) performed a quantum-mechanical calculation of librational frequencies of α-N_2, using a similar formalism to that in the previous subsection. His choice of variational wavefunctions, however, was different. He constructed wavefunctions which were expansions of free rotor wavefunctions of all J until convergence was obtained, and the expansion was determined by the molecular field approximation (James and Raich 1967). His results will be compared to ours later on.

The vibrational wavefunctions are chosen by the site symmetry of the problem, which in our case is S_6 (Curl et al. 1968). The center of inversion implies that only even spherical harmonics appear in an expansion of the effective potential acting on one molecule free to move under the combined effect of all its neighbors in their equilibrium orientations. The lowest non-trivial terms in this expansion are Y_{2m}. The trigonal symmetry further implies that only Y_{20} has to be considered. We thus look for wavefunctions which are solutions of Schrödinger's equation for a linear rotor in a force field

$$V(\theta, \varphi) = \tfrac{1}{2}K \sin^2\theta . \tag{55}$$

This potential differs from Y_{20} by an additive constant only, and has the convenient property of reducing to $\frac{1}{2}K\theta^2$ for large force constants and resulting low-amplitude oscillations ($\sin\theta \sim \theta$). This potential has been known and studied for a long time, both in the electronic problem of the hydrogen molecule ion (Baber and Hassé 1934), and in the context of molecular rotation in crystals (Kohin 1960, Curl et al. 1968). The solutions are the oblate spheroidal wavefunctions (Flammer 1957), which would serve as the most natural variational wavefunctions of our problem. In particular, these functions change continuously from spherical harmonics at vanishing K to harmonic oscillator-like functions for large K.

The spheroidal wavefunctions are of the form

$$\psi_{\text{gs}}(\theta, \varphi) = f_{\text{gs}}(\theta), \quad \psi_{\text{ex}}^{\pm 1}(\theta, \varphi) = f_{\text{ex}}^{\pm}(\theta) \exp(\pm \mathrm{i}\varphi), \tag{56}$$

where $f(\theta)$ are fairly complicated functions that cannot be expressed in simple closed form. In this work we did not use the general form, but only the two extreme limits. In the low-barrier region (o-H_2) the wavefunctions reduce to the proper spherical harmonics in (54). The high-barrier limit can be obtained by noting (Nielsen 1935) that a strongly localized oscillation on the surface of a sphere is essentially the motion of a two-dimensional isotropic harmonic oscillator. The solution to this problem is well-known

(Shaffer 1944), and for our purposes is most conveniently written down in planar polar coordinates in the form

$$\psi_{v,m}(\rho, \varphi) = N_{v,m}\rho^m L^m_{1/2\,(v+m)}(\alpha\rho^2)\exp(-\tfrac{1}{2}\alpha\rho^2)\exp(\pm im\varphi). \quad (57)$$

Here v is the vibrational quantum number, $m=v,\ v-2,\ v-4,\cdots$ is the vibrational angular momentum associated with degenerate vibrations, N_{vm} is a normalization constant, and L^s_r is the $(r-s)$-degree associated Laguerre polynomial. In particular, for the ground state $v=m=0$ and for the lowest excited state $v=m=1$. Comparing this planar oscillator with our spherical angular oscillator, the radius ρ is related to the spherical polar angle θ, as indicated in fig. 4. For the displacement ρ we will use the displacements

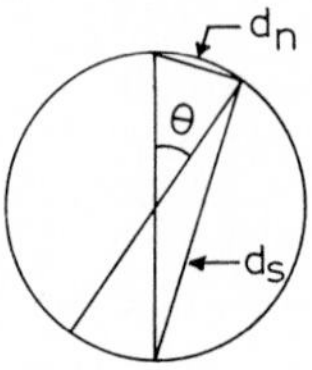

Fig. 4. Librational displacements for the quantum-mechanical treatment.

from equilibrium d_n and d_s, the latter being required for symmetrization of wavefunctions. By elementary geometry

$$d_n = 2\sin(\tfrac{1}{2}\theta), \quad d_s = 2\cos(\tfrac{1}{2}\theta). \quad (58)$$

Substituting these expression for ρ in (57) and constructing symmetric and anti-symmetric combinations we obtain the following single-particle vibrational wavefunctions:

$$\begin{aligned}\psi^{\pm}_{gs} &= N^{\pm}_{gs}[\exp(-\tfrac{1}{2}\alpha d_n^2) \pm \exp(-\tfrac{1}{2}\alpha d_s^2)] \\ &= N^{\pm}_{gs}\,{\cosh \atop \sinh}(\alpha\cos\theta),\end{aligned} \quad (59)$$

and

$$\begin{aligned}\psi^{\xi\pm}_{ex} &= N^{\pm}_{ex}[d_n\exp(-\tfrac{1}{2}\alpha d_n^2) \mp d_s\exp(-\tfrac{1}{2}\alpha d_s^2)]\exp(i\xi\varphi) \\ &= N^{\pm}_{ex}\exp(i\xi\varphi)\{[\sin(\tfrac{1}{2}\theta) \mp \cos(\tfrac{1}{2}\theta)]\cosh(\alpha\cos\theta) \\ &\qquad + [\sin(\tfrac{1}{2}\theta) \pm \cos(\tfrac{1}{2}\theta)]\sinh(\alpha\cos\theta)\}.\end{aligned} \quad (60)$$

Here $\xi = \pm 1$, the two values reflecting the two rotational degrees of freedom on the surface of a sphere.

Using these wavefunctions we next evaluate the matrix elements appearing in (47). The kinetic energy one-particle operator is

$$t = -\frac{\hbar^2}{2I}\left[\frac{1}{\sin\theta}\frac{\partial}{\partial\theta}\left(\sin\theta\frac{\partial}{\partial\theta}\right) + \frac{1}{\sin^2\theta}\frac{\partial^2}{\partial\varphi^2}\right] \tag{61}$$

and the matrix elements of (59) and (60) are (in wavenumbers)

$$\langle\psi^{\pm}_{\text{gs}}|\, t\,|\,\psi^{\pm}_{\text{gs}}\rangle = B\alpha\frac{[(\sinh 2\alpha)/2\alpha]\,L(2\alpha) \mp \frac{2}{3}\alpha}{(\sinh 2\alpha)/2\alpha \pm 1}, \tag{62}$$

$$\begin{aligned}\langle\psi^{\pm}_{\text{ex}}|\, t\,|\,\psi^{\pm}_{\text{ex}}\rangle &= B\alpha \\ &\times\left[\frac{(e^{2\alpha}/4\alpha)(1 - 3/4\alpha) + e^{-2\alpha}(1 + \frac{1}{2}\alpha^{-1} + \frac{3}{16}\alpha^{-2}) \mp \frac{1}{8}\pi(3\alpha^2 - 4\alpha + 1)}{(e^{2\alpha}/2\alpha) - e^{-2\alpha}(1 + 1/4\alpha) \mp \frac{1}{2}\pi\alpha}\right. \\ &\qquad\left. + \frac{\int_{-1}^{1}[e^{2\alpha\kappa}/(1+\kappa)]\,d\kappa \mp \pi}{(e^{2\alpha}/2\alpha) - e^{-2\alpha}(1 + 1/4\alpha) \mp \frac{1}{2}\pi\alpha}\right].\end{aligned} \tag{63}$$

In these expressions the upper (lower) sign refers to the symmetric (antisymmetric) combination, and $L(x)$ is Langevin's function. For high barriers we have the limits

$$\langle t\rangle_{\text{gs}} \xrightarrow[\alpha\to\infty]{} B\alpha, \quad \langle t\rangle_{\text{ex}} \xrightarrow[\alpha\to\infty]{} 2B\alpha.$$

Since for a harmonic librator α is related to the harmonic librational frequency ω_{h} by $\alpha = I\omega_{\text{h}}/h$ this gives

$$\langle t\rangle_{\text{ex}} - \langle t\rangle_{\text{gs}} \xrightarrow[\alpha\to\infty]{} \tfrac{1}{2}\hbar\omega_{\text{h}}.$$

This result is expected for the kinetic energy excitation of a harmonic oscillator, being half the total excitation energy. The ground and excited state kinetic energies, separately, tend to the expected limit of a two-dimensional oscillator.

The evaluation of the potential energy matrix elements is considerably more involved. First, the potential energy consists of two-body operators. Secondly, the wavefunctions (56) and the intermolecular potential (52) are expressed in different coordinate systems. The wavefunctions are most conveniently represented in the molecular systems, where the equilibrium symmetry axes serve as quantization axes. These systems usually vary from site to site in the unit cell, and in the structure considered here there are four such coordinate systems. The intermolecular potential is expressed in the bond system, where the intermolecular axis is chosen as the common z-axis, and this system varies from pair to pair. Since the potential is expanded in spherical harmonics, and the transformation properties of these functions are well-known (Rose 1957), it was found most natural to transform the expression for the potential (52) into the molecular systems, thus obtaining

$$v(1,2) = \sum_{l_1,l_2=0}^{\infty} \sum_{mpq} A_{l_1 l_2, m}(R)\, D_{pm}^{(l_1)}(\alpha\beta\gamma)_1\, D_{qm}^{(l_2)}(\alpha\beta\gamma)_2\, Y_{l_1 p}(\omega_1)\, Y_{l_2 q}(\omega_2). \tag{64}$$

Here ω are the angles with respect to the equilibrium orientations, $\alpha\beta\gamma$ are the eulerian angles specifying the transformation between the two coordinate systems, and $D_{mm'}^{(j)}$ are the corresponding rotation matrix coefficients (Rose 1957).

This expression is used in (47) and only the spherical harmonics appear in the integrand. Due to the general form (56) of the wavefunctions (over the whole range of barriers) the integration over ϕ is trivial and determines which values of p and q survive in the sum (64). There are three kinds of potential energy matrix elements in (47), a ground state term, a direct term, and an exchange term. Consider first the ground state term. Defining

$$A_{l_1 l_2, m}^{\mathrm{gs}}(R) = A_{l_1 l_2, m}(R) \times 4\pi\,[(2l_1+1)(2l_2+1)]^{-1/2} \int \mathrm{d}\omega\, Y_{l_1 0} \psi_{\mathrm{gs}}^2 \int \mathrm{d}\omega\, Y_{l_2 0} \psi_{\mathrm{gs}}^2 ,$$

it can be written in the form

$$\langle \psi_{\mathrm{gs}}^1 \psi_{\mathrm{gs}}^2 |\, v(1,2)\, | \psi_{\mathrm{gs}}^1 \psi_{\mathrm{gs}}^2 \rangle = \sum_{l_1 l_2, m} A_{l_1 l_2, m}^{\mathrm{gs}}(R)\, Y_{l_1 m}(\Omega_1^0)\, Y_{l_2 m}(\Omega_2^0). \tag{65}$$

Comparing the matrix element with the original potential energy (52), we see that the two are fairly similar and that the matrix element consists of two types of expressions: a) The spherical harmonic shape factor, where now the equilibrium orientations, rather than the instantaneous orientations, appear. This factor depends on the crystal structure only. b) An averaging factor $A^{\mathrm{gs}}(R)$, obtained by multiplying the radial function $A(R)$ by the corresponding averages of the terms in the potential over the librational wavefunctions. The integrals are functions of α only, and are one-dimensional integrals, as the ϕ-integration is trivial and has already been used to derive (65). In some cases the integrals can be evaluated analytically in terms of simple functions. In performing the lattice sums in (47) the averaged radial function $A^{gs}(R)$ can be taken out of the sum and the remaining lattice sum, depending for each pair (l_1, l_2) on the crystal structure only and not on α or the particular substance, can be evaluated readily on a computer.

The situation is practically the same for the direct and exchange terms. Defining

$$A^{\text{direct}}_{l_1 l_2, m}(R) = A_{l_1 l_2, m}(R) \int d\omega\, Y_{l_1, \xi-\xi'} \psi^{\xi*}_{\text{ex}} \psi^{\xi'}_{\text{ex}} \int d\omega\, Y_{l_2 0} \psi^2_{\text{gs}},$$

$$A^{\text{exchange}}_{l_1 l_2, m}(R) = A_{l_1 l_2, m}(R) \int d\omega\, Y_{l,\xi} \psi^{\xi*}_{\text{ex}} \psi_{\text{gs}} \int d\omega\, Y_{l_2, -\xi'} \psi^{\xi'}_{\text{ex}} \psi_{\text{gs}},$$

we have

$$\langle \psi^{1,\xi}_{\text{ex}} \psi^2_{\text{gs}} |\, v(1, 2)\, | \psi^{1,\xi'}_{\text{ex}} \psi^2_{\text{gs}} \rangle = \sum_{l_1 l_2, m} A^{\text{direct}}_{l_1 l_2, m}(R)\, D^{(l_1)}_{\xi-\eta, m}(\alpha\beta\gamma)_1\, D^{(l_2)}_{0m}(\alpha\beta\gamma)_2,$$

$$\langle \psi^{1,\xi}_{\text{ex}} \psi^2_{\text{gs}} |\, v(1, 2)\, | \psi^{2,\xi'}_{\text{ex}} \psi^1_{\text{gs}} \rangle = \sum_{l_1 l_2, m} A^{\text{exchange}}_{l_1 l_2, m}(R)\, D^{(l_1)}_{\xi, m}(\alpha\beta\gamma)_1\, D^{(l_2)}_{-\eta, m}(\alpha\beta\gamma)_2. \tag{66}$$

4.3. Applications and comparison with experiment

We discuss briefly the application of the self-consistent phonon treatment (De Wette et al. 1967, Koehler 1968) to translational modes of hydrogen and deuterium and of the formalism in the previous subsection to liberations in nitrogen and carbon dioxide and to librons in hydrogen.

4.3.1. Hydrogen

Solid parahydrogen has hexagonal close-packed structure at all temperatures below the melting point. If the sample contains at least 60% orthohydrogen a λ-type heat capacity anomaly occurs at 1.5–2 K. The lower-temperature phase is face-centered cubic and the accurate structure is believed to be Pa3 (Hardy et al. 1971).

The optical phonons of cubic hydrogen and deuterium were investigated in the far infrared (Hardy et al. 1968). Although two active modes of symmetry T_u are expected, three lines were in fact found. These results proved that long-range rotational ordering does occur in solid hydrogen as had been predicted by Raich and James (1966). The two lowest frequency lines in the spectrum (at 62.2 and 80,0 cm^{-1} for o-H_2 and at 57.4 and 74.5 cm^{-1} for p-D_2) were assigned as the optical modes of symmetry T_u. The third line (at 93 cm^{-1} for o-H_2 and at 85 cm^{-1} for p-D_2) is much broader and is believed to be a combination band. Klump et al. (1970) calculated the optical phonons of cubic hydrogen and deuterium using the RPA approximation and including short-range correlations. Using the gas phase Lennard–Jones parameters and the observed crystal spacing, these authors obtained optical mode frequencies of 63.8 and 87.0 cm^{-1} for o-H_2 and 53.1 and 74.4 cm^{-1} for p-D_2, in close agreement with experiment. The calculated ground state crystal energies are also in good agreement with thermodynamically determined energies (Schnepp 1970).

Klein and Koehler (1970) carried out a complete SCF calculation for the phonon frequencies, lattice energies and nearest neighbor distance for hcp H_2 and D_2. Their treatment gives very good results for the optical phonon mode as compared with experiment (McTague et al. 1970, Nielsen et al. 1970). The calculated crystal energies are within 10% of the experimental values.

4.3.2. *Nitrogen*

This substance was discussed in detail in the previous subsection (3.4). The librational frequencies at $\boldsymbol{q}=0$ were evaluated from (47) for a quadrupole–quadrupole potential. The same frequencies were also evaluated classically by rewriting this potential in the space-fixed crystal system (James and Raich 1967), expanding in angular displacements (Schnepp and Ron 1969), and solving the classical, harmonic equations of motion. These calculations are summarized in table 4, together with the experimental results (Anderson et al. 1970, Mathai and Allin 1971) and the calculation by Raich (1972), who performed the lattice sums up to two neighboring shells.

TABLE 4

Calculated and observed librational frequencies at $\boldsymbol{q}=0$ for $\alpha-N_2$. The molecular quadrupole moment used is 1.52×10^{-26} esu cm^2.

	Nearest neighbors only		Second nearest neighbors			All neighbors		Experiment[b,c]
	Classical	Present quantum	Classical	Raich[a]	Present quantum	Classical	Present quantum	
E_g	27.8	29.6	36.6	35.7	35.6	34.8	34.5	32
T_g	38.4	35.8	45.2	41.5	41.4	45.0	41.3	36.5
T_g	70.3	66.1	74.2	70.3	70.2	73.8	69.9	60

a. Raich (1972)
b. Anderson et al. (1970)
c. Mathai and Allin (1971)

These results lead to the following conclusions: a) The results with our vibrational wavefunctions and with Raich's combinations of rotational functions practically coincide. They coincide completely if account is taken of the slightly different molecular constants used in the two calculations and one more decimal place is kept. This means that the choice of oscillatory or rotational wavefunctions is a matter of technical convenience or taste, since each can be expanded in terms of the other. We feel, however, that oscillatory functions are more natural, as a single vibrational wavefunction gave the same result as an expansion up to high $J\,(\sim 10)$. Further, the strongly localized nature of the oscillations is confirmed by the fact that the symmetric and antisymmetric wavefunctions gave the same ground and excited state energies. b) Comparison between classical and quantum-mechanical calculations shows that the anharmonicities are small enough to be regarded as perturbations. In principle one could evaluate the corrections to the frequencies by classical perturbation theory, and the use of quantum mechanics in this case may be a more convenient scheme only for including anharmonicites. c) Comparison between calculations and experiment shows that the quadrupole potential accounts reasonably, though not completely, for the librational frequencies.

4.3.3. Carbon dioxide

The calculations are compared to experiment (Cahill and Leroi 1969a, b) in table 5. The main conclusion to be drawn is that the quadrupole potential is clearly insufficient for describing the librational frequencies, and further terms have to be included in the potential, as described above.

TABLE 5

Calculated and observed librational frequencies at $\boldsymbol{q} = 0$ for CO_2. The quadrupole moment used is 4.3×10^{-26} esu cm^2.

	Nearest neighbors only		All neighbors		Experiment[a]
	Classical	Quantum	Classical	Quantum	
E_g	36.2	42.5	45.2	49.0	72
T_g	50.0	51.3	58.6	58.4	92
T_g	91.5	94.8	96.0	99.4	136

a. Cahill and Leroi (1969a)

4.3.4. Librons in solid hydrogen

Using the free rotor wavefunctions (54) in (47) we evaluated the libron frequencies for o-H_2. The calculated frequencies were 10.7, 12.8, and 21.6 cm^{-1}, and when the quadrupole moment was reduced due to the high-amplitude translational motion (Harris 1970) the calculated frequencies became 9.0, 10.7, and 18.2 cm^{-1}. These results are still in poor agreement with the experimental results (Hardy et al. 1971) of 6.5, 8.2, and 11.3 cm^{-1}. To obtain good agreement with experiment higher order perturbation theory must be used (Coll et al. 1970).

List of symbols

Φ = potential of the solid
v = pair potential for a pair of molecules,
l, l' = designation of unit cell,
k', k' = designation of site,
Ω, Ω' = orientation of molecule,
R = distance,
σ = Lennard–Jones potential σ-parameter,
ε = Lennard–Jones potential ε-parameter,
Y_{jm} = spherical harmonic,
κ, κ' = designation of atom in molecule,
T = kinetic energy of solid,
u_i, u_j = displacement in translational coordinate i or j,
u_α, u_β = displacement in librational coordinate α or β,
u_s = displacement in translational or librational coordinate s,
m_k = mass of molecule at site k,
$\boldsymbol{I}$ = moment of inertia tensor,
$I_{\alpha\beta}$ = component of moment of inertia,
$\boldsymbol{I}^{\mathrm{p}}$ = moment of inertia tensor in principal axes system,
u_i^{p} = displacement in principal axes system,
Φ_{ij} = derivative of Φ with respect to displacement u_i, u_j, taken at equilibrium,
$\boldsymbol{q}$ = wave vector,
$\boldsymbol{R}(lk)$ = position vector of molecule (lk),
U_s = amplitude of displacement u_s,
ω = angular frequency,

t	=	time,
$\boldsymbol{M}$	=	dynamic matrix (classical),
$\boldsymbol{e}$	=	unit matrix 3-dimensional,
$\boldsymbol{E}$	=	unit matrix, general,
θ, ϕ	=	spherical coordinates,
B	=	rotational constant,
E	=	energy,
ΔE	=	excitation energy,
W	=	reduced energy in units of B,
ΔW	=	excitation energy,
r	=	displacement in distance R,
X, Y, Z	=	component of distance vector $\boldsymbol{R}$,
x, y, z	=	displacements in vector components X, Y, Z,
$\tilde{\boldsymbol{A}}$	=	adjoint of transformation matrix $\boldsymbol{A}$,
μ, ν	=	running indices in summation,
$\boldsymbol{B}^+$	=	adjoint of transformation matrix $\boldsymbol{B}$,
R^0, X^0, Y^0, Z^0	=	equilibrium values of distance R and of components X, Y, Z,
α, β, γ	=	rotation angles about cartesian axes x, y, z respectively,
Λ	=	direction cosine,
λ	=	direction cosine displacement,
l, m, n	=	symmetrized direction cosine displacements,
H	=	half the distance between the two centers of interaction in the diatomic potential,
$\boldsymbol{\Delta}$	=	net molecular displacement vector (extended point mass model),
u_ξ	=	imaginary librational displacement coordinate,
Γ	=	center of brillouin zone ($\boldsymbol{q}=0$),
Ψ	=	molecular wave function,
t	=	kinetic energy of molecule,
H	=	hamiltonian,
ψ	=	crystal wave function,
ξ	=	designation of state with respect to azimuthal variable ϕ,
$\delta_{k,k'}$	=	Kroneker delta,
ψ_{gs}	=	ground state molecular wave function,
ψ_{ex}	=	excited state molecular wave function,
α	=	nonlinear (exponential) variational parameter,
$\boldsymbol{D}$	=	dynamic matrix (quantum mechanical),
Θ	=	molecular quadrupole moment.

References

ANDERSON, A. and G.E. LEROI (1966), J. Chem. Phys. **45**, 4359.
ANDERSON, A. and T.S. SUN (1971), Chem. Phys. Letters **8**, 537.
ANDERSON, A., H.A. GEBBIE, and S.H. WALMSLEY (1969), Mol. Phys. **7**, 401.
ANDERSON, A., T.S. SUN, and M.C.A. DONKERSLOOT (1970), Can. J. Phys. **48**, 2265.
ANDERSON, A. and S.H. WALMSLEY (1964), Mol. Phys. **7**, 583.
BABER, W.G. and H.H. HASSÉ (1934), Proc. Cambridge Phil. Soc. **31**, 564.
BECKA, L.N. (1962), J. Chem. Phys. **37**, 431.
BERNSTEIN, E.R. (1970), J. Chem. Phys. **52**, 4701.
BONADEO, H., M.P. MARZOCCHI, E. CASTELLUCCI and S. CALIFANO (1971), J. Chem. Phys. **57**, 4299.
BRITH, M., A. RON, and O. SCHNEPP (1969), J. Chem. Phys. **51**, 1318.
BROWN, K.G. and W.T. KING (1970), J. Chem. Phys. **52**, 4437.
BUHRER, W., W. HÄLG and T. SCHNEIDER (1967), Rep. Inst. Reaktorforsch., Wurenlingen, no. AF-SSP-9.
CAHILL, J.E. and G.E. LEROI (1969a), J. Chem. Phys. **51**, 1324.
CAHILL, J.E. and G.E. LEROI (1969b), J. Chem. Phys. **51**, 97.
CHEUTIN, A. and J.P. MATHIEU (1956), J. Chem. Phys. **53**, 106.
CHIHARA, H., N. NAKAMURA, and M. TACHIKI (1971), J. Chem. Phys. **54**, 3540.
COCHRAN, W. and G.S. PAWLEY (1964), Proc. Roy. Soc. (London) **A280**, 1.
COLL III, C.F., A.B. HARRIS, and A.J. BERLINSKY (1970), Phys. Rev. Lett. **25**, 858.
COUTURE-MATHIEU, L., J.P. MATHIEU, J. Cremer, and H. POULET (1951), J. Chim. Phys. **48**, 1.
CRUICKSHANK, D.W. (1958), Rev. Mod. Phys. **30**, 163.
CURL, R.F., H.P. HOPKINS, and K.S. PITZER (1968), J. Chem. Phys. **48**, 4064.
DE BOER, J. (1942), Physica **9**, 363.
DEVONSHIRE, A.F. (1936), Proc. Roy. Soc., (London) **A153**, 601.
DE WETTE, F.W., L.H. NOSANOW, and N.R. WERTHAMER (1967), Phys. Rev. **162**, 824.
DOLLING, G. (1970), Trans. Am. Crystall. Assoc. **6**, 73.
DOLLING, G. and B.M. POWELL (1970), Proc. Roy. Soc. (London) **A319**, 209.
DONKERSLOOT, M.C.A. and S.H. WALMSLEY (1971), Chem. Phys. Lett. **11**, 105.
DOWS, D.A. (1962), J. Chem. Phys. **36**, 2836.
DOWS, D.A., *Physics and chemistry of the organic solid state* (1963, 1965), Wiley (Interscience), New York, Ch. 11.
DOWS, D.A. (1966), J. Chim. Phys. **63**, 168.
DURIG, J.R., C.B. PATE, Y.S. LI, and D.J. ANTION (1971), J. Chem. Phys. **54**, 4863.
DYMOND, J.H. and B.J. ALDER (1968), Chem. Phys. Lett. **2**, 54.
FLAMMER, C. (1957), *Spheroidal wave functions* (Stanford Univ. Press, Stanford, Cal., USA).
FRUEHLING, A. (1950), J. Chem. Phys. **18**, 1119.
GARTENHAUS, S. and C. SCHWARTZ (1957), Phys. Rev. **108**, 482.
GEDDES, A.L. and G.L. BOTTGER (1971), J. Chem. Phys. **55**, 1990.
GILLIS, N.S., T.R. KOEHLER, and N.R. WERTHAMER (1968), Phys. Rev. **175**, 1110.
GOODINGS, D.A. and M. HENKELMAN (1971), Can. J. Phys. **49**, 2898.
HARADA, I. and T. SHIMANOUCHI (1966), J. Chem. Phys. **44**, 2016.
HARADA, I. and T. SHIMANOUCHI (1967), J. Chem. Phys. **46**, 2708.

HARDY, W.N., I.F. SILVERA, K.N. KLUMP, and O. SCHNEPP (1968), Phys. Rev. Lett. **21**, 291.
HARDY, W.N., I.F. SILVERA, and J.P. MCTAGUE (1971), Phys. Rev. Lett. **26**, 127.
HARRIS, A.B. (1970), Phys. Rev. **B1**, 1881.
ITO, M. and T. SHIGEOKA (1966), Spectrochim. Acta **22**, 1029.
ITO, M. and M. SUZUKI (1968), unpublished work.
JACOBI, N. and O. SCHNEPP (1972), Chem. Phys. Lett. **13**, 344.
JAMES, H.M. and J.C. RAICH (1967), Phys. Rev. **162**, 649.
JORDAN, T.H., H.W. SMITH, W.E. STREIB, and W.N. LIPSCOMB (1964), J. Chem. Phys. **41**, 756.
KASTLER, A. and A. ROUSSET (1941), J. Phys. Radium **2**, 49.
KITAIGORODSKII, A. (1966), J. Chim. Phys. **63**, 9.
KLEIN, M.L. and T.R. KOEHLER (1970), J. of Physics **C3**, L102.
KLUMP, K.N., O. SCHNEPP, and L.H. NOSANOW (1970), Phys. Rev. **B1**, 2496.
KNOX, R.S. (1963), *Theory of excitons*, Solid State Physics, Suppl. 5, (Acad. Press, New York).
KOEHLER, T.R. (1968), Phys. Rev. **165**, 942.
KOHIN, B.C. (1960), J. Chem. Phys. **33**, 882.
KUAN, T.S. (1969), Ph.D. Thesis, Univ. of Southern Cal., USA.
KUAN, T.S., A. WARSHEL, and O. SCHNEPP (1970), J. Chem. Phys. **52**, 3012.
LAUFER, J.C. and G.E. LEROI (1971), J. Chem. Phys. **55**, 993.
LOGAN, K.W., S.F. TREVINO, H.J. PRASK and J.D. GAULT (1970), J. Chem. Phys. **53**, 3417.
MCTAGUE, J.P., I.F. SILVERA, and W.N. HARDY (1970), Bull. Am. Phys. Soc. **15**, 296.
MATHAI, P.M. and E.J. ALLIN (1971), Can. J. Phys. **49**, 1973.
MERTENS, F.G., W. BIEM and H. HAHN (1968), Z.f. Phys. **213**, 33.
NAKAMURA, M. and T. Miyazawa (1969), J. Chem. Phys. **51**, 3146.
NIELSEN, H.H. (1935), J. Chem. Phys. **3**, 189.
NIELSEN, M., H.B. MØLLER and L. MEYER (1970), Bull. Am. Phys. Soc. **15**, 383.
OLIVER, D.A. and S.H. WALMSLEY (1968), Mol. Phys. **15**, 141.
OLIVER, D.A. and S.H. WALMSLEY (1969), Mol. Phys. **17**, 617.
PAULING, L. (1930), Phys. Rev. **36**, 430.
PAWLEY, G.S. (1967), Physica Stat. Sol. **20**, 347.
PISERI, L. and G. ZERBI (1968), J. Mol. Spectr. **26**, 254.
POPLE, J.A. (1954), Proc. Roy. Soc. **A221**, 498.
RAFIZADEH, H.A. and S. YIP (1970), J. Chem. Phys. **53**, 315.
RAICH, J.C. (1972), J. Chem. Phys., **56**, 2395.
RAICH, J.C. and R.D. ETTERS (1971), J. Chem. Phys. **55**, 3901.
RAICH, J.C. and H.M. JAMES (1966), Phys. Rev. Lett. **16**, 173.
RON, A. and O. SCHNEPP (1967), J. Chem. Phys. **46**, 3991.
ROSE, M.E. (1957), *Elementary theory of angular momentum* (John Wiley and Sons, New York).
RUSH, J.J. (1967), J. Chem. Phys. **47**, 3936.
SAUER, P. (1966), Z.f. Physik, **194**, 360.
SHAFFER, W.H. (1944), Rev. Mod. Phys. **16**, 245.
SCHNEPP, O. (1969), Adv. in At. and Mol. Phys. **5**, 155.
SCHNEPP, O. (1970), Phys. Rev. **2A**, 2574.
SCHNEPP, O. and N. JACOBI (1972), Adv. Chem. Phys. **22**, 205.

SCHNEPP, O. and A. RON (1969), Disc. Faraday Soc., **48**, 26.
SCHOMAKER, V. and K.N. TRUEBLOOD (1968), Acta Cryst. **B24**, 63.
SHIMANOUCHI, T. (1970), private communication.
SHIMANOUCHI, T., M. TSUBOI, and T. MIYAZAWA (1961), J. Chem. Phys. **35**, 1597.
STENMAN, F. (1971), J. Chem. Phys. **54**, 4217.
ST. LOUIS, R.V. and O. SCHNEPP (1969), J. Chem. Phys. **50**, 5177.
STOGRYN, D.E. and A.P. STOGRYN (1966), Mol. Phys. **11**, 371.
SUZUKI, M. and O. SCHNEPP (1971), J. Chem. Phys. **55**, 5349.
SUZUKI, M., T. YOKOYAMA and M. ITO (1967), Spetrochim. Acta **24A**, 1091.
SWEET, J.R. and W.A. STEELE (1967), J. Chem. Phys. **47**, 3029.
TADDEI, G., H. BONADEO, M.P. MARZOCCHI, and S. CALIFANO (1972), J. Chem. Phys. **58**, 966.
TARINA, V. (1967), J. Chem. Phys. **46**, 3273.
VENKATARAMAN, G. and V.L. SAHNI (1970), Rev. Mod. Phys. **42**, 409.
WALMSLEY, S.A. (1968), J. Chem. Phys. **48**, 1438.
WALMSLEY, S.A. and A. ANDERSON (1964), Mol. Phys. **7**, 411.
WALMSLEY, S.H. and J.A. POPLE (1964), Mol. Phys. **8**, 345.
WIGNER, E. (1931), *Gruppentheorie*, Friedr. Vieweg and Sohn Akt. Ges., Braunschweig, Germany.
WILLIAMS, D.E. (1967), J. Chem. Phys. **47**, 4680.
WILLIAMS, D.R., L.J. SCHAAD, and J.N. MURRELL (1967), J. Chem. Phys. **47**, 12.
WILSON, E. B., J. C. DECIUS, and P. C. CROSS (1955), *Molecular vibrations* (McGraw-Hill, New York).

CHAPTER 4

Second Sound and Related Thermal Conduction Phenomena

H. BECK

Institut für Theoretische Physik der Universität Zürich
Schönberggasse 9, Zurich
Switzerland

Dynamical Properties of Solids, edited by
G.K. Horton and A.A. Maradudin

Contents

1. *Introduction*

The phenomena connected with the transport of heat in an insulating crystal can be divided into two groups. First there is 'common' diffusive heat conduction which can be observed in any solid. The corresponding properties of a specific material are characterized by its thermal conductivity κ, or, more generally, a tensor κ_{ij}. In addition to this, two exceptional types of behavior have been observed on a few special substances in a rather narrow temperature range: second sound, a wavelike propagation of heat, and Poiseuille flow, a special form of thermal conduction, which leads to an unusual temperature dependence of κ.

This chapter is mainly devoted to a description of second sound (SS) and Poiseuille flow (PF). Facts about 'ordinary' thermal conduction (TC), which have been reviewed by several authors, see e.g. Klemens (1958) and Carruthers (1961), will only be touched upon where they are related to the occurrence of SS and PF. This is mainly true for the temperature dependence of κ for very low T-values, in the neighbourhood of the thermal conductivity maximum. Moreover, the theoretical framework describing SS and PF will usually, at the same time, yield results for the static thermal conductivity κ.

It is interesting to note that, about at the same time when Debye (1914) explained the increase of κ with decreasing temperature observed in dielectric crystals in terms of travelling lattice waves which are scattered less and less for lower and lower T, the first speculation about SS was enunciated by Nernst (1917). We can probably only speculate today whether he had the modern picture of SS in his mind when he wrote: 'Since in all probability heat has inertia, it is possible that at very low temperatures, with the resulting high conductivity, an oscillatory discharge of thermal differences of potential might occur under certain circumstances.'

Concerning the history of the theory of 'ordinary' thermal conductivity, let us just mention some landmarks: Peierls (1929) developed a more rigorous approach based on a Boltzmann equation for the density of phonons, demonstrating that κ is infinite as long as there are only momentum conserving collisions between the phonons. Casimir (1938) showed that for very low temperatures scattering of phonons from the sample walls limits TC, which then depends on the dimensions of the crystal. Klemens (1951, 1955) also considered scattering from imperfections and impurities, which is the dominating collision mechanism at low temperatures.

In contrast to this gradual development starting in the early days of lattice dynamics, the idea of SS in solids did not emerge directly from Nernst's speculations. Tisza (1938, 1940) and Landau (1941a) predicted, on the basis of the two-fluid theory of He II, the existence of propagating temperature waves in superfluid helium, called second sound. Its velocity was expressed in terms of thermodynamic quantities by (2.34). Peshkov (1944) was first to detect this phenomenon by examining the response of the liquid to periodic heating at a boundary. Later on (Peshkov 1947) he suggested that SS might also exist in solids. Ward and Wilks (1951, 1952) and Dingle (1952) showed that it can be derived by considering a system of interacting phonons experiencing only momentum conserving collisions. In this sense SS can be viewed as an oscillation in the density of thermal phonons, analogous to an ordinary sound wave in a gas of particles. Under the condition that there are enough collisions between the phonons in order to reach approximate thermal equilibrium in a time much shorter than the oscillation period of this collective excitation, and provided that resistive (momentum destroying) processes are sufficiently rare, Sussman and Thellung (1963) and Gurzhi (1964, 1965) predicted the existence of SS and PF. They solved the phonon Boltzmann equation in a relaxation time approximation and derived hydrodynamic equations for local temperature and drift velocity of the phonon gas. In a series of papers by Krumhansl and coworkers (Prohovsky and Krumhansl 1964, Krumhansl 1965, Guyer and Krumhansl 1964, 1966a, b, Guyer 1966) the theoretical foundations and the conditions for an experimental detection were investigated in more detail.

Up to that time, the experimentalists had been looking for SS in such materials as quartz and sapphire (see the references quoted by Rogers 1971) without any success. Finally, the onset of PF was detected by Meshov-Deglin (1965, 1967) and SS was observed by Ackerman et al. (1966), both in solid ^{4}He. Since then, further successful experiments on ^{3}He, NaF and Bi have been reported. They will be discussed in section 3.

Theorists extended the earlier work which was based on solving approximately a Peierls–Boltzmann equation, in two directions. First, many-body techniques of statistical mechanics, such as Green's functions and linear response theory, were used to derive this Boltzmann equation and generalizations of it starting from a microscopic lattice hamiltonian. On the other hand, more sophisticated methods than the mean free time approximation to solve the Boltzmann equation were developed, although it must be admitted that there is much more to be done in this field.

The basic concept of phonon hydrodynamics from which the main parts of this chapter are developed is illustrated in fig. 1. The central issue is the transport equation for the phonon density, be it the simple Peierls–Boltzmann equation or a generalization including the 'quasi-particle interaction' between phonons and the coupling to the elastic deformation field and, perhaps, even taking into account the finite spectral width of the phonons. The analysis of section 2 starts from the simple Peierls equation and, after establishing the necessary notation, leads immediately to hydrodynamic equations describing SS and PF by treating the collision operator in the so-called relaxation time approximation. The well-known conditions for the existence of SS and PF as well as expressions for velocity and damping of SS are derived and the connection with Callaway's (1959) formulation of the static thermal conductivity κ is established. These results can, certainly qualitatively, account for the experimental facts which are summarized and discussed in section 3.

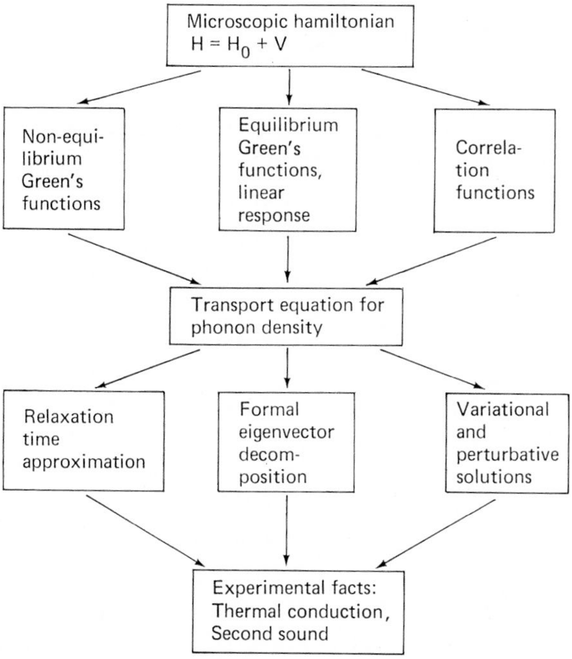

Fig. 1. Schematic representation of the different topics treated in this chapter and of their logical connections.

The whole of section 4 is then devoted to establishing the various links between the microscopic level and the experimentally accessible phenomena shown in fig. 1. Subsection 4.1 presents the main ideas underlying the derivation of a transport equation for phonons by the help of equilibrium and non-equilibrium Green's functions. Some details of the non-equilibrium approach following the concepts of Kadanoff and Baym (1962) are presented. In order to avoid duplications the equilibrium Green's function method is only sketched briefly since the evaluation of the heat current auto-correlation function in subsection 4.2, leading to expressions for κ, follows essentially the lines of an "equilibrium derivation" of the transport equation. The main point of these types of microscopic theories is to isolate the 'hydrodynamic singularities' of the pertinent correlation functions showing up for small wave-vectors and frequencies. In subsection 4.3 mathematically more rigorous methods to solve the transport equation are developed. This provides not only a better foundation of the more phenomenological theory of section 2, but also more rigorous, though partly rather formal, expressions for the mean relaxation times introduced there.

The final section presents four topics which do not strictly belong to the chain of arguments pictured in fig. 1. First, the coupling between phonon gas (second sound) and the 'elastic background' (first sound) is considered from the point of view of a two-fluid description of dielectric solids and some consequences of the coupling are discussed. In the second subsection, it is shown how to deal with quantum crystals which do not allow for the harmonic approximation of lattice dynamics, the starting point in section 2. Then the contributions to the problem of 'driftless versus drifting SS' are summarized and finally several theoretical concepts to describe and analyze heat pulse data are mentioned.

Although phonon hydrodynamics in dielectric solids is in some sense a rather narrow subject, it was, of course, impossible to present a complete account of all theoretical and experimental efforts made in this field. Let us therefore, before beginning our review, mention a few aspects which will not be covered.

First, the phonon transport equation will always be used in its linearized form, although the Green's function approach of section 4 yields a non-linear equation for the phonon density, including a non-linear collision operator [reducing under simplifying assumptions to the form given by Peierls (1955)]. In this way, we preclude the analysis of intensity dependent effects such as soliton-like heat pulses observed by Narayanamurti and Varma (1970). In principle, such effects would be an impressive demonstration of the lattice anharmonicity. However, it seems that more quantitative investigations are needed to determine how far the phenomena observed are really due to the properties of the crystal itself.

A second limitation of our presentation of the subject concerns theory: whereas most theoretical work aimed at obtaining information and insight about second sound and related phenomena involves, somehow or other, a phonon transport equation, there is a different approach making use of Mori's (1962, 1965a, b) formalism of evaluating correlation functions. As stated before, the crucial mathematical step in the derivation of a transport equation consists in isolating the singular behavior of certain quantities introduced in the framework of Green's functions. This somewhat complicated procedure can be circumvented by focussing on the hydrodynamic domain right at the beginning and taking into account all dynamical variables which, in a given physical situation, are 'almost conserved', thus contributing singularities for small frequencies and wave vectors to the pertinent correlation functions. Goetze and Michel (1972) have obtained closed microscopic expressions for thermal conductivity and lattice viscosity that are more easily amenable to numerical evaluation than some purely formal results obtained from an eigenfunction decomposition of the collision operator. Meier (1973) found drifting and driftless SS using this approach – see subsection 5.3 – but the formalism has not yet been developed far enough to yield expressions for the attenuation of these various excitations.

Finally, a recent numerical approach to second sound is worth mentioning. Tsai and McDonald (1973a) have identified the thermally equilibrated region following the main pulse in a computer experiment simulating shock waves with second sound. In further molecular dynamical calculations aimed at investigating the propagation of a heat pulse in a lattice of classical particles, Tsai and McDonald (1973b) found features similar to what is observed in heat pulse experiments on NaF (e.g. McNelly et al. 1970). Although the details of these calculations cannot yet be clearly related to the experimental findings and to the usual theoretical treatments, this approach appears to be a valuable complementary tool to investigate second sound in solids.

2. *Elementary theory of phonon transport*

2.1. Phonons in equilibrium

The main purpose of this short subsection is to introduce some basic concepts and the necessary notation. We treat an ideal insulating crystal with N unit cells, labeled by $\boldsymbol{n}$, each containing s particles. Departures from a perfectly periodic structure caused by impurities, defects, etc. can have a strong influence on phonon transport phenomena. They will be taken into account in a phenomenological manner (i.e. by means of relaxation times) throughout this section. Klemens (1955) has treated the scattering of phonons from imperfections and impurities on a more microscopic basis.

The hamiltonian

$$H = \sum_{\boldsymbol{n}\sigma} \frac{\boldsymbol{p}(\boldsymbol{n}\sigma)^2}{2m_\sigma} + V(\{\boldsymbol{R}(\boldsymbol{n}\sigma)\}) \tag{2.1}$$

is a function of the coordinates $\boldsymbol{R}(\boldsymbol{n}\sigma)$ and the momenta $\boldsymbol{p}(\boldsymbol{n}\sigma)$ of all particles ($\sigma = 1, \cdots, s$). In traditional lattice dynamics the potential energy V is expanded around the equilibrium positions $\boldsymbol{X}(\boldsymbol{n}\sigma)$ and only the first few terms are considered. Introducing normal coordinates by

$$\boldsymbol{u}(\boldsymbol{n}\sigma) = (m^\sigma N)^{-1/2} \sum_k \boldsymbol{e}^\sigma(k)\, \mathrm{e}^{i\boldsymbol{k}\cdot\boldsymbol{X}(\boldsymbol{n}\sigma)} A_k, \tag{2.2a}$$

$$\boldsymbol{p}(\boldsymbol{n}\sigma) = -\,\mathrm{i}(m_\sigma/N)^{1/2} \sum_k \boldsymbol{e}^\sigma(k)\, \mathrm{e}^{i\boldsymbol{k}\cdot\boldsymbol{X}(\boldsymbol{n}\sigma)} B_k, \tag{2.2b}$$

with the commutation relations

$$[A_k, B_{k'}] = \delta_{k,k'}, \tag{2.3}$$

we obtain the well-known anharmonic phonon hamiltonian

$$H = \sum_k \omega_k (a_k^\dagger a_k + \tfrac{1}{2}) + \sum_{\nu=3}^{4} \frac{1}{\nu!} V_\nu(k_1, \cdots, k_\nu)\, A_{k_1} \cdots A_{k_\nu}, \tag{2.4}$$

where

$$A_k = A_{-k}^\dagger = (2\omega_k)^{-1/2}(a_k + a_{-k}^\dagger), \tag{2.5a}$$

$$B_k = -\,B_{-k}^\dagger = (\tfrac{1}{2}\omega_k)^{1/2}(a_k - a_{-k}^\dagger), \tag{2.5b}$$

and $\pm k = (\pm \boldsymbol{k}, \lambda)$ summarizes phonon wave vector $\boldsymbol{k}$ (or 'quasimomentum') and polarization λ. In the case of a quantum crystal like solid helium such an expansion of (2.1) is meaningless since the harmonic phonon energies ω_k entering (2.4) and (2.5) are imaginary throughout the whole Brillouin zone.

In this situation, we consider (2.4) as a model hamiltonian with some effective ω_k and coupling parameters V_ν, which should adequately describe transport phenomena involving phonons of relatively long wavelength. This point of view will be justified in subsection 5.2.

If V_3 and V_4 are neglected, the phonons behave like an ideal Bose gas with occupation numbers

$$N(k) = N_0(\omega_k) = [\exp(\beta\omega_k) - 1]^{-1}, \quad \beta = (k_B T)^{-1}. \tag{2.6}$$

When the anharmonic corrections in (2.4) are taken into account, the phonons are no longer completely well-defined excitations. The effect of interaction processes among them is usually incorporated into an energy shift Δ_k and a damping Γ_k which, for small V_3 and V_4, can be calculated by perturbation theory. Explicit expressions, correct up to V_3^2 and V_4, can be found in the literature (e.g. Maradudin and Fein 1962). Such a form for Γ_k will be given in subsection 4.2.3 in the framework of a Green's function treatment of thermal conductivity.

2.2. The Peierls equation

In order to describe transport processes like heat conduction, we must allow for situations where the crystal is subjected to external disturbances which may vary in space and time. We assume that in such a non-equilibrium state the concept of phonons or of – more appropriately – wave packets of phonons of polarization λ and mean wave vector $\boldsymbol{k}$ which can be localized in regions smaller than a characteristic wavelength of the external perturbation is still valid and useful (Peierls 1955). All physical quantities of interest can then be calculated provided the distribution function $N(k, \boldsymbol{r}t)$ of phonons at position $\boldsymbol{r}$ and time t is known. Its time evolution is supposed to obey the 'Peierls–Boltzmann' equation

$$\frac{\partial N}{\partial t} + \boldsymbol{v}_{k'} \cdot \frac{\partial N}{\partial \boldsymbol{r}} = C[N], \tag{2.7}$$

with the phonon group velocity $\boldsymbol{v}_k \equiv \partial\omega_k/\partial\boldsymbol{k}$. The collision operator C is a sum of different terms describing various scattering processes, namely

$$C = C_N + C_R, \quad C_R = C_I + C_B + C_U,$$

where C_N comprises normal processes and the resistive part C_R can be broken into boundary scattering (C_B), scattering from impurities, dislocations, etc. (C_I), and an Umklapp term C_U. Explicit expressions for C_N and C_U, especially their linearized version will be written down in section 4 whereas the work of Klemens (1951, 1955) provides formulae for C_I. The simple transport equation (2.7) which is due to Peierls (1955) will be justified in subsection 4.1 in the framework of non-equilibrium Green's functions, which also yields generalizations taking into account the finite life time of the colliding quasi-particles and a mean field type interaction between the latter as well as their coupling to elastic deformations. Solving (2.7) in a mathematically satisfactory way is a difficult task which will be discussed in subsection 4.3. Here our elementary treatment of second sound and thermal conduction is based on the so-called relaxation time approximation to the full collision operator C. This can be made plausible in the following way: for all above mentioned scattering mechanisms the total energy of the phonons is conserved. Thus the local equilibrium distribution function

$$N_{\mathrm{LE}}(k, \boldsymbol{r}t) = \{\exp[\beta(\boldsymbol{r}t)\,\omega_k] - 1\}^{-1}, \tag{2.8}$$

$\beta(\boldsymbol{r}, t)$ being a space- and time-dependent inverse local temperature, is unaffected by C, i.e. $C\,[N_{\mathrm{LE}}]=0$. Furthermore, C_N also conserves momentum, which is not true for C_R which summarizes all resistive processes that are responsible for a finite thermal conductivity. So the 'drifting' local equilibrium function

$$N^{\mathrm{d}}_{\mathrm{LE}}(k, \boldsymbol{r}t) = (\exp\{\beta(\boldsymbol{r}t)\,[\omega_k - \boldsymbol{u}(\boldsymbol{r}t)\cdot\boldsymbol{k}]\} - 1)^{-1} \tag{2.9}$$

obeys $C_N\,[N^{\mathrm{d}}_{\mathrm{LE}}]=0$. Obviously $\boldsymbol{u}$ has the meaning of a local drift velocity of the phonon gas.

We now replace the full collision operator C by the following approximation

$$C[N(k)] = -\frac{N(k) - N^{\mathrm{d}}_{\mathrm{LE}}(k)}{\tau_{\mathrm{N}}(k)} - \frac{N(k) - N_{\mathrm{LE}}(k)}{\tau_{\mathrm{R}}(k)}. \tag{2.10}$$

The physical meaning of this approximation is clear: normal collisions reduce any deviations of the distribution function for wave vector and polarization $(\boldsymbol{k}, \lambda)$ from a drifting local equilibrium state to zero within a characteristic relaxation time $\tau_{\mathrm{N}}(k)$. In the same way C_R drives the phonon distribution back to N_{LE} within $\tau_{\mathrm{R}}(k)$. From a mathematical point of view this simplification is drastic although it will be justified to some extent in subsection 4.3. Since, on the other hand, more rigorous solutions of (2.7), other than purely formal ones, would have to be found for a specific solid by means of very extensive numerical work, the relaxation time approximation (2.10) has been very widely used to discuss phonon hydrodynamical phenomena in a qualitative and a quantitative way. Recently Maris (1972, 1973), and Meier and Beck (1973) have successfully applied numerical methods to solve the transport equation for the phonons in liquid He II and were able to explain the experimental frequency dependence of the sound velocity which could not be accounted for by a relaxation time approximation.

Before we write down the explicit solution of (2.7) using (2.10) we assume that for all our purposes the deviation $\delta f(\boldsymbol{r}t)$ of any quantity $f(\boldsymbol{r}t)$ from its equilibrium value f_0 is small, which allows for linearization of all equations with respect to the δf's involved. This procedure gives an adequate description for most experiments. Some data on non-linear behaviour of heat pulses are mentioned in the introduction.

Let us therefore expand

$$N(k, \boldsymbol{r}t) = N_0(k) + m(k)\, g(k, \boldsymbol{r}t), \tag{2.11}$$

$$N_{\mathrm{LE}}(k, \boldsymbol{r}t) \approx N_0(k) - m(k)\, \omega_k\, \delta\beta(\boldsymbol{r}t)/\beta_0\,, \tag{2.12}$$

$$N_{\mathrm{LE}}^{\mathrm{d}}(k, \boldsymbol{r}t) \approx N_0(k) - m(k)\, [\omega_k\, \delta\beta(\boldsymbol{r}t)/\beta_0 - \boldsymbol{u}(\boldsymbol{r}t)\cdot\boldsymbol{k}]\,, \tag{2.13}$$

with

$$m(k) = -\, \mathrm{d}N_0/\mathrm{d}\omega_k = -\, \beta_0 N_0 (N_0 + 1)\,. \tag{2.14}$$

After insertion of (2.11) – (2.14) into (2.10), the collision equation for the unknown function g reads

$$\left[\frac{\partial}{\partial t} + \boldsymbol{v}\cdot\frac{\partial}{\partial \boldsymbol{r}} + \tau^{-1}\right] g = -\frac{\omega_k}{\tau}\frac{\delta\beta}{\beta_0} + \frac{1}{\tau_{\mathrm{N}}}\, \boldsymbol{u}\cdot\boldsymbol{k}\,, \tag{2.15}$$

with the combined relaxation time

$$\tau(k)^{-1} = \tau_{\mathrm{N}}(k)^{-1} + \tau_{\mathrm{R}}(k)^{-1}\,. \tag{2.16}$$

Upon Fourier transforming all quantities according to

$$f(k, \boldsymbol{r}t) = \sum_{\boldsymbol{q}} \mathrm{e}^{\mathrm{i}\boldsymbol{q}\cdot\boldsymbol{r}} \int_{-\infty}^{+\infty} \mathrm{d}\Omega\, \mathrm{e}^{-\mathrm{i}\Omega t} f(k, \boldsymbol{q}\Omega)\,, \tag{2.17}$$

the solution of (2.15) is formally given by

$$g(k, \boldsymbol{q}\Omega) = [-\mathrm{i}\Omega + \mathrm{i}\boldsymbol{q}\cdot\boldsymbol{v}_k + \tau^{-1}(k)]^{-1} \times \left[-\frac{\omega_k}{\tau(k)} \frac{\delta\beta(\boldsymbol{q}\Omega)}{\beta_0} + \frac{1}{\tau_{\mathrm{N}}(k)} \boldsymbol{u}(\boldsymbol{q}\Omega)\cdot\boldsymbol{k} \right]. \tag{2.18}$$

Thus g depends on two unknown functions, $\delta\beta$ and u. These quantities have to be chosen such as to fulfill the conservation laws associated with the transport equation (2.7). We define local densities and currents by

energy density:

$$E(\boldsymbol{r}t) = V^{-1} \sum_k \omega_k N(k, \boldsymbol{r}t) = E_0 + \delta E(\boldsymbol{r}t), \tag{2.19}$$

energy current:

$$S_i(\boldsymbol{r}t) = V^{-1} \sum_k \omega_k (v_k)_i N(\cdot\cdot) = \delta S_i(\boldsymbol{r}t), \tag{2.20}$$

momentum density:

$$P_i(\boldsymbol{r}t) = V^{-1} \sum_k k_i N(\cdot\cdot) = \delta P_i(\boldsymbol{r}t), \tag{2.21}$$

momentum flux tensor:

$$T_{ij}(\boldsymbol{r}t) = V^{-1} \sum_k k_i (v_k)_j N(\cdot\cdot) = T_{ij}^{(0)} + \delta T_{ij}(\boldsymbol{r}t), \tag{2.22}$$

where, corresponding to the splitting of N into N_0 and g in (2.11), the deviations are given by

$$\delta E(\boldsymbol{r}t) = V^{-1} \sum_k \omega_k \, m(k) \, g(k, \boldsymbol{r}t), \text{ etc.} \tag{2.19a}$$

Multiplication of (2.7) by ω_k and k_i, respectively, and summation over k leads to

$$\frac{\partial \delta E}{\partial t} + \frac{\partial \boldsymbol{S}}{\partial \boldsymbol{r}} = 0, \quad \frac{\partial P_i}{\partial t} + \frac{\partial T_{ij}}{\partial r_j} = \sum_k k_i C_{\mathrm{R}}(N). \tag{2.23, 24}$$

These are, respectively, the conservation law for the energy density and a 'quasi-conservation law' for the 'quasi-momentum' density, the right-hand side of which shows the loss of quasi-momentum due to resistive scattering. In fact, if resistive collisions are at least as frequent as momentum conserving ones. i.e. '$C_R \gtrsim C_N$', the first term in (2.10) can be omitted and (2.23) is the only conservation law needed, since there is just $\delta\beta$ to be determined. By inserting the solution (2.18) for g into the expressions occurring in (2.23) and (2.24), we obtain a system of 'hydrodynamic equations' for $\delta\beta$ and $\boldsymbol{u}$. This will turn out to be a convenient framework to discuss thermal conduction and second sound.

2.3. Second sound

In subsection 5.4 the full solution (2.18) will be used to discuss heat pulse experiments at various temperatures. In order to get an immediate understanding of second sound as a collective motion in the phonon gas, we suppose that the mean frequencies Ω of the temperature deviation $\delta\beta$ are small compared to the relevant inverse relaxation times $\tau(k)^{-1}$. This means that sufficiently many collision events take place during one period of oscillation of the macroscopic quantity $\delta\beta$ so that, at anytime, the phonon gas is able to reach a local equilibrium state, characterized by $\beta(\boldsymbol{rt})$ and $\boldsymbol{u}(\boldsymbol{rt})$. This is the condition for a hydrodynamic description to be valid.

Thus the denominator in (2.18) is expanded:

$$g \approx [1 + \mathrm{i}\Omega\tau - \mathrm{i}\boldsymbol{v}\cdot\boldsymbol{q}\tau + \cdots]\left[-\omega_k \frac{\delta\beta}{\beta_0} + \frac{\tau}{\tau_N}\boldsymbol{u}\cdot\boldsymbol{k}\right]. \tag{2.25}$$

(Strictly speaking there may always be small values of $\boldsymbol{k}$ such that $\Omega\tau(k)$ is large, as we shall see from expressions like (2.51) to (2.54) for the various τ's. We anticipate, however, that in the final results these long wavelength contributions will have negligible weight.) Using (2.25) we can immediately evaluate the densities and currents (2.19) to (2.22). To this end we abbreviate the average of any quantity f over the distribution function (2.14) by

$$V^{-1}\sum_{\boldsymbol{k}} f(k)\, m(k) \equiv \langle f(k)\rangle .$$

Let us first drop all terms proportional to τ and furthermore assume that there is no resistive scattering such that $\tau = \tau_N$. For crystals showing inversion symmetry we find for these lowest order contributions

$$\delta E(\boldsymbol{q}\Omega) = -\langle\omega_k^2\rangle\,\delta\beta(\boldsymbol{q}\Omega)/\beta_0\,, \tag{2.26}$$

$$\delta P_i = \langle k_i k_j\rangle\, u_j\,, \tag{2.27}$$

$$\delta S_i = \langle\omega_k v_i k_j\rangle\, u_j\,, \tag{2.28}$$

$$\delta T_{ij} = -\langle\omega_k k_i k_j\rangle\,\delta\beta/\beta_0\,, \tag{2.29}$$

(repeated indices imply a summation) and the conservation laws read

$$\mathrm{i}\Omega\langle\omega_k^2\rangle\,\delta\beta/\beta_0 + \mathrm{i}q_i u_j\langle\omega_k v_i k_j\rangle = 0\,, \tag{2.30}$$

$$\mathrm{i}q_j\langle\omega_k v_j k_i\rangle\,\delta\beta/\beta_0 + \mathrm{i}\Omega u_j\langle k_i k_j\rangle = 0\,. \tag{2.31}$$

This system has non-trivial solutions for $\delta\beta$ and u_i provided that the determinant vanishes, which yields the desired relation $\Omega = \Omega(\boldsymbol{q})$ for the possible excitations.

For a cubic crystal we find

$$\Omega^2 = q^2\,\frac{\langle\omega_k \boldsymbol{v}\cdot\boldsymbol{k}\rangle^2}{3\langle\boldsymbol{k}^2\rangle\langle\omega_k^2\rangle} \equiv c_{\mathrm{II}}^2 q^2\,. \tag{2.32}$$

This is the dispersion relation for an undamped second sound wave. The averages entering the expression for c_{II}, which was first given in this general form by Kwok (1967), can be computed once the phonon spectrum $\omega_{\boldsymbol{k}\lambda}$ of the solid is known. Numerical calculations for some alkali halides for various temperatures were performed by Varshni and Konti (1972), Hardy and Jaswal (1971), and Jaswal and Hardy (1972). For NaF, for instance, c_{II} will be weakly temperature dependent, its value for $T = 18\,\mathrm{K}$ being about 7% smaller than the one for $T = 0\,\mathrm{K}$. If ω_k is approximated by a Debye spectrum, $\omega_k = c_\lambda|\boldsymbol{k}|$, the well-known temperature independent expression

$$c_{\mathrm{II}}^2 = \tfrac{1}{3}\Big(\sum_\lambda c_\lambda^{-3}\Big)\Big/\Big(\sum_\lambda c_\lambda^{-5}\Big) \tag{2.33}$$

results [see Süssmann and Thellung (1963) and many other papers]. If we consider the two transverse modes to be degenerate and c_{t} to be much smaller than c_ℓ, c_{II} is approximately given by $c_{\mathrm{t}}/\sqrt{3}$. This very simple approximation for (2.32) shows the analogy between second sound as a collective mode of the phonon gas and an ordinary sound wave in a gas of particles, since in the latter case one finds the same relation between the sound velocity c_{s} and the mean thermal velocity c_{T} of a single gas particle: $c_{\mathrm{s}} = c_{\mathrm{T}}/\sqrt{3}$.

The factor $\sqrt{3}$ can be thought of as expressing the fact that particles moving in all three spatial directions are equally taking part in the collective vibration.

It is also interesting to note the connection with Landau's (1941b) expression for c_{II} in superfluid helium, derived on the basis of the two-fluid equations. He obtained

$$c_{\text{II}}^2 = TS^2\rho_s/(C\rho_n\rho), \tag{2.34}$$

where S = entropy, C = specific heat (both per unit volume), ρ_s = density of superfluid phase and ρ_n = density of the normal fluid. Considering again the phonons to be an ideal Bose gas, we can easily compute these thermodynamic quantities (Khalatnikov 1965):

$$S = \langle \omega_k \boldsymbol{v} \cdot \boldsymbol{k} \rangle / (3T), \tag{2.35}$$

$$C = \langle \omega_k^2 \rangle / T, \tag{2.36}$$

$$\rho_n = \langle \boldsymbol{k}^2 \rangle / 3. \tag{2.37}$$

Thus (2.34) agrees with (2.32) as long as ϱ_s in (2.34) is replaced by ϱ, which is a good approximation for very low temperatures. Dynes et al. (1973) have used expression (2.34) to compute c_{II} for superfluid He by using the values for ω_k and v_k obtained from the measured phonon–roton dispersion curve. They find a T-dependent second-sound velocity which is in good agreement with their heat pulse data.

Let us finally mention that, in contrast to a cubic system, the second-sound velocity in a hexagonal crystal will in general depend on the propagation direction.

Next we calculate the contributions of order τ and those arising from a non-vanishing probability for resistive scattering. Here we are faced with a certain formal dilemma: on one hand, the more fundamental eigenvector analysis of the collision operator in subsection 4.3 will show that the expressions (2.26) and (2.27) for δE and P_i should hold to all orders in τ, since they are projections of the true solution g of (2.7) onto the eigenvector ω_k and k_i of C_{N}, respectively. On the other hand, insertion of our approximate relaxation time solution (2.25) into (2.19) and (2.21) leads to corrections of order τ which, in general, do not vanish. This is one of the differences between the treatments of Süssman and Thellung (1963) and Guyer and Krumhansl (1966a). In order to keep our discussion closely along the lines of the more general analysis in subsection 4.3, we simply omit the corrections of order τ to δE and P_i. Using expression (2.25) also for the loss term on the right-hand side of conservation law (2.24) we find, instead of (2.30), (2.31), the system (valid for cubic symmetry again):

$$(\delta\beta/\beta_0)\,[\mathrm{i}\Omega\langle\omega_k^2\rangle - \tfrac{1}{3}q^2\langle\omega_k^2 v_k^2\tau\rangle] \\ + \tfrac{1}{3}\boldsymbol{q}\cdot\boldsymbol{u}\,[\mathrm{i}\langle\omega_k \boldsymbol{k}\cdot\boldsymbol{v}\,(1-\alpha)\rangle - \Omega\langle\omega_k \boldsymbol{k}\cdot\boldsymbol{v}\tau\,(1-\alpha)\rangle] = 0\,, \tag{2.38}$$

$$(\delta\beta/\beta_0)\,[-\,\mathrm{i}q_i\langle\omega_k \boldsymbol{k}\cdot\boldsymbol{v}\,(1-\alpha)\rangle + \Omega q_i\langle\omega_k \boldsymbol{k}\cdot\boldsymbol{v}\tau\rangle] \\ + u_i[-\,\mathrm{i}\Omega\langle\boldsymbol{k}^2\rangle + q^2 B + \langle\boldsymbol{k}^2\,(1-\alpha)\,\tau_{\mathrm{R}}^{-1}\rangle + \mathrm{i}\Omega\langle\boldsymbol{k}^2\,(1-\alpha)\,\alpha\rangle] \\ + q_i\boldsymbol{q}\cdot\boldsymbol{u}A = 0\,, \tag{2.39}$$

with

$$A = \tfrac{1}{5}[3\langle(\boldsymbol{k}\cdot\boldsymbol{v})^2\,(1-\alpha)\,\tau\rangle - \langle\boldsymbol{k}^2\boldsymbol{v}^2\,(1-\alpha)\,\tau\rangle]\,, \tag{2.40}$$

$$B = \tfrac{1}{5}[2\langle\boldsymbol{k}^2\boldsymbol{v}^2\,(1-\alpha)\,\tau\rangle - \langle(\boldsymbol{k}\cdot\boldsymbol{v})^2\,(1-\alpha)\,\tau\rangle]\,. \tag{2.41}$$

$$\alpha = \tau/\tau_{\mathrm{R}} = 1 - \tau/\tau_{\mathrm{N}}\,. \tag{2.42}$$

For later use we write down the total expression for the heat current (2.20)

$$S_i = \tfrac{1}{3}[\langle\omega_k \boldsymbol{k}\cdot\boldsymbol{v}\,(1-\alpha)\rangle + \mathrm{i}\Omega\langle\omega_k \boldsymbol{k}\cdot\boldsymbol{v}\,(1-\alpha)\,\tau\rangle]\,u_i \\ + \tfrac{1}{3}\mathrm{i}\langle\omega_k^2 v_k^2\tau\rangle\,q_i\,\delta\beta/\beta_0\,. \tag{2.43}$$

These equations can now be used to find expressions for the thermal conductivity (see next section) and for attenuation and dispersion of second sound. For the latter purpose (2.39) is multiplied by q_i and summed over i. We specialize to the situation where normal processes are still much more frequent than resistive collisions, i.e. $\tau_{\mathrm{N}} \ll \tau_{\mathrm{R}}$ and $\tau \approx \tau_{\mathrm{N}}$. Then the condition for vanishing determinant of (2.38) and (2.39) reads

$$\Omega^2 + \mathrm{i}\Omega\,[\overline{\tau_{\mathrm{R}}^{-1}} + q^2 c_{\mathrm{II}}^2\bar{\tau}_{\mathrm{N}}] - q^2 c_{\mathrm{II}}^2 \approx 0\,, \tag{2.44}$$

with

$$\overline{\tau_{\mathrm{R}}^{-1}} = \langle\boldsymbol{k}^2\tau_{\mathrm{R}}^{-1}\rangle/\langle\boldsymbol{k}^2\rangle\,, \tag{2.45}$$

$$\bar{\tau}_{\mathrm{N}} = \langle\omega_k^2 v_k^2\tau_{\mathrm{N}}\rangle\,\langle\boldsymbol{k}^2\rangle/\langle\omega_k \boldsymbol{k}\cdot\boldsymbol{v}\rangle^2 \\ + \tfrac{1}{5}[\langle\boldsymbol{k}^2\boldsymbol{v}^2\tau_{\mathrm{N}}\rangle + 2\langle(\boldsymbol{k}\cdot\boldsymbol{v})^2\,\tau_{\mathrm{N}}\rangle]\,\langle\omega_k^2\rangle/\langle\omega_k \boldsymbol{k}\cdot\boldsymbol{v}\rangle^2 \\ - 2\langle\omega_k \boldsymbol{k}\cdot\boldsymbol{v}\tau_{\mathrm{N}}\rangle/\langle\omega_k \boldsymbol{k}\cdot\boldsymbol{v}\rangle\,. \tag{2.46}$$

This yields the dispersion relation

$$\Omega \approx \pm c_{\mathrm{II}} q \left[1 - \frac{1}{4} \left(\frac{\overline{\tau_{\mathrm{R}}^{-1}}}{q c_{\mathrm{II}}} + \bar{\tau}_{\mathrm{N}} q c_{\mathrm{II}} \right)^2 \right]^{1/2} - \mathrm{i} \left[\overline{\tau_{\mathrm{R}}^{-1}} + q^2 c_{\mathrm{II}}^2 \bar{\tau}_{\mathrm{N}} \right]. \tag{2.47}$$

It is obvious from this result that the damping of second sound has two sources: normal and resistive scattering. In order to have a weakly damped wave there should be many normal processes:

$$\Omega \bar{\tau}_{\mathrm{N}} \ll 1\,, \tag{2.48}$$

and momentum destroying collisions should be rare:

$$\Omega \gg \overline{\tau_{\mathrm{R}}^{-1}}\,. \tag{2.49}$$

The combination of these two inequalities is the well-known 'window' condition for the frequency of second sound (replacing $(\overline{\tau_{\mathrm{R}}^{-1}})^{-1}$ by some $\overline{\tau_{\mathrm{R}}}$)

$$\Omega \bar{\tau}_{\mathrm{N}} \ll 1 \ll \Omega \bar{\tau}_{\mathrm{R}}\,. \tag{2.50}$$

The quantities $\overline{\tau_{\mathrm{N}}}$ and $\overline{\tau_{\mathrm{R}}^{-1}}$ are weighted means of $\tau(k)$ and $\tau_{\mathrm{R}}^{-1}(k)$. In subsection 4.3 we shall relate them to matrix elements of the full collision operator. Here we can estimate the feasibility according to (2.50) of observing second sound by interpreting the various $\tau_i(k)$ as lifetimes for single phonons of wave vector $\boldsymbol{k}$ and polarization λ with respect to decay by a corresponding collision process. We list some well-known results (the subscripts have the meaning defined at the beginning of subsection 2.2) valid for very low temperatures:

Herring (1954)

$$\tau_{\mathrm{N}}^{-1} \propto T^m k^{5-m}, \quad 1 \leqslant m \leqslant 4\,; \tag{2.51}$$

e.g. Jackson and Walker (1971)

$$\tau_{\mathrm{U}}^{-1} \propto T^2 k^3 \exp\left(-\theta_{\mathrm{D}}/\alpha T\right), \quad \alpha \approx 2\,; \tag{2.52}$$

Klemens (1955)

$$\tau_{\mathrm{I}}^{-1} \propto k^4\,; \tag{2.53}$$

Casimir (1938)

$$\tau_B^{-1} \propto L^{-1}. \tag{2.54}$$

θ_D is the Debye temperature and L a characteristic sample length [see Jackson and Walker (1971) for more information about estimates differing from those given here]. For low temperatures the dispersion of the phonons in the averages of the type (2.45), (2.46) can be neglected and we can expect the following temperature dependence for the mean values

$$\overline{\tau_N} \approx A_N T^{-5}, \text{ independent of } m \text{ in (2.51)}, \tag{2.55}$$

$$\overline{\tau_R^{-1}} \approx A_B/L + A_I T^4 + A_U T^5 \exp(-\theta_D/\alpha T). \tag{2.56}$$

Since Umklapp processes die out exponentially for $T \to 0$, the main requirement for satisfying (2.49) consists in growing sufficiently large (L big enough) and pure (A_I small!) crystals. On the other hand, A_N should be large enough such that normal collisions are still frequent at those values of T for which τ_R^{-1} is negligible. In section 3, where we describe second-sound experiments, the various materials used for this purpose, successfully and otherwise, will be considered from this point of view.

Expression (2.47) shows that the velocity of second sound depends rather strongly on τ_R^{-1}. It is close to c_{II} only if (2.49) is well satisfied and it goes to zero as soon as τ_R^{-1} is comparable to $2qc_{II}$. If τ_R^{-1} is still larger, such that inequality (2.49) is reversed, we find, instead of (2.47),

$$\Omega \approx -\mathrm{i}q^2 c_{II}^2 \bar{\tau}. \tag{2.57}$$

This corresponds to diffusive heat conduction (see next section) instead of a propagating temperature wave.

If, however, (2.49) is well satisfied the solutions (2.47) can be approximated by $\Omega \approx \pm c_{II}q - iq^2 c_{II}\bar{\tau}_N$. Then a one-dimensional temperature distribution $\delta\beta(rt)$ with initial value $\delta\beta(r0)$ propagates as

$$\delta\beta(rt) \propto (\bar{\tau}_N t)^{-1/2} \int \mathrm{d}r' \exp\left[-\frac{(r - r' \pm c_{II}t)^2}{4c_{II}^2\bar{\tau}_N t}\right] \delta\beta(r'0). \tag{2.58}$$

Such a pulse propagates with velocity c_{II}, but its width is spread proportional to $(\bar{\tau}_N t)^{1/2}$ (see Ackerman and Guyer 1968). This fact was used to determine $\bar{\tau}_N$ from heat pulse experiments on solid He.

2.4. Steady state thermal conductivity. Poiseuille flow

Phenomenologically the thermal conductivity κ is defined by Fourier's law

$$S_i = -\kappa\, \partial T/\partial x_i\,, \tag{2.59}$$

which postulates proportionality between heat current $\boldsymbol{S}$ and gradient of the local temperature. (For a crystal other than cubic, κ has to be replaced by a tensor κ_{ij}.) $\boldsymbol{S}$ and T, or rather $\delta\beta/\beta_0 = -\delta T/T_0$, have appeared explicitly in our treatment of the phonon Boltzmann equation in the previous subsection. For the time-independent situation ($\Omega = 0$), eq. (2.43) reads in $\boldsymbol{r}$-space:

$$S_i = -(1/3T_0)\,\langle \omega_k^2 v_k^2 \tau\rangle\, \nabla_i\, \delta T + \tfrac{1}{3}\langle \omega_k \boldsymbol{k}\cdot\boldsymbol{v}\,(1-\alpha)\rangle\, u_i\,. \tag{2.60}$$

If resistive scattering is strong, no local drift can develop, and therefore $\boldsymbol{u} = 0$ and κ can be approximated by the well-known expression

$$\kappa = (1/3T_0)\,\langle \omega_k^2 v_k^2 \tau\rangle \approx \tfrac{1}{3} C \bar{c}^2 \tau_{\text{eff}}\,, \tag{2.61}$$

where (2.36) was used for the specific heat and τ_{eff} and $\bar{c}$ denote appropriate mean values for the phonon relaxation time and group velocity. For the general case, we have to use eq. (2.39) with $\Omega = 0$ to express u_i again in terms of δT:

$$\begin{aligned}[\langle k^2 (1-\alpha)\,\tau_{\text{R}}^{-1}\rangle - B\nabla^2]\, u_i - A\nabla_i \nabla\cdot\boldsymbol{u}&\\ = -(1/T_0)\,\langle \omega_k \boldsymbol{k}\cdot\boldsymbol{v}\,(1-\alpha)\rangle\, \nabla_i\, \delta T\,.&\end{aligned} \tag{2.62}$$

Let us assume that the gradient of δT is uniform over the whole sample, say parallel to the z-axis, and that $\boldsymbol{u}$ has the same direction. Furthermore, we want to describe a situation where u_z and S_z depend only on x and y. Insertion of (2.62) into (2.60) then yields a differential equation for S_z:

$$S_z - \tfrac{3}{5} c_{\text{II}}^2 \tau_{\text{p}} \tau_z \nabla^2 S_z = -\left[\langle \omega_k^2 v_k^2 \tau\rangle + \frac{\langle \omega_k \boldsymbol{k}\cdot\boldsymbol{v}\,(1-\alpha)\rangle^2}{\langle k^2 (1-\alpha)\,\tau_{\text{R}}^{-1}\rangle}\right] \frac{1}{3T_0}\, \nabla_i\, \delta T, \tag{2.63}$$

with

$$\tau_z^{-1} = \langle k^2 (1-\alpha)\,\tau_{\text{R}}^{-1}\rangle / \langle k^2\rangle\,, \tag{2.64}$$

$$\tau_{\text{p}} = \frac{\langle \omega_k^2\rangle}{\langle \omega_k^2 \boldsymbol{k}\cdot\boldsymbol{v}\rangle^2}\,[2\langle k^2 v^2 (1-\alpha)\,\tau\rangle - \langle (\boldsymbol{k}\cdot\boldsymbol{v})^2 (1-\alpha)\,\tau\rangle]\,. \tag{2.65}$$

For a cylindrical sample the solution $S_z(r)$, r being $(x^2+y^2)^{1/2}$, is given by a Bessel function. Guyer and Krumhansl (1966b) have discussed the behavior of S_z in detail. Two limiting situations are specially simple:

(i) The second derivative of S_z is of the order $R^2 S_z$, R being the radius of the sample. The first term on the left-hand side of (2.63) can be neglected, provided that

$$\tfrac{3}{5}c_{II}^2 \tau_p \tau_z R^2 \gg 1 ,$$

or, in terms of mean free paths $l_p = \sqrt{3}c_{II}\tau_p$ and $l_z = \sqrt{3}c_{II}\tau_z$, if

$$l_z \gg R^2/l_p . \tag{2.66}$$

This means that the resistive mean free path l_z has to be at least as large as the radial sample dimension since, on the other hand, our expansion (2.25) is only valid as long as the total mean free path l_p is smaller than the spatial variation of quantities like $\boldsymbol{S}$, i.e. $l_p < R$. Therefore, τ_N has to be much smaller than τ_R, and l_p is essentially l_N, the normal process mean free path, and our second condition for case (i) reads

$$l_p \approx l_N \ll R . \tag{2.67}$$

Under these circumstances, the solution $S_z(r)$ which vanishes on the sample wall is [using again (2.36) and (2.64), (2.65)]:

$$S_z(r) = -\tfrac{1}{2}(R^2 - r^2)\tfrac{5}{3}(C/\tau_p)\nabla_z \delta T . \tag{2.68}$$

This stationary motion of the phonon gas corresponds to Poiseuille flow in a liquid (Süssman and Thellung 1963). Heat current and drift velocity have a parabolic shape as functions of r. The total heat flow S_z is found by integrating (2.68) over the sample cross section:

$$\bar{S}_z = -\pi R^2 \kappa_{PF} \nabla_z \delta T , \tag{2.69}$$

with the Poiseuille flow thermal conductivity

$$\kappa_{PF} = \tfrac{5}{12}R^2 C/\tau_p . \tag{2.70}$$

The R^4 dependence of the total heat current has been verified experimentally (e.g. Hogan et al. 1969). Since according to (2.55) τ_p, which is about equal to τ_N, should vary as T^{-5} for low temperatures, we expect κ_{PF} to rise with T as T^8. This fact will be discussed in section 3. The conditions (2.66) and (2.67) for the observation of Poiseuille flow are more stringent than the 'window' (2.50) for second sound, since there l_R, the resistive mean free path, does not have to meet (2.66) but it has merely to be larger than the wavelength of second sound, which in a typical heat pulse experiment is much smaller than the sample length. This may be the reason why NaF shows second sound but nobody has as yet observed Poiseuille flow even in the purest NaF crystals. Expression (2.70) for κ_{PF} can also be cast into the general form (2.61) for a thermal conduction coefficient

$$\kappa_{PF} = \tfrac{1}{3} C\bar{c} l_{PF} \quad \text{with} \quad l_{PF} = \tfrac{5}{4} R^2/(\bar{c}\tau_p). \tag{2.71}$$

As in the very low temperature Casimir region (see below), scattering from the sample walls is the mechanism which produces a finite thermal resistance in the Poiseuille flow domain. However, in contrast to the Casimir case, normal processes, according to (2.67) are very frequent. So the mean distance a phonon travels until it reaches the wall, where it loses momentum, is $\bar{l} \approx R^2/(\bar{c}\tau_N)$, a result typical for a brownian type motion, instead of $R/\bar{c}$.

(*ii*) τ_z is so small that the $\Delta^2 S_z$-term in (2.63) is of no importance. Then the heat current is constant and the thermal conductivity is given by

$$\kappa = \frac{1}{3T_0}\left[\langle \omega_k^2 v_k^2 \tau\rangle + \frac{\langle \omega_k \boldsymbol{k}\cdot\boldsymbol{v}\tau/\tau_N\rangle^2}{\langle k^2(1-\tau/\tau_N)/\tau_N\rangle}\right]. \tag{2.72}$$

This is the obvious generalization to a system with s polarizations and arbitrary dispersion $\omega_{k\lambda}$ of the well-known Callaway expression for κ (Callaway 1959, Holland 1963), which has been used very frequently and often quite successfully to analyze experimental data. Some aspects of such 'Callaway fits' will be discussed in section 3.

In conclusion, the general temperature behavior of κ in the various regions where different scattering processes dominate can be summarized by the help of the form (2.61). Taking the relaxation times in (2.72) out of the averaging brackets and replacing them by appropriate mean values, we find as in (2.61)

$$\kappa \approx \tfrac{1}{3} C\bar{c}^2 \tau_{\text{eff}}, \tag{2.73}$$

with

$$\tau_{\text{eff}} \approx \bar{\tau}\left[1 + (c_{II}^2/c_{II}'^2)\,\bar{\tau}_R/\bar{\tau}_N\right] 3c_{II}'^2/\bar{c}^2 \tag{2.74}$$

and

$$c_{\mathrm{II}}'^2 = \tfrac{1}{3}\langle \omega_k^2 v_k^2 \rangle / \langle \omega_k^2 \rangle . \tag{2.75}$$

The last expression is the velocity of 'driftless second sound' discussed in subsection 5.3. Depending on the strength of the various collision processes, we can distinguish between five different regions of thermal conduction listed in table 1 with the corresponding inequalities between mean relaxation times, the expected T-dependence of κ and an estimate for τ_{eff} in (2.73).

TABLE 1

Casimir region		
$\tau_R \approx \tau_B$; τ_U and $\tau_I \gg \tau_B$; $\tau_N \gg \tau_B$;	$\kappa \propto T^3$ (specific heat),	$\tau_{\mathrm{eff}} \approx \tau_B$
'Defect region'		
$\tau_R \approx \tau_I$; $\tau_B \gtrsim \tau_I$; $\tau_U \gg \tau_B$; τ_N/τ_R depends on purity	κ approaches its peak,	τ_{eff} given by (2.74)
Poiseuille region		
$\tau_R \approx \tau_B$; τ_U, $\tau_I \gg \tau_B$; $\tau_N \ll \tau_B$;	$\kappa \propto T^8$ (at least in theory),	τ_{eff} acc. to (2.71)
Ziman region		
$\tau_R \approx \tau_U$; $\tau_U \ll \tau_B$, τ_I; $\tau_N \ll \tau_U$;	$\kappa \propto T^{-2} \exp(\theta_D/\alpha T)$ [see (2.52) and (2.56)], $\tau_{\mathrm{eff}} \approx \tau_U$	
Kinetic region		
$\tau_R \approx \tau_U$; $\tau_U \ll \tau_B$, τ_I; $\tau_N \gtrsim \tau_R$	$\kappa \propto T^{-1}$, $\tau_{\mathrm{eff}} \approx \tau$	

Fig. 2 (see p. 230) shows two typical κ versus T curves, one for an impure crystal and one for a very pure one, which shows Poiseuille flow.

Except for Poiseuille flow, where τ_p, or l_p, are essentially the relaxation quantities for normal processes, see (2.67) and (2.71), τ_N does not show up explicitly in table 1. Since normal processes conserve momentum and therefore do not destroy a phonon drift, they do, as such, not lead to a finite thermal resistance (Peierls 1955). This is true, although the heat current (2.20) is, in general, not proportional to the momentum density (2.21) which is actually the conserved quantity under normal processes. Normal processes can still influence κ, namely in the 'defect region' of very pure crystals, where τ_N is comparable with τ_R. There the full Callaway expression (2.74), which does involve τ_N, has to be used. Physically the influence of normal processes on the mechanism of thermal conduction can be understood in the following way: according to (2.53) scattering from impurities, etc. affects predominantly high frequency phonons. Now normal collisions, e.g. three-phonon processes, can help to provide more phonons of those kinds which are scattered strongly by all kinds of imperfections. Thus normal processes usually have a 'resistive' effect in that they lower the thermal conductivity (Berman and Brock 1965). This fact will be discussed in section 3.

3. *Experimental findings*

Before we develop a more rigorous mathematical framework justifying our elementary treatment of phonon hydrodynamics in section 2, it is useful to discuss, at least briefly, some experiments. Besides demonstrating the physical realizability of the phenomena postulated in the previous chapter, this will also show what specific questions a more fundamental theory should be able to answer.

As stated in the introduction, it is not the purpose of this chapter to review extensively the vast amount of experimental data on 'ordinary' low temperature thermal conduction. This has been done by a number of authors (see, e.g., Klemens 1956, 1958, or Carruthers 1961). Among other substances, alkali halides, such as NaF (Rogers 1971, Jackson and Walker 1971), LiF (Pohl 1968, Narayanamurti and Pohl 1970, Berman and Brock 1965) and KCl (Carruthers 1961) as well as solid helium (Berman et al. 1965, Berman et al. 1968, Berman and Day 1970, Bertman et al. 1966, Hogan et al. 1969) have proved to be best suited for testing the theoretical predictions. The theorist is humbled, however, by the fact that the Callaway formulation (and similar approximative schemes) which we derived from the relaxation time approximation to the phonon Boltzmann equation, is virtually the only level on which the theory can make quantitative statements. The results of the more rigorous treatment in subsection 4.3, are, with some exceptions, too formal to be compared directly with experimental data obtained on some specific sample, since in most cases knowledge of the full spectrum of the collision operator would be required. On the other hand it may be surprising how well Callaway-type models work in many instances.

Let us state briefly what an analysis of thermal conductivity data reveals about magnitude and temperature dependence of the mean relaxation times entering expressions like (2.73).

(*i*) κ is for very low T limited by boundary collisions. The T^3-dependence coming from the specific heat and the influence of the sample dimensions have been verified quite accurately (Pohl 1969).

(*ii*) The effect of impurities can best be studied by examining κ for samples to which a known amount of isotopes with different mass (e.g., some ^{3}He in ^{4}He) has been added. According to Klemens (1955)

$$\tau_I^{-1}(k) = Ak^4\,, \tag{3.1}$$

which yields $\overline{\tau_I^{-1}} \propto T^4$. Whereas the power four seems to fit the data well when analysed by (2.61), the total scattering is usually stronger than predicted by the constant A. This seems surprising since a variational treatment of the Boltzmann equation (Ziman 1956) including a collision operator for mass defect scattering (Klemens 1955) yields a rigorous upper bound for the effect of these collisions. Usually, the excess scattering is explained by assuming that the lattice is slightly distorted around the sites occupied by a foreign atom. Thus scattering of phonons from strain fields and local variations of the force constants has also to be considered (Carruthers 1961). In the case of helium, the quantum crystal effects have been taken into account by Varma (1971) and Nelson and Hartmann (1972). Such addditional scattering mechanisms again lead to mean relaxation times varying with T^4 (Carruthers 1961). There is some theoretical uncertainty about their magnitude and thus the comparison with experimental data is not quite satisfactory yet (Lawson and Fairbank 1973).

(*iii*) As to Umklapp processes, the exponential dependence

$$\overline{\tau_U^{-1}} = A_U T^n \exp(-\theta_D/\alpha T) \tag{3.2}$$

seems to be well verified. (bcc ^{3}He shows some anomalies, see Thomlinson 1972.) The number α in the exponent has to be chosen between about 2 and 4 in order to fit the data for most substances. It is, however, difficult to determine the exponent n since it does not influence the behavior of $\overline{\tau_U^{-1}}$ appreciably. In hcp ^{4}He a sizable anisotropy in thermal conductivity has been found: fitting the data for $\kappa_{\|}$ and $\kappa_{\perp}$ for temperature gradients parallel and orthogonal to the c-axis in the Ziman regime by

$$\kappa_{\|,\perp} = A_{\|,\perp} \exp(\theta_{\|,\perp}/T)\,, \tag{3.3}$$

Hogan et al. (1969) found that

$$A_{\parallel} \approx 20A_{\perp}, \quad \theta_{\parallel} \approx 0.5\theta_{\perp}. \tag{3.4}$$

Werthamer and Chui [1972a, b] have examined the matrix element (4.114) for thermal conduction in the Ziman limit and found that the large differences (3.4) between the parameters for $\kappa_{\parallel}$ and $\kappa_{\perp}$ can be accounted for by using the properties of the phonon spectrum of hcp ^{4}He.

(*iv*) The role of normal processes in thermal conduction was mentioned at the end of subsection 2.4. They only influence κ where τ_N and τ_R are comparable, which is expected to be true in the 'defect region' of crystals of high quality. Indeed it turns out to be impossible to fit the data for LiF (Berman and Brock 1965) and He (Berman et al. 1965, Bertman et al. 1966) in this region by simply assuming (2.61) with τ_{eff} given by τ, i.e. by neglecting the second term in the bracket of (2.74). On the other hand, the use of the full expression (2.74) in (2.61) for isotopically mixed systems can yield information about τ_N. This is usually done in the following way: it is assumed that τ_I is known and has a magnitude that is in agreement with the known concentration of isotopic defects. Then different power laws for $\tau_N(T)$ are used to find the best fit for the data using (2.74). It must be stated, however, that (2.74) does not depend on τ_N in a very sensitive way. Also, the results of this fitting procedure are not in agreement with each other:

LiF:

Berman and Brock (1965): $\tau_N^{-1} \propto T^4$ is better than T^5,

Ackerman and Guyer (1968): $\tau_N^{-1} \propto T^5$,

He: (3.5)

Ackerman and Guyer (1968): $\tau_N^{-1} \propto T^5$,

Berman et al. (1965): $\tau_N^{-1} \propto T^4$,

Agrawal (1967): $\tau_N^{-1} \propto T^5$.

Usually, the fact that τ_N^{-1} may deviate from the expected T^5 behavior in (2.55) is explained (Berman et al. 1965) by assuming that T^5 would only be valid for very low T, whereas the experiments show the transition to the high-T behavior expected to be $\tau_N^{-1} \propto T^2$ or T^3 (Herring 1954).

Concluding these few statements about static thermal conduction, let us remark that the curve for κ, which always looks like fig. 2, is a good indicator for the possibility of detecting second sound in a specific sample, since the mean free times determining the 'window' can be estimated from the analysis of κ. Second sound can be expected in the region where κ shows its maximum, provided that the latter is high enough.

There are four materials which have lent themselves to successful experiments demonstrating second sound (SS) and/or Poisieulle flow (PF): ^{3}He, ^{4}He, NaF and Bi (see table 2). Single crystals of He and Bi can both be

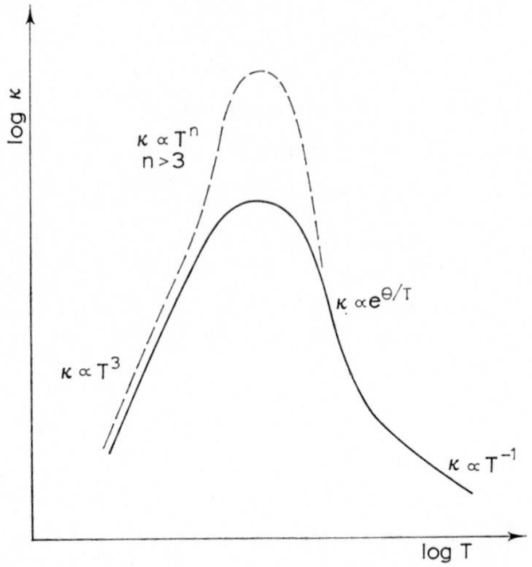

Fig. 2. Typical log–log plot of thermal conductivity versus temperature as measured on helium or alkali halides. Full curve: average single crystal of moderate quality, showing no Poiseuille flow. Dashed curve: high quality sample with a considerably higher maximum in κ and a domain where $\kappa \propto T^n$ with $n > 3$. The theoretical value $n=8$ for fully developed Poiseuille flow is, however, never reached in practice.

TABLE 2

^{4}He	for SS	(Ackerman et al. 1966, Ackerman and Guyer 1967, 1968)
	for PF	(Meshov-Deglin 1965, 1967, Seward et al. 1969, Hogan et al. 1969)
^{3}He	for SS	(Ackerman and Overton 1969)
	for PF	(Thomlinson 1969)
NaF	for SS	(McNelly et al. 1970, Jackson et al. 1970, Jackson and Walker 1971, Rogers 1971)
Bi	for SS	(Narayanamurti and Dynes 1972)
	for PF	(Kopylov and Meshov-Deglin 1971)

prepared with a high degree of chemical and physical perfection, whereas for NaF the main problem is purity (OH^- !) since Na and F both exist with but one isotope. LiF, NaI, synthetic sapphire and quartz have also been tried (see the references quoted by Rogers 1971) without, however, leading to positive results. Recently, it has been suggested by Rogers (1972) that isotopically pure neon might be another candidate for SS if one succeeds in growing defect-free crystals.

PF is observed for temperatures just below the maximum of κ in fig. 2. If κ shows in this domain a T-dependence of the form T^n with $n > 3$, it is usually interpreted as PF or at least the onset of the latter. The R^2 dependence in (2.70) is confirmed by the experiments, whereas the temperature variation differs between different experiments, see table 3. Further experiments have only shown slight departures of $\kappa(T)$ from T^3, e.g. $T^{3.4}$ to $T^{3.7}$ in ^3He (Thomlinson 1969) and may, therefore, show incipient PF, since conditions (2.66), (2.67) apparently cannot be fulfilled well enough. Whereas the usual observation of PF is only through measuring an 'overall' feature like $\kappa(T)$, Griffin (1968b) proposed light scattering experiments which might reveal more detailed insight into the 'local pattern' of Poiseuille flow.

TABLE 3

Meshov-Deglin (1965, 1967)	^4He: τ_{PF}^{-1} (2.71)	$\propto T^3$ to T^5,	$\kappa_{PF} \propto T^6$ to T^8
Hogan et al. (1969)	^4He: τ_{PF}^{-1} (2.71)	$\propto T^3$	$\kappa_{PF} \propto T^6$
Lawson and Fairbank (1973)	^4He: τ_{PF}^{-1} (2.71)	$\propto T^3$	$\kappa_{PF} \propto T^6$

In order to observe SS, one has to perform time-dependent experiments. Most authors use a heat pulse technique: a heater produces short temperature deviations at one end of the sample at some time t_0 and a thermometer detects the local temperature $T(t)$ for $t > t_0$ at the opposite end (von Gutfeld 1968). The main features of such experiments, which are described in detail in the experimental papers quoted above, depend on the ambient temperature: for very low T (on some temperature scale appropriate for the sample and the pulse duration) the pulse propagates ballistically without appreciable scattering, except at the boundaries. (This can be observed very clearly in NaF and Bi, whereas for He only hints of ballistic phonon pulses have been seen so far, see Fox et al. 1972.) For high T, heat propagates in a diffusive way, whereas for intermediate temperatures a secondary pulse can be detected with varying shape and velocity, which is interpreted as second sound, see fig. 3. In addition to merely demonstrating the existence of SS, these experiments also yield information about $\tau_N(T)$. For He, where a fully developed SS-peak can be observed over an appreciable range of T, the pulse width is an immediate measure for $\overline{\tau_N}$ [see (2.47) and (2.58)]. The analysis of helium data (Ackerman and Guyer 1968) yields

$$\bar{\tau}_N \propto T^{-3}. \tag{3.6}$$

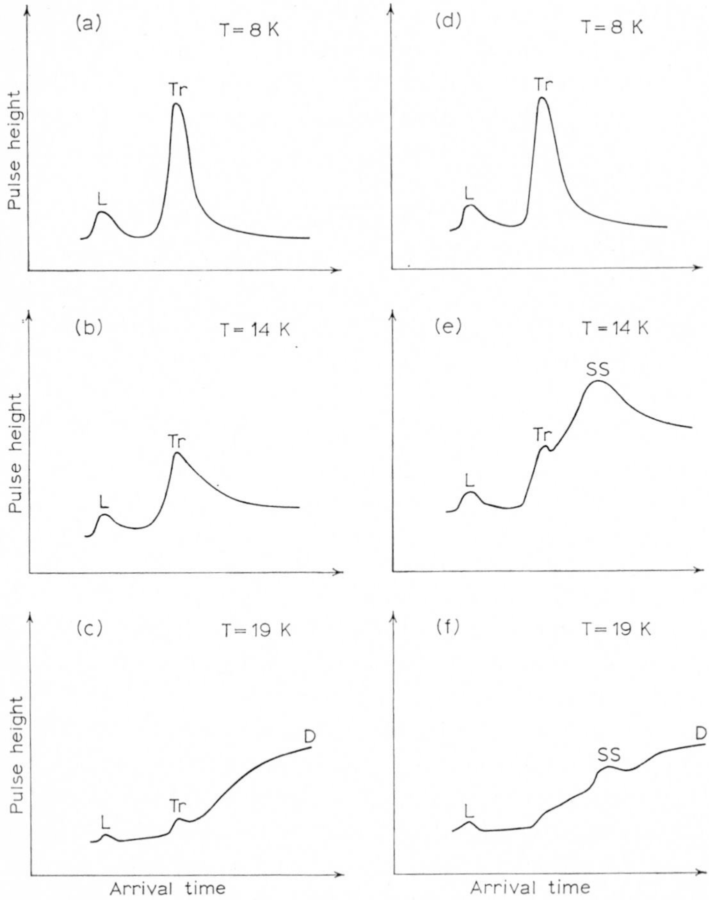

Fig. 3. Heat pulses in average NaF crystal (a–c) and in a very pure sample (d–f). The pulse intensity measured at the end of the crystal is plotted versus the arrival time. The temperatures T indicated are merely representative values and do not correspond to some specific experiment. (The temperature where SS is observed also depends on sample size and pulse duration.) The different peaks are denoted by L (longitudinal), Tr (transverse), SS (second sound) and D (diffusive signal).

The influence of τ_N on the width of the SS-peak cannot be used to determine τ_N for NaF and Bi, since, due to stronger resistive scattering, the SS-peak goes over into a broad diffusive ramp before it has fully developed. In Rogers' (1971) model, see subsection 5.4, τ_N also influences the velocity of the SS-peak. His analysis yields for NaF

$$\bar{\tau}_N \propto T^{-3.71}, \tag{3.7}$$

and, according to Narayanamurti and Dynes (1972) for Bi

$$\bar{\tau}_N \propto T^{-4}. \tag{3.8}$$

Ranninger (1972), and Beck and Beck (1973) have used the relaxation time concept to discuss heat pulse propagation, see subsection 5.4. In this formalism, the experimental velocity $c_{II}(T)$ of SS can also be used to find $\tau_N(T)$. Beck (1975b) finds, using the results of Beck and Beck (1973), for NaF

$$\bar{\tau}_N \propto T^{-3}. \tag{3.9}$$

In addition to this variety of heat pulse experiments, there is one experiment (Brown and Matthews 1970) performed on Bi using a continuous oscillatory temperature disturbance on the crystal. Information about the way heat propagates can then be found by analyzing amplitude and phase of the signal arriving at the detector. They do not find conclusive evidence for SS in Bi. However, this method could be used for the other materials as a complementary technique to observe SS.

There is yet another promising way of detecting SS, namely by Brillouin scattering of light. Some theoretical aspects of such experiments and some preliminary experimental work is discussed at the end of subsection 5.1. So far, however, no results concerning second sound in solids seen by light scattering have been published.

It is impossible to enter into the details of the experimental work reported in all the papers listed above. Concerning the theoretical understanding of the data, it should be mentioned that the most serious problem seems to be the interpretation of the discrepancy between the different temperature dependences of τ_N for the various ways it is extracted from experiment (3.5) to (3.9) and also the deviation of these results from theoretical considerations (Herring 1954, Meier 1969, Weiss 1968) which all lead to

$$\tau_N \propto T^{-5}. \tag{3.10}$$

Some more comments about these facts will be made in subsection 5.2, on quantum crystals.

4. *Theoretical refinements*

4.1. Derivation of transport equations by means of Green's functions

4.1.1. General remarks

Green's functions are a powerful tool to describe properties of many-body systems and to find suitable approximations for the quantities of physical interest. Details of the mathematical procedure which will be used in this section can be found in various textbooks (Kadanoff and Baym 1962, Abrikosov et al. 1965, etc.) For a solid, one usually considers the phonon Green's function

$$G(1,2) = \mathrm{i}^{-1}\langle T(A(1)\,A^{\dagger}(2))\rangle - \mathrm{i}^{-1}\langle A(1)\rangle\,\langle A^{\dagger}(2)\rangle\,. \tag{4.1}$$

Here $(1)\equiv(k_1t_1)$ and T denotes the time ordering operator. The effect of the latter as well as the time dependence of A and the meaning of the ensemble average $\langle\cdots\rangle$ can be defined such as to fulfill the needs of the special situation, see below. In order to find information about equilibrium properties of the phonon system, it is useful to introduce imaginary times between 0 and $-\mathrm{i}\beta$ and to define

$$A(t) = \mathrm{e}^{\mathrm{i}Ht}A\mathrm{e}^{-\mathrm{i}Ht} \quad \text{and} \quad \langle\cdots\rangle_{\mathrm{eq}} = (\mathrm{Tr}\,\mathrm{e}^{-\beta H})^{-1}\,\mathrm{Tr}[\mathrm{e}^{-\beta \mathrm{H}}\cdots]\,. \tag{4.2}$$

The invariance properties of the equilibrium state imply

$$G_{\mathrm{eq}}(\boldsymbol{k}_1\lambda_1t_1, \boldsymbol{k}_2\lambda_2t_2) = \delta_{\boldsymbol{k}_1,\boldsymbol{k}_2}\mathscr{G}_{\lambda_1\lambda_2}(\boldsymbol{k}_1, t_1 - t_2)\,. \tag{4.3}$$

The Fourier transform of the real time correlation function

$$G^{<}_{\lambda\lambda'}(\boldsymbol{k}\omega) \equiv (1/\mathrm{i}) \int_{-\infty}^{+\infty} \mathrm{d}t\,\mathrm{e}^{\mathrm{i}\omega t}\langle A_{\boldsymbol{k}\lambda}(t)\,A_{\boldsymbol{k}\lambda'}(0)\rangle_{\mathrm{eq}} \tag{4.4}$$

is related to the spectral function χ, the expectation value of the commutator between $A(t)$ and $A(0)$, by

$$G^{<}_{\lambda\lambda'}(\boldsymbol{k}\omega) = (1/\mathrm{i})\,N_0(\omega)\,\chi_{\lambda\lambda'}(\boldsymbol{k}\omega)\,. \tag{4.5}$$

The fact that all these quantities are matrices in polarization space makes their interpretation somewhat difficult. Usually, only the diagonal elements, $\lambda = \lambda'$, are considered. Then $\chi_{\lambda\lambda'}(\boldsymbol{k}, \omega) \equiv \chi(\boldsymbol{k}\lambda, \omega)$ is related to the probability for a phonon with wave vector $\boldsymbol{k}$ and polarization λ to have energy ω, which is particularly clear in the harmonic approximation for χ:

$$\chi^{(\text{harm})}(k, \omega) = 2\pi \frac{\omega}{|\omega|} \delta(\omega^2 - \omega_k^2). \tag{4.6}$$

Anharmonic corrections to (4.6) are usually calculated by means of perturbation theory. It can be shown that the non-diagonal elements ($\lambda \neq \lambda'$) are of order V_3^2 and V_4, which justifies their neglect in anharmonic perturbation theory. (A possible different point of view would be to diagonalize $\chi_{\lambda\lambda'}$ at a given stage of approximation by means of a frequency dependent, orthogonal transformation and thus to introduce renormalized phonons whose frequency distribution would then be given by the diagonal elements of the new χ).

In order to be able to account for transport phenomena by means of Green's functions, our concept can be extended in two ways: one is described in detail in the book by Kadanoff and Baym (1962) and consists in adding a perturbation

$$H_1(t) = \sum_k A_k J_k(t). \tag{4.7}$$

to the hamiltonian of the system. The external force $J_k(t)$, which may depend on the (real) time t breaks the symmetry leading to (4.3). We then work with the same definition (4.1) for a non-equilibrium real-time Green's function

$$G_J(1, 2) = (1/\mathrm{i}) \langle T(A(1) A^\dagger(2))\rangle_J - (1/\mathrm{i}) \langle A(1)\rangle_J \langle A^\dagger(2)\rangle_J, \tag{4.8}$$

the expectation value $\langle \cdots \rangle_J$ now being evaluated under inclusion of H_1. This is easily done in the interaction picture:

$$\langle T(A(1) A^\dagger(2))\rangle_J = \langle U^{-1}(\infty, -\infty)\, T[U(\infty, t_2) \times A^\dagger(2)\, U(t_2, t_1)\, A(t_1)\, U(t_1, -\infty)]\rangle_{\text{eq}}. \tag{4.9}$$

The different parts of the U-matrix

$$U(t_2, t_1) = T\left[\exp\left(-\mathrm{i}\int_{t_1}^{t_2} \mathrm{d}t'\, H_1(t')\right)\right] \tag{4.10}$$

can then be summarized into an S-matrix by replacing the usual real time ordering by a suitable time ordering operation on a double path along the time axis, see subsection 1.2 of this chapter, where equations of motion will be derived for G_J. Here we merely summarize the relevant ideas which will lead to a generalized transport equation.

First of all, one has to find a suitable physical interpretation of the non-equilibrium correlation functions

$$g^{\gtrless}(1,2) = G_J(1,2) \ \text{for} \ t_1 \gtrless t_2 . \tag{4.11}$$

This is facilitated by going over to the functions $g^{\gtrless}_{\lambda\lambda'}(\boldsymbol{Kq}, t\tau)$ of the 'center of mass' and 'relative' variables

$$\begin{aligned} \boldsymbol{K} &= \tfrac{1}{2}(\boldsymbol{k}_1 + \boldsymbol{k}_2), \qquad & t &= \tfrac{1}{2}(t_1 + t_2), \\ \boldsymbol{q} &= \boldsymbol{k}_1 - \boldsymbol{k}_2, & \tau &= t_1 - t_2, \end{aligned} \tag{4.12}$$

and to their Fourier transforms

$$g^{\gtrless}_{\lambda\lambda'}(\boldsymbol{Kr}, t\omega) = \sum_{\boldsymbol{q}} e^{i\boldsymbol{q}\cdot\boldsymbol{r}} \int_{-\infty}^{+\infty} d\tau \, e^{-i\omega\tau} g^{\gtrless}_{\lambda\lambda'}(\boldsymbol{Kq}, t\tau). \tag{4.13}$$

In equilibrium we obviously find independence of $\boldsymbol{r}$ and t:

$$g^{<}_{\lambda\lambda'}(\boldsymbol{Kr}, t\omega)_{\text{eq}} = N_0(\omega)\, \chi_{\lambda\lambda'}(\boldsymbol{K}\omega)/i . \tag{4.14}$$

If $J_\lambda(\boldsymbol{r}, t) = \sum_{\boldsymbol{k}} e^{i\boldsymbol{k}\cdot\boldsymbol{r}} J_{\boldsymbol{k}\lambda}(t)$ varies slowly with position $\boldsymbol{r}$ and time t we may assume that $g^{>}$ and $g^{<}$ also vary slowly in space and time. Following Kadanoff and Baym (1962) we write for the diagonal part of $g^{<}$:

$$g^{<}_{\lambda\lambda'}(\boldsymbol{Kr}, t\omega) = n(\boldsymbol{K}\lambda\boldsymbol{r}; t\omega)\, \chi(\boldsymbol{K}\lambda\boldsymbol{r}, t\omega)/i , \tag{4.15}$$

with

$$\chi(\boldsymbol{K}\lambda\boldsymbol{r}, t\omega) = i\left[g^{>}_{\lambda\lambda}(\boldsymbol{Kr}, t\omega) - g^{<}_{\lambda\lambda}(\boldsymbol{Kr}, t\omega)\right]$$

and we interpret $\chi(\boldsymbol{K}\lambda\boldsymbol{r}, t\omega)$ as the space and time dependent spectral function for phonons with wave vector $\boldsymbol{k}$ and polarization λ, and $n(\boldsymbol{K}\lambda\boldsymbol{r}, t\omega)$ as a distribution function giving the number of phonons with $(\boldsymbol{K}, \lambda)$ and energy ω at $\boldsymbol{r}$ and t. The non-diagonal part $g^{<}_{\lambda\lambda'}$, again has no immediate physical meaning. It is usually either neglected or expressed by the diagonal part since, in some sense to be defined more precisely in the following subsection, it is expected to lead only to small corrections to the generalized transport equation for the quantity n defined by (4.15). If the system is not too anharmonic, we can suppose that the non-equilibrium spectral function χ is again sharply peaked for some $\omega = E(K, \boldsymbol{r}t)$, which is a suitably defined $\boldsymbol{r}$- and t-dependent mean phonon energy. Then $n(\cdots\omega)$ needs only be evaluated for this value of ω and

$$N(K\boldsymbol{r}, t) = n\big(K\boldsymbol{r}, t, \omega = E(K, \boldsymbol{r}t)\big) \tag{4.16}$$

will then obey a Boltzmann equation of the form (2.7), which was our starting point in section 2.

In addition to yielding generalizations going beyond (2.7), this Green's function treatment also furnishes an equation for the expectation value

$$d(\boldsymbol{k}\lambda, t) \equiv \langle A_{\boldsymbol{k}\lambda}(t)\rangle_J \tag{4.17}$$

which can be different from zero in a non-equilibrium case and describes the motion of the elastic lattice. The physical meaning of this 'two-fluid' aspect of phonon hydrodynamics, where N (4.16) and d (4.17) obey two coupled equations of motion will be discussed in subsection 5.1.

The present non-equilibrium approach was used in the early work of Horie and Krumhansl (1964), and later by Kwok and Martin (1966) to demonstrate that second sound can be obtained as a second pole in the displacement autocorrelation function (see subsection 5.1). In a series of papers, Niklasson and Sjölander (1968), and Niklasson (1969, 1970) used the scheme sketched above to obtain transport equations for interacting phonon systems and general expressions for transport coefficients. Meier (1969) used similar methods, which were extended by Beck and Meier (1970) to account for quantum crystals on the level of the self-consistent harmonic approximation.

The equations obtained in this framework are in principle valid for large deviations from equilibrium, as long as their space and time variation is slow. In reality, the external perturbation is usually small. Thus, it should be sufficient to consider the linear response of the important observables with respect to the external force. This procedure yields linearized equations and, furthermore, they involve only equilibrium expectation values, which are functional derivatives of non-equilibrium quantities like (4.8) with respect to $J_k(t)$, evaluated for $J=0$. As an example, let us consider the displacement field

$$d(kt) \equiv \langle A_k(t)\rangle_J \approx \langle A_k(t)\rangle_{\mathrm{eq}} - \mathrm{i}\sum_{k'} \int_{-\infty}^{+\infty} \theta(t-t')\,\langle [A_k(t), A_{k'}(t')]\rangle_{\mathrm{eq}}\, J_{k'}(t')\,\mathrm{d}t'. \tag{4.18}$$

The retarded commutator showing up in the response function

$$R(kt, k't') = \frac{\delta d(kt)}{\delta J(k't')} \tag{4.19}$$

for the displacement field is, of course, closely connected with the equilibrium Green's function (4.3). If we are interested in small ('hydrodynamic') wave vectors $\boldsymbol{k}$ and frequencies Ω in the Fourier transform $d(\boldsymbol{k}, \Omega)$, it does not suffice to use a simple perturbative result for R based on a corresponding approximation for $\mathcal{G}$ since in the hydrodynamic regime an expansion in powers of anharmonicities breaks down, owing to 'hydrodynamic singularities' in the self-energy σ of $\mathcal{G}$. Technically, this means that the series of 'ladder graphs' determining part of σ has to be summed up as a whole.

This procedure, leading immediately to a linearized transport equation, has certain advantages over the non-equilibrium approach described before. It does not necessitate an 'ad hoc' definition for a non-equilibrium phonon density n, such as (4.15), since an examination of the hydrodynamic behavior of the contributions to σ quite naturally leads to a function n, which obeys a generalized transport equation and can thus – a posteriori – be interpreted as a phonon distribution. Furthermore, the treatment of certain non-diagonal terms ($\lambda \neq \lambda'$) in σ is much more straightforward. Although these statements can only become clear to the reader when the single steps are exhibited in detail, we shall not present it in this section since a very similar technique will be used in subsection 4.2 to determine the heat current auto-correlation function for a phonon system yielding information about the thermal conductivity.

The equilibrium Green's function method, sometimes called 'ladder graph approach', was used by Sham (1967) to derive the linearized Peierls–Boltzmann equation for interacting phonons. Goetze and Michel (1969) also used the framework of linear response in their microscopic foundation of the two-fluid description of dielectric solids. Their transport equations are also valid for quantum crystals on the level of the renormalized harmonic treatment of the equilibrium properties. Klein and Wehner (1968, 1969) took the

'Wigner operator' $a^{\dagger}_{\boldsymbol{k}+\frac{1}{2}\boldsymbol{q},\lambda} a_{\boldsymbol{k}-\frac{1}{2}\boldsymbol{q},\lambda}$ for the $\boldsymbol{q}$-Fourier component $n(\boldsymbol{k}\lambda, \boldsymbol{q})$ of the phonon density as their starting point and calculated its time behavior in response to an external field of the form (4.7). In a recent review, Beck et al. (1974) described briefly both approaches – non-equilibrium and equilibrium – and indicated how the key quantities used in both procedures, namely $g^{\gtrless}(1,2)$ and $d(1)$ – (4.8), (4.11) and (4.17) – in the former case and the linear response functions like (4.19) for the second method, are related to each other.

4.1.2. Non-equilibrium Green's functions

Here a few details of the description of phonon transport by means of the non-equilibrium Green's function (4.8) are presented. For more information the interested reader is referred to the references given in the course of the analysis.

First it is useful to replace the complicated sequence of U-matrices in (4.9) by

$$\langle T(A(1)\, A^{\dagger}(2))\rangle_J = \langle T_L(A(1)\, A^{\dagger}(2)\, S_L)\rangle_{\text{eq}} \tag{4.20}$$

with

$$S_L = T_L \left[\exp\left(-\mathrm{i} \int_L \mathrm{d}\tau\, H_1(\tau)\right)\right]. \tag{4.21}$$

T_L orders all times occurring along a path L which stretches along the real time axis from $-\infty$ to $+\infty\,(L_+)$ and back to $-\infty\,(L_-)$. This double path was introduced by Craig (1968) and used by Niklasson (1968, 1969, 1970) as well as by Beck and Meier (1970) in order to avoid the analytic continuation from complex to real times proposed by Kadanoff and Baym (1962). $G_J(1,2)$ defined in this way has different meanings depending on whether t_1 and t_2 lie on L_+ or L_-, e.g.

$$\begin{aligned} G_J(1,2) &= g^{<}(1,2) \quad \text{for } t_1 \in L_-,\ t_2 \in L_+, \\ G_J(1,2) &= g^{T}(1,2) \quad \text{for } t_1 \in L_+,\ t_2 \in L_+, \text{ etc.} \end{aligned} \tag{4.22}$$

$g^{\gtrless}$ being the ordinary real time correlation function and g^T the time ordered Green's function. The Heisenberg equations of motion for A_k, derived from the hamiltonian (2.4) lead to an equation for the displacement field (4.17), which reads, neglecting non-linear terms in d:

$$\theta(1)\, d(1) = J(-1) + V_3(-k_1, \bar{k}_2, -\bar{k}_3)\, G_J(\bar{k}_2 t_1, \bar{k}_3 t_1) + V_4(-k_1, \bar{k}_2, \bar{k}_3, \bar{k}_4)\, G_J^{(3)}(\bar{k}_2 t_1, \bar{k}_3 t_1, \bar{k}_4 t_1), \tag{4.23}$$

where the bars denote summation over momenta and polarizations,

$$\theta(1) = -\left[\frac{\partial^2}{\partial t_1^2} + \omega_{k_1}^2\right] \tag{4.24}$$

and $G_J^{(3)}$ abbreviates a time ordered expectation value of three A's. By means of functional derivation and the usual anharmonic decoupling procedure for higher order functions like $G_J^{(3)}$ (Meier 1969, Niklasson 1969, 1970, Niklasson and Sjölander 1968) two Dyson equations for G_J can be derived

$$\theta(1)\, G_J(1,2) = \delta(1-2) + \int_L \mathrm{d}t'\, \sigma(k_1 t_1, \bar{k} t')\, G_J(\bar{k} t', k_2 t_2), \tag{4.25a}$$

$$\theta(2)\, G_J(1,2) = \delta(1-2) + \int_L \mathrm{d}t'\, G_J(k_1 t_1, \bar{k} t')\, \sigma(\bar{k} t', k_2 t_2). \tag{4.25b}$$

Up to terms $\propto V_3^2$ and V_4 the self-energy $\sigma = \sigma_d + \sigma_1 + \sigma_c$ is given by

$$\sigma_d(1,2) = \delta(t_1 - t_2)\, V_3(-k_1, \bar{k}, k_2)\, d(\bar{k} t_1), \tag{4.26}$$

$$\sigma_1(1,2) = \tfrac{1}{2}\mathrm{i}\, \delta(t_1 - t_2)\, V_4(-k_1, \bar{k}, -\bar{k}', k_2)\, G_J(\bar{k} t_1, \overline{k' t_2}), \tag{4.27}$$

$$\sigma_c(1,2) = \tfrac{1}{2}\mathrm{i}\, V_3(-k_1, \bar{k}_3, \bar{k}_5)\, V_3(k_2, -\bar{k}_4, -\bar{k}_6) \times G_J(\bar{k}_3 t_1, \bar{k}_4 t_2)\, G_J(\bar{k}_5 t_1, \bar{k}_6 t_2). \tag{4.28}$$

Since we are interested in $g^<$ we fix t_1 on L_- and t_2 on L_+, and vice versa, and we reduce the time integral along L to simple integrations from $-\infty$ to $+\infty$ by identifying the different 'pieces' of $G_J(1,2)$ according to (4.22). Using

$$\operatorname{Re} g \equiv g^T - \tfrac{1}{2}(g^> + g^<)$$

and a similar definition for Re σ in terms of σ^T, $\sigma^>$ and $\sigma^<$, and subtracting (4.25b) from (4.25a) we find

$$-[\theta(1) - \theta(2)]\, g^{\gtrless} = \operatorname{Re} g \cdot \sigma^{\gtrless} - \sigma^{\gtrless} \cdot \operatorname{Re} g + g^{\gtrless} \cdot \operatorname{Re} \sigma - \operatorname{Re} \sigma \cdot g^{\gtrless} + I, \tag{4.29}$$

with

$$I = \tfrac{1}{2}(\sigma_c^> \cdot g^< + g^> \cdot \sigma_c^< - g^< \cdot \sigma_c^> - \sigma_c^> \cdot g^<). \tag{4.30}$$

The dot between two quantities stands for

$$A \cdot B = \int_{-\infty}^{+\infty} dt' \sum_{k'} A(1, k't')\, B(k't', 2). \tag{4.31}$$

Now all quantities are expressed as functions of the variables (4.12). Thus (4.31) goes over into

$$A \cdot B = \int_{-\infty}^{+\infty} d\tau' \sum_{\boldsymbol{q}'\lambda'} A_{\lambda_1\lambda'}(\boldsymbol{K} + \tfrac{1}{2}(\boldsymbol{q} - \boldsymbol{q}'), \boldsymbol{q}'; t + \tfrac{1}{2}(\tau - \tau'), \tau')$$
$$\times B_{\lambda'\lambda_2}(\boldsymbol{K}' - \tfrac{1}{2}\boldsymbol{q}', \boldsymbol{q} - \boldsymbol{q}'; t - \tfrac{1}{2}\tau', \tau - \tau') \tag{4.32}$$

involving functions of the type occurring on the right-hand side of (4.13). A and B are then expanded to first order with respect to small $\boldsymbol{q}$ and $\boldsymbol{q}'$ (corresponding to slow spatial variation) and to τ and τ' [corresponding to the fact that the variation with the 'center-of-mass time' t is much slower than the dependence on τ, which is 'conjugate' to the energy variable ω in the Fourier transformation (4.13)]. The left-hand side of (4.29) then reads

$$- [\theta(1) - \theta(2)]\, g^{\gtrless}(1, 2)$$
$$\approx \left[2 \frac{\partial}{\partial t} \frac{\partial}{\partial \tau} + \omega_{\boldsymbol{K}\lambda}^2 - \omega_{\boldsymbol{K}\lambda'}^2 + \tfrac{1}{2}\boldsymbol{q} \cdot \frac{\partial}{\partial \boldsymbol{K}} (\omega_{\boldsymbol{K}\lambda}^2 + \omega_{\boldsymbol{K}\lambda'}^2) \right] g_{\lambda\lambda''}^{\gtrless}(\boldsymbol{K}\boldsymbol{q}, t\tau). \tag{4.33}$$

There is now a fundamental difference between $\lambda \neq \lambda'$ and $\lambda = \lambda'$. For the diagonal terms the difference $\omega_{\boldsymbol{k}\lambda}^2 - \omega_{\boldsymbol{k}\lambda'}^2$ vanishes and the 'operator' acting on $g_{\lambda\lambda'}^{\gtrless}(\cdots)$ is 'singular in the hydrodynamic limit', in which $\boldsymbol{q} \to 0$ and the functions vary slowly with t. On the other hand, for $\lambda \neq \lambda'$ we can assume that, except for isolated points of degeneracy in the Brillouin zone, $\omega_{\boldsymbol{k}\lambda}^2 - \omega_{\boldsymbol{k}\lambda'}^2$ is the dominant term in (4.33) such that in the hydrodynamic limit the operator acting on $g_{\lambda\lambda'}^{\gtrless}$, remains non-zero. Therefore, we proceed as follows: the equation for $\lambda = \lambda'$ is Fourier transformed according to (4.13), yielding

$$\{\omega^2 - \omega_{\boldsymbol{K}\lambda}^2 - \operatorname{Re}\sigma_{\lambda\lambda}, g_{\lambda\lambda}^{\gtrless}\} + \{\operatorname{Re} g_{\lambda\lambda}, \sigma_{\lambda\lambda}^{\gtrless}\} = \mathrm{i}[\sigma_{\lambda\lambda}^{>} g_{\lambda\lambda}^{<} - \sigma_{\lambda\lambda}^{<} g_{\lambda\lambda}^{>}]. \tag{4.34}$$

This is a generalized transport equation as discussed by Kadanoff and Baym (1962), with the 'Poisson brackets' defined by

$$\{A, B\} = \frac{\partial A_{\lambda\lambda}(\boldsymbol{K r}, t\omega)}{\partial \boldsymbol{r}} \frac{\partial B}{\partial \boldsymbol{K}} - \frac{\partial A}{\partial \boldsymbol{K}} \frac{\partial B}{\partial \boldsymbol{r}} + \frac{\partial A}{\partial \omega} \frac{\partial B}{\partial t} - \frac{\partial A}{\partial t} \frac{\partial B}{\partial \omega}. \tag{4.35}$$

Introducing now the functions $\chi = \mathrm{i}(g^{>} - g^{<})$ and n according to (4.15), which is, as in the work of Kadanoff and Baym, in some sense the 'key' definition for the interpretation of the non-equilibrium correlations $g^{>}$ and $g^{<}$, we find that χ is unaffected by the right-hand side of (4.34) and is given by

$$\chi_{\lambda\lambda}(\boldsymbol{K r}, t\omega) = \frac{1}{2} \frac{\Gamma_{\lambda\lambda}}{(\omega^2 - \omega_{\boldsymbol{K}\lambda}^2 - \mathrm{Re}\, \sigma_{\lambda\lambda})^2 + \frac{1}{4}\Gamma_{\lambda\lambda}^2} \tag{4.36}$$

with $\Gamma = \mathrm{i}(\sigma^{>} - \sigma^{<})$. This means that the phonons have space and time dependent energies and lifetimes since Re σ and Γ, according to (4.26) to (4.28) again involve $\chi(\boldsymbol{r}t)$ and $n(\boldsymbol{r}t)$ as well as the displacement field d. Of course Re $\sigma_{\lambda\lambda}$ and $\Gamma_{\lambda\lambda}$ also involve the nondiagonal parts of $g_{\lambda\lambda'}^{\gtrless}$. These are usually neglected (see Meier 1969), since in order to make (4.34) tractable a number of other simplifications have to be made anyway, or they can be expressed by means of $g_{\lambda\lambda}^{\gtrless}$ by inverting (4.33) which, as we saw before, remains 'regular' in the hydrodynamic limit. This procedure was rigorously carried out by Goetze and Michel (1969). Neglecting here the non-diagonal terms on the right-hand side of (4.34) the latter reads, using (4.28) for the self-energy:

$$\mathrm{i}[\sigma^{>} g^{<} - g^{>} g^{<}] = -\frac{1}{4\pi} \int \mathrm{d}\omega' \, \mathrm{d}\omega'' \, \delta(\omega + \omega' + \omega'') \times \sum_{\boldsymbol{K}'\boldsymbol{K}''} |V_3(K, K', K'')|^2 \, [g^{>} g^{>\prime} g^{>\prime\prime} - g^{<} g^{<\prime} g^{<\prime\prime}], \tag{4.37}$$

where $g^{>\prime} = g^{>}(\boldsymbol{K}'\boldsymbol{r}, t\omega')$, etc. Eq. (4.37) has already the appearance of a 'balance term' between $g^{>}$'s and $g^{<}$'s and will finally yield the collision term of the phonon Boltzmann equation. Also, by similar manipulations, the right-hand side of eq. (4.23) for the displacement field d can be brought into a form involving χ and n. This equation, together with (4.34) and (4.37), where $g^{<} = \chi n/\mathrm{i}$ and $g^{>} = g^{<} + \chi/n$, and the explicit form (4.36) for χ as well as expressions (4.26) to (4.28) giving σ in terms of d, n, χ have been inserted, form a complete (although highly non-linear) system describing the transport behavior of our crystal under the influence of the external perturbation (4.7). In order to obtain more physical insight, we make the following approximation: we neglect the damping Γ of the phonon spectral function χ (4.36):

$$\chi(Kr, t\omega) \approx 2\pi \frac{\omega}{|\omega|} \delta(\omega^2 - \omega_K^2 - \operatorname{Re}\sigma(K, rt)), \tag{4.38}$$

which defines new phonon energies

$$E(K, rt) = [\omega_K^2 + \operatorname{Re}\sigma]^{1/2} \tag{4.39}$$

which depend on space and time through the functional dependence of σ on the displacement field d in (4.26) and the phonon density n in (4.27) via (4.15). Since according to (4.38) the phonons have sharply defined energies E, we can deal with the phonon distribution function (4.16). The equation of motion for this function is found by integrating (4.34) over ω and using (4.38):

$$\frac{\partial N(\boldsymbol{K}, \boldsymbol{r}t)}{\partial t} - \frac{\partial E}{\partial \boldsymbol{r}} \frac{\partial N}{\partial \boldsymbol{K}} + \frac{\partial E}{\partial \boldsymbol{K}} \frac{\partial N}{\partial \boldsymbol{r}} = C[N]. \tag{4.40}$$

C formally agrees with Peierl's expression (Peierls 1955, Meier 1969) for the non-linear collision operator

$$\begin{aligned} C[N] = -\tfrac{1}{8}\pi \sum_{K'K''} \frac{1}{EE'E''} \{ & 2|V_3(K, K', -K'')|^2 \delta(E + E' - E'') \\ & \times [(N+1)(N'+1)N'' - NN'(N''+1)] \\ & + |V_3(K, -K', -K'')|^2 \delta(E - E' - E'') \\ & \times [(N+1)N'N'' - N(N'+1)(N''+1)]\}, \end{aligned} \tag{4.41}$$

although the phonon energies $E = E(\boldsymbol{k}, \boldsymbol{r}, t)$ etc. can still be dependent on space and time.

In order to linearize (4.40) with respect to deviations from equilibrium, we define, following (2.11), (2.14)

$$N(K, \boldsymbol{r}t) = N_0(E) + m(\omega_K)\,\varphi(K, \boldsymbol{r}t). \tag{4.42}$$

$N_0(E)$ is the equilibrium distribution involving, however, the space- and time-dependent energies $E(K, \boldsymbol{r}t)$, whereas φ describes how N deviates from such a Bose distribution. Furthermore, in order to come as close as possible to the phenomenological results of subsection 5.1, we replace the displacement field $d(\boldsymbol{k}\lambda, t)$ by a continuous function of the space variable $\boldsymbol{r}$

$$s_i(\boldsymbol{r}t) = (mN)^{-1/2} \sum_{k} e_i(k)\, \mathrm{e}^{\mathrm{i}\boldsymbol{k}\cdot\boldsymbol{r}}\, d(kt). \tag{4.43}$$

[For a non-Bravais lattice this definition has to be generalized, see Goetze and Michel (1969).] Then we express the dependence of E on $\boldsymbol{s}$ and N by introducing the functional derivatives

$$f(K, K') = \frac{\delta E(K, \boldsymbol{r}t)}{\delta N(K', \boldsymbol{r}t)}, \qquad h_{ij}(K) = -\frac{\delta E(K, \boldsymbol{r}t)}{\delta u_{ij}(\boldsymbol{r}t)}, \tag{4.44, 45}$$

with

$$u_{ij} = \frac{1}{2}\left[\frac{\partial s_i}{\partial r_j} + \frac{\partial s_j}{\partial r_i}\right]. \tag{4.46}$$

f corresponds to the quasi-particle interaction introduced by Landau (1956) in his theory of normal Fermi liquids, whereas h represents a generalized Grüneisen parameter. These quantities were incorporated by Goetze and Michel (1967a, b, 1969) into their two-fluid description of dielectric solids summarized in subsection 5.1. They also derive integral equations determining f and h in terms of the lattice anharmonicities. To lowest order (for a Bravais lattice):

$$f(K, K') = (4E(K)\, E(K'))^{-1}\, V_4(K, -K, K', -K'), \tag{4.47}$$

$$h_{ij}(K) = +\mathrm{i}\,(m/N)^{1/2} \times \partial\Big[\sum_{\lambda} E(K)^{-1}\, e_i(\boldsymbol{Q}\lambda)\, V_3(\boldsymbol{Q}\lambda, K, -K)\Big]_{\boldsymbol{Q}=\boldsymbol{0}} / \partial Q_j \tag{4.48}$$

and the linearized transport equation reads

$$I^{-1}\frac{\partial\varphi(K, \boldsymbol{r}t)}{\partial t} - \boldsymbol{v}_K\cdot\frac{\partial\varphi}{\partial\boldsymbol{r}} + I^{-1}h_{ij}(K)\frac{\partial^2 s_i}{\partial r_j\partial t} = L[\varphi]. \tag{4.49}$$

I is the integral operator

$$I\,\varphi(K) = \sum_{K'} \left[\delta_{K,K'} + f(K, K')\, m(K')\right] \varphi(K') \tag{4.50}$$

and the linearized collision integral has the form

$$L[\varphi] = -\frac{\pi}{8m(K)} \sum_{K'K''} \sum_{Q} \left(\frac{mm'm''}{\beta}\right)^{1/2} \frac{1}{EE'E''}$$

$$\times \{2|V_3(K, K', -K'')|^2 \, \delta(E + E' - E'') \, \delta_{\boldsymbol{K}+\boldsymbol{K}'-\boldsymbol{K},\boldsymbol{Q}} [\varphi + \varphi' - \varphi'']$$

$$+ |V_3(K, -K', -K'')|^2 \, \delta(E - E' - E'') \, \delta_{\boldsymbol{K}-\boldsymbol{K}'-\boldsymbol{K}'',\boldsymbol{Q}} [\varphi - \varphi' - \varphi'']\},$$

(4.51)

where $\boldsymbol{Q}$ is a vector of the reciprocal lattice.

The physical significance of the coupling between the phonon density φ and the displacement field $\boldsymbol{s}$ will be discussed in subsection 5.1, where the final form of the 'elastic' equation determining the latter will also be given. Eq. (4.49) is the generalization of (2.7), which was our starting point of section 2. Eq. (2.7) follows from (4.49) by neglecting the anharmonic effects described by the quantities $f(k, k')$ and h_{ij}.

4.2. Correlation function formulation of thermal conduction

4.2.1. Densities and currents

In section 2 we started from the phonon Boltzmann equation in order to arrive at explicit expressions for the thermal conductivity κ. Here we present a way that takes the phenomenological law

$$S_i = -\kappa \, \partial T/\partial r_i \tag{4.52}$$

as its starting point and uses microscopic prescriptions to calculate the energy current $\boldsymbol{S}$ in a dielectric solid. Operator forms for S_i have been derived by a number of authors: Choquard (1963), Hardy (1963), Enz (1968) and others. Enz starts from

$$A(\boldsymbol{r}) = \tfrac{1}{2} \sum_{n} [A(n), \delta(\boldsymbol{r} - \boldsymbol{R}(n))]_+ \tag{4.53}$$

which expresses the density of some physical quantity, say energy, by means of a sum over all particles n involving the corresponding one-particle operator $A(n)$. $[\cdots,\cdots]_+$ denotes the anticommutator. Specializing to the energy density $E(\boldsymbol{r})$ we find, using an expansion of (2.1) up to fourth order in the atomic displacement [for brevity we treat a Bravais lattice]:

$$E(n) = \frac{p^2(n)}{2m} + \sum_{\nu=2}^{4} \frac{1}{\nu!} \sum_{\substack{n_2 \cdots n_\nu \\ i_2 \cdots i_\nu \\ i}} \Phi_\nu(in, i_2 n_2, \cdots)\, u_i(n)\, u_{i_2}(n_2) \cdots u_{i_\nu}(n_\nu)\,. \tag{4.54}$$

When we evaluate the Fourier transform

$$E(\boldsymbol{q}) = \tfrac{1}{2} \sum_n [E(n), \exp\{-\mathrm{i}\boldsymbol{q}\cdot(\boldsymbol{X}(n) + \boldsymbol{u}(n))\}]_+ \tag{4.55}$$

we separate the terms quadratic in the u's and p's from those of higher order. Contributions of the latter type are found by taking the anharmonic summands $\nu > 2$ in (4.54) on one hand and also by performing a 'multipole' expansion of the exponential

$$\exp\{-\mathrm{i}\boldsymbol{q}\cdot(\boldsymbol{X}(n) + \boldsymbol{u}(n))\} \approx \exp\{-\mathrm{i}\boldsymbol{q}\cdot\boldsymbol{X}(n)\}\,[1 - \mathrm{i}\boldsymbol{q}\cdot\boldsymbol{u}(n) + \cdots] \tag{4.56}$$

in powers of $\boldsymbol{u}(n)$, the instantaneous displacement of particle n from its equilibrium position $\boldsymbol{X}(n)$. Throughout the subsequent analysis anharmonic corrections to the operator expressions for densities and currents will be systematically neglected. This ought to be sufficient for treating low temperature phenomena, for which it seems useful to think of, say, the local energy density $E(\boldsymbol{r}t)$, eq. (2.19), as the sum of the contributions of each phonon present in the neighbourhood of $\boldsymbol{r}$ at time t. However, we shall definitely have to take into account anharmonicities in those equations which determine the time behavior of the quadratic, phonon-like, contributions to $E(\boldsymbol{r}t)$. Otherwise, we would deal with an unrealistic harmonic system showing infinite thermal conductivity. Also, we remark that for temperatures comparable with the Debye temperature, anharmonic terms in the densities themselves will yield observable corrections to the transport coefficients (Ranninger 1965).

At the same time, all but the first term in (4.56) are rejected, since for slowly varying phenomena only the lowest powers of $\boldsymbol{q}$ in $E(\boldsymbol{q})$ are of importance. [The term linear in $\boldsymbol{q}$ will yield a $\boldsymbol{q}$-independent contribution to the energy current involving, however, products of three u's and p's whose expectation values will be of the same order as anharmonic terms from (4.54).]

Making use of a given approximate expression for $E(\boldsymbol{q})$, the corresponding energy current $\boldsymbol{S}(\boldsymbol{q})$ is constructed by calculating $\partial E/\partial t$ by means of the

Heisenberg equations for the operators showing up in $E(\boldsymbol{q})$. Identifying $\partial E/\partial t$ with $-\mathrm{i}\boldsymbol{q}\cdot\boldsymbol{S}(\boldsymbol{q})$, the longitudinal part of $\boldsymbol{S}$ is determined. Using the transformations (2.2) we find for the lowest order terms:

$$S_i(\boldsymbol{q}) = \tfrac{1}{2} \sum_{\boldsymbol{k}\lambda\lambda'} C_i(\boldsymbol{k}\lambda\lambda') \left[B_{\boldsymbol{k}+\frac{1}{2}\boldsymbol{q}\lambda} A^{\dagger}_{\boldsymbol{k}-\frac{1}{2}\boldsymbol{q}\lambda'} + A_{\boldsymbol{k}+\frac{1}{2}\boldsymbol{q}\lambda} B^{\dagger}_{\boldsymbol{k}-\frac{1}{2}\boldsymbol{q}\lambda'}\right], \tag{4.57}$$

with

$$C_i(\boldsymbol{k}\lambda\lambda') = \delta_{\lambda\lambda'} (v_{\boldsymbol{k}\lambda})_i\, \omega_{\boldsymbol{k}\lambda} + \tfrac{1}{2}(\omega^2_{\boldsymbol{k}\lambda} - \omega^2_{\boldsymbol{k}\lambda'}) \frac{\partial \boldsymbol{e}(\boldsymbol{k}\lambda)}{\partial k_i} \cdot \boldsymbol{e}^*(\boldsymbol{k}\lambda'). \tag{4.58}$$

The first part of C_i is diagonal in the polarizations and will turn out to be more important than the non-diagonal part which vanishes for $\lambda = \lambda'$. In order to be able to use Green's functions of the type (4.1), in the following analysis we have expressed S_i in terms of A's and B's instead of the phonon creation and annihilation operators defined in (2.5). It is easy to derive the well-known expression

$$S_i^{\mathrm{d}}(\boldsymbol{q}) \approx \sum_{\boldsymbol{k}\lambda} (v_{\boldsymbol{k}\lambda})_i\, \omega_{\boldsymbol{k}\lambda}\, a^{\dagger}_{\boldsymbol{k}+\frac{1}{2}\boldsymbol{q}\,\lambda}\, a_{\boldsymbol{k}-\frac{1}{2}\boldsymbol{q}\,\lambda} \tag{4.59}$$

for the diagonal part, and the non-diagonal contribution is equivalent to S^i calculated by Enz (1968).

4.2.2. Linear response

Now we have to calculate the expectation value $s_i(\boldsymbol{q}t) = \langle S_i(\boldsymbol{q})\rangle_t$ in a – possibly time dependent – density matrix appropriate for a non-equilibrium situation allowing for heat conduction and to relate s_i to the gradient of the local temperature $T(\boldsymbol{q}t)$. In subsection 4.1 an external mechanical force (4.7) was used to disturb the system, which enabled us to derive transport equations. On this level, there is no a-priori mention of a local temperature nor of a heat current produced by this external perturbation. It is not until we solve the Boltzmann equation, either in a simple-minded way as in section 2 or by an eigenfunction expansion, that the concept of a local temperature can be defined by means of (4.107). The results for transport coefficients are independent of the external perturbation since the latter merely served as a device to derive relations between non-equilibrium quantities.

From a rigorous point of view, 'thermal perturbations', such as heaters which create heat currents in the system, cannot by represented by an additional hamiltonian of the type (4.7). The appropriate method would be to include external reservoirs with some given temperature in the scheme of deriving equations of motion for observable quantities of the crystal. It can be shown, however, (Enz 1968, Kadanoff and Martin 1963) that it is reasonable to describe the effect of such reservoirs by the additional hamiltonian

$$H_1(t) = \int \mathrm{d}^3r\, E(\boldsymbol{r})\, \alpha(\boldsymbol{r}t) = \sum_{\boldsymbol{q}} E(-\boldsymbol{q})\, \alpha(\boldsymbol{q}t) \tag{4.60}$$

relating α to the deviation $\delta T(\boldsymbol{r}t)$ of the local temperature from its average value T_0, which is forced upon the system by the external sources:

$$\alpha(\boldsymbol{r}t) = -\,\delta T/(T_0 + \delta T) \approx -\,\delta T(\boldsymbol{r}t)/T_0\,. \tag{4.61}$$

Indeed, if α is space and time independent, a new canonical density matrix

$$\rho \propto \exp\left[-\,\beta_0 (H + H_1)\right] = \exp(-\,\beta' H)$$

with a new inverse temperature $\beta' = [k_\mathrm{B}(T_0 + \delta T)]^{-1} = \beta_0(1+\alpha)$ can be introduced. Eq. (4.60) can now be treated like the external perturbation (4.7).

The linear response of the time Fourier transform of $s_i(\boldsymbol{q}t)$ under the influence of (4.60) is

$$s_i(\boldsymbol{q}\Omega) = -\,\mathrm{i} \int_0^\infty \mathrm{d}t\, \langle [S_i(\boldsymbol{q}t), E(-\boldsymbol{q})] \rangle_{\mathrm{eq}}\, \mathrm{e}^{\mathrm{i}\Omega t} \alpha(\boldsymbol{q}\Omega)\,. \tag{4.62}$$

By the help of Kubo's operator identity (Kubo 1957, 1965) and of the conservation law (2.23) the response function in (4.62) is equivalent to

$$\begin{aligned} s_i(\boldsymbol{q}\Omega) &= -\,(\mathrm{i}/T_0) \int_0^\infty \mathrm{d}t\, \mathrm{e}^{\mathrm{i}\Omega t} \int_0^{-i\beta} \mathrm{d}\tau\, \langle S_j(-\boldsymbol{q}\tau)\, S_i(\boldsymbol{q}t) \rangle_{\mathrm{eq}}\, \mathrm{i}\boldsymbol{q}_j\, \delta T(\boldsymbol{q}\Omega) \\ &= -\,\kappa_{ij}(\boldsymbol{q}\Omega)\, \mathrm{i}q_j\, \delta T(\boldsymbol{q}\Omega)\,. \end{aligned} \tag{4.63}$$

Thus the ($\boldsymbol{q}$- and Ω-dependent) thermal conductivity tensor is essentially given by the equilibrium heat current auto-correlation function.

Actually κ_{ij} should be defined by an equation like (4.63) with, however, the 'externally impressed' temperature δT replaced by the 'true local temperature variations' δT_{L}, which in the case of small $\boldsymbol{q}$, can be defined by means of the specific heat C

$$\delta E(\boldsymbol{q}t) = C\,\delta T_{\mathrm{L}}(\boldsymbol{q}t), \tag{4.64}$$

see Martin (1965) and Griffin (1965, 1968a). The thermal conductivity $\kappa_{ij}(\boldsymbol{q}\Omega)$ is then given by a response function different from (4.63). It can be shown that – except for pathological cases – the result essentially reduces to (4.63) when $\boldsymbol{q}$ and Ω approach zero. Note, however, that it was exactly the difference between δT and δT_{L} which Griffin (1965, 1968a) used as an argument for obtaining 'driftless' second sound, see subsection 5.3.

Verboven (1960) has reduced (4.63) to an expression involving only a single time integration. For the homogeneous static limit that we are interested in, his result can be cast into the form

$$\kappa_{ij}^{(0)} = \lim_{\Omega\to 0}\lim_{\boldsymbol{q}\to \boldsymbol{0}} \kappa_{ij}(\boldsymbol{q}\Omega) = \frac{1}{2T_0}\lim_{\Omega\to 0}\lim_{\boldsymbol{q}\to \boldsymbol{0}} \chi_{S_jS_i}(\boldsymbol{q}\Omega)/\Omega\,. \tag{4.65}$$

Here $\chi_{S_iS_j}$ is the spectral function of the imaginary-time current–current Green's function:

$$\chi_{S_jS_i}(\boldsymbol{q}\Omega) = \mathrm{i}\left[G_{S_jS_i}(\boldsymbol{q},\,\Omega + \mathrm{i}\varepsilon) - G_{S_jS_i}(\boldsymbol{q},\,\Omega - \mathrm{i}\varepsilon)\right], \tag{4.66}$$

where

$$G_{S_jS_i}(\boldsymbol{q}z_\nu) = (1/\mathrm{i})\int_0^{-\mathrm{i}\beta} \mathrm{d}\tau\,\exp(-\,\mathrm{i}z_\nu\tau)\,\langle T(S_j(-\,\boldsymbol{q}\tau)\,S_i(\boldsymbol{q}0))\rangle_{\mathrm{eq}}\,,$$
$$z_\nu = 2\pi\nu/(-\,\mathrm{i}\beta)\,, \tag{4.67}$$

is, as usual, continued analytically to a function of all non-real z. Thus the determination of κ is reduced to evaluating the equilibrium Green's function (4.67). The analysis of the following subsection shows that this inevitably leads back to solving a linearized Boltzmann equation, although, at first sight, there is no immediate connection between a transport equation and an equilibrium function like (4.67).

4.2.3. Evaluation of the current-current Green's function ('ladder graphs')

Ranninger (1967, 1968, 1969) has devoted a series of papers to the evaluation of (4.65). Although somewhat different in appearance, his analysis is related to the derivation of the linearized phonon transport equation (Sham 1967, Klein and Wehner 1968, 1969, Goetze and Michel 1969, Beck 1971) by means of equilibrium Green's functions. The main point is to unravel those contributions to the self-energy of Green's functions like (4.75) which behave in a singular way for $\boldsymbol{q} \to \mathbf{0}$ and $z \to 0$, in the sense that a perturbation expansion in powers of anharmonicities breaks down. Again the algebra of the various steps of the analysis is quite involved and therefore we only present the most important ideas.

In order to find an explicit expression for (4.67), we introduce an imaginary time Green's function (Kadanoff and Baym 1962) by

$$G_{\mathrm{R}}(1,2) = -\mathrm{i}\langle T(A(1)\,A^{\dagger}(2)\,S_{\mathrm{R}})\rangle, \quad 0 \geqslant t_{\mathrm{i}} \geqslant -\mathrm{i}\beta, \tag{4.68}$$

where S_{R} is now the S-matrix appropriate for an external 'force' coupling to the heat current

$$S_{\mathrm{R}} = T\left[\exp\left(-\mathrm{i}\int_0^{-\mathrm{i}\beta} \mathrm{d}\tau \sum_{qi} S_i(\boldsymbol{q}\tau)\,R_i(\boldsymbol{q}\tau)\right)\right]. \tag{4.69}$$

Remembering definition (4.57) for S_i, we can express (4.67) as

$$G_{S_jS_i}(\boldsymbol{q}z_\nu) = \tfrac{1}{2}\sum_{\boldsymbol{k}\lambda\lambda'} C_i(\boldsymbol{k}\lambda\lambda') \times \int_0^{-\mathrm{i}\beta} \mathrm{d}\tau \exp(\mathrm{i}z_\nu\tau)\left(\frac{\partial}{\partial\tau} - \frac{\partial}{\partial\tau'}\right) F_j(\boldsymbol{kq}\lambda\lambda';\tau\tau')|_{\tau'=\tau}, \tag{4.70}$$

where

$$F_j(\boldsymbol{kq}\lambda\lambda';\tau\tau') = \left.\frac{\delta G_R(\boldsymbol{k}-\tfrac{1}{2}\boldsymbol{q}\;\lambda\tau,\,\boldsymbol{k}+\tfrac{1}{2}\boldsymbol{q}\;\lambda'\tau')}{\delta R_j(\boldsymbol{q}0)}\right|_{\boldsymbol{R}=\mathbf{0}} \tag{4.71}$$

is the functional derivative of (4.68) with respect to the external force when the latter is zero. G_R obeys a Dyson equation formally similar to (4.25):

$$\theta(1)\,G_R(1,2) = \delta(1,2) + [\sigma_R(1,\bar{3}) + \sigma_1(1,\bar{3}) + \sigma_{\mathrm{c}}(1,\bar{3})]\,G_R(\bar{3},2) \tag{4.72}$$

the bar including a time integration from 0 to $-\mathrm{i}\beta$, $\theta(1)$ being given by (4.24). In the self-energy, we have omitted σ_{d} (4.26) since this term would only introduce small corrections to the final result, corresponding to the coupling between the thermal phonons carrying the heat and the elastic displacement field, as discussed in subsubsection 4.1.2 and subsection 5.1. Instead, σ includes the contribution σ_R originating in the external force (4.69):

$$\sigma_R(1,3)=\frac{\partial\delta(t_1-t_3)}{\partial t_1}$$
$$\times\sum_{qi}R_i(\boldsymbol{q}t_1)\,\delta_{\boldsymbol{k}_1,\boldsymbol{k}_3-\boldsymbol{q}}\left[C_i(\boldsymbol{k}_1+\tfrac{1}{2}\boldsymbol{q}\ \lambda_3\lambda_1)-C_i(-\boldsymbol{k}_1-\tfrac{1}{2}\boldsymbol{q}\ \lambda_1\lambda_3)\right].\quad(4.73)$$

We can immediately obtain an approximate integral equation for F_j(4.71) from (4.72) with the help of

$$\frac{\delta G_R(1,2)}{\delta R(3)}=G_R(1,\bar{4})\frac{\delta\sigma(\bar{4},\bar{5})}{\delta R(3)}G(\bar{5},2)\qquad(4.74)$$

which is a consequence of (4.72), see Kadanoff and Baym (1962). After the derivatives with respect to $\boldsymbol{R}$ are taken the external perturbation is switched off ($\boldsymbol{R}=0$), so all quantities are equilibrium expectation values and G_R reduces to the usual one-phonon Green's function

$$G_R(1,2)|_{\boldsymbol{R}=0}=\mathscr{G}_{\lambda_1\lambda_2}(\boldsymbol{k}_1,t_1-t_2)\,\delta_{\boldsymbol{k}_1,\boldsymbol{k}_2}.\qquad(4.75)$$

$G_{S_jS_i}$ is expressed by means of the Fourier coefficients of F_j with respect to τ and τ'

$$G_{S_jS_i}(\boldsymbol{q}z_\nu)=-\frac{1}{\beta}\sum_{\boldsymbol{k}\lambda\lambda'}C_i(\boldsymbol{k}\lambda\lambda')$$
$$\times\sum_{z_\mu}(2z_\mu-z_\nu)F_j(\boldsymbol{kq}\lambda\lambda';z_\mu,z_\nu-z_\mu).\qquad(4.76)$$

Beck (1971) has given more details about the analytic behaviour of functions like our F_j, which is closely related to the 'vertex part' of G. It is the solution of

$$F_j(\boldsymbol{kq}\lambda\lambda';z_1z_2)=\sum_{\alpha\beta}\mathscr{G}_{\lambda\alpha}(\boldsymbol{k}-\tfrac{1}{2}\boldsymbol{q},z_1)$$
$$\times X^j_{\alpha\beta}(\boldsymbol{kq},z_1z_2)\,\mathscr{G}_{\beta\lambda'}(\boldsymbol{k}+\tfrac{1}{2}\boldsymbol{q},-z_2),\qquad(4.77)$$

with

$$X^j_{\alpha\beta}(\boldsymbol{kq}, z_1 z_2) = 2z_2 C_j(\boldsymbol{k}\alpha\beta) + \tfrac{1}{2}\mathrm{i} \sum_{\boldsymbol{k}'\mu\mu'} V_4(-\boldsymbol{k}\alpha, \boldsymbol{k}\beta; \boldsymbol{k}'\mu, -\boldsymbol{k}'\mu')$$

$$\times \frac{1}{-\mathrm{i}\beta} \sum_{z_\alpha} F_j(\boldsymbol{k}'\boldsymbol{q}\mu\mu'; z_\alpha, z_1 + z_2 - z_\alpha)$$

$$+ \mathrm{i} \sum V_3(-\boldsymbol{k}\alpha, \boldsymbol{k}'\mu, \boldsymbol{k}''\rho)\, V_3^*(-\boldsymbol{k}\beta, \boldsymbol{k}'\mu', \boldsymbol{k}''\rho')$$

$$\times \frac{1}{-\mathrm{i}\beta} \sum_{z_\alpha} F_j(\boldsymbol{k}'\boldsymbol{q}\mu\mu'; z_\alpha, z_1 + z_2 - z_\alpha)\, \mathscr{G}_{\rho\rho'}(\boldsymbol{k}'', z_1 - z_\alpha). \tag{4.78}$$

Here, we have already neglected the small wave vector $\boldsymbol{q}$ with respect to $\boldsymbol{k}, \boldsymbol{k}'$, etc. in the arguments of V_3 and V_4. Eq. (4.78) looks fairly complicated. Considering $|V_3|^2$ and V_4 as small, we can write down an iterative solution for (4.77) and (4.78). In terms of graphs, we then build up F_j by means of 'ladder graphs', coming from the last term in (4.78), see Sham (1967), Ranninger (1967, 1968), and 'chain graphs' due to the V_4-term. Summing 'ladder' terms will lead to the 'indirect' or 'back-scattering' part of the linearized collision operator; whereas the chains yield the equivalent of the integral operator I^{-1} in (4.49), (4.50) describing the quasi-particle interaction between phonons. In our final equation determining the static thermal conductivity, this interaction will not enter, since in (4.49) it accompanies the time derivative.

The sums over $z_\alpha[=2\pi\alpha/(-\mathrm{i}\beta)]$ are performed by using the identity (Kadanoff and Baym 1962):

$$\frac{1}{-\mathrm{i}\beta} \sum_{z_\alpha} F_j(z_\alpha, z_\nu - z_\alpha) = \oint_\Gamma \mathrm{d}z' \, \frac{N_0(z')}{2\pi} F_j(z', z_\nu - z'), \tag{4.79}$$

the path Γ leading along the branch cuts of F_j occurring for Im $z'=0$ and Im $(z_\nu - z')=0$. In the end, we need the limits $z_\nu \to \Omega \pm \mathrm{i}\delta$ in order to express $\kappa^{(0)}_{ij}$ (4.65) by F_j using (4.66), (4.67), (4.76):

$$\kappa^{(0)}_{ij} = \frac{1}{2T_0} \lim_{\Omega\to 0} \lim_{\boldsymbol{q}\to 0} \sum_{\boldsymbol{k}\lambda\lambda'} C_i(\boldsymbol{k}\lambda\lambda')$$

$$\times \int_{-\infty}^{+\infty} \frac{\mathrm{d}\omega}{2\pi} \, \omega m(\omega) \left[F_j^{++} + F_j^{--} - F_j^{-+} - F_j^{+-}\right]. \tag{4.80}$$

$m(\omega)$ is given by (2.14) and

$$F_j^{\pm\pm}(\boldsymbol{kq}\lambda\lambda', \omega\Omega) = F_j(\boldsymbol{kq}\lambda\lambda'; \omega + \tfrac{1}{2}\Omega \pm \mathrm{i}0, -\omega + \tfrac{1}{2}\Omega \pm \mathrm{i}0). \qquad (4.81)$$

Eq. (4.79) also serves to transform (4.77), (4.78) into an integral equation for the different functions $F_j^{\pm\pm}$ obtained by letting z_1 and z_2 in (4.77) go to the corresponding limits in (4.81). It is now crucial to examine the behavior of (4.81) in the limit of very small $\boldsymbol{q}$ and Ω. This can be done most easily by looking at the product of two $\mathscr{G}$'s on the right-hand side of (4.77). For the sake of simplicity, we approximate $\mathscr{G}_{\lambda\lambda'}$ by its diagonal part and use a form obtained in anharmonic perturbation theory for the latter:

$$\mathscr{G}_{\lambda\lambda'}(\boldsymbol{k}, \nu \pm \mathrm{i}\varepsilon) \approx [\nu^2 - \omega_{\boldsymbol{k}\lambda}^2 + \tfrac{1}{2}\mathrm{i}\,\mathrm{sg}\,\varepsilon \cdot \Gamma(\boldsymbol{k}\lambda, \nu)]^{-1}\,\delta_{\lambda\lambda'}. \qquad (4.82)$$

The real part of the self energy has been neglected (or incorporated into some renormalized frequencies ω_k^2) and Γ is given in a self-consistent way in terms of $\chi(k, \nu) = \mathrm{i}[\mathscr{G}_{\lambda\lambda}(\nu + \mathrm{i}\varepsilon) - \mathscr{G}_{\lambda\lambda'}(\nu - \mathrm{i}\varepsilon)]$ by

$$\Gamma(k, \nu) = \tfrac{1}{2}\sum_{k'k''} |V_3(-k, k', k'')|^2$$
$$\times \int \frac{\mathrm{d}\omega}{2\pi} N_0(\omega)\,[\chi(k', \omega)\,\chi(k'', \nu - \omega) + \chi(k', \nu + \omega)\,\chi(k'', \omega)]. \qquad (4.83)$$

Let us take a look at the right-hand side of (4.77), taking the limits used in (4.81) and putting $\boldsymbol{q} = 0$:

$$Z_{\lambda\lambda'} \equiv \mathscr{G}_{\lambda\lambda}(\boldsymbol{k}, \omega + \tfrac{1}{2}\Omega + \mathrm{i}\varepsilon_1)\,\mathscr{G}_{\lambda'\lambda'}(\boldsymbol{k}, \omega - \tfrac{1}{2}\Omega + \mathrm{i}\varepsilon_2)$$
$$\approx [-2\omega\Omega + \Delta_{\lambda\lambda'}(\boldsymbol{k}) + \tfrac{1}{2}\mathrm{i}(\mathrm{sg}\,\varepsilon_1\,\Gamma(\boldsymbol{k}\lambda, \omega) - \mathrm{sg}\,\varepsilon_2\,\Gamma(\boldsymbol{k}\lambda', \omega))]^{-1}$$
$$\times [\mathscr{G}_{\lambda\lambda}(\boldsymbol{k}, \omega + \mathrm{i}\varepsilon_1) - \mathscr{G}_{\lambda'\lambda'}(\boldsymbol{k}, \omega + \mathrm{i}\varepsilon_2)] + \mathrm{O}(\Omega) \qquad (4.84)$$

which can be obtained by using $A^{-1}B^{-1} = (B - A)^{-1}(A^{-1} - B^{-1})$. The quantity

$$\Delta_{\lambda\lambda'}(\boldsymbol{k}) = \omega_{\boldsymbol{k}\lambda}^2 - \omega_{\boldsymbol{k}\lambda'}^2 \qquad (4.85)$$

vanishes for $\lambda = \lambda'$ and is supposed to be non-zero for most parts of the Brillouin zone for $\lambda \neq \lambda'$. This important argument was already invoked in subsubsection 4.1.2 in order to be able to express the non-diagonal part of the non-equilibrium Green's function by means of the diagonal, hydrodynamically singular one. In the limit $\Omega \to 0$ we obtain the following forms for (4.84):

$$\lambda = \lambda', \quad \varepsilon_1 = \varepsilon_2, \quad Z_{\lambda\lambda'} \approx 0, \tag{4.86a}$$

$$\lambda = \lambda', \quad \varepsilon_1 = -\varepsilon_2, \quad Z_{\lambda\lambda'} \approx \chi(\boldsymbol{k}\lambda, \omega)/\Gamma(\boldsymbol{k}\lambda, \omega), \tag{4.86b}$$

$$\lambda \neq \lambda', \quad Z_{\lambda\lambda'} \approx [\mathscr{G}_{\lambda\lambda}(\boldsymbol{k}, \omega + \mathrm{i}\varepsilon_1) - \mathscr{G}_{\lambda'\lambda'}(\boldsymbol{k}, \omega + \mathrm{i}\varepsilon_2)]/\Delta_{\lambda\lambda'}(\boldsymbol{k}). \tag{4.86c}$$

Insertion of (4.86c) for $\lambda \neq \lambda'$ into (4.80) shows that this contribution vanishes. Thus the non-diagonal part of the heat current $\boldsymbol{S}$ would only contribute anharmonic corrections to $\kappa_{ij}^{(0)}$ stemming from higher order terms of an iterative solution of (4.78). Equally F_j^{++} and F_j^{--} vanish up to this order owing to (4.86a). So we are left with (4.86b). This result, however, has a surprising form: according to (4.83) it is $o(V_3^{-2})$, i.e. it is very *large* for small anharmonicities. This expresses the fact that $F_j^{+-}(\cdot\cdot\lambda\lambda;\cdot\cdot)$ is 'singular' in the hydrodynamic limit $\boldsymbol{q}\to 0$, $\Omega \to 0$. A closer examination of (4.78) reveals that all higher order terms of an iterative solution would again contribute such singularities, which causes the usual anharmonic perturbation expansion to break down. This problem is typical of the treatment of hydrodynamic phenomena in many-body systems: hydrodynamic excitations are based on the existence of many collisions between the quasi-particles considered, which produces local equilibrium. This is, of course, in contradiction with the idea of weak interactions that could be treated in a perturbative way.

We now proceed as follows: in the expression (4.80) for $\kappa_{ij}^{(0)}$ we replace those parts of $F_j^{\pm\pm}(\lambda\lambda')$ which are, according to (4.86), 'regular' for $\Omega \to 0$ by their lowest order values (4.86). Thus, we are left with

$$\kappa_{ij}^{(0)} \approx \frac{1}{2T_0} \sum_{\boldsymbol{k}\lambda} C_i(\boldsymbol{k}) \int \mathrm{d}\omega\, \omega m(\omega)\, [F_j^{-+}(\boldsymbol{k}\boldsymbol{0}\lambda\lambda; \omega 0) + F_j^{+-}(\cdots)], \tag{4.87}$$

where $C_i(k)$ is the diagonal part $C_i(\boldsymbol{k}\lambda\lambda)$ in (4.58). For $F_j^{-+}(\lambda\lambda)$ and $F_j^{+-}(\lambda\lambda)$, however, we have to treat the full integral equation (4.77), (4.78), whereby we neglect the regular parts of F_j wherever they appear. Putting $F_j^{+-}(\boldsymbol{k}\boldsymbol{0}\lambda, \lambda; \omega 0) + F_j^{-+}(\cdots) = \chi(k, \omega)\, h_j(k, \omega)$ with $k = (\boldsymbol{k}\lambda)$ we find

$$h_j(k\omega) = \Gamma^{-1}(k\omega) \Big[4\omega\, C_i(\boldsymbol{k}\lambda\lambda) + \frac{1}{2\pi} \sum_{k'k''} |V_3(-k, k', k'')|^2 \times \int \mathrm{d}\omega'\, N_0(\omega')\, (\chi(k'', \omega)\, h_j(k', \omega + \omega') + \chi(k'', \omega - \omega')\, h_j(k', \omega')) \Big]. \tag{4.88}$$

The term containing V_4 in (4.78) does not contribute since it would involve $-i\Omega(F_j^{+-}+F_j^{-+})$ which vanishes for $\Omega\to 0$ as does $I^{-1}\partial\varphi/\partial t$ in (4.49). $\kappa_{ij}^{(0)}$ is determined provided that we can solve the homogeneous integral equation (4.88). Let us, in conclusion, summarize some aspects of this problem.

If we replace, in (4.88), h_j by the inhomogeneity $4\omega C_i/\Gamma$ we find

$$\kappa_{ij}^{(0)} = \frac{1}{T_0}\sum_k C_i(k)\, C_j(k) \int \frac{d\omega}{\pi}\, \omega^2 m(\omega)\, \chi(k\omega)\, \Gamma^{-1}(k\omega). \tag{4.89}$$

This is a familiar result, since by introducing the specific heat $C(\omega) = \omega^2 m(\omega)/T_0$ for the frequency ω and putting

$$\frac{1}{\pi}\sum_k v_i(k)\, v_j(k)\, \chi(k\omega)\, \Gamma^{-1}(k\omega) \equiv \tfrac{1}{3}c^2(\omega)\, \tau(\omega)\, \delta_{ij}, \tag{4.90}$$

$\kappa_{ij}^{(0)}=\kappa^{(0)}\delta_{ij}$ can be expressed as a frequency integral over specific heat, relaxation time τ and group velocity c:

$$\kappa^{(0)} = \tfrac{1}{3}\int d\omega\, c^2(\omega)\, \tau(\omega)\, C(\omega). \tag{4.91}$$

Since $\Gamma(k\omega)$ is the damping function in the one-phonon spectral function, $\tau(\omega)$ is, correspondingly, the mean life time of a single phonon with frequency ω. The effect of inserting the solution h_j of the full equation (4.88) instead of its lowest order term can be visualized according to Ranninger (1967, 1968) as replacing the single phonon relaxation time $\tau(\omega)$ by a collective 'transport life-time' $h_j(k,\omega)$.

Multiplying (4.88) by Γ and taking the left-hand side Γh_j from (4.83) together with the second term on the other side we find

$$\tilde{L}[h_j(k\omega)] = 4\omega C_i(k). \tag{4.92}$$

This is nothing else than a linearized collision equation for the case of a space- and time-independent deviation from equilibrium caused by the external force $4\omega C_i$. $\tilde{L}$ may be found by linearizing the general collision term (4.37): it describes collisions between quasi-particles with spectral function χ. Approximating the latter by its harmonic form (4.6) and putting $h_j(k,\omega=\pm\omega_k)=\varphi_j(k)$ we can simplify our problem to

$$\kappa_{ij}^{(0)} = (1/T_0)\sum_k v_i(k)\, \omega_k\, m(k)\, \varphi_j(k) \tag{4.93}$$

and

$$L[\varphi_j(k)] = v_j \omega_k , \tag{4.94}$$

L being the usual linearized collision term (4.51). Thus we have been led back to the old formulation of the thermal conductivity problem (Peierls 1955, Ziman 1960, etc.): in the steady state situation, the left-hand side o (2.7) is approximated by the local equilibrium (2.12) and the linearized Boltzmann equation reads

$$L[\varphi] = - \omega_k v_j(k) \nabla_j \delta T / T_0 . \tag{4.95}$$

The prescriptions (4.52) and (2.20) for evaluating energy current and $\kappa_{ij}^{(0)}$ leads immediately back to the system (4.93), (4.94). In the following section, we shall use the eigenfunctions of L to find formally exact expressions for $\kappa_{ij}^{(0)}$, which can then be compared to the relaxation time approximations of subsection 2.4.

4.3. Solutions of the Peierls–Boltzmann equation

4.3.1. Eigenfunctions of the collision operator

In subsection 4.1 it was shown how a transport equation of the form (4.49) can be derived from the microscopic hamiltonian (2.4). Although one may be proud of the mathematical formulation of section 1, one has to admit that it has as yet not been possible to solve (4.49) in a really satisfactory way, even approximating the quasi-particle interaction operator I by 1.

Our problem consists in finding functions $\varphi(k, \boldsymbol{q}\Omega)$ which are Fourier transforms of the phonon distribution function $\varphi(k, \boldsymbol{r}t)$, and which satisfy

$$[-\mathrm{i}\Omega + \mathrm{i}\boldsymbol{q} \cdot \boldsymbol{v}_k - L]\, \varphi(k, \boldsymbol{q}\Omega) = F(k, \boldsymbol{q}\Omega) . \tag{4.96}$$

F is some external force: in the two-fluid framework (subsect. 5.1) it describes the effect of elastic deformations on the phonon gas whereas in the preceding section the inhomogeneity of (4.95) involved the gradient of the local temperature. L is a linearized collision operator splitting into a normal and a resistive part, $L = L_\mathrm{N} + L_R$. To lowest order in the anharmonicities, L_N is given by (4.51) with $\boldsymbol{Q} = 0$, whereas the Umklapp part L_R summarizes all terms with reciprocal lattice vectors $\boldsymbol{Q} \neq 0$. Operators describing further momentum non-conserving processes have been considered by Klemens (1951, 1955). All these operators fit into the scheme

$$L\varphi(k) = L^{(D)}(k)\,\varphi(k) + \sum_{k'} L^{(I)}(k,k')\,\varphi(k'), \tag{4.97}$$

i.e. they consist of a 'direct', multiplicative part $L^{(D)}$ and an integral expression with kernel $L^{(I)}$.

Let us introduce a Hilbert space of functions $\varphi(k, \boldsymbol{q}\Omega)$ considering $k = (\boldsymbol{k}\lambda)$ as the independent variables and treating $\boldsymbol{q}$ and Ω as given parameters. A scalar product is defined by

$$\langle \varphi_1 \mid \varphi_2 \rangle = (1/V) \sum_k m(k)\,\varphi_1^*(k)\,\varphi_2(k). \tag{4.98}$$

The following properties

$$L(\varphi_1 + \varphi_2) = L\varphi_1 + L\varphi_2, \tag{4.99}$$

$$\langle \varphi_1 \mid L\varphi_2 \rangle = \langle L\varphi_1 \mid \varphi_2 \rangle, \tag{4.100}$$

$$\langle \varphi \mid L\varphi \rangle \leqslant 0 \tag{4.101}$$

are true for L_N and all different terms of L_R. We are mainly interested in the spectral properties of L_N. Since it conserves energy and momentum, we find four eigenfunctions with eigenvalue zero

$$L_N\chi_0 = 0 \quad \text{with} \quad \chi_0 = \alpha_0\omega_k, \qquad \text{(phonon energy)} \tag{4.102}$$

$$L_N\chi_{1_i} = 0 \quad \text{with} \quad \chi_{1_i} = \alpha_1 k_i, \qquad \text{(phonon momentum)} \tag{4.103}$$

The constants α_0 and α_1 normalize χ_0 and χ_{1_i} in the norm given by (4.98). Furthermore, according to (4.101) the spectrum of L_N is bounded from above by zero. It can be expected that there is no other eigenfunction with (discrete) eigenvalue zero since there are no further collision invariants. For an infinite system $L^{(D)}$, $L^{(I)}$ and the functions φ are functions of the continuous variable $\boldsymbol{k}$, and $V^{-1}\sum_{\boldsymbol{k}}$ is replaced by $[1/(8\pi^3)]\int d^3k$, the integration extending over the first Brillouin zone. Using the fact that the spectrum of $L^{(D)}$, which is a continuous function with values between zero and some negative lower bound, is given by all possible values $L^{(D)}(\boldsymbol{k}\lambda)$, Jäckle (1970) and Buot (1972) have shown that the continuous spectrum of L_N extends right up to zero. The proof is based on the so-called Weyl–Von Neumann theorem (Riesz and Sz-Nagy 1955) stating that the continuous spectrum and the accumulation points of $L^{(D)}$, a self-adjoint operator, do not change when the compact part $L^{(I)}$ is added. Thus the usual procedure to treat those eigenvalues of $L_N - i\boldsymbol{q}\cdot\boldsymbol{v}_k$ which emerge from zero when 'switching on' the drift term $-i\boldsymbol{q}\cdot\boldsymbol{v}_k$ in order to derive hydrodynamic equations cannot be rigorously justified as can be done in the case of a gas of particles interacting through 'hard enough' pair potentials. There we have a critical quantity λ_c such that the continuous spectrum of L_N includes no values $\lambda > \lambda_c$. Thus for small enough $\boldsymbol{q}$ the above mentioned eigenvalues of the operator $L_N - i\boldsymbol{q}\cdot\boldsymbol{v}_k$ are well separated from its continuous spectrum. Heuristically this unpleasant situation can be remedied by the help of the following argument: obviously that part of the spectrum of $L_N^{(D)}$ which lies close to zero stems from values of $L_N^{(D)}(\boldsymbol{k}\lambda)$ for very small $\boldsymbol{k}$'s, i.e. from long wavelength phonons whose damping goes to zero for $\boldsymbol{k}\to 0$ owing to translational invariance of the lattice. These 'acoustic' small $\boldsymbol{k}$ phonons contribute, however, very little to observable hydrodynamic quantities such as (2.19)–(2.22), at least for temperatures that are not too low. Thus it should be possible to truncate the Brillouin zone by omitting all values of $\boldsymbol{k}$ with $|\boldsymbol{k}| < k_0$ and to build up the Hilbert space on this range of variables. Then the spectrum of L_N would show a gap between λ_c and zero with λ_c being given by the smallest value of $L_N^{(D)}(k)$ in the truncated zone. In any case we shall sketch the above mentioned procedure of calculating the 'hydrodynamic' eigenvalues of $L_N - i\boldsymbol{q}\cdot\boldsymbol{v}_k$ in subsubsection 4.3.3 although this procedure has as yet no rigorous mathematical justification, since these eigenvalues lie in the continuum.*

In the following, we shall again assume a finite system. Then L_N has a set of discrete eigenvalues $\lambda_l \leqslant 0$. The eigenfunctions χ_0 and χ_1 will always be identified with (4.102), (4.103) whereas all nonzero eigenvalues will be labelled with $l \geqslant 2$. (In order to be consistent with a fine but discrete grid in $\boldsymbol{k}$-space, we have to replace the energy conserving δ-functions in L_N by some appropriate functions with a finite width).

Inserting the expansion of φ in terms of eigenfunctions χ_l of L_N

$$\varphi(k, \boldsymbol{q}\Omega) = a_0(\boldsymbol{q}\Omega)\,\chi_0(k) + \sum_{j=1}^{3} a_j(\boldsymbol{q}\Omega)\,\chi_{1_i}(k) + \sum_{l \geqslant 2} a_l(\boldsymbol{q}\Omega)\,\chi_l(k) \tag{4.104}$$

into (4.96) and taking the scalar product with $\chi_{l'}$ yields a system of linear equations for the vector of coefficients $a_0, a_{1_x}, a_{1_y}, a_{1_z}, a_2, \cdots$, which we summarize into $(a_0, \boldsymbol{a}_1, a_2)$:

* Recently, Beck (1975a) has performed calculations on a model with $\boldsymbol{k}$-dependent relaxation times, showing that taking into account the gapless spectrum of L in an appropriate way may lead to important modifications of the hydrodynamic equations describing second sound and Poiseuille flow.

$$\begin{pmatrix} -\mathrm{i}\Omega & \mathrm{i}\boldsymbol{q}\cdot\boldsymbol{V}_{01} & \mathrm{i}\boldsymbol{q}\cdot\ _{02} \\ \mathrm{i}\boldsymbol{q}\cdot\boldsymbol{V}_{10} & -\mathrm{i}\Omega-(L_{\mathrm{R}})_{11} & \mathrm{i}\boldsymbol{q}\cdot\boldsymbol{V}_{12}-(L_{\mathrm{R}})_{12} \\ \mathrm{i}\boldsymbol{q}\cdot\boldsymbol{V}_{20} & \mathrm{i}\boldsymbol{q}\cdot\boldsymbol{V}_{21}-(L_{\mathrm{R}})_{21} & -\mathrm{i}\Omega+\mathrm{i}\boldsymbol{q}\cdot\boldsymbol{V}_{22}-(L_{\mathrm{N}})_{22}-(L_{\mathrm{R}})_{22} \end{pmatrix}$$

$$\times\begin{pmatrix} a_0 \\ \boldsymbol{a}_1 \\ a_2 \end{pmatrix} = \begin{pmatrix} F_0 \\ \boldsymbol{F}_1 \\ F_2 \end{pmatrix}. \qquad (4.105)$$

Here $F_l = \langle \chi_l \mid F\rangle$ and the quantities like $\boldsymbol{V}_{01}$, $(L_{\mathrm{R}})_{12}$, etc. are matrices defined in an obvious way, e.g.

$$(L_{\mathrm{R}})_{12} = \langle \chi_{1_i} \mid L_{\mathrm{R}}\chi_l\rangle, \quad l \geqslant 2. \qquad (4.106)$$

Obviously $(L_{\mathrm{N}})_{22}$ is diagonal with $\langle \chi_l | L_{\mathrm{N}} | \chi_{l'}\rangle = \delta_{ll'}\lambda_l$. The coefficients a_0 and $\boldsymbol{a}_1$ have the physical meaning of the deviations of E and $\boldsymbol{P}$ from equilibrium. Comparison of (4.98), (4.104) with (2.19), (2.21), (2.19a) shows

$$a_0 = \langle \chi_0 \mid \varphi\rangle = \langle \omega_k \mid \omega_k\rangle^{-1/2}\,\delta E = \langle \omega_k \mid \omega_k\rangle^{1/2}\,\delta T/T_0, \qquad (4.107)$$

$$a_{1_i} = \langle k_i \mid \varphi\rangle = \langle k_i \mid k_i\rangle^{-1/2}\,\delta P_i \qquad (4.108)$$

and obviously the first equation of (4.105) is the conservation law for energy with the heat current given by

$$S_i = \sum_{j=1}^{3} a_{1_j}(V_i)_{oj} + \sum_{l\geqslant 2} a_l (V_i)_{ol}. \qquad (4.109)$$

This formal expansion of φ in terms of the eigenfunctions of L_{N} (or also of $L = L_{\mathrm{N}} + L_{\mathrm{R}}$) was used by Guyer and Krumhansl (1966a, b), Goetze and Michel (1967a, b; 1969), Niklasson (1969, 1970) and others in order to find 'exact' expressions for transport coefficients and to justify the hydrodynamic equations of section 2 for second sound. We use (4.105) as a starting point for calculating the static thermal conductivity as well as dispersion and damping of second sound in the next subsubsection and for demonstrating the coupling between first sound and the collective excitations of the phonon gas in subsection 5.1.

4.3.2. *Static thermal conductivity and second sound*

There are two ways of finding $\kappa_{ij}^{(0)}$ from the solutions of (4.96). Either the homogeneous part of (4.105) is considered and the heat current S_i (4.109) is expressed in terms of $\mathrm{i}\boldsymbol{q}a_0$ and thus of the gradient of the local temperature, or the inhomogeneous equation with the force term from (4.94) is solved. Whereas Guyer and Krumhansl (1966, a, b) and most other authors used the first method, we proceed according to the second, and thus complete Ranninger's (1967, 1968) program presented in subsection 4.2.

In the static limit, eq. (4.105) with the force term of eq. (4.94) reduces to

$$-\begin{pmatrix}(L_{\mathrm{R}})_{11} & (L_{\mathrm{R}})_{12}\\ (L_{\mathrm{R}})_{21} & (L_{\mathrm{N}}+L_{\mathrm{R}})_{22}\end{pmatrix}\begin{pmatrix}\boldsymbol{a}_1\\ a_2\end{pmatrix}=\begin{pmatrix}\boldsymbol{F}_1\\ F_2\end{pmatrix}, \tag{4.110}$$

with $\boldsymbol{F}_1=\langle\boldsymbol{\chi}_1|\, v_j\, |\omega\rangle$ and $F_2=\langle\chi_l|\, v_j\, |\omega\rangle$, whereas $a_0=0$. The coefficient vectors $\boldsymbol{a}_1$ and a_2 are found by solving formally (4.110), and $\kappa_{ij}^{(0)}$ is immediately calculated by using (4.93), (4.94), and (4.104):

$$\kappa_{ij}^{(0)}=CK_{ij},$$
$$K_{ij}=\langle 0|V_i(1-P)\,L^{-1}(1-P)\,V_j|\,0\rangle + \sum_{rs}\langle 0|A_i|\,s\rangle\, M_{rs}^{-1}\langle s|A_j^{\dagger}|\,0\rangle, \tag{4.111}$$

where

$$|0\rangle=|\chi_0\rangle,\ |s\rangle=|\chi_{1_s}\rangle$$

and

$$A_i=v_i-v_i(1-P)\,L^{-1}(1-P)\,L_{\mathrm{R}}. \tag{4.112}$$

M_{rs}^{-1} is the inverse in the three-dimensional subspace of the matrix

$$M_{rs}=\langle r|\,L_{\mathrm{R}}-L_{\mathrm{R}}(1-P)\,L^{-1}(1-P)\,L_{\mathrm{R}}\,|s\rangle \tag{4.113}$$

and finally P is the projector onto the subspace spanned by χ_0 and χ_{1_s}, $s=1,3$. L^{-1} is the inverse of L in this subspace.

This is of course a very formal result, given e.g. by Guyer and Krumhansl (1966a). In general, it does not have much practical use since a numerical evaluation would require knowledge of the eigenfunctions χ_l. There are two limiting situations, in which κ_{ij} has a much simpler form:

(1) '$L_N \gg L_R$'; Ziman limit:

$$K_{ij}\approx\langle 0|\,v_i\,|r\rangle\,\langle r|\,L_{\mathrm{R}}\,|s\rangle^{-1}\,\langle s|\,v_j\,|0\rangle. \tag{4.114}$$

K_{ij} is independent of L_N, a fact already pointed out in subsection 2.4, and furthermore it can be calculated by simply inverting a three by three matrix which can be evaluated numerically. Werthamer and Chui (1972a, b) have started from (4.114) and estimated the matrix elements of L_R by a saddle point technique. Thus they were able to account for the large anisotropy of K_{ij} in hcp ^{4}He, see section 3. Eq. (4.114) is also essentially what one finds by applying a variational principle for K_{ij} using a trial function φ of the form $\varphi = \text{const.}\ \boldsymbol{q}\cdot\boldsymbol{k}$ (Ziman 1960).

(2) '$L_N \ll L_R$'

$$K_{ij} \approx \langle 0|\, v_i \,|r\rangle \,\langle r|\, L_R^{-1}\,|s\rangle\, \langle s|\, v_j\,|0\rangle\,. \tag{4.115}$$

This result can be derived (Guyer and Krumhansl 1966a) by carefully combining the different matrices entering (4.111) and considering $L_N \ll L_R$. In this limit, it is not sufficient to calculate simple matrix elements of L_R; its inverse has to be known. It is interesting to note that perturbative methods like the one described in subsubsection 4.3.3, also using variational arguments, lead to the result (4.132), so the inverse of L_R is again replaced by the inverse of a matrix element.

Guyer and Krumhansl (1966a) have suggested an interpolation scheme for situations between the extremes (1) and (2) which in our framework can be formulated as

$$K_{ij} \approx \langle 0|\, v_i \,|r\rangle \left[\frac{1}{1+t}\langle r|\, L_R|\, s\rangle^{-1} + \frac{t}{1+t}\langle r|\, L_R^{-1}\,|s\rangle\right] \langle s\,|v_j\,|0\rangle \tag{4.116}$$

with

$$t \approx \langle r|\, L_R^{-1}\,|r\rangle\,\langle r|\,(1-P)\,L_N^{-1}\,(1-P)\,|r\rangle\,. \tag{4.117}$$

(Guyer and Krumhansl worked with a simple one-branch model.) This is a modification of Callaway's formulation (2.72). Hogan et al. (1969) have used a formula of the type (4.116), with the collision operators replaced by wave-vector dependent relaxation times to fit thermal conductivity data obtained on helium with fair success.

Second sound can also be obtained under certain conditions from (4.105). The 'external force' F is set equal to zero, and we look for solutions of the homogeneous system. The coefficients a_2 are eliminated by the help of the third equation, which leads to

$$[-\mathrm{i}\Omega + \langle 0|\, \boldsymbol{q}\cdot\boldsymbol{v}(1-P)\, A^{-1}(1-P)\, \boldsymbol{q}\cdot\boldsymbol{v}\,|0\rangle]\, a_0 + \sum_s \langle 0|\, \mathrm{i}\boldsymbol{q}\cdot\boldsymbol{v} - \mathrm{i}\boldsymbol{q}\cdot\boldsymbol{v}(1-P)\, A^{-1}(1-P) \times (\mathrm{i}\boldsymbol{q}\cdot\boldsymbol{v} - L_{\mathrm{R}})\,|s\rangle\, a_{1_s} = 0, \quad (4.118)$$

$$\langle s|\, \mathrm{i}\boldsymbol{q}\cdot\boldsymbol{v} - (\mathrm{i}\boldsymbol{q}\cdot\boldsymbol{v} - L_{\mathrm{R}})\,(1-P)\, A^{-1}(1-P)\, \mathrm{i}\boldsymbol{q}\cdot\boldsymbol{v}\,|0\rangle\, a_0 + \sum_{s'} [-\mathrm{i}\Omega\delta_{ss'} - \langle s|\, L_{\mathrm{R}} - (\mathrm{i}\boldsymbol{q}\cdot\boldsymbol{v} - L_{\mathrm{R}})\,(1-P)\, A^{-1}(1-P) \times (\mathrm{i}\boldsymbol{q}\cdot\boldsymbol{v} - L_{\mathrm{R}})|s'\rangle\, a_{1s'}] = 0, \quad (4.119)$$

with

$$A = -\mathrm{i}\Omega + \mathrm{i}\boldsymbol{q}\cdot\boldsymbol{v} - L\,. \quad (4.120)$$

Again it is impossible to make any precise statements about possible excitations in the phonon system described by (4.118), (4.119) for arbitrary relative magnitude of Ω, $|\boldsymbol{q}|$ and the matrix elements of the collision operators. This will be done for the analysis of heat pulse experiments in the framework of the relaxation time model in subsection 5.4. Here we are interested in 'exact' results and we specialize to the situation where second sound was found to exist in the phenomenological framework of section 2. At first sight, we are tempted to incorporate the window condition (2.50) into the system (4.118), (4.119) by simply neglecting $-\mathrm{i}\Omega$ and $\mathrm{i}\boldsymbol{q}\cdot\boldsymbol{v}$ with respect to L_{N}, and L_{R} with respect to $-\mathrm{i}\Omega$, $\mathrm{i}\boldsymbol{q}\cdot\boldsymbol{v}$ and L_{N}. For the first of these approximations we have to consider, however, that there will always be matrix elements of L_{N} which are arbitrarily close to zero, since the spectrum of L_{N} has no gap. According to what we said in subsection 3.1. we can, however, hope that these eigenvalues of L_{N} have only negligible weight (see, however, footnote on p. 258). Thus we find, for cubic symmetry, the following condition for vanishing determinant of (4.118), (4.119):

$$\Omega^2 + \mathrm{i}\Omega\,[\overline{\tau_{\mathrm{R}}^{-1}} + q^2 c_{\mathrm{II}}^2 \bar{\tau}_{\mathrm{N}}] - q^2 c_{\mathrm{II}}^2 = 0\,. \quad (4.121)$$

This is exactly (2.44), but the relaxation times are now given the following precise, though formal meaning:

$$\overline{\tau_{\mathrm{R}}^{-1}} = -\,\langle \boldsymbol{k}|\, L_{\mathrm{R}}\,|\boldsymbol{k}\rangle / \langle \boldsymbol{k}\,|\,\boldsymbol{k}\rangle\,, \quad (4.122)$$

$$\bar{\tau}_{\mathrm{N}} = c_{\mathrm{II}}^{-2}\left[\sum_{ij}\left(\frac{\langle k_i\,|v_j\tilde{L}_{\mathrm{N}}\,v_j\,|k_i\rangle}{5\langle \boldsymbol{k}\cdot\boldsymbol{k}\rangle} + \frac{2\langle k_i\,|v_i\tilde{L}_{\mathrm{N}}^{-1}v_j\,|k_j\rangle}{5\langle \boldsymbol{k}\cdot\boldsymbol{k}\rangle}\right) - \frac{1}{3}\frac{\langle \omega_k|\,\boldsymbol{v}\cdot\tilde{L}_{\mathrm{N}}^{-1}\boldsymbol{v}\,|\omega_k\rangle}{\langle \omega_k\,|\,\omega_k\rangle}\right], \tag{4.123}$$

where

$$\tilde{L}_{\mathrm{N}}^{-1} = (1-P)\,L_{\mathrm{N}}^{-1}\,(1-P).$$

Guyer and Krumhansl (1966b) have also formulated the Poiseuille flow problem in this framework. Again one finds the equations of subsection 2.4 and obtains 'exact' expressions for τ_p and τ_z, defined as mean relaxation times in (2.64, 65). We have seen that the more rigorous treatment of this section which was first presented in detail by Guyer and Krumhansl (1966a, b), leads to equations for our phonon hydrodynamic phenomena that are formally the same as those obtained in the relaxation time approximation. This fact may serve as a justification for this approximation.

4.3.3. *Perturbation theory*

Weiss (1968), Thellung and Weiss (1969), and Beck (1971) used a method to solve (4.96) which is well-known in the case of gas particles (Reif 1965). Again, one assumes one type of collision processes to be stronger than anything else: $L_{\mathrm{N}} \gg |\boldsymbol{q}\cdot\boldsymbol{v}|$, $L_{\mathrm{N}} \gg L_{\mathrm{R}}$, or $L_{\mathrm{R}} \gtrsim L_{\mathrm{N}} \gg |\boldsymbol{q}\cdot\boldsymbol{v}|$. We treat the case $F=0$ and write (4.96) as

$$\frac{\partial\varphi}{\partial t} - O\varphi = 0, \tag{4.124}$$

with $O = L_{\mathrm{N}} + L_{\mathrm{R}} - \mathrm{i}\boldsymbol{q}\cdot\boldsymbol{v}$. If we knew the eigenfunctions ψ_l of O with

$$O\psi_l = \eta_l\psi_l$$

the solution of (4.124) could immediately be written down:

$$\varphi(t) = \sum_l c_l \exp(\eta_l t)\,\psi_l\,. \tag{4.125}$$

The eigenvalues η_l will be complex since O is no longer symmetric. According to the assumption of $L_X = L_{\mathrm{N}}$ or L being the most important part of O, we try to find ψ_l by adding the rest as a small perturbation to L_X and expand

$$[L_X + \varepsilon(O - L_X)]\,[\psi_l^{(0)} + \varepsilon\psi_l^{(1)} + \cdots] = [\eta_l^{(0)} + \varepsilon\eta_l^{(1)} + \cdots]\,[\psi_l^{(0)} + \varepsilon\psi_l^{(1)} + \cdots]\,. \quad (4.126)$$

ε is a parameter used to group the terms with respect to powers of the disturbance. Since we are interested in hydrodynamic phenomena, we only need to know those η_l with $|\eta_l| \approx 0$. For small perturbations, we can assume that the small η's are those which reduce to small λ's – eigenvalues of L_X alone – when the perturbation is switched off. Again, we neglect the fact that there are always many λ's arbitrarily close to zero, see subsubsection 4.3.1, and we consider only those eigenvalues of L_X which are exactly zero, belonging to the collision invariants. Thus, we have to solve (4.126) for $l=0$, 1 if we want to find second sound, i.e. we perturb the eigenfunctions (4.102), (4.103) of L_{N}. We can also consider the extreme case of very strong resistive scattering by choosing the eigenfunction (4.102) alone and treating only the drift term $-\mathrm{i}\boldsymbol{q}\cdot\boldsymbol{v}$ as a perturbation.

Details of the procedure can be found in the papers quoted above. The eigenvalues are usually evaluated to second order in ε and the eigenfunctions to order ε. In the course of the analysis, an integral equation of the form

$$L_X f = Z\,, \quad (4.127)$$

with $L_X = L_{\mathrm{N}}$ or $L_X = L$ has to be solved, Z being some given function. Solving (4.127) exactly would again require knowledge of the full spectrum of L_X. A useful and probably satisfactory approximation consists in making the ansatz

$$f = \text{const.} \times Z\,.$$

The constant is determined by using a variational principle based on (4.101). We list the results for two special cases:

(i) $L_R \ll |\boldsymbol{q}\cdot\boldsymbol{v}| \ll L_N$

This is the window condition for second sound, so (4.126) is solved for $l=0$, 1, as stated above. The four perturbed eigenvalues for an isotropic system with $\boldsymbol{q}$ in the z-direction are

$$\eta_0 = \eta_{1_z} = \mathrm{i}qc_{\mathrm{II}} + \tfrac{1}{2}R + aq^2c_{\mathrm{II}}^2/N\,, \quad (4.128)$$

$$\eta_{1_x} = \eta_{1_y} = R + bq^2c_{\mathrm{II}}^2/N\,, \quad (4.129)$$

where

$$R = \langle \chi_{1_z} | L_R | \chi_{1_z} \rangle < 0, \tag{4.130}$$

$$N = \langle \chi_{1_z} + \chi_0 | (c_{II} - v_z) L_N (c_{II} - v_z) | \chi_{1_z} + \chi_0 \rangle < 0, \tag{4.131}$$

and a and b are unimportant constants. According to (4.125) η_0 and η_{1_z} describe longitudinal propagating second sound (the heat current associated with this motion is parallel to $\boldsymbol{q}$), whereas η_{1_x} and η_{1_y} give non-propagating transverse excitations, which we did not consider in section 2. Eqs. (4.130), (4.131) give explicit expressions for the damping of second sound, corresponding to the more formal results (4.122), (4.123). Weiss (1968), and Thellung and Weiss (1969) have estimated the temperature dependence of N and R and find $N \propto T^5$, $R \propto \exp(-\theta_D/2T)$ in agreement with our statements in section 2.

(*ii*) $L_R \gtrsim L_N \gg |\boldsymbol{q} \cdot \boldsymbol{v}|$

We only treat the eigenfunction χ_0 (4.102) which is also an eigenfunction of $L = L_N + L_R$. The resulting η_0 reads

$$\eta_0 = \tfrac{1}{3} q^2 \frac{\langle \chi_0 | \boldsymbol{v}^2 | \chi_0 \rangle^2}{\langle \chi_0 | \boldsymbol{v} \cdot L \boldsymbol{v} | \chi_0 \rangle} < 0. \tag{4.132}$$

This is an excitation decaying exponentially in time, it describes diffusive heat conduction, $\eta_0 \propto q^2 \kappa$. In contrast to the exact expression (4.115), the formula (4.132) involves the inverse of a simple matrix element of L instead of a matrix element of L^{-1}. This is typical of variational solutions of the Boltzmann equation (4.96). The closed microscopic expression for the lattice thermal conductivity obtained by Goetze and Michel (1972) in the framework of the Mori theory for correlation functions – see our introduction and subsection 5.3 – is also essentially the same as our result (4.132).

5. *Some special topics*

5.1. Two-fluid description of dielectric solids

In subsubsection 4.1.2, we derived a generalized transport equation for the phonon density $N(k, rt)$ or for its deviation φ from equilibrium. This equation, in the form (4.49) involved the integral operator I (4.50) and a coupling to the elastic displacement field $\boldsymbol{s}$(4.43). In this section, we derive (4.49) from a more phenomenological point of view. We also use the same framework to find an equation for $\boldsymbol{s}$. [We did not present the microscopic derivation of the latter in section 4 in order to keep the analysis short]. Furthermore, some consequences of the coupling between φ and $\boldsymbol{s}$ will be discussed.

A complete and detailed introduction into the two-fluid picture of dielectric solids which was put forward by Goetze and Michel (1967a, 1969) can be found in their papers as well as in a recent review of Enz (1974) where the significance of a two-fluid concept for several important many-body systems is investigated. Again, we can only present some important ideas here.

For a semi-phenomenological description of transport phenomena in insulating crystals, we assume that the state of the lattice can be specified by giving, for every point in space and time, the elastic deformation $u_{ij}(\boldsymbol{r}t)$ and the density $N(k, \boldsymbol{r}t)$ of quasi-particles, or phonons. These quantities should be meaningful as long as wave vector and frequency of the variation of macroscopic observables are small compared to wave vector and frequency of thermal phonons. To find equations of motion for u_{ij} and N, we assume that the energy of our system is a local functional $E(\boldsymbol{r}t)=E[N(k,\boldsymbol{r}t), u_{ij}(\boldsymbol{r}t)]$ of the two parameters. The most important quantities are the derivatives of E:

stress tensor $$\frac{\delta E}{\delta u_{ij}} = \sigma_{ij}, \tag{5.1}$$

elastic constants $$\frac{\delta \sigma_{ij}}{\delta u_{rs}} = S_{ijrs}, \tag{5.2}$$

quasi particle energies $$\frac{\delta E}{\delta N(k)} = \omega_k, \tag{5.3}$$

interaction energy between quasi particles $$\frac{\delta \omega_k}{\delta N(k')} = f(k, k'), \tag{5.4}$$

Grüneisen tensor $$\frac{\delta \omega_k}{\delta u_{ij}} = -\, h_{ij}(k). \tag{5.5}$$

Definitions (5.3), (5.4) are borrowed from Landau's (1956) theory of normal Fermi liquids. The deformation tensor u_{ij} gives the spatial variation of $\boldsymbol{s}$:

$$u_{ij} = \frac{1}{2}\left(\frac{\partial s_i}{\partial r_j} + \frac{\partial s_j}{\partial r_i}\right)$$

and the time behavior of $\boldsymbol{s}$ is governed by the classical relation (Landau and Lifschitz 1959):

$$\rho \frac{\partial^2 s_i}{\partial t^2} = \frac{\partial \sigma_{ij}}{\partial r_j} = F_i + \frac{\partial \sigma_{ij}}{\delta u_{mn}} \frac{\partial u_{mn}}{\partial r_j} + \sum_k \frac{\delta \sigma_{ij}}{\delta N(k)} \frac{\partial N(k)}{\partial r_j}$$

$$= F_i + S_{ijmn} \frac{\partial^2 s_m}{\partial r_j \partial r_n} - \sum_k h_{ij}(k) \frac{\partial N(k)}{\partial r_j}. \quad (5.6)$$

Here, ρ is the density, F_i is a possible external mechanical force and the usual summation convention is used. Next we consider the quasi-particle energy $\omega_k(\boldsymbol{r}t)$ as a 'Hamilton function' for the phonon system and we form the Poisson bracket to find the time development of N:

$$\frac{\partial N}{\partial t} + \frac{\partial N}{\partial \boldsymbol{r}} \cdot \frac{\partial \omega}{\partial \boldsymbol{k}} - \frac{\partial N}{\partial \boldsymbol{k}} \cdot \frac{\partial \omega}{\partial \boldsymbol{r}} = C[N]. \quad (5.7)$$

The term on the right-hand side takes into account the collisions between the quasi-particles. If we again identify the quantity given by (4.39) with the energy of a phonon with wave vector $\boldsymbol{k}$ and polarization λ, our eq. (5.7) is identical with (4.40). Splitting N into two parts as in (4.42) and linearizing (5.6) and (5.7), we end up with two coupled equations for φ and $\boldsymbol{s}$:

$$I^{-1} \frac{\partial \varphi}{\partial t} + \boldsymbol{v} \cdot \frac{\partial \varphi}{\partial \boldsymbol{r}} + I^{-1} h_{ij} \frac{\partial^2 s_i}{\partial r_j \partial t} = L[\varphi] \quad (5.8)$$

and

$$\rho \frac{\partial^2 s_i}{\partial t^2} = F_i + [S_{ijmn} - \sum_k m(k)\, h_{ij} I^{-1} h_{mn}] \frac{\partial^2 s_{mn}}{\partial r_j \partial r_n}$$

$$- \sum_k h_{ij} m(k)\, I^{-1}\, \partial \varphi / \partial r_j. \quad (5.9)$$

(5.8) is, of course, identical with (4.49), and I operates as defined in (4.50). Eq. (5.9) could also be found in the Green's function treatment of subsubsection 4.1.2 where we obtained microscopic expressions for h_{ij}, $f(k, k')$ and L.

Thus, we can describe transport phenomena by means of two 'interacting fluids', the elastic deformation and the gas of thermal phonons. Their equations of motion are coupled:

(*i*) The phonon gas exerts a force on the elastic background whose effect is to attenuate a sound wave by means of thermal conduction and viscous friction. In equilibrium, this coupling gives rise to thermal expansion.

(*ii*) The phonon gas is influenced by deformations of the lattice: a variation in the mean distance between two particles changes the respective force constants, which amounts to a local change in the harmonic phonon energies ω_k. Other parameters determining the behavior of the phonon gas, like the local temperature, are also modified, which creates a deviation φ of the phonon distribution from equilibrium. It is, however, important for the static limit of certain correlation functions (Goetze and Michel 1969) that this coupling of φ to $\boldsymbol{s}$ in (5.8) vanishes in the limit of time-independent deformations.

Formally, this two-fluid picture has much in common with two-fluid hydrodynamics for helium II (Landau 1941b). There are, however, some important differences. For instance, the quantum liquid has no Umklapp scattering between phonons. The interested reader is referred to the review by Enz (1974) who treats and compares both systems from the two-fluid point of view. Furthermore, it should be stressed that – at least for very low temperatures, where the coupling between φ and $\boldsymbol{s}$ is weak – the occurrence of second sound is not bound to a two-fluid theory: it can be interpreted as a collective motion in the phonon gas *alone*, which is only weakly modified by the coupling to $\boldsymbol{s}$.

Let us now mention situations where the two-fluid coupling does have some importance. The system (5.8) and (5.9) can be solved formally by going to the Fourier transforms $\boldsymbol{s}(\boldsymbol{q}\Omega)$ and $\varphi(k, \boldsymbol{q}\Omega)$. For the sake of simplicity, we neglect the quasi-particle interaction $f(k, k')$ $(I \approx 1)$ and we obtain

$$(-\mathrm{i}\Omega + \mathrm{i}\boldsymbol{q}\cdot\boldsymbol{v}_k - L)\,\varphi = -\,\Omega q_r h_{rj}(k)\, s_j\,, \tag{5.10}$$

$$\rho\Omega^2 s_i = F_i + q_r q_s \bar{S}_{ijrs} s_j - \mathrm{i}q_r \langle h_{ir} \mid \varphi\rangle\,. \tag{5.11}$$

Here, $\bar{S}_{ijrs} = S_{ijrs} - \langle h_{ij} \mid h_{rs}\rangle$ and the bracket $\langle\cdot\cdot \mid \cdot\cdot\rangle$ is defined by (4.98). Our aim is to find the response of s_i with respect to the external force F_j:

$$s_i(\boldsymbol{q}\Omega) = G_{ij}(\boldsymbol{q}\Omega)\, F_j(\boldsymbol{q}\Omega) \tag{5.12}$$

by eliminating the phonon density φ. This is achieved formally by solving (5.10), or equivalently (4.105), treating the right-hand side of (5.10) as a given force term. As a simplification, we assume that the Grüneisen tensor

(4.48) can be approximated by

$$h_{is}(k) \approx g_{is}\omega_k , \tag{5.13}$$

where g_{is} is a measure of the strength of the cubic coupling parameter V_3. Such an approximation is used frequently for practical calculations, see e.g. Leibfried and Schlömann (1954). Then s_i couples only to that part of φ lying in the subspace of $\chi_0 = \alpha_0\omega_k$, see (4.104), and

$$\langle h_{is} \mid \varphi\rangle \approx (a_0/\alpha_0)\, g_{is} . \tag{5.14}$$

The coefficient a_0 is found from an inhomogeneous counterpart of the system (4.118, 119) which has the form

$$\begin{aligned} B_{00}a_0 + \sum_s B_{0s}a_{1s} &= F_0 , \\ B_{s0}a_0 + \sum_{s'} B_{ss'}a_{1s'} &= F_s . \end{aligned} \tag{5.15}$$

We find the formal result

$$G_{ij}(\boldsymbol{q}\Omega) = \left[\rho\Omega^2\delta_{ij} - q_r q_s \bar{S}_{ijrs} - \mathrm{i}\Omega q_r q_t C T_0 g_{ir} g_{jt} \frac{R(\boldsymbol{q}\Omega)}{D(\boldsymbol{q}\Omega)}\right]^{-1} . \tag{5.16}$$

The inverse has to be taken with respect to the cartesian indices i and j. The function R is a combination of the coefficients of (5.15) and $D(\boldsymbol{q}\Omega)$ is the determinant of the matrix B on the left-hand side of (5.15).

First, we can draw the following general conclusion from (5.16): whatever collective excitations are possible in the phonon gas – showing up as a zero in $D(\boldsymbol{q}\Omega)$ – will also yield a singularity in the 'elastic propagator' G_{ij}. A special case was pointed out by Kwok and Martin (1966), and Sham (1967), who showed that the displacement–displacement correlation function, whose long wavelength limit is just our G_{ij}, can have poles for both first and second sound. The ratio of the intensities of the two excitations, $r = I^{(\mathrm{ss})}\, I^{(\mathrm{1st\ sound})}$, is usually rather small, being given by the square of the coupling coefficients g_{ir}, or

$$r \approx \frac{C_p}{C_v} - 1 . \tag{5.17}$$

Recently, Franck and Hewko (1973) have found unusual features in the temperature dependence of the (first) sound velocity in hcp ^{4}He, which might be attributed to the coupling between an ordinary sound wave and second sound. However, a detailed analysis of their data, which the authors carried out by using Niklasson's (1970) theoretical results, leaves some basic questions open. A fit of the measurements requires certain matrix elements of L to be strongly different from one another, which seems quite unlikely, even for the rather anisotropic hcp helium crystal.

Eq. (5.16) is also valid for the case that the only hydrodynamic excitation of the phonon gas is heat conduction. Then $D(\boldsymbol{q}\Omega) \approx \mathrm{i}\Omega - q^2\kappa/C$ involves the thermal conductivity κ. A more general analysis, not using approximation (5.13), can also furnish a microscopic expression for the lattice viscosity introduced in classical thermo-elasticity theory (Landau and Lifschitz 1959). See the papers by Goetze and Michel (1969), Maris (1969), Niklasson (1970), and others. Last but not least, explicit forms for $R(\boldsymbol{q}\Omega)$ and $D(\boldsymbol{q}\Omega)$ in (5.16) can be used to calculate dispersion and damping of acoustic waves due to coupling with the phonon fluid. This was done in the early work of Akhiezer (1939), Boemmel and Dransfeld (1960), and Woodruff and Ehrenreich (1961).

The fact that second sound is a singularity of G_{ij} is a hint that it might be excited by a mechanical force $\boldsymbol{F}$. Due to the very small ratio (5.17) between the intensities of a first (acoustic) and a second (thermal) sound wave created in this way, such an experimental observation of the latter is hardly feasible. Instead, several authors (Griffin 1968a, Wehner and Klein 1972) propose observation of second sound by means of light scattering. Light waves couple to the local dipole moment $\boldsymbol{p}(\boldsymbol{r}t)$ of the crystal, which can be expressed in terms of the normal coordinates (2.2a):

$$\boldsymbol{p}(\boldsymbol{q}) = \sum_{\lambda} \boldsymbol{p}_1(\lambda)\, A_{\boldsymbol{q}\lambda} + \sum_{q'q''} \boldsymbol{p}_2(q'q'')\, A_q A_{q''}\, \Delta(\boldsymbol{q} + \boldsymbol{q}' + \boldsymbol{q}'') + \cdots .$$

The quadratic term causes a direct coupling of the light wave to thermal fluctuations whose strength is determined by p_2, whereas p_1 gives rise to the same indirect coupling via an elastic deformation as discussed before. Wehner and Klein (1972) have shown that the effective ratio $\bar{r}$ between the scattered light intensities from first and from second sound may differ markedly from r (5.17) owing to the direct coupling. According to recent measurements by Pohl and Schwartz (1973) $\bar{r}$ will, unfortunately, be even smaller than (5.17) at very low temperatures. Therefore, Pohl and Schwartz suggest scattering light from 'forced' thermal excitations which may be created by heating the crystal or shining laser light on it.

5.2. Quantum crystals

In subsection 2.1, we found our basic hamiltonian (2.4) by expanding the potential energy of the crystal with respect to the displacements $\boldsymbol{u}(\boldsymbol{n}\sigma)$ of the particles from their mean position. Such a procedure is not feasible for quantum solids like He and the light rare-gas crystals. Due to their light mass, the particles have large zero-point motions. Thus, the u's are by no means small – $\langle u_n^2 \rangle^{1/2}$ is typically one third of the lattice constant for solid He – which makes an expansion of (2.1) in terms of $\boldsymbol{u}(\boldsymbol{n}\sigma)$ slowly convergent. Furthermore, the equilibrium distance of two neighboring particles is so large that the second derivative of the interparticle potential evaluated for this distance is negative. So the harmonic phonon frequencies ω_k for solid He turn out to be imaginary in the whole Brillouin zone (De Wette and Nijboer 1965). On the other hand, the first and so far most successful experiments revealing second sound and Poiseuille flow have been performed on helium and have confirmed the validity of the theory of phonon hydrodynamics also for this solid. How can we justify the application of a theory based on the concept of almost harmonic phonons to a substance where the latter do not seem to exist?

First, there is now plenty of experimental evidence for the existence of phonon-like elementary excitations in He, see, for example, the neutron-scattering data on ^{4}He [Osgood et al. (1972) and references quoted therein] and results concerning sound propagation (Greywall 1971). At the same time, much progress has been made during the past few years in developing sophisticated renormalization procedures which can be used to calculate the properties of these phonons in quantum crystals without using an anharmonic hamiltonian like (2.4) as a starting point. Among other work we mention Horner (1972), who used equations of motion for the equilibrium phonon Green's function, Glyde (1971), who found phonon frequencies by the help of a T-matrix formalism, and Koehler and Werthamer (1972), who constructed one- and multi-phonon states from a ground-state wave function, including the necessary correlations between the particles. Although the spectral functions χ [see (4.5)] of such phonon excitations, calculated by the above mentioned techniques, may be rather broad and distorted near the boundary of the zone, the 'thermal' phonons involved in hydrodynamic phenomena at very low temperatures are essentially not more anharmonic than in a well-behaved classical solid.

As far as the transport problems are concerned, one may take the point of view that, once the existence of 'normal' anharmonic phonons has been shown, a hamiltonian of the form (2.4) can be postulated as the starting point for the usual Green's function methods sketched in section 4. Expressions for ω_k and the V_ν's are furnished by either of the above mentioned methods to treat the equilibrium lattice dynamics of quantum crystals. Besides this, there are some attempts to derive transport equations valid for such strongly anharmonic systems directly from the general many-body hamiltonian (2.1). Goetze and Michel (1969) as well as Beck and Meier (1970) did this on the level of the so-called renormalized harmonic approximation. Beck and Meier (1971) also included the short-range correlations between particles which is essential for treating the hard core of the interaction. The general result is that one ends up with formally the same linearized system of equations for $\boldsymbol{s}$ and φ as in our section 4 and in subsection 5.1, involving, however, renormalized frequencies $\tilde{\omega}_k$ and coupling parameters $\tilde{V}_\nu$. These quantities have to be calculated by means of the equilibrium pair-correlation function of the crystal. Concerning the applicability to solid He, it must be said that the renormalized harmonic approximation – where the pair correlation function is gaussian – is insufficient because of the hard core. Even the 'true' pair correlation entering the results of Beck and Meier (1971) yields phonon frequencies that are larger than the experimental ones by about a factor of two (Noolandi and Van Kranendonck 1972). Thus, the (renormalized) anharmonic corrections would still be very large. It would therefore – at least for the sake of formal completeness of the formalism – be desirable to derive transport equations for the phonon system of quantum crystals directly along the lines used in the aforementioned work on equilibrium properties, which did yield, for the phonon frequencies, results which are quite satisfactory when compared to experimental values.

These few remarks show that the application of our equations to solid He seems to be justified, although a complete, gapless chain of arguments leading from (2.1) to transport equations for quantum crystals involving parameters that are in good agreement with experimental data has yet to be given. It seems, however, to be clear that the discrepancy between the T-dependence of τ_N^{-1}, as extracted from second sound and Poiseuille flow data, and the expected T^5 behavior is not due to the quantum nature of solid He, since NaF shows similar effects (Beck 1975b).

5.3. Drifting and driftless second sound

Our discussion of second sound (SS) in subsection 2.3 was based on the system of eqs. (2.38), (2.39) for $\delta\beta$ and $\boldsymbol{u}$, the local (inverse) temperature deviation and the drift velocity of the phonon gas, respectively. In that framework, the capability of the phonon system to maintain a drift motion was crucial to obtain SS, since for $\boldsymbol{u}=0$ there are no propagating solutions for (2.38), (2.39). However, several authors have discussed wave-like collective excitations of the phonon fluid without a drift, so-called driftless SS (Griffin 1965, 1968a, Enz 1968, Hardy 1970, Meier 1973). Although, for several reasons, this seems to be merely a playground for theoreticians, we want to sketch these approaches briefly and list the main conditions for an experimental realization of driftless SS.

Enz (1968) treats thermal motion in dielectric crystals within the correlation function formalism. The equilibrium is disturbed by external 'forces' of the type (4.60). Two different situations are considered:

(*a*) The perturbation hamiltonian is given by (4.60), i.e.

$$H_{1_a} = \int \mathrm{d}^3 r\, \alpha(\boldsymbol{r}t)\, E(\boldsymbol{r}), \tag{5.18}$$

where E is the energy density of the crystal and the meaning of α as an 'externally impressed' temperature was explained in subsubsection 4.2.2. Then the linear response of E and the heat current $\boldsymbol{S}$ under the influence of H_{1_a} is calculated. The usual conservation law (2.23) linking E and $\boldsymbol{S}$ leads to

$$[\mathrm{i}\Omega C(\boldsymbol{q}\Omega) - q_i q_j K_{ij}(\boldsymbol{q}\Omega)]\, \alpha(\boldsymbol{q}\Omega) = 0\,. \tag{5.19}$$

$C(\boldsymbol{q}\Omega)$ and $K_{ij}(\boldsymbol{q}\Omega)$ are proportional to the Fourier transforms of the time dependent energy–energy and current–current correlation functions, respectively. Possible thermal excitations will have a dispersion relation $\Omega(\boldsymbol{q})$ fulfilling

$$\mathrm{i}\Omega\, C(\boldsymbol{q}\Omega) = q_i q_j\, K_{ij}(\boldsymbol{q}\Omega)\,. \tag{5.20}$$

Using the fact that $C(\boldsymbol{0}, 0)$ reduces to the specific heat C and assuming that the current auto-correlation function, denoted by $\langle\!\langle S_i S_j(t)\rangle\!\rangle$, decays exponentially in time:

$$\langle\!\langle S_i S_j(t)\rangle\!\rangle = K_{ij}^{(0)} \exp(-t/\tau_{\mathrm{SS}})\,, \tag{5.21}$$

we find from (5.20) for small $\boldsymbol{q}$ and Ω

$$\mathrm{i}\Omega = q_i q_j (K_{ij}^{(0)}/C) \frac{\tau_{\mathrm{SS}}}{1 - \mathrm{i}\Omega\tau_{\mathrm{SS}}} = q^2 c_{\mathrm{II}}'^2 \frac{\tau_{\mathrm{SS}}}{1 - \mathrm{i}\Omega\tau_{\mathrm{SS}}}\,. \tag{5.22}$$

The fact that $q_i K_{ij}^{(0)} q_j/(q^2 C)$ is equal to our expression (2.75) for c_{II}^2 can be verified by using the explicit forms of $K_{ij}^{(0)}$ and C. For $\Omega\tau_{\mathrm{SS}} \ll 1$ we recover the usual dispersion relation for thermal conduction

$$\Omega = -\,\mathrm{i}q^2 c_{\mathrm{II}}^{\prime 2}\tau_{\mathrm{SS}}\,, \tag{5.23}$$

whereas for $\Omega\tau_{\mathrm{ss}} \gg 1$ a propagating mode with

$$\Omega^2 = q^2 c_{\mathrm{II}}^2 \tag{5.24}$$

is possible. It is called driftless second sound since there was no drift velocity introduced into our equations nor was any use made of a conservation law for the momentum density $\boldsymbol{P}$, the dynamical variable conjugate to the drift velocity.

(*b*) We use

$$H_{1_b} = H_{1_a} + \int \mathrm{d}^3 r\, \boldsymbol{u}(\boldsymbol{r}t)\cdot\boldsymbol{P}(\boldsymbol{r}) \tag{5.25}$$

as a perturbation. Since there are now two external parameters, the temperature and the drift velocity $\boldsymbol{u}$, we have to calculate the response of E, $\boldsymbol{S}$, $\boldsymbol{P}$ and T_{ij}, all quantities being defined in subsection 2.2, and to use both conservation laws, (2.23) and (2.24). This situation is completely analogous to the one discussed in section 2 and the possible excitations are 'drifting' second sound ($\Omega^2 = c_{\mathrm{II}}^2 q^2$) or again diffusive heat conduction.

From this semi-phenomenological treatment, we can draw the following conclusions:

(*i*) In order for case (*a*) to be a valid description, momentum density correlations must decay rapidly, i.e.

$$\langle\!\langle P_i P_j(t)\rangle\!\rangle \propto \exp(-\,t/\tau_{\mathrm{PP}})$$

with τ_{PP} being small on a macroscopic time scale. If this were not true, we would have to include the conservation law for $\boldsymbol{P}$, which would lead us back to case (*b*) showing drifting SS.

(*ii*) Driftless SS with frequency Ω is then possible provided that $\Omega\tau_{\mathrm{SS}} \gg 1$. This yields a kind of window condition for driftless SS

$$\Omega\tau_{\mathrm{SS}} \gg 1 \gg \Omega\tau_{\mathrm{PP}}\,. \tag{5.26}$$

So the physical requirement is to find a situation where the momentum density $\boldsymbol{P}(\boldsymbol{r}t)$ created in some non-equilibrium situation is dissipated much faster than the energy current $\boldsymbol{S}$.

For an isotropic Debye solid $c_{\text{II}}'^2$ is found to be

$$c_{\text{II}}'^2 = \tfrac{1}{3}\left(\sum_\lambda c_\lambda^{-1}\right)/\left(\sum_\lambda c_\lambda^{-3}\right) \tag{5.27}$$

which has to be compared with (2.33) for c_{II}^2. For a real crystal, it is more difficult to estimate the difference between c_{II} and c_{II}', since both involve angular averages of inverse powers of the sound velocities. Enz (1968) states that for He the difference between c_{II} and c_{II}' is probably less than about 6%.

Griffin (1965, 1968a) discusses driftless SS along similar lines as in our previous case (*a*). He calculates $\langle E(\boldsymbol{r}t)\rangle$ in response to H_{1_a} and defines a 'true' local temperature by

$$\delta E(\boldsymbol{r}t) = C\,\delta T_{\text{true}}(\boldsymbol{r}t),$$

as opposed to the 'external' temperature $\delta T_{\text{ex}} = -T_0\alpha$. δT_{true} is then given by

$$\delta T_{\text{true}}(\boldsymbol{q}\Omega) = X^{-1}(\boldsymbol{q}\Omega)\,\delta T_{\text{ex}}(\boldsymbol{q}\Omega)\,. \tag{5.28}$$

The zeros of X yield the possible eigenmodes of the system, among which, under the same conditions as before, Griffin finds driftless SS.

Recently, Meier (1973) approached the problem of hydrodynamic excitations in an interacting phonon system by means of Mori's (1962, 1965a, b) treatment of correlation functions. It is well-known that a perturbative calculation of, say, the displacement auto-correlation function for small $\boldsymbol{q}$ and Ω has to treat correctly the hydrodynamical singularities of the type encountered in subsubsection 4.2.3. These singularities are the consequence of a coupling between the quantity whose auto-correlations one wants to know and some further slowly varying dynamical quantity. Instead of summing up infinite series of terms in a perturbation expansion as we did in subsubsection 4.2.3, one tries to take into account right from the outset all important, slowly decaying quantities which might introduce hydrodynamic poles. Without going into the details of such a 'correlation matrix' formalism, we state below some results.

Goetze and Michel (1972) use A_k, B_k [defined in (2.2)] and the Fourier transform $E(\boldsymbol{k})$ of the energy density as their dynamical variables. The various correlation functions between these variables show poles corresponding to first sound propagation and heat conduction. These excitations are coupled by anharmonic parameters in a similar way as in our general form (5.16) for the displacement respose function G_{ij}.

Meier (1973) considered two cases: using as the basic variables A_k, B_k, $E(\boldsymbol{k})$ and $\partial E(\boldsymbol{k})/\partial t$, which is equal to $\mathrm{i}\boldsymbol{k}\cdot\boldsymbol{S}(\boldsymbol{k})$, he finds first and driftless second sound as possible modes. Taking instead A_k, B_k, $E(\boldsymbol{k})$ and $\boldsymbol{P}(\boldsymbol{k})$, the poles of the correlation functions describe first and drifting second sound.

This again makes it clear that driftless SS is expected to exist under circumstances where the energy density and the heat current are the only almost conserved quantities, whereas the momentum density decays in a short time and does not contribute to phenomena on a hydrodynamic time scale. Unfortunately, Meier's analysis does not furnish results about the attenuation of driftless SS. Also, it does not seem straightforward to extend the formalism to include anharmonic corrections in a consistent way. Such a procedure might, in a six-variable theory including A_k, B_k, $E(\boldsymbol{k})$, $\partial E(\boldsymbol{k})/\partial t$, $\boldsymbol{P}(\boldsymbol{k})$, $\partial \boldsymbol{P}(\boldsymbol{k})/\partial t$, reveal which type of second sound has the smaller damping in a given situation. Quite generally, the heat current can be decomposed into a component decaying by normal processes and one which is dissipated by resistive scattering. The latter mechanism, however, is expected to influence the momentum density $\boldsymbol{P}$ equally strongly whereas $\boldsymbol{P}$ is not affected by normal collisions. So, in a loose sense, one would expect the heat current to be at least as strongly damped as $\boldsymbol{P}$. This would, however, never allow for a window like (5.26).

A further attempt to discriminate between the possibilities of detecting either of the two forms of SS on a more mathematical ground was published by Hardy (1970). He works with the eigenfunctions of the collision operator L. These can be grouped into even and odd ones with respect to the transformation $\boldsymbol{k}\to-\boldsymbol{k}$. An eigenvalue of special importance, denoted by $\Omega^{(1)}$, is the one that goes to zero for $L_{\mathrm{R}}\to 0$. It is, for $L_{\mathrm{R}}=0$, associated with our (odd) eigenfunctions $\chi_{1_i}=\alpha_1 k_i$ of L_{N}, introduced in subsubsection 4.3.1. Hardy shows that

(*i*) in order to have second sound of any kind, we need

$$\Omega^{(1)} \ll \Omega^{(l)}_{\text{even}} \tag{5.29}$$

for all even eigenvalues of L.

(*ii*) If, furthermore

$$\Omega^{(1)} \ll \Omega^{(l)}_{\text{odd}} \tag{5.30}$$

is satisfied for all $\Omega^{(l)}_{\text{odd}}$ [except, of course $\Omega^{(1)}$ itself], then drifting second sound is possible. Indeed, (5.29) and (5.30) are roughly equivalent to the condition $\tau_R \gg \tau$ for relaxation times, which allows for the window (2.50) for appropriate frequencies.

(*iii*) If, however, $\Omega^{(1)}$ is comparable to most odd eigenvalues,

$$\Omega^{(1)} \gtrsim \Omega^{(l)}_{\text{odd}}, \tag{5.31}$$

then there will be driftless SS.

Physically, the fact that all $\Omega^{(l)}_{\text{even}}$ are 'large' implies that the even part of a given distribution φ is reduced to local equilibrium within a short time. If (5.30) is valid, the odd component of φ will also be reduced quickly to a simple drift motion allowing for drifting SS. On the other hand, (5.31) implies that odd parts of φ other than just an overall drift can live at least as long and therefore contribute to the heat current $\boldsymbol{S}$ which, according to (2.20), is built up exclusively of the odd part of φ. Thus, we expect driftless SS to be possible.

If normal processes dominate, then $\Omega^{(1)}$ is almost zero, so (5.30) should be true and drifting SS is more likely to occur in this case. In heat pulse experiments, second sound seems indeed to show up in domains where normal scattering is stronger than resistive processes. The rapid delay and broadening of the pulses in NaF with rising temperature is consistent with the growing influence of Umklapp processes as described by (2.47), see Beck (1975b). Therefore, what one sees there is probably the drifting kind of SS. This point of view is also corroborated by the fact that SS in helium is observed in very much the same temperature interval as Poiseuille flow, which is intrinsically associated with a drift motion of the phonon fluid.

Concerning Hardy's work, one should add that the numerical work on the collision operator for phonons in liquid helium II (Maris 1973, and unpublished calculations by Meier and Beck) do not give any hint that even and odd eigenfunctions should have eigenvalues lying typically in different domains Furthermore, the fact that L has a continuous part extending to zero would also require a mathematically more careful analysis of the collision equation than the usual eigenfunction decomposition.

5.4. Relaxation time analysis of heat pulse experiments

In solid helium there is a relatively large temperature interval in which heat pulses propagate with the T-independent velocity c_{II}. In contrast to this, the speed of a second sound pulse in NaF and Bi monotonically decreases with rising temperature. Thus, one should be able to describe theoretically not only the truly hydrodynamical region for which the theories in section 2 and subsubsection 4.3.2 are valid, but also the whole transition from the ballistic, low-temperature region ($\Omega\tau \gg 1$) through the second sound domain characterized by (2.50) to the high-temperature diffusive behavior.

Rogers (1971) has analyzed his pulse data with the assumption that the thermal excitations of the crystal can be described by an isotropic gas of phonons, the motion of which is governed by hydrodynamic equations appropriate for a viscous fluid. A frequency-dependent second viscosity

$$\zeta \propto \frac{\tau(1 - c_2^2/c_1^2)}{1 - \mathrm{i}\Omega\tau} \tag{5.32}$$

as introduced into the equation of motion for the local temperature, leading to the following dispersion relation for collective thermal modes

$$\Omega^2 + \frac{\mathrm{i}\Omega}{\tau_{\mathrm{R}}} + \frac{\mathrm{i}\Omega q^2 \tau (c_1^2 - c_2^2)}{1 - \mathrm{i}\Omega\tau} = q^2 c_2^2 . \tag{5.33}$$

For $\Omega\tau \gg 1$, (5.33) describes first-sound waves (velocity c_1), whereas for $\Omega\tau \ll 1$ the wave propagates as second sound with velocity c_2.

Neglecting resistive scattering ($\tau = \tau_{\mathrm{N}}$), the solution

$$\Omega(q) = c(\Omega\tau_{\mathrm{N}}, q)\cdot q \tag{5.34}$$

of (5.33) can be used to find the T-dependence of τ_{N} by comparing $c(\Omega\tau_{\mathrm{N}}(T), q)$ with the velocity of experimental second-sound peaks. Rogers finds $\tau_{\mathrm{N}}^{-1} \propto T^{3.71}$ for NaF.

Ranninger (1972) has presented a semi-phenomenological theory of heat-pulse propagation valid for all magnitudes of $\Omega\tau$. He starts from the equations of motion for energy–energy and similar correlation functions using microscopic expressions like (4.57) for the densities and currents. The time behavior of these correlation functions is then approximated by an exponential decay. The possible excitations of the interacting phonon system in this framework are ballistic pulses travelling with the speed of sound of either of the three acoustic polarizations for $\Omega\tau \gg 1$ and second sound for $\Omega\tau \ll 1$. The latter is influenced by resistive scattering in the sense that its velocity decreases as τ_{R}^{-1} increases, but in a weaker way than in our eq. (2.47). In this theory the transition between $\Omega\tau \gg 1$ and $\Omega\tau \ll 1$ is smooth and continuous in contrast to the approach described below. Ballistic heat pulses as well as second sound are seen to be merely different forms of the same collective oscillation of the energy density of the phonon gas.

Finally, Beck and Beck (1973) described heat pulse experiments by using the full relaxation time solution of the phonon Boltzmann equation (4.96). It has the form (2.18), but it includes further terms stemming from a suitably chosen force term in (4.96). The conservation laws (2.23), (2.24) lead to the system

$$[\Omega + C_{11}(q\Omega)]\frac{\delta\beta}{\beta_0} + C_{12}(q\Omega)\frac{\boldsymbol{u}\cdot\boldsymbol{q}}{q} = f_1(q\Omega), \tag{5.35}$$

$$C_{21}(q\Omega)\frac{\delta\beta}{\beta_0} + [\Omega + C_{22}(q\Omega)]\frac{\boldsymbol{u}\cdot\boldsymbol{q}}{q} = f_2(q\Omega) \tag{5.36}$$

which is the generalization of (2.38), (2.39) for arbitrary values of $\Omega\tau$. For an isotropic three-branch Debye model, the coefficients in (5.35), (5.36) can be evaluated explicitly. The result can be summarized in the following way:

(i) $\Omega\tau \gg 1$

The determinant $D = (\Omega + C_{11})(\Omega + C_{22}) - C_{12}C_{21}$ of (5.35), (5.36) has no zeros (except for $\Omega = 0$). The only possible excitations are ballistic heat pulses travelling with the speed c_l and c_t of longitudinal and transverse sound, respectively.

(ii) $\Omega\tau \ll 1$

The usual hydrodynamic modes (second sound, diffusive heat conduction) are found as zeros of D.

(iii) Intermediate range

There is a critical value $(\Omega\tau)_c$ such that

a) there is a zero of D describing second sound for $\Omega\tau < (\Omega\tau)_c$,

b) there is no second sound for $\Omega\tau > (\Omega\tau)_c$.

The effective velocity c_2 of such second-sound peaks strongly depends on τ_N and τ_R and, therefore, on T. In the model of Beck and Beck (1973), c_2 is about half way between c_t and c_{II} (given by (2.33)) for $\Omega\tau \approx (\Omega\tau)_c$. In the 'window', $\Omega\tau_N \ll 1 \ll \Omega\tau_R$, c_2 is about equal to c_{II} and for decreasing values of τ_R, c_2 goes to zero as described in (2.47).

In contrast to Ranninger's point of view, this treatment suggests that it is more adequate to think of ballistic pulses as single-particle-like excitations, as distinct from the collective second sound oscillations, although this may be more a semantic question.

Beck (1975b) has used the numerical results for $c_2(T)$ from this model calculation to compare it with the experimental heat pulse velocities. He finds that τ_N should vary like T^{-3} in order to reproduce the experimental $c_2(T)$ and that an expression like (2.56) for τ_R reproduces the behavior for crystals of different purities and the Umklapp damping quite satisfactorily.

Unfortunately, the correct limiting behavior of such models for $\Omega\tau \gg 1$ and $\Omega\tau \ll 1$ does not guarantee that the intermediate range is also described correctly, since there the explicit form of the eigenfunctions χ_l of L_N, with $l \geq 2$, will also be important. For a full clarification of the domain $\Omega\tau \approx 1$, it would be necessary to solve the collision equation without any further approximation, probably with the help of extensive numerical work, as has been done for the phonon system of liquid helium II (Maris 1972, 1973, Meier and Beck 1973). Even then, one would have to account in some way for the missing gap in the spectrum of L (see subsection 4.3), which may even influence the behavior of hydrodynamic excitations for $\Omega\tau \ll 1$ (see footnote on p. 258).

Acknowledgements

The author would like to thank N.R. Werthamer for suggestions concerning the formal framework of this chapter. During his stay at Cornell University, which was mainly financed by the 'Erziehungsrat des Kantons Zürich', he has benefited from many discussions with J.A. Krumhansl, R.O. Pohl and T.F. McNelly. He is also indebted to T. Gallie for carefully reading the manuscript.

References

Abrikosov, A.A., L.P. Gorkov and L.Y. Djaloshinsky (1965), *Quantum field theoretical methods in statistical physics* (Pergamon Press, Oxford).

Ackerman, C.C., B. Bertman, H.A. Fairbank and R.A. Guyer (1966), Phys. Rev. Lett. **16**, 789.

Ackerman, C.C. and R.A. Guyer (1967), Sol. State Commun. **5**, 671.

Ackerman, C.C. and R.A. Guyer (1968), Ann. Physics (N.Y.) **50**, 128.

Ackerman, C.C. and W.C. Overton (1969, Phys. Rev. Lett. **22**, 764.

Agrawal, B. (1967), Phys. Rev. **162**, 731.

Akhiezer, A. (1939), J. Phys. (USSR) **1**, 277.

BECK, H. (1971), Phys. Cond. Matter **12**, 330.
BECK, H. (1975a), Z. für Physik, B**20**, 313.
BECK, H. (1975b), Z. für Physik, to appear.
BECK, H. and P.F. MEIER (1970), Phys. Cond. Matter **12**, 16.
BECK, H. and P.F. MEIER (1971), Z. für Physik **247**, 189.
BECK, H. and R. BECK (1973), Phys. Rev. B**8**, 1669.
BECK, H., P.F. MEIER and A. THELLUNG (1974), Phys. Stat. Sol. (a) **24**, 11.
BERMAN, R. and J.C.F. BROCK (1965), Proc. Roy. Soc. (London) A**289**, 46.
BERMAN, R., C.L. BOUNDS and S.J. ROGERS (1965), Proc. Roy. Soc. (London) A**289**, 66.
BERMAN, R., C.L. BOUNDS, C.R. DAY and H.H. SAMPLE (1968), Phys. Lett. **26A**, 185.
BERMAN, R. and C.R. DAY (1970), Phys. Lett. **33A**, 329.
BERTMAN, B., H.A. FAIRBANK, R.A. GUYER and C.W. WHITE (1966), Phys. Rev. **142**, 79.
BOEMMEL, H.E. and K. DRANSFELD (1960), Phys. Rev. **117**, 1245.
BROWN, C.R. and P.W. MATTHEWS (1970), Can. J. Physics **48**, 1200.
BUOT, F.A. (1972), J. Phys. C**5**, 5.
CALLAWAY, J. (1959), Phys. Rev. **113**, 1046.
CARRUTHERS, P. (1961), Rev. Mod. Physics **33**, 92.
CASIMIR, H.B.G. (1938), Physica **5**, 495.
CHOQUARD, Ph. (1963), Helv. Phys. Acta **36**, 415.
CRAIG, R.A. (1968), J. Math. Phys. **9**, 605.
DEBYE, P. (1914), in *Vorträge über die kinetische Theorie der Materie und Elektrizität* (Teubner, Berlin).
DE WETTE, F.W. and B.R.A. NIJBOER (1965), Phys. Lett. **18**, 19.
DINGLE, R.B. (1952), Proc. Roy. Soc. (London) A**65**, 374.
DYNES, R.C., V. NARAYANAMURTI and K. ANDRES (1973), Phys Rev. Lett. **30**, 1129.
ENZ, Ch. (1968), Ann. Physics (N.Y.) **46**, 114.
ENZ, Ch. (1974), Rev. Mod. Phys. (to appear).
FOX, J.N., J.U. TREFNY, J. BUCHANAN, L. SHEN and B. BERTMAN (1972), Phys. Rev. Lett. **28**, 16.
FRANCK, J.P. and R.A.D. HEWKO (1973), Phys. Rev. Lett. **31**, 1291.
GLYDE, H.R. (1971), Can. J. Phys. **49**, 761.
GOETZE, W. and K.H. MICHEL (1967a), Phys. Rev. **156**, 963.
GOETZE, W. and K.H. MICHEL (1967b), Phys. Rev. **157**, 738.
GOETZE, W. and K.H. MICHEL (1969), Z. für Physik **223**, 199.
GOETZE, W. and K.H. MICHEL (1972), in *Dynamical properties of solids*, ed. by G.K. Horton and A.A. Maradudin (North-Holland Publ.Co., Amsterdam), Vol. 1, ch. 9, p. 499.
GREYWALL, D.S. (1971), Phys. Rev. A**3**, 2106.
GRIFFIN, A. (1965), Phys. Letters **17**, 208.
GRIFFIN, A. (1968a), Rev. Mod. Phys. **40**, 167.
GRIFFIN, A. (1968b), Can. J. Phys. **46**, 2843.
GURZHI, R.N. (1964), Zh. E.T.F. **46**, 719 [English transl.: Sov. Phys. JETP **19** (1964) 490].
GURZHI, R.N. (1965), Fiz. Tverd. Tela **7**, 3315 [English transl.: Sov. Phys. Sol. State **7** (1966) 2838].
GUYER, R.A. (1966), Phys. Rev. **148**, 789.
GUYER, R.A. and J.A. KRUMHANSL (1964), Phys. Rev. A **133**, 1411.
GUYER, R.A. and J.A. KRUMHANSL (1966a), Phys. Rev. **148**, 766.
GUYER, R.A. and J.A. KRUMHANSL (1966b), Phys. Rev. **148**, 778.

HARDY, R.J. (1963), Phys. Rev. **132**, 168.
HARDY, R.J. (1970), Phys. Rev. B**2**, 1193.
HARDY, R.J. and S.S. JASWAL (1971), Phys. Rev. B**3**, 4385.
HERRING, C. (1954), Phys. Rev. **95**, 954.
HOGAN, E.M., R.A. GUYER and H.A. FAIRBANK (1969), Phys. Rev. **185**, 356.
HOLLAND, M.G. (1963), Phys. Rev. **132**, 2461.
HORIE, C. and J.A. KRUMHANSL (1964), Phys. Rev. **136**, A 1397.
HORNER, H. (1972), J. Low Temp. Phys. **8**, 511.
JÄCKLE, J. (1970), Phys. Cond. Matt. **11**, 139.
JACKSON, H.E. and C.T. WALKER (1971), Phys. Rev. B**3**, 1428.
JACKSON, H.E., C.T. WALKER and T.F. MCNELLY (1970), Phys. Rev. Lett. **25**, 26.
JASWAL, S.S. and R.J. HARDY (1972), Phys. Rev. B**5**, 753.
KADANOFF, L.P. and G. BAYM (1962), *Quantum statistical mechanics* (Benjamin, N.Y.).
KADANOFF, L.P. and P.C. MARTIN (1963), Ann. Physics (N.Y.) **24**, 419.
KHALATNIKOV, I.M. (1965), *An introduction to the theory of superfluidity* (Benjamin, N.Y.).
KLEIN, R. and R.K. WEHNER (1968), Phys. Cond. Matt. **8**, 141.
KLEIN, R. and R.K. WEHNER (1969), Phys. Cond. Matt. **10**, 1.
KLEMENS, P.G. (1951), Proc. Roy. Soc. (London) A**208**, 108.
KLEMENS, P.G. (1955), Proc. Phys. Soc. (London) A**68**, 1113.
KLEMENS, P.G. (1956), *Handbuch der Physik* **14**/1 (Springer, Berlin) p. 198.
KLEMENS, P.G. (1958), Solid State Phys. **7**, 1.
KOEHLER, T.R. and N.R. WERTHAMER (1972), Phys. Rev. A**5**, 2230.
KOPYLOV, V.N. and L.P. MESHOV-DEGLIN (1971), Sov. Phys. JETP Lett. **14**, 21.
KRUMHANSL, J.A. (1965), Proc. Phys. Soc. **85**, 921.
KUBO, R. (1957), J. Phys. Soc. Japan **12**, 570.
KUBO, R. (1965), in *Statistical mechanics of equilibrium and non-equilibrium*, ed. J. Meixner (North-Holland Publ. Co., Amsterdam), p. 81.
KWOK, P.C. (1967), Physics **3**, 221.
KWOK, P.C. and P.C. MARTIN (1966), Phys. Rev. **142**, 495.
LANDAU, L.D. (1941a), Zh. E.T.F. **11**, 592.
LANDAU, L.D. (1941b), J. Physics (Moscow) **5**, 71.
LANDAU, L.D. (1956), Zh. E.T.F. **30**, 1058 [English transl.: Sov. Phys. JETP **3** (1956) 920].
LANDAU, L.D. and E.M. LIFSCHITZ (1959), *Theory of elasticity* (Pergamon Press, London).
LAWSON, D.T. and H.A. FAIRBANK (1973), J. Low Temp. Physics **11**, 263.
LEIBFRIED, G. and E. SCHLÖMANN (1954), Nachr. Gött. Akad. Wiss. **2a**, 71.
MARADUDIN, A.A. and A.E. FEIN (1962), Phys. Rev **128**, 2589.
MARIS, H.J. (1969), Phys. Rev. **188**, 1303.
MARIS, H.J. (1972), Phys. Rev. Lett. **28**, 377.
MARIS, H.J. (1973), Phys. Rev. Lett. **30**, 312; Phys. Rev. A**7**, 2074.
MARTIN, P.C. (1965), in *Statistical mechanics of equilibrium and non-equilibrium*, ed. J. Meixner (North-Holland Publ. Co., Amsterdam), p. 100.
MCNELLY, T.F., S.J. ROGERS, D.J. CHANNIN, R.J. ROLLEFSON, W.M. GOUBAU, G.E. SCHMIDT, J.A. KRUMHANSL and R.O. POHL (1970), Phys. Rev. Lett. **24**, 100.
MEIER, P.F. (1969), Phys. Cond. Matt. **8**, 241.
MEIER, P. F. (1973), Phys. Cond. Matt. **17**, 17.
MEIER, P.F. and H. BECK (1973), Phys. Rev. A**8**, 569.

MESHOV-DEGLIN, L.P. (1965), Zh. E.T.F. **49**, 66 [English transl.: Sov. Phys. JETP **22** (1966) 47].
MESHOV-DEGLIN, L.P. (1967), Zh. E.T.F. **52**, 866 [English transl.: Sov. Phys. JETP **25** (1967) 568].
MORI, H. (1962), Progr. Theor. Phys. **28**, 763.
MORI, H. (1965a), Progr. Theor. Phys. **33**, 423.
MORI, H. (1965b), Progr. Theor. Phys. **34**, 399.
NARAYANAMURTI, V. and R.O. POHL (1970), Rev. Mod. Phys. **42**, 201.
NARAYANAMURTI, V. and C.M. VARMA (1970), Phys. Rev. Lett. **25**, 1105.
NARAYANAMURTI, V. and R.C. DYNES (1972), Phys. Rev. Lett. **28**, 1461.
NELSON, R.O. and W.M. HARTMA (1972), Phys. Rev. Lett. **28**, 1261.
NERNST, W. (1917), *Die theoretischen Grundlagen des neuen Wärmesatzes* (Knapp, Halle).
NIKLASSON, G. (1969), Fortschr. der Physik **17**, 235.
NIKLASSON, G. (1970), Ann. Phys. (N.Y.) **59**, 263.
NIKLASSON, G. and A. SJÖLANDER (1968), Ann. Phys. (N.Y.) **49**, 249.
NOOLANDI, J. and J. VAN KRANENDONCK (1972), Can. J. Phys. **50**, 1815.
OSGOOD, E. B., V.J. MINKIEWICZ, T.A. KITCHENS and G. SHIRANE (1972), Phys. Rev. A**5**, 1537.
PEIERLS, R. (1929), Ann. der Physik **3**, 1055.
PEIERLS, R. (1955), *The quantum theory of solids* (Clarendon Press, Oxford).
PESHKOV, V. (1944), J. Phys. (USSR) **8**, 131.
PESHKOV, V. (1947), in *Report on an internat. conf. on fundamental particles and low temperature physics* (Phys. Soc. of London), vol. II, p. 19.
POHL, R.O. (1968), in *Internat. conf. on localized excitations in solids*, ed. R.F. Wallis (Plenum Press, N.Y.), p. 434.
POHL, R.O. (1969), in *Internat. conf. on elementary excitations in solids*, ed. R.F. Wallis (Plenum Press, N.Y.), p. 259.
POHL, D.W. and S.E. SCHWARTZ, (1973), Phys. Rev. B**7**, 2735.
PROHOVSKY, E.W. and J.A. KRUMHANSL (1964), Phys. Rev. A **133**, 1403.
RANNINGER, J. (1965), Phys. Rev. A **140**, 2031.
RANNINGER, J. (1967), Ann. Physics (N.Y.) **45**, 452.
RANNINGER, J. (1968), Ann. Physics (N.Y.) **49**, 297.
RANNINGER, J. (1969), J. Phys. C**2**, 929.
RANNINGER, J. (1972), Phys. Rev. B**5**, 3315.
REIF, F. (1965), *Fundamentals of statistical and thermal physics* (McGraw Hill, N.Y.).
RIESZ, F. and B. SZ-NAGY (1955), *Functional analysis* (Frederic Ungar, N.Y.).
ROGERS, S.J. (1971), Phys. Rev. B**3**, 1440.
ROGERS, S.J. (1972), J. de Physique (France) **33**, Suppl. C4, 111.
SEWARD, W.O., O. LAZARUS and S.C. FAIN Jr. (1969), Phys. Rev. **178**, 345.
SHAM, L. J. (1967), Phys. Rev. **156**, 494.
SÜSSMAN, J.A. and A. THELLUNG (1963), Proc. Phys. Soc. **81**, 1122.
THELLUNG, A. and K. WEISS (1969), Phys. Cond. Mat. **9**, 300.
THOMLINSON, W.C. (1969), Phys. Rev. Lett. **23**, 1330.
THOMLINSON, W.C. (1972), J. Low Temp. Phys. **9**, 167.
TISZA, L. (1938), C.R. Acad. Sci. (Paris) **207**, 1035 and 1186.
TISZA, L. (1940), J. Phys. Rad. **1**, 164 and 350.
TSAI, D.H. and R.A. MCDONALD (1973a), J. Phys. C**6**, L 171.

TSAI, D.H. and R.A. MCDONALD (1973b), Preprint.
VARMA, C.M. (1971), Phys. Rev. A**4**, 313.
VARSHNI, Y.P. and A. KONTI (1972), Phys. Rev. B**6**, 1532.
VERBOVEN, E. (1960), Physica **26**, 1091.
VON GUTFELD, R.J. (1968), in *Physical acoustics*, ed. N.P. Mason (Acad. Press Inc., N.Y.), **5**, p. 233.
WARD, J.C. and J. WILKS (1951), Phil. Mag. **42**, 314.
WARD, J.C. and J. WILKS (1952), Phil. Mag. **43**, 48.
WEHNER, R.K. and R. KLEIN (1972), Physica **62**, 161.
WEISS, K. (1968), Phys. Cond. Mat. **7**, 201.
WERTHAMER, N.R. and S.T. CHUI (1972a), Phys. Lett. **41**A, 157.
WERTHAMER, N.R. and S.T. CHUI (1972b), Sol. State Commun. **10**, 843.
WOODRUFF, T.O. and H. EHRENREICH (1961), Phys. Rev. **123**, 1553.
ZIMAN, J.M. (1956), Can. J. Phys. **34**, 1256.
ZIMAN, J.M. (1960), *Electrons and phonons* (Clarendon Press, Oxford).

CHAPTER 5

Dynamics of Impurities in Crystals

D.W. TAYLOR

Physics Department, McMaster University
Hamilton, Ontario
Canada

Dynamical Properties of Solids, edited by*
G.K. Horton and A.A. Maradudin

© *North-Holland Publishing Company, 1975*

Contents

1. *Introduction*

The introduction of impurities into a crystal lattice modifies both the vibrational eigenfrequencies and the eigenfunctions or normal modes. Large perturbations can so modify the eigenfrequencies that modes are driven out of the host crystal continuum (local modes) or resonances may occur within the continuum. The most obvious manifestation of the perturbation of the normal modes is due to the loss of translational symmetry of the disordered crystal. This leads to the relaxation of selection rules that depend upon the conservation of crystal momentum $\boldsymbol{k}$ and one consequence is the possibility of infra-red absorption in the acoustic frequency region of the host crystal. As well as this loss in translational symmetry, atoms near an impurity atom have their point symmetry modified. In particular any inversion symmetry will be removed so that first-order Raman scattering can occur even though it is symmetry forbidden in the host crystal. Hence the dynamical effects can be readily detected by well developed optical methods.

Another way to view the consequences of disorder is via the ideas of linear response theory. Such experiments as infra-red absorption and inelastic neutron scattering can be viewed as investigating the response of the crystal to a probe of well defined wave vector, $\boldsymbol{k}$. What is then detected is the $\boldsymbol{k}$ component of the normal modes, and, as a consequence of the disorder, almost all the normal modes will have such a non-zero component. Hence the crystal responds over a wide frequency range rather than at just a few isolated frequencies, as in a pure crystal.

This linear response viewpoint naturally leads to the use of Green's functions as described in section 2. The evaluation of these functions in the presence of disorder can be a difficult problem which is the subject of the following chapter (ch. 6). However, for low concentrations of impurities the theory is relatively simple and can be evaluated in considerable detail and in some cases with great precision. We will confine ourselves to this concentration range in the present chapter, discussing both the theory and its relation to experiment.

The basic disorder theory is developed in section 3 and its general properties are investigated in section 4 for the simplest impurity model i.e. when only the different mass of the impurity is taken into account. In the following section (sect. 5) we discuss the somewhat more complicated situation that arises when force constant changes are associated with the impurity. In section 5 we also describe the various impurity models that have been adopted for substitutional impurities (our major topic), for interstitials and for clusters of impurities.

Before embarking on a discussion of the many experiments on dilute disordered crystals, in section 6 we give a brief description of the range of the disturbance produced by an impurity in order to attempt to understand what is meant by 'dilute'. In the following sections we then discuss the calculations that have been made in order to understand a variety of experimental results. It is the intention of these sections to at least reference all such recent calculations up to the end of 1973. Not all the experimental results will be referenced directly, especially when we refer to a separate calculational paper.

Section 7 contains the results obtained by optical methods, including infra-red absorption, first-order Raman scattering, vibronic and local mode sidebands. Particularly for the highly investigated alkali halides, many of the calculations attempt to describe the overall shape of the spectra rather than just fix the local mode or resonant mode frequencies.

Inelastic neutron scattering probes the details of the disordered crystal lattice dynamics in even more detail and so requires more of the theory, particularly for coherent scattering. This topic is discussed in section 8 where it will be seen that the experimental results support the basic theoretical predictions although the numerical agreement is not always very satisfactory. This is partly due to the relatively large impurity concentrations that are necessary for there to be a detectable effect, and these tend to be on the edge of the range of validity of low concentration disorder theory.

In section 9 we close with a discussion of impurity effects on frequency distributions. These include incoherent neutron scattering, the frequency distribution $\alpha^2 f(\omega)$ that can be extracted from the tunnelling currents in sufficiently strong coupling superconductors and finally the specific heat which involves an integral over the density of states. None of these experiments have yielded quite the same detailed information as those considered in previous sections. Section 10 is devoted to a conclusion.

What we will not consider are special impurity systems such as those where the impurity substitutes off-centre and those where internal states couple strongly to the phonons (molecular levels, spin states). Anharmonic effects are only mentioned in passing and impurities in quantum crystals are not discussed at all.

Even so, there is a considerable amount of material as the field has been under intensive investigation for over a decade. Earlier reviews include the very comprehensive one due to Maradudin (1966) whilst both Ludwig (1967) and Maradudin et al. (1971) have described the theoretical methods in considerable detail. Other reviews have considered impurities in alkali halides (Klein 1968), the infra-red absorption due to dilute concentrations of impurities (Newman 1969) and electron and hydrogen centres in ionic crystals (Bauerle 1973). The summer school lectures of Elliott (1965) and those to be found in Elementary Excitations in Solids (Maradudin and Nardelli 1969) should also be noted. Further, McCombie (1970) has discussed the dynamics of an impurity from a rather different viewpoint compared with that adopted in this chapter. Finally, the 'Localised Excitations in Solids' conference proceedings (Wallis 1968) contain much material relevant to this chapter. The conference, roughly speaking, marks the beginning of the era of detailed calculations of the lattice dynamics of impurities in crystals. Most of the calculations that we will discuss post-date this conference.

2. *Green's functions for lattice dynamics*

2.1. Couplings to lattice vibrations

Photons, neutrons and electrons have been used extensively as probes to measure the lattice dynamics of both ordered and disordered crystals. The interaction of the probe with the crystal lattice depends, in part, upon the atomic positions $\boldsymbol{R}(l\kappa)+\boldsymbol{u}(l\kappa, t)$. Here $\boldsymbol{u}(l\kappa, t)$ is the atomic displacement from the equilibrium position $\boldsymbol{R}(l\kappa)$ with l referring to the unit cell and κ the site within the unit cell. In all the examples that we will consider it is sufficient to retain just the linear term of the expansion of the interaction hamiltonian in terms of the displacements

$$H_{\mathrm{I}} = \sum_{l\kappa} \boldsymbol{F}(l\kappa, t)\cdot \boldsymbol{u}(l\kappa, t).$$

The various forms of the coupling coefficient $\boldsymbol{F}$ will be considered later in sections 7–9.

Experimentally determined quantities such as transition rates or scattering cross sections can be determined using Fermi's golden rule on the assumption that H_I is weak. As this requires calculations of $|\langle f|H_I|i\rangle|^2$ it is clear that the required function of the lattice dynamics is almost always the displacement–displacement correlation function,

$$S_{\alpha\beta}(l\kappa, l'\kappa'; \omega) = (1/2\pi) \int_{-\infty}^{\infty} \langle u_\alpha(l\kappa; t)\, u_\beta(l'\kappa')\rangle_T\, e^{i\omega t}\, d\omega, \tag{2.1}$$

where $\langle\cdots\rangle_T$ denotes a thermal average.

Such correlation functions are readily calculated via Green's functions (Fetter and Walecka 1971). In fact Green's functions naturally arise if we use the methods of linear response theory to calculate the consequences of the coupling between the probe and the lattice via H_I. The Green's functions in turn are obtained by solving, in some approximation, their equation of motion. For this we need to introduce the hamiltonian for the crystal.

2.2. Disordered crystal hamiltonian

In the harmonic approximation, the hamiltonian for an ordered crystal is

$$\mathscr{H}^0 = \tfrac{1}{2}\sum_{l\kappa} \frac{\boldsymbol{P}(l\kappa)^2}{M_0(\kappa)} + \tfrac{1}{2}\sum_{\substack{l\kappa \\ l'\kappa'}} \boldsymbol{u}(l\kappa)\cdot\boldsymbol{\Phi}^0(l\kappa, l'\kappa')\cdot\boldsymbol{u}(l'\kappa'), \tag{2.2}$$

with the force constant matrix, $\boldsymbol{\Phi}^0$, being translationally invariant. We take the same form for the alloy, i.e.,

$$\mathscr{H}^A = \tfrac{1}{2}\sum_{l\kappa} \frac{\boldsymbol{P}(l\kappa)^2}{M(l\kappa)} + \tfrac{1}{2}\sum_{\substack{l\kappa \\ l'\kappa'}} \boldsymbol{u}(l\kappa)\cdot\boldsymbol{\Phi}(l\kappa, l'\kappa')\cdot\boldsymbol{u}(l'\kappa'). \tag{2.3}$$

Note that the mass now depends upon l and that $\boldsymbol{\Phi}$ is not translationally invariant. The passage from $\mathscr{H}^0$ to $\mathscr{H}^A$ is not completely straightforward. Suppose $\mathscr{H}^0$ describes the host crystal into which substitutional impurity atoms are added to form the alloy. Due to the differing interatomic forces there will be a distortion of the host lattice as well as a volume change and the atomic positions will no longer be periodic. However, the structure can be visualised as consisting of an effective periodic lattice, appropriate to the average atomic spacing as measured by a diffraction experiment, with the atomic equilibrium positions being displaced from the effective lattice sites by amounts dependent upon the local environment. Due to this relaxation of the host lattice sites, a derivation of the force constant matrix appearing in (2.3) would require higher order derivatives of the interatomic potentials than are needed for $\boldsymbol{\Phi}^0$.

Although a systematic discussion of these effects does not appear to have been given, there is a simple way to approximate them. This proceeds by first using the host crystal mode Grüneisen parameters to estimate $\boldsymbol{\Phi}$ appropriate to the effective lattice, this matrix still being translationally invariant, along with the experimentally determined change in atomic spacing due to alloying. Then the local variations in the force constants, appropriate to the various atomic species present, may be estimated although these are usually taken as parameters to be determined experimentally.

2.3. Lattice Green's functions

We choose to use Green's functions given by [see Fetter and Walecka (1971), especially ch. 9, for details of the theory in this subsection],

$$G_{\alpha\beta}(l\kappa, l'\kappa'; \omega) = (1/\hbar) \int_{-\infty}^{\infty} \langle\langle u_\alpha(l\kappa, t); u_\beta(l'\kappa')\rangle\rangle \, \mathrm{e}^{\mathrm{i}\omega t} \, \mathrm{d}t, \tag{2.4a}$$

where

$$\langle\langle A(t); B\rangle\rangle = \mp \mathrm{i}\theta(\pm t)\langle[A(t), B]\rangle_{\mathrm{T}} \tag{2.4b}$$

is a double time Green's function as described by Zubarev (1960). The upper and lower signs give, respectively, the retarded and advanced Green's functions with $\theta(t)$ being the usual step function.

These Green's functions are related to the correlation function (2.1) via the spectral representation

$$\boldsymbol{G}(l\kappa, l'\kappa'; z) = (1/\hbar) \int_{-\infty}^{\infty} \frac{(1 - \mathrm{e}^{-\beta\omega})\, \boldsymbol{S}(l\kappa, l'\kappa'; \omega)}{z - \omega} \, \mathrm{d}\omega,$$

where $\beta = \hbar/k_{\mathrm{B}}T$. Continuation into the upper and lower half planes gives, respectively, the retarded and advanced Green's functions. A more explicit relation between these functions is obtained from the discontinuity of the Green's functions across the real axis, i.e.,

$$\boldsymbol{G}(\omega + \mathrm{i}0^+) - \boldsymbol{G}(\omega - \mathrm{i}0^+) = 2\mathrm{i}\,\mathrm{Im}\,\boldsymbol{G}(\omega) = -(2\pi\mathrm{i}/\hbar)\,(1 - \mathrm{e}^{-\beta\omega})\,\boldsymbol{S}(\omega). \tag{2.5}$$

For clarity, we have absorbed the site indices $(l\kappa)$ as well as the cartesian components (α) into the formal matrix notation. We will follow a convention in all that follows of suppressing indices where possible, with the understanding that all matrices refer to the full lattice space (α, l, κ) unless otherwise indicated.

Differentiating the formal Green's function (2.4) with respect to time gives the equation of motion,

$$\mathrm{i}\hbar\, \mathrm{d}\langle\langle A(t); B\rangle\rangle/\mathrm{d}t = \hbar\,\delta(t)\,\langle[A, B]\rangle_{\mathrm{T}} + \langle\langle[A(t), \mathscr{H}]; B\rangle\rangle\,. \tag{2.6}$$

As

$$[\boldsymbol{u}(l\kappa), \mathscr{H}^{\mathrm{A}}] = \mathrm{i}\hbar\,\boldsymbol{P}(l\kappa)/M(l\kappa)$$

and

$$[\boldsymbol{P}(l\kappa), \mathscr{H}^{\mathrm{A}}] = -\,\mathrm{i}\hbar \sum_{l'\kappa'} \boldsymbol{\Phi}(l\kappa, l'\kappa')\cdot\boldsymbol{u}(l'\kappa'),$$

applying the equation of motion twice gives an equation entirely in terms of the u–u Green's function (2.4). On Fourier transforming with respect to time the result is

$$-\,M(l\kappa)\,\omega^2\,\boldsymbol{G}(l\kappa, l'\kappa'; \omega) + \sum_{l''\kappa''} \boldsymbol{\Phi}(l\kappa, l''\kappa'')\,\boldsymbol{G}(l''\kappa'', l'\kappa'; \omega) + \boldsymbol{I}\delta_{ll'}\delta_{\kappa\kappa'} = 0\,.$$

Written in the full matrix notation this is

$$-\,\boldsymbol{M}\omega^2\boldsymbol{G}(\omega) + \boldsymbol{\Phi}\boldsymbol{G}(\omega) + \boldsymbol{I} = 0,$$

or

$$\boldsymbol{G}(\omega)^{-1} = \boldsymbol{M}\omega^2 - \boldsymbol{\Phi}\,. \tag{2.7}$$

The Green's function for a perfect crystal described by the hamiltonian $\mathscr{H}^0$ (2.2) satisfies a similar equation

$$\boldsymbol{G}^0(\omega)^{-1} = \boldsymbol{M}_0\omega^2 - \boldsymbol{\Phi}^0\,. \tag{2.8}$$

Hence on introducting the perturbation matrix

$$\boldsymbol{C}(\omega) = (\boldsymbol{M}_0 - \boldsymbol{M})\,\omega^2 + \boldsymbol{\Phi} - \boldsymbol{\Phi}^0\,, \tag{2.9}$$

we can obtain the basic Dyson equation relating $\boldsymbol{G}(\omega)$ and $\boldsymbol{G}^0(\omega)$,

$$\boldsymbol{G}(\omega) = \boldsymbol{G}^0(\omega) + \boldsymbol{G}^0(\omega)\boldsymbol{C}(\omega)\boldsymbol{G}(\omega)\,. \tag{2.10}$$

Solutions to this equation will be described below in section 3, however, it is clear that a detailed knowledge of $\boldsymbol{G}^0(\omega)$ is required and we now direct our attention to this problem.

To evaluate $\boldsymbol{G}^0(\omega)$ we need to transform to a representation that diagonalises eq. (2.8). Let us rewrite this equation as

$$(\boldsymbol{M}_0^{1/2}\boldsymbol{G}^0(\omega)\,\boldsymbol{M}_0^{1/2})^{-1} = \boldsymbol{I}\omega^2 - \boldsymbol{M}_0^{-1/2}\boldsymbol{\Phi}^0\boldsymbol{M}_0^{-1/2}. \tag{2.11}$$

From the basic theory of lattice dynamics discussed in ch. 1 of vol. 1, it is readily seen that the required transformation matrix is just

$$\langle \boldsymbol{k}j | l\kappa\alpha\rangle = N^{-1/2} w_\alpha^*(\kappa|\boldsymbol{k}j)\exp[-\mathrm{i}\boldsymbol{k}\cdot\boldsymbol{R}(l\kappa)],$$

where $\boldsymbol{w}(\kappa|\boldsymbol{k}j)$ is the eigenvector for a phonon mode of wave vector $\boldsymbol{k}$ and branch j and N is the number of unit cells in the crystal. Effecting this transformation yields

$$G_j^0(\boldsymbol{k},\omega)^{-1} = \omega^2 - \omega_j(\boldsymbol{k})^2,$$

where $\omega_j(\boldsymbol{k})$ is the eigenfrequency of the phonon mode $(\boldsymbol{k}j)$. The Green's function in the site representation is then given by

$$G_{\alpha\beta}^0(l\kappa, l'\kappa';\omega) = [M_0(\kappa)\,M_0(\kappa')]^{-1/2}\,N^{-1}\sum_{jk} w_\alpha(\kappa|\boldsymbol{k}j)\,w_\beta^*(\kappa'|\boldsymbol{k}j) \times \exp\{\mathrm{i}\boldsymbol{k}\cdot[\boldsymbol{R}(l\kappa) - \boldsymbol{R}(l'\kappa')]\}\,G_j^0(\boldsymbol{k},\omega). \tag{2.12}$$

Numerical values for this function are obtained by first examining its imaginary part (2.5)

$$\mathrm{Im}\,G_{\alpha\beta}^0(l\kappa, l'\kappa';\omega) = -(\pi/N)\,[M_0(\kappa)\,M_0(\kappa')]^{-1/2} \times \sum_{jk} w_\alpha(\kappa|\boldsymbol{k}j)\,w_\beta(\kappa'|\boldsymbol{k}j)\exp\{\mathrm{i}\boldsymbol{k}\cdot[\boldsymbol{R}(l\kappa) - \boldsymbol{R}(l'\kappa')]\} \times [\delta(\omega-\omega_j(\boldsymbol{k})) - \delta(\omega+\omega_j(\boldsymbol{k}))]/2\omega_j(\boldsymbol{k}). \tag{2.13}$$

The analysis of the high-resolution optical spectra now available require precise evaluations of $\mathrm{Im}\,\boldsymbol{G}^0(\omega)$. This can be achieved by using a large number of $\boldsymbol{k}$ points in the first Brillouin zone supported by either staggered bin techniques (Caldwell and Klein 1967) or preferably by interpolation techniques (Gilat and Raubenheimer 1966, Gilat 1972). In cubic crystals it is only necessary to sum over the irreducible 1/48th of the Brillouin zone (see for instance the appendix to Timusk and Klein, 1966), typically using 1686 points equivalent to 64,000 points in the full zone. In the alkali halides this leads to smooth histograms of bin width $\approx 0.5\ \mathrm{cm}^{-1}$ (c.f. maximum frequencies $\gtrsim 150\ \mathrm{cm}^{-1}$) with clearly defined Van Hove singularities. MacPherson and Timusk (1970b) show such histograms for six alkali halides.

The real part of $\boldsymbol{G}^0(\omega)$ is then obtained via a Hilbert transform

$$\operatorname{Re} \boldsymbol{G}^0(\omega) = -(2/\pi)\, \mathrm{P} \int_0^\infty \frac{\omega' \operatorname{Im} \boldsymbol{G}^0(\omega')\, \mathrm{d}\omega'}{\omega^2 - \omega'^2} \tag{2.14}$$

The principal value integral can be done analytically if $\operatorname{Im} \boldsymbol{G}^0(\omega')$ is taken to be a constant within each bin of the histogram. An alternative, and faster procedure (Sievers et al. 1965), is to add and subtract $\omega \operatorname{Im} \boldsymbol{G}^0(\omega)$ in the numerator in order to eliminate the zero in the denominator. Simpson's rule can then be used and the additional integral arising from the above addition is readily done.

An alternative to the above procedures is to evaluate $\boldsymbol{G}^0(\omega)$ a small but finite distance, $\mathrm{i}\Delta$, off the real axis. This allows the evaluation of the real and imaginary parts of $\boldsymbol{G}^0(\omega)$ simultaneously. Δ has to be sufficiently big to remove fluctuations ariring from the finite number of $\boldsymbol{k}$ points used yet must not obscure real structure. For instance Benedek and Nardelli (1968b) using 4096 $\boldsymbol{k}$ points took $\Delta = 1\ \mathrm{cm}^{-1}$ and evaluated $\boldsymbol{G}^0(\omega)$ at $4\ \mathrm{cm}^{-1}$ intervals whereas Grim et al. (1972) used 11,664 $\boldsymbol{k}$ points, $\Delta = 0.01\omega_{\max}$, with a bin width of $0.02\omega_{\max}$.

2.4. General properties of the Green's function

From (2.11), (2.13) we can readily see that the phonon density of states, $\nu^0(\omega)$, is given by

$$\begin{aligned}\operatorname{Tr} \operatorname{Im} \boldsymbol{M}_0^{1/2} \boldsymbol{G}^0(\omega)\, \boldsymbol{M}_0^{1/2} &= -(\pi/2\omega) \sum_{j\boldsymbol{k}} \delta(\omega - \omega_j(\boldsymbol{k})) \\ &= -(3rN\pi/2\omega)\, \nu^0(\omega)\end{aligned}$$

for $\nu^0(\omega)$ normalised to unity. In this equation r is the number of atoms per unit cell and we have restricted ourselves to $\omega > 0$.

Eq. (2.7) for $\boldsymbol{G}(\omega)$ can also be put in the same form as (2.11). As we are still dealing with a quadratic hamiltonian there exist well defined normal modes analogous to phonons. Hence, in principle, there is a representation that diagonalises $\boldsymbol{M}^{-1/2}\boldsymbol{\Phi}\boldsymbol{M}^{-1/2}$ so that even for a disordered crystal

$$(3rN\pi/2\omega)\,\nu(\omega) = -\operatorname{Tr}\boldsymbol{M}^{1/2}\boldsymbol{G}(\omega)\,\boldsymbol{M}^{1/2} = -\operatorname{Tr}\boldsymbol{MG}(\omega)\,. \tag{2.15}$$

Of course, for a disordered crystal we do not know the required transformation and it is an approximation for $\boldsymbol{MG}(\omega)$ that yields $\nu(\omega)$.

These Green's functions can be readily shown to satisfy a useful sum rule. This is an *f*-sum rule and can be derived in the usual way by taking the thermal average of the identity

$$[u_\alpha(l\kappa),\,[u_\beta(l'\kappa'),\,\mathscr{H}^{\mathrm{A}}]] = -\,[\hbar^2/M(l\kappa)]\,\delta_{\alpha\beta}\delta_{ll'}\,\delta_{\kappa\kappa'}$$

to obtain

$$\int_{-\infty}^{\infty} \omega\,(1-\mathrm{e}^{-\beta\omega})\,\boldsymbol{S}(\omega)\,\mathrm{d}\omega = -\,[\hbar/M(l\kappa)]\,\boldsymbol{I}\,.$$

Using (2.5) this gives

$$(2/\pi)\int_{0}^{\infty} \omega\,\operatorname{Im}\boldsymbol{M}\,\boldsymbol{G}(\omega)\,\mathrm{d}\omega = -\,\boldsymbol{I} \tag{2.16}$$

as $\operatorname{Im}\boldsymbol{G}(\omega)$ is an odd function of ω. As only the kinetic energy part of the hamiltonian is used in this derivation the result is exact, irrespective of anharmonicity and any of the difficulties mentioned in subsection 2.2. It is of use in optical absorption studies.

Other derivations of this sum rule can be found in the literature but they do not always emphasize its exactness. We note that our result for the normalised density of states $\nu(\omega)$, (2.15), is in full accord with this result. Other sum rules, or moments of $\operatorname{Im}\boldsymbol{G}(\omega)$ can be obtained by considering higher order commutators although they do not appear to have any general application in the context of this chapter. An inverse moment has also been derived by the author (Taylor and Vashishta 1972),

$$\int_{0}^{\infty} \omega^{-1}\,\operatorname{Im}\boldsymbol{G}(\omega)\,\mathrm{d}\omega = -\,\tfrac{1}{2}\pi\boldsymbol{\Phi}^{-1}$$

for use in superconductivity. The appearance of the force constant matrix $\boldsymbol{\Phi}$ renders it difficult to apply in the most general situation.

3. Disorder theory

3.1. On-diagonal disorder approximation

It is essential for the following that the perturbation matrix, $\boldsymbol{C}(\omega)$, (2.9) can be split into independent matrices, $\boldsymbol{C}^i(\omega)$, due to each impurity, i.e.

$$\boldsymbol{C}(\omega) = \sum_i \boldsymbol{C}^i(\omega), \tag{3.1}$$

where the sum is over all impurity atoms. This follows automatically if only the mass difference between the impurity and host atoms is taken into account (mass defect). Then

$$\boldsymbol{C}^i(l\kappa, l'\kappa'; \omega) = M^0(\kappa)\varepsilon(\kappa)\omega^2 \boldsymbol{I}\delta_{ll'}\,\delta_{\kappa\kappa'}\,\delta_{ll_i} \tag{3.2a}$$

for the ith impurity at l_i on sublattice κ. Here $\varepsilon(\kappa)$ is the relative mass difference

$$\varepsilon(\kappa) = 1 - M(\kappa)/M^0(\kappa). \tag{3.2b}$$

For simplicity we assume only one kind of impurity substituting in one sublattice. Note in this case that the $\boldsymbol{C}^i(\omega)$ and hence $\boldsymbol{C}(\omega)$ are diagonal matrices, hence the name on-diagonal disorder.

When the force constant changes associated with the impurities are taken into account, $\boldsymbol{C}(\omega)$ has off-diagonal contributions, a situation known in the general theory of alloys as off-diagonal disorder. However, because of the requirement (see ch. 1, vol. 1)

$$\sum_{l'\kappa'} \boldsymbol{\Phi}(l\kappa, l'\kappa') = 0,$$

there are also diagonal contributions to $\boldsymbol{C}(\omega)$ associated with the above off-diagonal contributions. Note that these diagonal contributions are at all the sites associated with the force constant changes due to the ith impurity, not just at the impurity site. These sites are said to form the impurity space of this particular impurity.

The general distortion of the alloy lattice, as discussed in subsection 2.2, seems to preclude the validity of (3.1) in that there are contributions to $\boldsymbol{C}(\omega)$ associated with the overall volume change due to alloying. However if we follow the approximation discussed at the end of subsection 2.2, the use of a

$G^0(\omega)$ calculated for the effective lattice takes into account the effects due to this volume change. Then the changes local to each impurity may be approximated by independent $C^i(\omega)$. For this to be at all possible the impurity concentration must be sufficiently low in order that diagonal contributions to $C(\omega)$ at non-impurity sites are not significantly affected by more than one impurity, i.e. impurity spaces rarely overlap.

At very low concentrations, c, much less than 0.01, the effective lattice is very well represented by the host lattice and (3.1) is well satisfied. This situation applies to a large class of optical experiments (see section 7). However, in inelastic neutron scattering experiments c has to exceed 0.01 for there to be observable effects. In this case, at the present, it is necessary to fall back on the effective crystal estimated via the mode Grüneisen parameters and also to use (3.1) somewhat beyond its strict range of validity (for further discussion, see section 6)

Adopting these approximations, the non-zero elements of an individual $C^i(\omega)$ constitute a submatrix of relatively small dimension connecting only those sites in the impurity space of the ith impurity. Other $C^j(\omega)$ will only differ by the location of this submatrix. Our approximations imply that we neglect the overlap of the submatrices in forming the total C and so reduce the problem to the same form as on-diagonal disorder.

3.2. Multiple scattering theory

Although the general problem of solving (2.10) is the subject of the next chapter, we will develop sufficient theory to discuss disordered crystals with low impurity concentrations. We follow the methods of Lax (1951, 1952) as used by Taylor (1967) for lattice vibrations.

The insertion of (3.1) in (2.10) yields

$$G(\omega) = G^0(\omega) + G^0 \sum_i C^i(\omega)\, G(\omega). \tag{3.3}$$

It is natural to single out the effects of a single impurity, say the ith, by writing (3.3) as

$$G(\omega) = G^i(\omega) + G^0(\omega)\, C^i(\omega)\, G(\omega),$$

where

$$G^i(\omega) = G^0(\omega) + G^0(\omega) \sum_{j \neq i} C^j(\omega)\, G(\omega).$$

On formally solving for $\boldsymbol{G}(\omega)$ in terms of $\boldsymbol{G}^i(\omega)$ and substituting into (3.3) we obtain

$$\boldsymbol{G}(\omega) = \boldsymbol{G}^0(\omega) + \boldsymbol{G}^0(\omega) \sum_i \boldsymbol{t}^i(\omega)\, \boldsymbol{G}^i(\omega), \tag{3.4a}$$

and $\boldsymbol{G}^i(\omega)$ is similarly given by

$$\boldsymbol{G}^i(\omega) = \boldsymbol{G}^0(\omega) + \boldsymbol{G}^0(\omega) \sum_{j \neq i} \boldsymbol{t}^j(\omega)\, \boldsymbol{G}^j(\omega). \tag{3.4b}$$

The t-matrix, $\boldsymbol{t}^i(\omega)$, describes the complete scattering of a wave off the ith defect and is given by

$$\boldsymbol{t}^i(\omega) = \boldsymbol{C}^i(\omega)\, [\boldsymbol{I} - \boldsymbol{G}^0(\omega)\, \boldsymbol{C}^i(\omega)]^{-1}. \tag{3.5}$$

Its evaluation requires the inversion of a matrix the size of the impurity space. As this can be an appreciable undertaking a discussion of the methods used will be put off to section 5.

The Green's function $\boldsymbol{G}^i(\omega)$ can be interpreted as describing the propagation of the effective field that is incident of the ith impurity space. This field clearly contains information about the dynamics of the rest of the crystal. It is related to all the other effective fields by (3.4b) and clearly we need to know all the impurity locations before a solution can be attempted. Further, such a solution is only practical when there are but a few impurities present.

3.3. The few impurity problem

The solution is trivial for just one impurity as then $\boldsymbol{G}^i(\omega) = \boldsymbol{G}^0(\omega)$ and we do not need multiple scattering theory. All that is required is the evaluation of the t-matrix to calculate

$$\boldsymbol{G}(\omega) = \boldsymbol{G}^0(\omega) + \boldsymbol{G}^0(\omega)\, \boldsymbol{t}^i(\omega)\, \boldsymbol{G}^0(\omega). \tag{3.6}$$

This equation, in one form or another, has been derived in many places in the literature. We will see below that the evaluation of this equation is often sufficient for very low concentration experiments.

This result is readily extended to more than one defect. Such extensions are usually only of interest when the impurities are close together but then the requirement (3.1) is no longer satisfied, except in the mass defect approximation. However, if only an isolated pair is considered then (2.10) can be solved even though (3.1) is not satisfied. The pair of impurities (or any size cluster) has to be considered as a single more extensive impurity with the perturbation matrix $\boldsymbol{C}^i(\omega)$ containing all the mass and force constant changes. Calculations for a variety of pairs of impurities will be described in subsection 5.6.

3.4. The many impurity problem

In a physical situation where the number of impurities in a crystal may approach or exceed 10^{20} per cm^3 and we cannot know their locations we must average the equations over all impurity configurations appropriate to the given concentration. This is known as a configuration average and is equivalent to ensemble averaging in statistical mechanics. Denoting this average by pointed brackets, (3.4a) becomes

$$\langle \boldsymbol{G}(\omega)\rangle = \boldsymbol{G}^0(\omega) + \sum_l \boldsymbol{G}^0(\omega)\langle \boldsymbol{t}^l(\omega)\,\boldsymbol{G}^l(\omega)\rangle,$$

where the sum is now over all unit cells. The average on the right-hand side of this equation can be rewritten by introducing a conditional average,

$$\langle \boldsymbol{t}^l(\omega)\boldsymbol{G}^l(\omega)\rangle = c\,\boldsymbol{t}^l(\omega)\langle \boldsymbol{G}^l(\omega)\rangle_l.$$

Here $\langle\ \rangle_l$ denotes an average over all configurations conditional on there being an impurity at l, and the factor c arises from the explicit average over what can be at l.

Noting that we only need the conditionally averaged effective field Green's functions (3.4) finally becomes

$$\langle \boldsymbol{G}(\omega)\rangle = \boldsymbol{G}^0(\omega) + \sum_l \boldsymbol{G}^0(\omega)\,c\,\boldsymbol{t}^l(\omega)\,\langle \boldsymbol{G}^l(\omega)\rangle_l, \tag{3.7a}$$

$$\langle \boldsymbol{G}^l(\omega)\rangle_l = \boldsymbol{G}^0(\omega) + \sum_{l'\neq l} \boldsymbol{G}^0(\omega)\,c\,\boldsymbol{t}^{l'}(\omega)\,\langle \boldsymbol{G}^{l'}(\omega)\rangle_{ll'}, \tag{3.7b}$$

where now an average conditional on two sites has appeared. Clearly we do not have a closed set of equations and must approximate.

In the presence of short range order (S.R.O.) the factor c in (3.7b) should be replaced by $\rho(l'|l)$ which is the probability that there is an impurity at l', given one at l. However, for want of more information and because of the nature of the approximation we will make to close the equations, it is usual to ignore S.R.O. (see, however, Hartmann 1968). Except for a brief comment in subsection 4.4, we will neglect any possible effects due to S.R.O.

At very low concentrations, particularly in optical work, it is sufficient to evaluate $\langle \boldsymbol{G}(\omega) \rangle$ to terms linear in c. It is immediately clear from (3.7) that these are obtained by setting $\langle \boldsymbol{G}^l(\omega) \rangle_l = \boldsymbol{G}^0(\omega)$, with the result

$$\langle \boldsymbol{G}(\omega) \rangle = \boldsymbol{G}^0(\omega) + \sum_l \boldsymbol{G}^0(\omega)\, c\, \boldsymbol{t}^l(\omega)\, \boldsymbol{G}^0(\omega). \tag{3.8}$$

This is an obvious extension of (3.6).

A more satisfactory low concentration approximation is one that is based on the single site approximation. This kind of approximation is also employed in the average-t-matrix and coherent potential approximations discussed in ch. 6. It is based on neglecting any explicit influence of one impurity on another. Thus $\langle \boldsymbol{G}^{l'}(\omega) \rangle_{ll'}$ in (3.7) is replaced by its average over l, i.e., $\langle \boldsymbol{G}^{l'}(\omega) \rangle_{l'}$ and so that a given impurity 'sees' only an average environment.

The above equations are now closed and can be solved to give

$$\langle \boldsymbol{G}(\omega) \rangle = \boldsymbol{G}^0(\omega) + \boldsymbol{G}^0(\omega)\, \Sigma(\omega) \langle \boldsymbol{G}(\omega) \rangle, \tag{3.9a}$$

where

$$\Sigma(\omega) = c \sum_l \boldsymbol{X}^l(\omega), \tag{3.9b}$$

and

$$\boldsymbol{X}^l(\omega) = \boldsymbol{C}^l(\omega)\,[\boldsymbol{I} - (1-c)\,\boldsymbol{G}^0(\omega)\,\boldsymbol{C}^l(\omega)]^{-1}. \tag{3.9c}$$

$\boldsymbol{X}^l(\omega)$ differs from $\boldsymbol{t}^l(\omega)$, (3.5), by just the factor $(1-c)$ which is connected with the multi-occupancy corrections discussed in ch. 6.

The implications of (3.9) are best seen by transforming to the $(\boldsymbol{k}, j)$ representation exactly as in (2.12). The result is

$$\langle G_{jj'}(\boldsymbol{k}, \omega) \rangle^{-1} = [\omega^2 - \omega_j^2(\boldsymbol{k})]\, \delta_{jj'} - \Sigma_{jj'}(\boldsymbol{k}, \omega), \tag{3.10a}$$

with the self energy given by

$$\Sigma_{jj'}(\boldsymbol{k}, \omega) = \sum_{\substack{\alpha\beta \\ \kappa\kappa'}} [M_0(\kappa)\, M_0(\kappa')]^{-1/2} \times w_\alpha(\kappa \,|\, \boldsymbol{k}j)\, w_\beta^*(\kappa' \,|\, \boldsymbol{k}j')\, \Sigma_{\alpha\beta}(\kappa, \kappa'; \boldsymbol{k}, \omega), \tag{3.10b}$$

where

$$\Sigma_{\alpha\beta}(\kappa, \kappa'; \boldsymbol{k}, \omega) = c \sum_{ll'} \exp\{-\mathrm{i}\boldsymbol{k}\cdot[\boldsymbol{R}(l\kappa) - \boldsymbol{R}(l'\kappa')]\} \times \boldsymbol{X}_{\alpha\beta}^{l_1}(l\kappa, l'\kappa'; \omega). \tag{3.10c}$$

In (3.10c) the sum is confined to a single impurity space which we have arbitrarily taken to be associated with an impurity in unit cell $l_1 = 0$. The configuration average, in restoring translational invariance, guarantees that (3.10) be diagonal on $\boldsymbol{k}$. However, there is no reason for it be diagonal on the branch labels j, j' although we will see below that we are often interested in situations where it is diagonal.

Although (3.10) is diagonal in $\boldsymbol{k}$ we know that in a disordered crystal the eigenstates cannot be wave-like. Hence we expect the self energy to have a finite imaginary part to simulate the damping of wave-like excitations in the crystal. To investigate this, and other consequences of (3.10) we need simple models for the impurities. These we consider in the next two sections.

There has been very little published on the extension of the above theory beyond the single site approximation to include the scattering off clusters of impurities. The problem is simplest in the mass defect approximation and the extension to pairs has been given by Langer (1961) for one dimension and for three dimensions by Aiyer et al. (1969). No numerical work has been published.

Further there are no calculations that evaluate either $\langle \boldsymbol{G}(\omega) \rangle$ or $\Sigma(\omega)$ to order c^2 yet correctly take into account the overlap of impurity spaces, (see subsection 3.1). The recent calculation of De Jong et al. (1973) explicitly neglects the possibility of this overlap. However it should be noted that Schwartz et al. (1973) have suggested a special model for the force constant changes that exactly reduces the problem back to ondiagonal disorder.

3.5. Conditionally averaged Green's functions

It often occurs that the external probe couples differently to the host and impurity atoms. If this difference is significant it is useful to have Green's functions that are conditionally averaged with respect to what kind of atom is at a given site. Hence we introduce

$$
\begin{aligned}
\boldsymbol{G}^{\mathrm{i}}(l, l'; \omega) &= \langle \boldsymbol{G}(l, l'; \omega) \rangle_l, \\
(1-c)\boldsymbol{G}^{\mathrm{h}}(l, l'; \omega) &= \langle \boldsymbol{G}(l, l'; \omega) \rangle - c\langle G(l, l'; \omega) \rangle_l, \\
\boldsymbol{G}^{\mathrm{ii}}(l, l'; \omega) &= \langle \boldsymbol{G}(l, l'; \omega) \rangle_{ll'}, \\
(1-c)\boldsymbol{G}^{\mathrm{ih}}(l, l'; \omega) &= \langle \boldsymbol{G}(l, l'; \omega) \rangle_l - c\langle \boldsymbol{G}(l, l'; \omega) \rangle_{ll'}, \\
(1-c)^2\boldsymbol{G}^{\mathrm{hh}}(l, l'; \omega) &= \langle \boldsymbol{G}(l, l'; \omega) \rangle \\
&\quad - c[\langle \boldsymbol{G}(l, l'; \omega) \rangle_l + \langle G(l, l'; \omega) \rangle_{l'}] + c^2\langle \boldsymbol{G}(l, l'; \omega) \rangle_{ll'}.
\end{aligned}
$$

$G^i(\omega)$ is readily obtained by configuration averaging (3.3) and noting that

$$\langle C^l(\omega)G(\omega) = cC^l(\omega)\langle G(\omega)\rangle_l .$$

Hence on comparison with (3.9)

$$\langle G(\omega)\rangle_l = [C^l(\omega)]^{-1} X^l(\omega)\langle G(\omega)\rangle . \tag{3.11}$$

$G^{ii}(\omega)$ is obtained by first noting that $G(\omega)$ also satisfies

$$G(\omega) = G^0(\omega) + \sum_i G^0(\omega)\, C^i(\omega)\, G^0(\omega) + \sum_{ij} G^0(\omega)\, C^i(\omega)\, G(\omega)\, C^j(\omega)\, G^0(\omega) . \tag{3.12}$$

On configuration averaging this equation we see that $\langle G(\omega)\rangle_{ll'}$ can be extracted from the third term on the right-hand side. This procedure has only been carried through for a mass defect (Kagan and Iosilevskii 1963, Elliott and Taylor 1967) and applied to the neutron scattering problem. We will defer discussion of the result until section 8.

In a number of experiments, such as the measurement of vibronic sidebands and impurity induced Raman scattering, only the impurity and its immediate neighbours couple to the probe. In such cases the problem is simple and all that is needed to obtain a result proportional to c is $G^i(\omega)$. To lowest order in c we can replace $\langle G(\omega)\rangle$ by $G^0(\omega)$ in (3.11) to obtain

$$\langle G(\omega)\rangle_l = c[C^l(\omega)]^{-1} t^l(\omega) G^0(\omega) . \tag{3.13}$$

This result is completely equivalent to the single impurity result (3.6) as can be seen by substituting the explicit form of the t-matrix (3.5) into (3.6).

4. *The mass defect approximation*

In order to examine the basic structure of the above results it is convenient to take the simplest model for the impurity. This is the mass defect approximation (3.2) and it ignores any force constant changes. In this case the impurity space reduces to just the impurity site (0κ) and the self energy (3.10) becomes

$$\Sigma_{jj'}(\boldsymbol{k}, \omega) = [c/M_0(\kappa)] \sum_{\alpha\beta} w_\alpha(\kappa\,|\,\boldsymbol{k}j)\, w_\beta(\kappa\,|\,\boldsymbol{k}j')\, X^0_{\alpha\beta}(0\kappa, 0\kappa; \omega) .$$

In a cubic structure symmetry ensures that

$$G^0_{\alpha\beta}(0\kappa, 0\kappa; \omega) = \delta_{\alpha\beta}\, G^0(\kappa, \omega).$$

As $\boldsymbol{C}^0(\omega)$ is also completely diagonal so are both $\boldsymbol{t}^0(\omega)$ and $\boldsymbol{X}^0(\omega)$, and we now have

$$\sum_{jj'}(\boldsymbol{k}, \omega) = [c/M_0(\kappa)] \sum_{\alpha} w_\alpha(\boldsymbol{\kappa}\,|\,\boldsymbol{k}j)\, w_\beta(\boldsymbol{\kappa}\,|\,\boldsymbol{k}j')\, X(\kappa, \omega), \tag{4.1}$$

with

$$X(\kappa, \omega) = X^0_{\alpha\alpha}(0\kappa, 0\kappa; \omega).$$

Only for a Bravais structure, when we can drop κ, does this generally simplify as then the orthogonality of the phonon eigenvectors reduces (4.1) to

$$\Sigma_{jj'}(\boldsymbol{k}, \omega) = \delta_{jj'}\, \Sigma(\omega), \tag{4.2a}$$

with

$$\Sigma(\omega) = \frac{c\varepsilon\omega^2}{1 - (1 - c)\, M_0\varepsilon\omega^2\, G^0(\omega)}. \tag{4.2b}$$

It can also be demonstrated that the transverse optic (TO) Green's function in a diatomic cubic structure can also be written in terms of a diagonal self energy, i.e.,

$$\langle G_{\mathrm{TO}}(\omega)\rangle = \langle G_{\mathrm{TT}}(\boldsymbol{0}, \omega)\rangle = (\omega^2 - \omega^2_{\mathrm{TO}} - \Sigma_{\mathrm{TO}}(\omega))^{-1}, \tag{4.3a}$$

with

$$\Sigma_{\mathrm{TO}}(\omega) = \frac{cm(2)\, \varepsilon(1)\, \omega^2}{1 - cm(1)\, \varepsilon(1) - (1 - c)\, \varepsilon(1)\, \omega^2 M_0(1)\, G^0(1, \omega)} \tag{4.3b}$$

assuming the impurities to be on sublattice 1. Here

$$m(1) = \frac{M_0(1)}{M_0(1) + M_0(2)}, \qquad m(2) = \frac{M_0(2)}{M_0(1) + M_0(2)}.$$

This result is useful in optical absorption studies. The mode mixing implied by (4.1) remains as $\boldsymbol{k} \to 0$. However, the eigenvectors appearing in (4.1) are very simply given in terms of the atomic masses $M_0(\kappa)$ in this limit (see ch. 1

of vol. 1) and the inversion of (3.10) can be readily done by hand to obtain (4.3). (The mode mixing is only between acoustic and optic branches of the same symmetry).

Our result, (4.3), differs from earlier results which neglected this mixing (Maradudin 1963, and Elliott and Taylor 1967) by the term $cm(1)\,\varepsilon(1)$. One consequence of the omission was that the resulting Green's functions did not exactly satisfy the sum rule (2.16) whereas our results, both (4.2) and (4.3), do satisfy it. However, at low concentrations this small change should not affect numerical results. We note that Benedek and Nardelli (1967) initially include this mode mixing in their calculations.

Central to all these results is the t-matrix

$$t_{\alpha\beta}(0\kappa, 0\kappa;\,\omega) = \delta_{\alpha\beta}\, t(\kappa, \omega) = \delta_{\alpha\beta}\, \frac{M_0(\kappa)\,\varepsilon(\kappa)\,\omega^2}{1 - M_0(\kappa)\,\varepsilon(\kappa)\,\omega^2\, G^0(\kappa, \omega)} \tag{4.4}$$

or its modifications in (4.2) and (4.3). t-matrices may exhibit poles on the real axis indicating bound states split off the continuum or poles off the real axis indicating resonances in the continuum, depending on the sign of the scattering potential. We will now discuss the consequences of these possibilities.

4.1. Local modes

It is clear from (2.13), (2.14) that $G^0(\kappa, \omega)$ is real and positive for $\omega > \omega_m$. Hence the possibility of a pole in the t-matrix arises if $\varepsilon > 0$. This corresponds to a light impurity mass splitting states off the top of the host crystal phonon continuum or band. The localised nature of these states leads to them being called local modes (Montroll and Potts 1955). As $\mathrm{Re}\, G^0(\kappa, \omega_m)$ is finite for any realistic phonon density of states there is a minimum critical value of ε for the occurrence of local modes and this critical value is host dependent. The results shown in figs. 5, 7 indicate that it is 0.35 for an impurity in Cu. For a diatomic crystal it will depend upon the sublattice, for instance Jaswal (1965a) found 0.45, 0.89 to be the values for the positive and negative ion sublattices of NaI.

From (3.5) it can be seen that, in general, these poles occur at frequencies for which

$$\det\,[\boldsymbol{I} - \boldsymbol{G}^0(\omega)\,\boldsymbol{C}^l(\omega)] = 0\,. \tag{4.5}$$

For $\omega > \omega_m$ there can be up to three different roots to this equation. The discussion given above refers to the case of cubic symmetry when these roots are degenerate. However, when the symmetry is reduced this degeneracy may be lifted. For instance, in the wurtzite structure there are two local mode frequencies corresponding to motion in the basal plane (2-fold degenerate) and perpendicular to this plane. Nusimovici et al. (1970b) have given calculations for the case of CdS.

For host crystals having a gap in their phonon density of states (e.g. some alkali halides and III–V compounds) the impurity may introduce local modes into the gap. This was first discussed by Mazur et al. (1956) for a linear chain

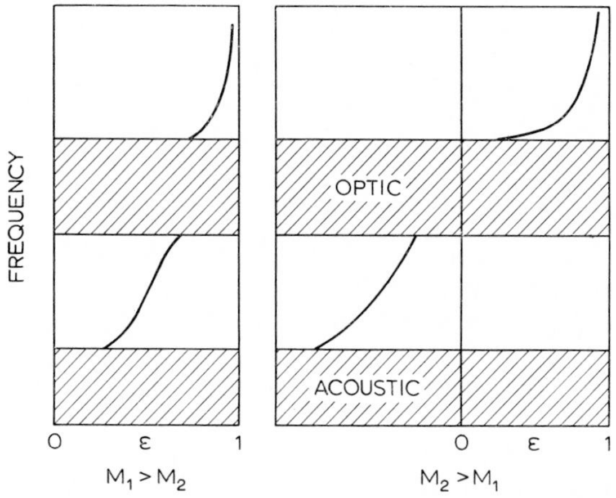

Fig. 1. The occurrence of gap and local modes (Sketch based on Jaswal 1965a).

and later by Mitani and Takeno (1965) and Jaswal (1965a) for three dimensions. Mitani and Takeno used a nearest neighbour force model to calculate $\boldsymbol{G}^0(\omega)$ whereas Jaswal used the deformation dipole model of Karo and Hardy (1963) (see ch. 3, vol. 1) for NaI. The latter case is sketched in fig. 1 for an impurity on sublattice $\kappa = 1$. It can readily be seen that either local or gap modes are split off the acoustic and optic bands depending upon the relationship between the masses. For instance, if the impurity mass is heavier than the lighter host atom ($\varepsilon < 0$, $M_2 > M_1$) a gap mode is split off the bottom of the optic band. Notice also that there are limits on the values of ε for the appearance of either gap or local modes. In performing equivalent calculations for materials of the zinc blende structure Gaur et al. (1971) found, in addition to the kind of behaviour shown in fig. 1, that when ε is negative and $M_1 > M_2$ a gap mode may split off the bottom of the optic band. This has not been found to occur in any alkali halide calculation.

4.2. Resonant modes

The resonant behaviour of the t-matrix may occur for ω within the host phonon band if $\varepsilon(\kappa)<0$, i.e., for a heavy impurity mass. Rewriting (4.4) with explicit real and imaginary parts,

$$t(\kappa, \omega)=\frac{M_0(\kappa)\,\varepsilon(\kappa)\,\omega^2\,[\alpha(\kappa, \omega)+\mathrm{i}\beta(\kappa, \omega)]}{\alpha^2(\kappa, \omega)+\beta^2(\kappa, \omega)},$$

with

$$\alpha(\kappa, \omega)=1-M_0(\kappa)\varepsilon(\kappa)\omega^2\,\mathrm{Re}\,G^0(\kappa, \omega),$$
$$\beta(\kappa, \omega)=M_0(\kappa)\varepsilon(\kappa)\omega^2\,\mathrm{Im}\,G^0(\kappa, \omega),$$

we readily see that such a resonance occurs near

$$\alpha(\kappa, \omega_\mathrm{R})=0. \tag{4.6}$$

It is important to realise, as pointed out by Callaway (1964), that this only leads to a lorentzian-type behaviour for $\mathrm{Im}\,t(\kappa, \omega)$ providing

$$\frac{\mathrm{d}\,\mathrm{Re}\,\omega^2\,G^0(\kappa, \omega)}{\mathrm{d}\omega}<0 \quad \text{at} \quad \omega=\omega_\mathrm{R}.$$

This lorenztian behaviour can be demonstrated by expanding the Green's function $G^0(\kappa, \omega)$ about ω_R. Then, using the not essential but simplifying assumption that

$$\frac{\mathrm{d}\,\mathrm{Im}\,\omega^2\,G^0(\kappa, \omega)}{\mathrm{d}\omega} \ll \frac{\mathrm{d}\,\mathrm{Re}\,\omega^2\,G^0(\kappa, \omega)}{\mathrm{d}\omega},$$

the t-matrix becomes approximately,

$$t(\kappa, z)=\frac{-\,\omega_\mathrm{R}^2\gamma(\kappa, \omega_\mathrm{R})}{z-\omega_\mathrm{R}+\mathrm{i}\omega_\mathrm{R}^2\gamma(\kappa, \omega_\mathrm{R})\,\mathrm{Im}\,G^0(\kappa, \omega_\mathrm{R})},$$

with

$$\gamma(\kappa, \omega)=\left[\frac{\mathrm{d}\,\omega^2\,\mathrm{Re}\,G^0(\kappa, \omega)}{\mathrm{d}\omega}\right]^{-1}.$$

As the retarded Green's function must be analytic in the upper half plane then, because $\mathrm{Im}\,G^0(\kappa, \omega+\mathrm{i}0^+)<0$ [see (2.13)], $\gamma(\kappa, \omega)$ must be negative for $t(\kappa, z)$ to have the correct analytic behaviour. Presumably if $\gamma(\kappa, \omega)>0$

the above expansion is invalid. That the damping is related to the phonon density of states via $\operatorname{Im} G^0(\kappa, \omega)$ reflects the decay of the induced mode into the host phonon states of a similar energy. A numerical illustration of this resonant behaviour is shown in fig. 2, the resonant frequencies being indicated by the vertical lines.

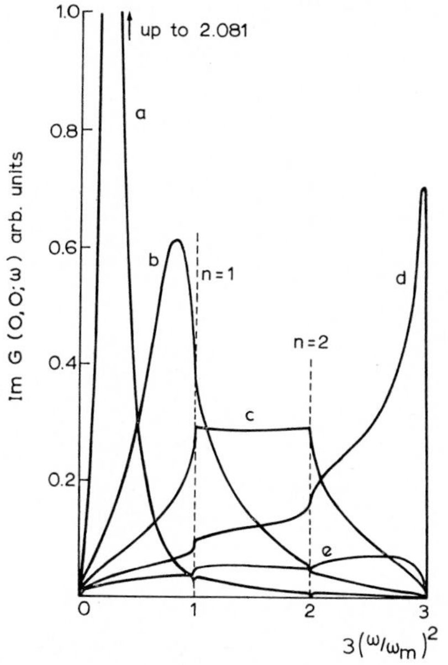

Fig. 2. Resonan mode peaks and the metamorphosis of Van Hove singularities as seen in a simple cubic mass defect Green's function: (a)$\varepsilon=-3$, (b)$\varepsilon=-0.56$, (c)$\varepsilon=0$, (d)$\varepsilon=0.31$, (e)$\varepsilon=0.49$; n labels singularity type (see subsection 4.5) (after Okazaki et al. 1967)

The possibility of such resonances was first realised independently by Brout and Visscher (1962), Kagan and Iosilevskii (1962), and Takeno (1963). It is customary to call them resonant modes (or quasi-localised modes) although it has to be realised that they are not individual normal modes of the crystal.

4.3. Finite concentrations

We must now consider how the above behaviour of the t-matrix is reflected in the Green's function $G_j(\boldsymbol{k}, \omega)$, (3.10). We concentrate on

$\operatorname{Im}\langle G_j(\boldsymbol{k}, \omega)\rangle$ which is related to the correlation function $\boldsymbol{S}(\omega)$ (2.5) and is given by

$$\operatorname{Im}\langle G_j(\boldsymbol{k}, \omega)\rangle = \frac{\operatorname{Im}\Sigma(\omega)}{[\omega^2 - \omega_j^2(\boldsymbol{k}) - \operatorname{Re}\Sigma(\omega)]^2 + [\operatorname{Im}\Sigma(\omega)]^2}.$$

A peak is expected at ω_{p} satisfying

$$p(\omega_{\mathrm{p}}) = \omega_{\mathrm{p}}^2 - \operatorname{Re}\Sigma(\omega_{\mathrm{p}}) = \omega_j^2(\boldsymbol{k}).$$

The function $p(\omega)$ is plotted in fig. 3 where it appears that three peaks may be expected. However, a careful analysis of the kind described above for

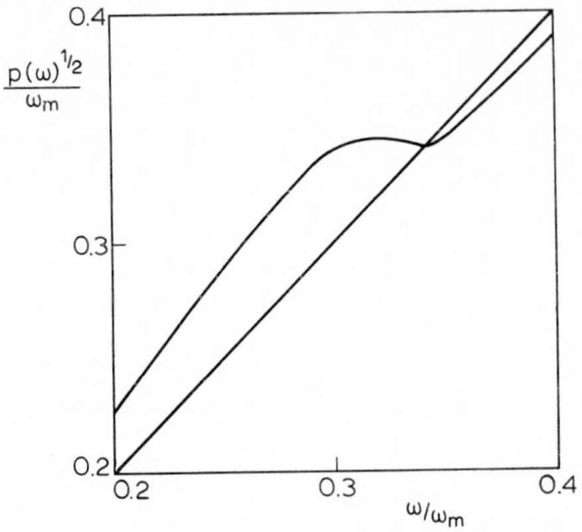

Fig. 3. Graphical solution for occurrence of peaks in the spectral function, see subsection 4.3.

$t(\omega)$ indicates that in the lorenztian approximation the width function for the peak is positive only when

$$\mathrm{d}p(\omega)/\mathrm{d}\omega > 0 \quad \text{at} \quad \omega = \omega_{\mathrm{p}}.$$

Hence we can see that, at the most, only two peaks can be expected, and then only for $\omega_j(\boldsymbol{k})$ very close to the resonant frequency ω_{R} for which $\operatorname{Re} t(\omega)$ and hence Re $\Sigma(\omega)$ are zero. At low concentrations ($\lesssim 5\%$) when the amplitude of the variations in Re $\Sigma(\omega)$ is small this structure is not well defined, at most a shoulder appearing at the position of the weaker peak, as illustrated in fig. 4.

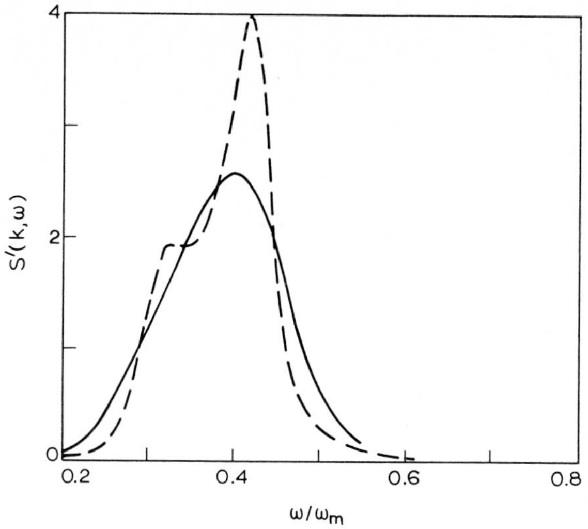

Fig. 4. Spectral function for $\varepsilon=2.1$, $c=0.1$. ——— without resolution, ... resolution broadened by folding with a Gaussian of FWHM$=0.1\omega_m$ (Elliott and Taylor 1967).

On the assumption that $\Sigma(\omega)$ is sufficiently slowly varying this analysis also yields that the dominant peak has been shifted by

$$\Delta(\omega) = [\mathrm{Re}\,\Sigma(\omega)]/2\omega \tag{4.7a}$$

from $\omega_j(\boldsymbol{k})$ and has a full width at half maximum (fwhm) of

$$\Gamma(\omega) = -\,[\mathrm{Im}\,\Sigma(\omega)]/\omega\,. \tag{4.7b}$$

A comparison of determining the shift by (4.7) and examining the peak position shows the error in using (4.7) is fairly small. This point will be considered further in section 8.

A numerical example of this resonant behaviour is shown in fig. 5 for a copper host with $\varepsilon=-2$. The sequence $\nu^0(\omega)$, $M_0\omega^2\,\mathrm{Re}\,G^0(\omega)$, $\Delta(\omega)$ and $\Gamma(\omega)$ shows how the position of a resonance is related to the structure in $\nu^0(\omega)$. Fig. 5 also shows an example of an incipient resonance at $\omega/\omega_m=0.86$ where although $\Delta(\omega)$ does not pass through zero it becomes sufficiently small for a peak to develop in $\Gamma(\omega)$. We see how a resonance can be interpreted as being due to an impurity splitting modes off a region of high density of states into regions of low density of states.

The appearance of a local mode has a different effect on $\mathrm{Im}\langle G_j(\boldsymbol{k},\omega)\rangle$ due to the fact that $G^0(\omega)$ does not have a finite imaginary part for $\omega>\omega_m$.

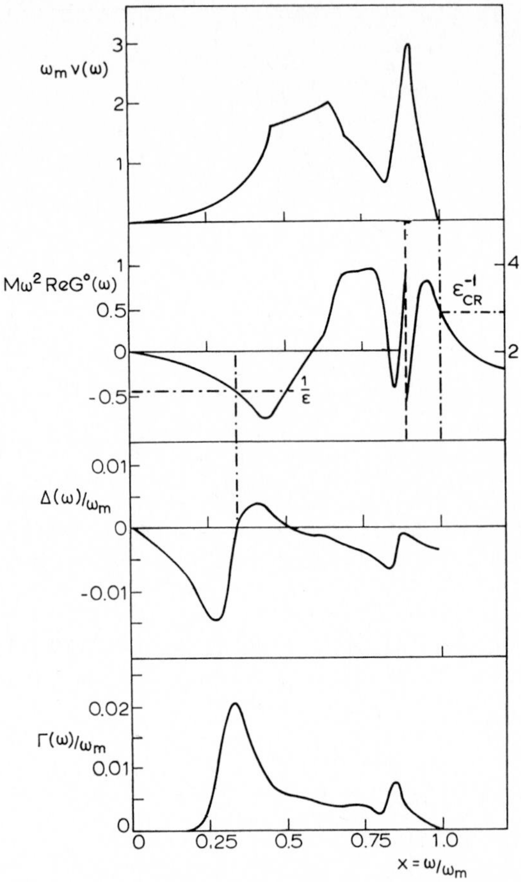

Fig. 5. Relations between the functions $v^0(\omega)$, $\omega^2 \operatorname{Re} G^0(\omega)$, $\Delta(\omega)$, and $\Gamma(\omega)$ for resonant and local modes. Note scale change for $\omega \gtrsim 0.9\omega_m$ for $\omega^2 \operatorname{Re} G^0(\omega)$.

The peak in $\operatorname{Im}\langle G_j(\boldsymbol{k}, \omega)\rangle$ at ω_p is replaced by a delta function and, for very small c, $\operatorname{Im}\langle G_j(\boldsymbol{k}, \omega)\rangle$ can be written as

$$\operatorname{Im}\langle G_j(\boldsymbol{k}, \omega)\rangle = -\frac{c\pi\omega_p\,\delta(\omega - \omega_p)}{2[\omega_p^2 - \omega_j^2(\boldsymbol{k})]^2\, B(\omega_p)}, \tag{4.8}$$

with

$$B(\omega) = \int_0^\infty d\omega'\, \omega'^2 v^0(\omega')/[\omega^2 - \omega'^2]^2 .$$

It can be shown that the position of the delta function relative to the local mode frequency, ω_L, is given by

$$\omega_p - \omega_L = \frac{c\,[\omega_j^2(\boldsymbol{k}) - (1-\varepsilon)\,\omega_L^2]}{2\varepsilon\omega_L B(\omega_L)\,[\omega_L^2 - \omega_j^2(\boldsymbol{k})]}. \tag{4.9}$$

It is here that the $(1-c)$ factor in $X(\omega)$, (3.9c), becomes important. Without it $\Sigma(\omega_L)$ would be divergent with the result that $\omega_p > \omega_L$ for all $\omega_j(\boldsymbol{k})$. As is shown by Elliott and Taylor (1967) this factor has the consequence of shifting the divergence of $\Sigma(\omega)$ such that the range of ω_p now includes ω_L. Thus we have the desirable result that the response at a single frequency ω_L due to one impurity has broadened out to a range whose width is proportional to c.

However, there is a very undesirable property of this result, namely the absence of any width to $\mathrm{Im}\,G_j(\boldsymbol{k}, \omega)$. This absence is contrary to our earlier general expectation that there can be no modes of well defined $\boldsymbol{k}$ in a disordered crystal. Further if $\mathrm{Im}\,G(\omega)$ is constructed by summing $\mathrm{Im}\langle G_j(\boldsymbol{k}, \omega)\rangle$ $(\boldsymbol{k}, j)$ then we have the inconsistency that there is a width to the density of states but not to an individual spectral function. It was one of the motivations behind the development of the CPA discussed in ch. 6, to remove this inconsistency.

In optical absorption studies it is just $G_{TO}(\omega)$, (4.3) that is of interest. It is common to use the approximation (3.8) which gives

$$\mathrm{Im}\langle G_{TO}(\omega)\rangle = (\pi/2\omega)\,\delta(\omega - \omega_{TO}) + \frac{cm(2)\,\mathrm{Im}\,t(1,\omega)}{M_0(1)\,[\omega^2 - \omega_{TO}^2]^2}. \tag{4.10}$$

The single site approximation, however, gives

$$\mathrm{Im}\langle G_{TO}(\omega)\rangle = \frac{\mathrm{Im}\,\Sigma_{TO}(\omega)}{[\omega^2 - \omega_{TO}^2 - \mathrm{Re}\,\Sigma_{TO}(\omega)]^2 + [\mathrm{Im}\,\Sigma_{TO}(\omega)]^2}.$$

If the concentration is very low, say $c < 0.01$ as is common in optical absorption studies, then for ω well away from ω_{TO} this reduces to

$$\mathrm{Im}\langle G_{TO}(\omega)\rangle = [\mathrm{Im}\,\Sigma_{TO}(\omega)]/(\omega^2 - \omega_{TO}^2)^2.$$

Neglecting the factor of c in the denominator in (4.3b) this is then identical to the second term in (4.10). Thus, (4.10) is only in error in not shifting ω_{TO}.

4.4. Short-range order

The inclusion of S.R.O. via $\rho(l'|l)$, as described after eq. (3.7), can be carried through in the single site approximation. As this approximation neglects the coherent scattering off cluster of impurities, building in S.R.O. is somewhat inconsistent. However, its inclusion may be viewed as at least modifying the average concentration of impurities around a given impurity.

Introducing the Warren S.R.O. parameter $\alpha(l', l)$.(see, for instance, Cowley 1950) via

$$\rho(l'|l) = c + (1-c)\alpha(l, l'),$$

the self energy (3.10c) becomes for, a cubic Bravais crystal,

$$\Sigma_{\alpha\beta}(\boldsymbol{k}, \omega) = \frac{cM_0\varepsilon\omega^2\delta_{\alpha\beta}}{1-(1-c)\,\varepsilon\omega^2 N^{-1}\sum_{\boldsymbol{q}}\alpha(\boldsymbol{k}-\boldsymbol{q})\,G^0_{\alpha\alpha}(\boldsymbol{q}, \omega)},$$

where

$$\alpha(\boldsymbol{k}) = \sum_{l}\alpha(l', l)\exp(\mathrm{i}\boldsymbol{k}\cdot\boldsymbol{R}_l),$$

and

$$G^0_{\alpha\alpha}(\boldsymbol{k}, \omega) = N^{-1}\sum_{ll'}G_{\alpha\alpha}(l, l')\exp[-\mathrm{i}\boldsymbol{k}\cdot(\boldsymbol{R}_l-\boldsymbol{R}_{l'})].$$

In the absence of S.R.O., $\alpha(l, l')=\delta(l, l')$ and the above reduces to (4.2).

Hartmann (1968) has explored the consequences of this approximation in considerable detail. In particular, he has examined the on-shell phonon shifts in the Debye approximation and found quite noticeable but not dramatic effects, even with rather extreme S.R.O., for $\varepsilon=-2$ and $c=0.093$.

We note that it only appears feasible to carry through this analysis in the mass defect approximation.

4.5. Metamorphosis of critical points

One of the consequences of the use of perturbation theory to calculate $\boldsymbol{G}(\omega)$ is that the Van Hove singularities in $\boldsymbol{G}^0(\omega)$ are preserved, possibly in different forms. This can be seen in fig. 2 where the detailed shape of $\mathrm{Im}\,\boldsymbol{G}(\omega)$ is seen to change as the impurity mass is changed. This behaviour has been discussed by Toyozawa et al. (1967) who called it the metamorphosis of the critical points. Extensive numerical examples are given by Okazaki et al. (1967) from which fig. 2 is taken.

Sumi (1970) has described how this behaviour arises from the interference between the incident and scattered waves from an impurity. Although Sumi describes the general problem involving force constant changes we will illustrate the effect in the mass defect approximation.

The behaviour of $G^0(\omega)$ in the region of a singularity can be written as

$$\begin{aligned} G^0(\omega) - G^0(\omega_n) &= g_n\sqrt{\omega_n^2 - \omega^2}\, \mathrm{e}^{-\mathrm{i}n\pi/2}, \qquad \omega < \omega_n; \\ &= \mathrm{i}g_n\sqrt{\omega^2 - \omega_n^2}\, \mathrm{e}^{-\mathrm{i}n\pi/2}, \qquad \omega > \omega_n; \end{aligned} \tag{4.11}$$

where g_n is a constant and ω_n is the frequency of the singularity. Here $n=0, 1, 2, 3$ labels the ordinary singularities corresponding to minima, saddle points and maxima in the phonon dispersion curves (see for instance Maradudin et al. 1971).

Now from (3.6), (4.4)

$$G(\omega) = G^0(\omega)/[1 - \varepsilon\omega^2 M_0 G^0(\omega)]$$

and we can introduce the phase shift $\eta(\omega)$ (Takeno 1963) so that

$$G(\omega) = \frac{\mathrm{e}^{-\mathrm{i}\eta(\omega)}}{|1 - \varepsilon\omega^2 M_0 G^0(\omega)|}\, G^0(\omega).$$

On substituting (4.11) it can be seen that $G(\omega) - G(\omega_n)$ is given by a very similar expression to (4.11) but with the phase advanced to $\frac{1}{2}n\pi + \eta(\omega)$. This has the consequence of mixing the various kinds of behaviour in the region of a singularity.

For instance for the singularity $n=1$ in fig. 2, as the impurity mass is increased $\eta(\omega)$ moves from the second to third quadrant due to the resonant frequency moving to lower values. However, when the impurity mass is lighter than the host mass, the sign of the scattering potential has changed and $\eta(\omega)$ is in the fourth quadrant. The case of an impurity mass not sufficiently heavy for a resonance so that $\eta(\omega)$ is in the first quadrant, is not shown.

Of course, this singular behaviour can only be expected to be preserved at very low concentrations. Harrington and Walker (1970) have demonstrated how the sharpness is eroded as c increases by examining the infra-red absorption in $CaF_2{:}H^-$. However, some form of self-consistent theory such as CPA (chapter 6), would be required to describe this erosion. We note that

Yacoby and Yust (1972) have indicated how differential techniques applied to the experimental spectra for very low impurity concentrations can be used to extract the precise positions of these singularities.

5. *The inclusion of force constant changes*

5.1. The general method

The introduction of force constant changes associated with an impurity complicates the calculation of the Green's function but does not alter the basic ideas discussed above in connection with a mass defect. This complication arises because of the relatively large size of the impurity space [$=3\times$ (number of neighbours involved + 1)]. Thus the matrix inversion in (3.5) necessary to obtain $\boldsymbol{t}(\omega)$ is no longer trivial. Further, even for a cubic Bravais lattice, $\Sigma_{jj'}(\boldsymbol{k}, \omega)$, (3.10) will not be diagonal in the branch label for general $\boldsymbol{k}$.

The exploitation of the symmetry of the impurity space, via group theory, to facilitate this inversion has been described in many places. The most recent and detailed review is given by Maradudin et al. (1971). The problem is equivalent to diagonalising the hamiltonian of a molecule the size of the impurity space, although here the pure translational and rotational modes are not removed.

Group theory yields the transformation matrix $\psi_\alpha^{(sa\lambda)}(l\kappa)$ that transforms $\boldsymbol{C}^{l_1}(\omega)$ [and $\boldsymbol{G}^0(\omega)$] to its irreducible representations. It is to be understood that $(l\alpha)$ range over just the impurity space associated with the impurity at $(l_1\kappa_1)$. Here λ labels the row of the sth irreducible representations of the point group, G, of the impurity space. The label a allows for the possibility that this representation may appear c_s times (i.e., $a=1,\dots,c_s$).

Although the c_s are not particularly difficult to calculate, the task of determining the ψ can be quite laborious. However, for the common structures, SC, BCC, FCC and diamond, they have been tabulated by Maradudin (1965). Note that the FCC result is in error and a correction has been published by Agrawal (1969). They are also quoted for other structures in some of the references in the following subsections.

The consequence of this transformation is to reduce $\boldsymbol{C}^{l_1}(\omega)$ to block diagonal form

$$\sum_{\substack{l\kappa\alpha\\ l'\kappa'\beta}} \psi_\alpha^{sa\lambda}(l\kappa)\, C_{\alpha\beta}^{l_1}(l\kappa, l'\kappa'; \omega)\, \psi_\beta^{s'b\lambda'}(l'\kappa') = \delta_{ss'}\delta_{\lambda\lambda'} C_{ab}^{s}(\omega). \tag{5.1}$$

The dimensions of the matrices $C^s(\omega)$ are given by c_s and their form naturally depends upon the impurity model chosen. Depending upon the crystal symmetry there may be up to three independent parameters (f_i, $i=1, 2, 3$) required to specify the force constant matrix between two atoms. In describing impurity models it is convenient to take f_L to label the force constant along the interatomic direction and f_{T_1}, f_{T_2} to refer to the constants transverse to this direction [e.g. for the nearest neighbour (nn) force constant in the FCC structure $f_L \equiv 1XX+1XY, f_{T_1}=1XX-1XY, f_{T_2}=1ZZ$]. The corresponding force constant changes are then denoted by Δf_i. To illustrate the size of the remaining problem Table 1 contains a list of the various impurity models that will be discussed in this chapter along with the irreducible representations (i.r.) of their perturbation matrices. As $G^0(\omega)$ has the same point group as $C^{l_1}(\omega)$ it is then relatively simple to solve the matrix equations for $t^s(\omega)$ or $X^s(\omega)$.

One of the consequences of introducing force constant changes is the possibility of resonances and local modes occuring in i.r.'s other than that for which a mass defect resonance might occur (T_{1u} in a cubic system). In

TABLE 1

Defect models and their irreducible representations.

Host structure	Forces changed	Symmetry	Irreducible representations
S.C.	n.n.	O_h	$A_{1g}+E_g+T_{1g}+T_{2g}+3T_{1u}+T_{2u}$
	Δf		$A_{1g}+E_g+2T_{1u}$
	Δf, Δg		$2A_{1g}+2E_g+3T_{1u}$
	Δf, Δg, Δk		$2A_{1g}+2E_g+4T_{1u}$
BCC	n.n	O_h	$A_{1g}+E_g+T_{1g}+2T_{2g}+A_{2u}+E_u+3T_{1u}+T_{2u}$
	n.n. and n.n.n.		$2A_{1g}+2E_g+2T_{1g}+3T_{2g}+A_{2u}+E_u+5T_{1u}+2T_{2u}$
FCC	n.n.	O_h	$A_{1g}+A_{2g}+2E_g+2T_{1g}+2T_{2g}+E_u+4T_{1u}+2T_{2u}$
Diamond	n.n. interstitial	T_d	$A_1+E+T_1+3T_2$
Fluorite	cation site	O_h	as for BCC n.n.
	anion site		$A_1+E+T_1+2T_2$
Rutile	cation Δf	D_{2h}	$3A_{1g}+2B_{1g}+2B_{2g}+2B_{3g}+A_{1u}+4B_{1u}+3B_{2u}+4B_{3u}$
	anion Δf	C_{1h}	$7A'+5A''$
FCC.	n.n. pair	D_{2h}	$A_{1g}+B_{2g}+B_{3g}+B_{1u}+B_{2u}+B_{3u}$
NaCl	model I pair	D_{2h}	$2A_{1g}+2B_{1g}+B_{2g}+B_{3g}+2B_{1u}+2B_{2u}+2B_{3u}$
	model II pair	D_{4h}	$A_{1g}+E_g+2A_{2u}+2E_u$
Diamond	dissimilar n.n. pair	C_{3v}	$2A_1+2E$
	n.n. pair	D_{3d}	$A_{1g}+E_g+A_{1u}+E_u$
	Interstitial Impurity	C_{3v}	$5A_1+A_2+6E$
Zinc blende	Vacancy/Impurity	C_{2v}	$6A_1+2A_2+8E$

the presence of force constant changes the usual criteria for the occurrence of either local or resonance modes is the generalisation of (4.6)

$$\mathrm{Re}\det\left[\boldsymbol{I}-\boldsymbol{C}^{l}(\omega)\boldsymbol{G}^{0}(\omega)\right]^{s}=0. \tag{5.2}$$

There is ample evidence from optical absorption experiments for (5.2) to be satisfied in several i.r.'s in a given material (see subsection 7.3).

A detailed description of the resonant mode behaviour on lines following that for the mass defect in section 4 is only possible for those representations for which $c_s=1$ (see, however, Klein 1968). Maradudin (1971) has discussed such cases in a manner very similar to our mass defect discussion.

In the use of the one impurity result, (3.6), or the linear result (3.8), for calculating infra-red, Raman and sideband absorption only specific irreducible representations are required (see section 7 for details). In these cases, having evaluated the t-matrix and hence the Green's functions in the i.r.'s, the calculation is essentially complete although there may remain difficulties with coupling constants. However, to calculate the self energy, $\Sigma_{jj'}(\boldsymbol{k},\omega)$ it is necessary to transform back from these i.r.'s to the real lattice space $(l\kappa\alpha)$ using the matrix introduced above and then to the $(\boldsymbol{k}j)$ representation as indicated in (3.10). Although in general $\Sigma(\omega)$ is not diagonal on j, j', it has to be for those cases where the eigenvectors $\boldsymbol{w}(\kappa|\boldsymbol{k}j)$ are determined completely by symmetry. This occurs, for instance, for $\boldsymbol{k}$ along symmetry directions in Bravais lattices. The effects of impurities on the lattice dynamics can then be discussed, approximately, by examining the on shell behaviour of the self energy using a generalisation of (4.7).

$$\Delta(\boldsymbol{k}j)=\frac{\mathrm{Re}\,\Sigma_{jj}(\boldsymbol{k};\omega_j(\boldsymbol{k}))}{2\omega_j(k)},\qquad \Gamma(j\boldsymbol{k})=\frac{\mathrm{Im}\,\Sigma_{jj}(\boldsymbol{k},\omega_j(\boldsymbol{k}))}{\omega_j(\boldsymbol{k})}. \tag{5.3}$$

Otherwise it is necessary to calculate the full expression for the experimental quantity of interest (e.g. neutron scattering cross section) although it may turn out on investigation that the off diagonal parts of $\Sigma(\omega)$ are not significant. However some preliminary investigations by Bruno (unpublished) indicate that this is not the case in the alkali halides (note the branch mixing in the mass defect discussion given above).

5.2. Nearest neighbour force models

Before describing the more general impurity models it is worth considering a set of nearest neighbour models that lead to a very simple result. It is clear from the above that many different independent elements of $\boldsymbol{G}^0(\omega)$ feature in general calculations. However if only n.n. force constants are used to describe both the host and defect lattice dynamics then the equation of motion (2.8) for $\boldsymbol{G}^0(\omega)$ enables sufficient relations to be generated between the elements of $\boldsymbol{G}^0(\omega)$ such that the Green's function for a single impurity can be written in terms of just $G^0_{\alpha\alpha}(0, 0, \omega)$.

This has been realised by several authors. For the case of isotropic force constants ($f_L = f_T = f$) the manipulations were carried through by Patnaik and Mahanty (1967) and when further simplified give

$$M_0\,\omega_m^2\,G_{\alpha\alpha}(0,0;\omega) = \frac{F + (1 - x^2F)\,M_0\,\omega_m^2\,G^0_{\alpha\alpha}(0,0;\omega)}{1 + (1-\varepsilon)\,x^2F - [\varepsilon + (1-\varepsilon)\,x^2F]\,M_0\,\omega^2\,G^0_{\alpha\alpha}(0,0;\omega)}, \tag{5.4}$$

with

$$F = 2r\Delta f/(f + \Delta f), \qquad x = \omega/\omega_m.$$

$r = 1$ corresponds to SC and BCC and $r = 3/2$ to FCC. For the case of just longitudinal forces ($f_1 = f, f_2 = f_3 = 0$) this same result was found by Mannheim (1968) [see also Mannheim and Cohen (1971) for corrections] with $r = 1$ for both BCC and FCC. The denominator of (5.4) was also obtained by Sievers and Takeno (1965).

Finally if M_0, ω_m^2 and $G^0_{\alpha\alpha}(0, 0, \omega)$ are replaced by $M(1)$, $6f/M(1)$ and $G^0_{\alpha\alpha}(01, 01; \omega)$ then (5.4) corresponds to the result of Takeno (1967) for an impurity on sublattice $\kappa = 1$ in the NaCl lattice.

Although the models of Patnaik and Mahanty (1967) and of Takeno (1967) are not really suitable for detailed comparison with experiment, that of Mannheim (1968) is a good approximation for impurities in solid rare gases (and in some metals). Its use is mentioned in subsection 7.2

5.3. Cubic monatomic hosts

The results of carrying through the procedures outlined in subsection 5.1 are given by Lakatos and Krumhansl (1968) for both the FCC and BCC structures. In the latter case both nearest and next nearest neighbours force constant changes were considered.

These authors also performed a numerical investigation of the effects of force constant changes on resonances by examining the behaviour of the resonant peak in $\operatorname{Im} G_{\alpha\alpha}(0, 0; \omega)$ for a single impurity at the origin. They only considered the FCC structure taking aluminium as the host material confining themselves largely to just changes in the longitudinal force constant. In a subsequent paper (Lakatos and Krumhansl 1969) they extended their investigation to $\Sigma_{jj}(\boldsymbol{k}, \omega)$ finding in particular that the resonant frequency $\omega_R = \omega_j(\boldsymbol{k})$, suchthat $\Delta(\boldsymbol{k}j) = 0$, lies slightly higher than that given by the peak in the Green's function.

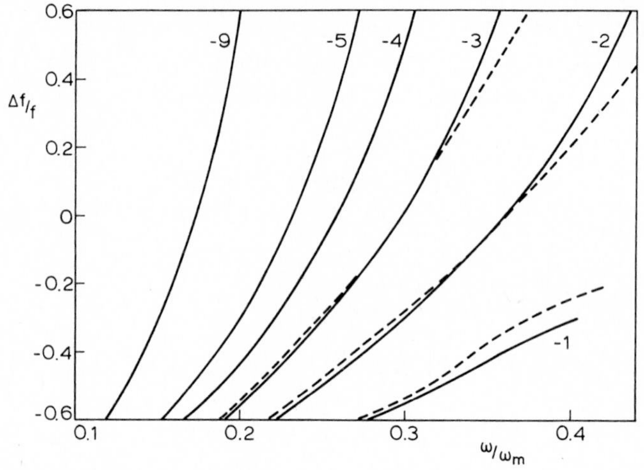

Fig. 6. Relation between the resonant frequency and longitudinal force constant change for several values of ε with Cu as as host. ——— T [00ζ] branch, ----- T_1 [0ζζ] branch.

However they did not examine the systematics of this definition of ω_R. This we do in fig. 6 for different values of ε and Δf_L taking copper as host material. The general behaviour is readily understood. That the slope is steeper for larger impurity masses merely reflects the dominance of the mass change over the force constant change. It can also be seen that weakening the force constants can cause the appearance of a resonance that would not occur in the presence of just a mass change.

The behaviour of the local mode frequency, ω_L, as a function of ε and $\Delta f/f$ has been investigated by Martin (1967a) for the FCC structure using only nearest neighbour longitudinal forces. In fig. 7 we show an equivalent result taking copper as host.

The examples quoted above and the experiments to be discussed in section 8 all refer to metallic alloys involving transition metals. As there appears to be no good microscopic theories for transition metal phonons all our discussions are in terms of the Born – von Karman model. In any case the interaction of electrons and phonons in alloys is problematic.

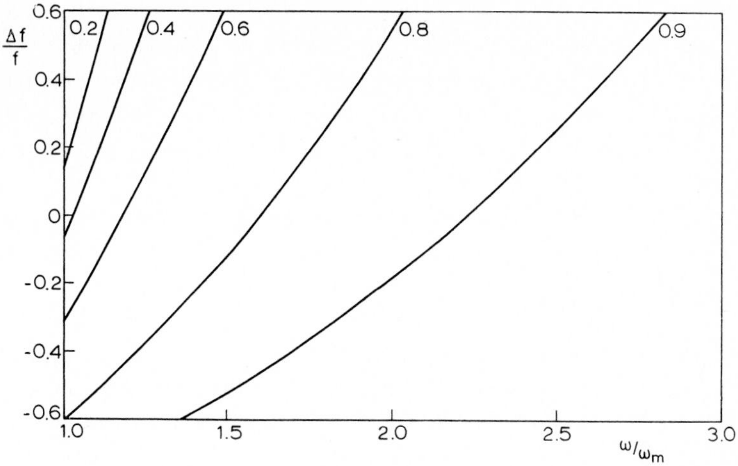

Fig. 7. Relation between the local mode frequency and longitudinal force constant change for several values of ε with Cu as host.

5.4. Diatomic cubic hosts

For an impurity in an alkali halide for which only $f=f_L$ is changed the results of the *t*-matrix inversion, for all the i.r.'s, have been given by Sennett (1965), Klein (1966) and Benedek and Nardelli (1967). The latter authors carry the calculations right through to the use of the finite concentration Green's function (3.9) to calculate the optical absorption. As a numerical example they took KBr as host material using the deformation dipole model (Karo and Hardy 1963) to calculate the unperturbed Green's functions. Subsequently, (Benedek and Nardelli 1968), they have applied their results to a whole sequence of alkali halides, in particular, investigating the depence of the T_{1u} resonance on ε and Δf. However they show the relation between ε and Δf_L for a series of given resonant frequencies. Mitani and Takeno (1965) do plot ω_L against ε and Δf_L, but only for a n.n. force constant model of the host crystal phonons. Grim et al. (1972) present results for ω_R and ω_L that are appropriate to GaAs. The only such plot for when Coulomb forces are included is that given by Benedek and Maradudin (1968) for the gap mode due to Cl isotopes in KI.

Other host crystals, besides the alkali halides, have been examined in detail. Agrawal (1969) has given, in copius detail, the *t*-matrix inversion for impurities in diatomic BCC and FCC crystals but gives no numerical results (however, see subsection 7.4 for applications). As we have already mentioned above GaAs has been considered by Grim et al. (1972). The case of the alkaline earth fluorides as host crystals has been spelled out by Lacina and Pershan (1970) whereas Benson (1973) has considered manganese fluoride as host crystal. These latter calculations were all performed in order to compare with experimental results, rather than as general investigations.

As introduced above, Δf refers to a change in the n.n. overlap force constant to which it should be compared in order to appreciate its magnitude (Timusk and Klein 1966). However when it is fitted to experimental results it will also approximate the effects of changes in Coulomb and dipolar forces. Such considerations lead Benedek and Nardelli (1967) to introduce the idea of the effective force constant f^* that in some sense incorporates the nearest neighbour effects of these forces. They introduced two definitions. By analogy with a linear chain they defined

$$f^* = -\Delta f_{\mathrm{L}}(\omega_{\mathrm{R}} = 0), \tag{5.5}$$

with $\Delta f_{\mathrm{L}}(\omega_{\mathrm{R}}=0)$ being that force constant change that makes the T_{1u} resonant frequency go to zero. This can be interpreted as meaning that the system becomes unstable under no net force. They also gave a definition in terms of an effective n.n. force that would reproduce the longitudinal optic frequency and found it had a very similar magnitude to that predicted by (5.5). Benedek and Nardelli (1968b) give extensive tables for f^* in a variety of alkali halides, including its dependence on the interatomic separation. Klein (1968) also discusses the effective force constant, giving a definition appropriate to high frequency local modes as well as pointing out that the definition (5.5) depends upon in which sublattice the impurity sits. Agrawal and Ram (1971, 1972) have given a more elaborate definition of f^* appropriate to all frequencies. Like Klein, they find that f^* tends to be larger when determined at high frequencies. It should be noted that Benedek and Nardelli's definition of f^* differs by a factor of 2 from that of Klein. We will follow Klein.

In fitting the high-resolution experimental results that are now available more elaborate models have become necessary. In order to allow for the effects of the relaxation of atomic positions around an impurity, Gethins et al. (1967) included a longitudinal force constant change, Δg, between the nearest and fourth nearest neighbour atoms, see fig. 8. Benedek and Mulazzi (1969) have described a variant on this relaxation model that relates Δg to the relaxation, ξ, of the n.n. atoms of the impurity via the effective force constant $f^*(r)$. Thus ξ, not Δg, becomes the parameter to be fitted. As might be expected these authors found that local mode frequencies and, to a lesser extent, gap mode frequencies depend mainly on Δf. This enables Δg to be used to fit other aspects of the experimental spectra.

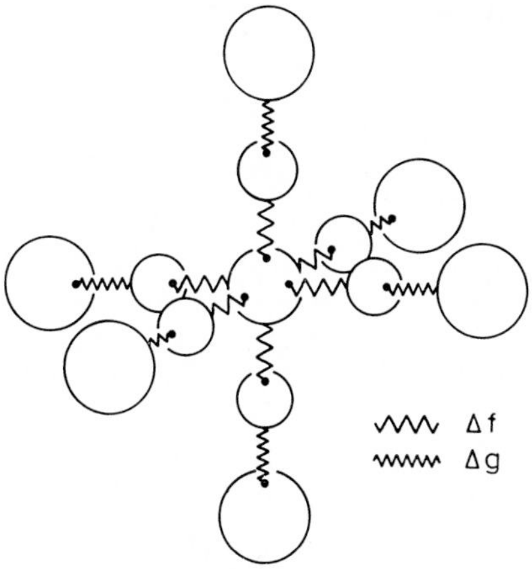

Fig. 8. Relaxation model incorporating Δf and Δg due to Gethins et al. (1967).

It will be noted that Δf_T is not employed in these models. For the alkali halides this is supported by strong evidence for central potentials from the elastic constants. Further, Benedek and Mulazzi (1969), and Page and Dick (1967) found that the experimental spectra were insensitive to Δf_T. It is rather different for the cesium halides where Δf_T is used rather extensively. In most other impurity systems only the use of Δf is warranted, as we will see in section 7.4.

When shell models (see ch. 3, vol. 1) are used for the host crystal lattice dynamics most authors relate Δf and Δg to the shell–shell force constant. However, once the shell model is introduced more extensive changes suggest themselves. Page and Strauch (1967, 1968), in the context of the U centre, have considered the impurity core–shell force constant change, Δk. Further they have shown how to include the potentially longrange effects due to changes in the core and shell charges within the general theory of short-range force constant changes described in this chapter. It was found that the local mode frequencies depend strongly on Δk as well as Δf so that fitting these frequencies leads to just a relation between Δf and Δk. This flexibility along with the remaining parameter, Δg, allows good fits to experiment (see subsection 7.3).

This additional parameter, Δk has also been found useful by Bilz et al. (1966), and MacPherson and Timusk (1970) again for the U centre in alkali halides. The latter authors describe the algebraic results in some detail. However, Δk has not been used for other impurities, presumably because the differences in polarizability between host and impurity ions are only of significance in the case of the U centre.

TABLE 2

Representation dependence of fitted force constants

	Force constant changes in 10^4 dyne cm^{-1}			
	T_{1u}	A_{1g}	E_g	T_{2g} (transverse Δf)
$NaCl:Ag^+$ (a) Δf	−0.50	0.59	−0.75	−0.08
Δg	−0.10	0.0	−0.16	0.0
$NaCl:Ca^{2+}$ (b) Δf	–	4.80	2.22	0.0
		1.36		
NaCl f^*	1.58(c)	4.62(a)	2.89(a)	3.57(b)
		4.0(b)	2.77(b)	
$KCl:Tl^+$ (d) Δf	–	–	0.12	0.0
$KBr:Tl^+$ Δf	0.80(e)	–	0.0(d)	0.0(d)
	−0.20(f)			
$KI:Tl^+$ Δf	−0.37(f)	–	0.0(d)	0.0(d)
$RbCl:Tl^+$ (d) Δf	–	–	−0.11	0.0

a) Montgomery et al. (1972b).
b) Kaiser et al. (1973).
c) Klein (1968).
d) Harley et al. (1971)
e) Ward and Timusk (1972).
f) Benedek and Terzi (1973).

Recent experimental results for $NaCl:Ag^+$ by Montgomery et al. (1972b) have shown that the relaxation model is insufficient to account for the infra-red absorption and the first-order Raman scattering results. They found it necessary to use substantially different Δf and Δg for different irreducible representations as is shown in table 2. Similar results due to Kaiser et al. (1973) and Harley et al. (1971) are also included. On the introduction of different irreducible representations the use of the T_{1u} representation to define f^* is no longer appropriate. Instead (5.5) has to be applied to each representation in turn leading to rather different values of f^* as can be seen in table 2.

Montgomery et al. (1972b) point out that this representation dependence arises, at least, from the Coulomb forces. As was pointed out above, the relaxation model of Gethins et al. (1967) ignores any effect that relaxation may have on the Coulomb force constants. This problem has been followed up by Mostoller and Wood (1973) who considered the system NaCl:Ag^+ using Coulomb, Van der Waals and Born-Mayer potentials, taking the parameters from the pure crystal data for NaCl and AgCl. They determined the force constants and the atomic relaxation in a self-consistent manner and were able to reproduce the E_g contribution to the Raman scattering quite well but not that due to the A_{1g} representation. Their inclusion of second nearest neighbour forces means that it is not possible to extract representation dependent Δf and Δg from the calculations for comparison with the fitted values of Montgomery et al. (1972b).

Other attempts to calculate force constant changes have not explored this representation dependence. Rather they aimed at estimates for Δf (and occasionally Δg). Calswell and Klein (1967) give estimates for Δf for several impurities in NaCl using the effective force constant of Benedek and Nardelli (1967), with $f^*(r)$ between the impurity and host atoms being determined from the appropriate pure crystal data. The comparison with the fitted values of MacDonald et al. (1969) in table 3 shows that the estimates are qualitatively reasonable. The results of Benedek and Nardelli (1968b) for impurities in KCl, also shown in table 3, were not so successful. Benedek and Terzi (1973), making rather crude estimates for the atomic relaxation were, also, not very successful in determining Δf and Δg. Estimates for force constant changes have also been made by Singh and Mitra (1972) and Mitra and Singh (1973) ignoring any relaxation. We refer to their work again at the end of subsection 5.7.

TABLE 3

Comparison between fitted and calculated force constant changes

	NaCl			KCl		
	$\Delta f/f^*$		$\xi(\%)$	$\Delta f/f^*$		$\xi(\%)$ (d)
	Fitted[(a)]	Cal.[(b)]	(b)	Fitted[(c)]	Cal.[(d)]	
Na^+				−0.04	−0.59	−4.0
K^+	0.19	0.52	6.5			
F^-	−0.91	−0.61	−6.5	−0.80	−0.75	−5.1
Br^-	0.04	0.33	2.5	−0.22	0.26	2.0
I^-	0.20	0.80	6.2	−0.22	0.30	6.0

a) MacDonald et al. (1969).
b) Caldwell and Klein (1967).
c) Ward and Timusk (1972).
d) Benedek and Nardelli (1968b).

The only quantum-mechanical calculations of force constant changes have been for hydrogen impurities. Wood and Gilbert (1967) were able to obtain good agreement with experiment for the local mode frequencies of U centres in KCl, KBr and KI. As the local mode frequency ω_L is at least twice the host lattice frequency they assumed just the impurity to be moving and so made a direct calculation of ω_L due to just nearest neighbour interactions. The relaxation of these nearest neighbours was taken into account in determining these interactions and they found that inclusion of the H^- ion polarizability to be important in obtaining this agreement. Good agreement with the experimental local mode frequency was obtained in a similar manner for an interstitial hydrogen atom in CaF_2 by Hartmann et al. (1970b). They found it important to make corrections for the motion of the nearest neighbour F^- ions but did not take into account any relaxation of these ions from their unperturbed positions.

One way to attempt to make sense of fitted force constants is to examine the ratio of the size of the impurity ion to that of the host ion it replaces. We will call this ratio R and include it in most of the following tables taking the ion sizes from Pauling (1960). It is expected that for $R>1$ the overlap forces are stronger leading to $\Delta f>0$ and vice versa. This is a rather simplified argument and, as we will see, is not always satisfied. Further it cannot be expected to be valid when the nature of the ions is considerably different (e.g. different valence, transition-metal ion for alkali ion).

5.5. Interstitial impurities

So far we have not considered an interstitial impurity. This particular defect requires an extension of the methods used above for a single substitutional impurity. As described by Brice (1965) (see also Izyumov et al. 1969) it is necessary to extend the pure crystal Green's function $\boldsymbol{G}^0(\omega)$ to include a term for the completely decoupled interstitial

$$\boldsymbol{G}^0(\omega)' = \boldsymbol{Q}\boldsymbol{G}^0(\omega)\boldsymbol{Q} + \frac{1}{M\omega^2}\boldsymbol{P},$$

where $\boldsymbol{Q}=\boldsymbol{I}-\boldsymbol{P}$ and $\boldsymbol{P}$ projects onto just the interstitial coordinate space.

The impurity matrix $C(\omega)$ has to be suitably augmented to include the interaction of the interstitial to the rest of the crystal. This interaction has to be parameterised and in principle fitted to experiment. This does not appear to have been done but Brice (1965) and later Elliott and Pfeuty (1967) with an improved $\boldsymbol{G}^0(\omega)$ have given graphs showing the behaviour of interstitial resonant and local modes as a function of these parameters. It is also to be noted that Bellomonte and Pryce (1966) attempted to estimate the coupling of the interstitial Li^+ in Si using tight binding theory.

Blaesser et al. (1968) have described a rather different technique that uses many body theory to couple the interstitial modes to the host crystal phonons. The generalisation of this method to a finite concentration of interstitials is discussed by Vanamu (1972) whereas Murtazin (1971) has generalised the more conventional method described above. However, no numerical results have been presented.

5.6. Impurity clusters

As mentioned in subsection 3.3 the effects of clusters of impurities are not readily incorporated in the general theory of finite impurity concentrations when force constant changes are considered. However, the behaviour of a given cluster in an otherwise pure crystal is readily calculated. The perturbation matrix $C(\omega)$ has to be enlarged to cover the impurity space of the whole cluster and then the t-matrix inversion is handled by the method described in subsection 5.1.

Takeno (1962, 1965) has described the behaviour of a mass defect pair in an idealised model of a simple cubic lattice. In particular he showed how the 6-fold degenerate local mode is split into two three-fold degenerate modes whose frequency splitting depends upon the separation of the pair of impurity atoms. A linear cluster of three impurities was also considered. Subsequently, Martin (1967b) has examined a nearest neighbour pair of impurity atoms in a FCC lattice, as is shown in fig. 9. The local mode in this case is split into 6 non-degenerate modes of symmetry $A_{1\mathrm{g}}$, $B_{2\mathrm{u}}$, $B_{3\mathrm{u}}$, $B_{2\mathrm{g}}$, $B_{3\mathrm{g}}$, $B_{1\mathrm{u}}$. Martin also investigated the resonant mode absorption due to a pair. His result, which is a combination of the odd representation of Green's functions, is compared in fig. 10 with that due to isolated impurities for $\varepsilon=-1$. The pair resonant peak is somewhat broader, indicating unresolved splitting, and shifted to lower frequencies. The generalisation to a diatomic host crystal has been given by Striefler and Jaswal (1969) for pairs in mixed LiH–LiD crystals.

The inclusion of force constant changes has been investigated by Elliott and Pfeuty (1967) for a pair of nearest neighbour impurity atoms in Si. Just the force constant between the impurities was changed. These authors further examined the local modes of a cluster comprising a B atom and an

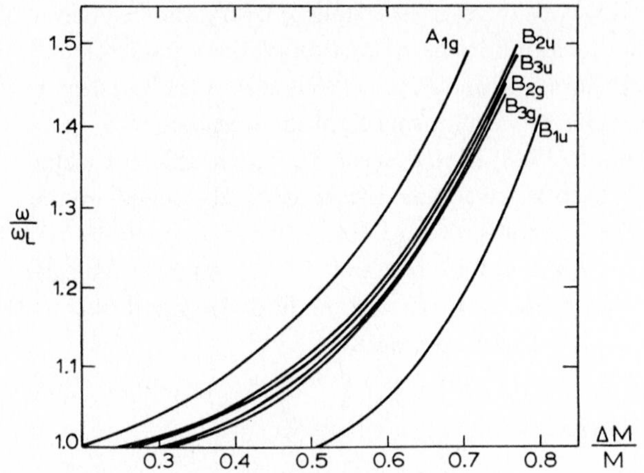

Fig. 9. Relation between local mode frequencies and impurity mass for n.n. pair in an FCC crystal (Martin 1967b).

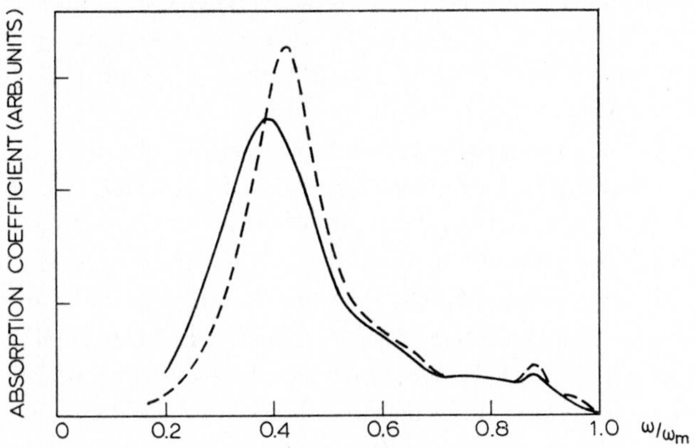

Fig. 10. Absorption due to a pair of heavy impurities ($\varepsilon=-1$) in an FCC crystal. ——— n.n. pair, ----- well separated pair (after Martin 1967b).

adjacent interstitial ion, again in Si. In the latter case they were able to make a good comparison with experiment. We note that Thompson and Newman (1972) made use of these results in discussing B and Si pair clusters in GaAs.

In the insulators when an impurity atom of a different valency is added there is usually an accompanying charge compensating vacancy. The dynamics of an impurity–vacancy pair have been investigated by two sets of authors. Kuhner and Wagner (1970) have examined the case of a Sm^{2+} ion in KBr using the model shown in fig. 11. This is an elaboration of a previous model due to Wagner and Bron (1965). It seems rather incomplete, omitting any force constant changes out of the plane shown and not setting to zero the force constants between the vacancy and its nearest neighbours not shown in the diagram. However the result of the calculation for the vibronic

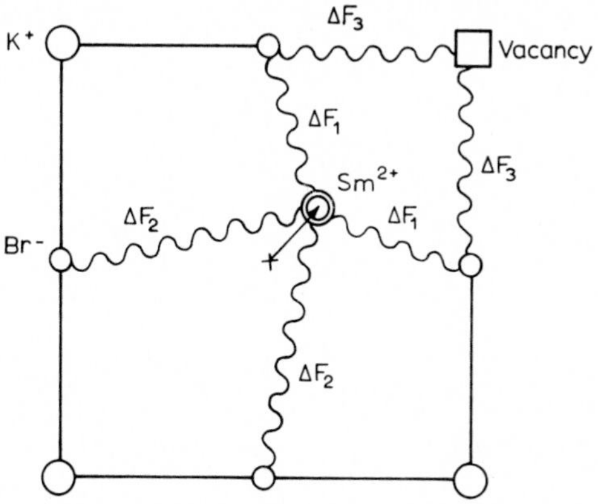

Fig. 11. Sm^{2+}/vacancy model of Kuhner and Wagner (1970).

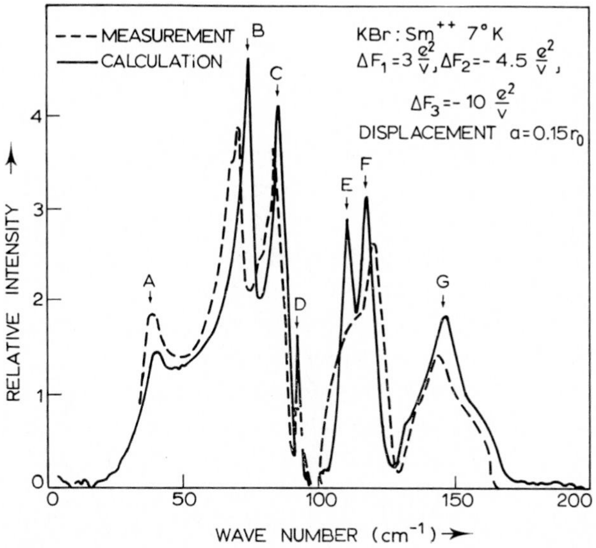

Fig. 12. Side band of Sm^{2+} in KBr; ----- calculation of Kuhner and Wagner (1970), ——— experiment (Timusk and Buchanan 1967), $e^2/v = 0.25 f^*$.

sideband (see section 7) is in very good agreement with experiment, as can be seen in fig. 12. Moreover it does constitute an improvement over the calculation of Buchanan and Woll (1969) who used Δf and Δg but no vacancy.

Grim et al. (1973) have considered a vacancy that is nearest neighbour to Cu substituting for Ga in GaAs but using an impurity space comprising of the vacancy site, the Cu site and all their nearest neighbour sites. They also described an approximate calculation for a cluster containing two Cu atoms and a vacancy.

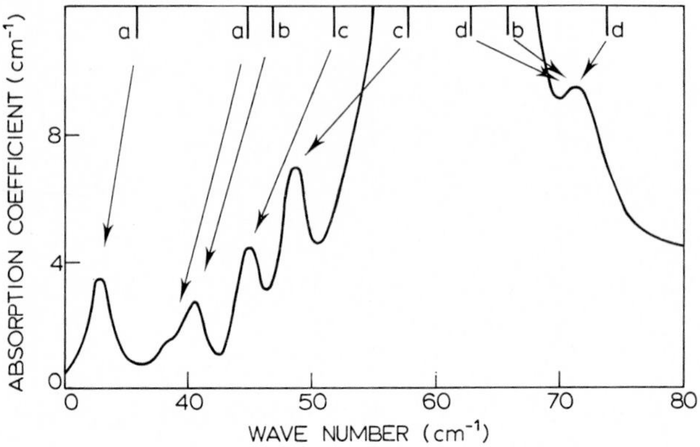

Fig. 13. F^- ion pair absorption in NaCl (Becker and Martin 1972). Bars indicate the calculated frequencies of Haridasan et al. (1973a) with suggested assignments indicated; (a) E_u, (b) B_{3u}, (c) B_{1u}, (d) A_{2u} (c=0.018).

Haridasan et al. (1973a) have presented a calculation for the low frequency resonant modes due to F^- ion pairs as seen by Becker and Martin (1972) and shown in fig. 13. The pairs were assumed to be either next n.n. (model I) or fourth n.n. (model II) and, because the experimental resonances are narrow, they ignore the motion of ions other than the F^- ions and their common nearest neighbours. The numerical results and suggested assignments are also indicated in fig. 13. Considering that they only fitted to the F^- single ion resonance at 59.5 cm^{-1} the agreement is quite promising. They have also applied this model to H^- ion pairs in KCl (Haridasan et al. 1973b) and obtained similar agreement with experiment (de Sousa et al. 1970).

Jaswal (1966, 1972) has examined clusters within the molecular model (see subsection 5.7). His initial calculation was for U centres in mixed alkali halides, where subsidiary structure appears along side the local mode frequency. Later he examined a Na^+ ion pair in KCl for comparison with the work of Templeton and Clayman (1971). However he predicts a rather large value for Δf that is inconsistent with that used by Ward and Timusk (1972) to fit the far infra-red absorption (see subsection 7.3).

We note that Haridasan et al. (1973a) reference a series of experimental papers for which no detailed calculations have been performed.

5.7. Approximate methods

When the defect space becomes very large the above analysis becomes intractable and approximations are needed. If the perturbation can be separated into a part that is strong and localised around the impurity and another that is weak and of long range then some form of perturbation expansion may be applied to the latter.

One such approach is described by Oitmaa and Maradudin (1969) who expand the equation of motion in terms of the host crystal eigenvectors for only one impurity in the crystal. They then apply the Fredholm method to the resulting integral equation and use their results to investigate the behaviour of local modes frequencies in a one-dimensional chain. Oitmaa (1970) has extended the calculation to resonant modes and finds that their frequencies are much more sensitive to the range of the perturbation than are the local mode frequencies. Other approximations have been described by Izyumov (1965), Croitoru and Grecu (1970), Bryksin and Firsov (1970) and Litzman and coworkers [see Litzman and Rosa (1973) and references therein].

The difficulty of separating the impurity spaces for a long range perturbation makes it impossible to apply the above approximations in the multiple scattering theory of section 3. However, Bruno (1973) has suggested an approach that would include the long range effects within an effective host lattice and apply the conventional t-matrix approach to the remaining short range perturbation. This is also the approach suggested in subsections 2.2, 3.1 for the inclusion of the effects of the volume change on adding impurities.

Bruno and Taylor (1972) have described a direct expansion of $\boldsymbol{X}^l(\omega)$ (3.9) for the situation where the mass difference dominates the effects of the force constant changes. However, their interest was in reducing the computation time needed when $\boldsymbol{X}^l(\omega)$ is used to calculate $\Sigma(\omega)$ and hence $\langle \boldsymbol{G}(\omega) \rangle$ via (3.9).

The molecular model, as introduced by Jaswal (1965b), is a different type of approximation. This involves solving the equations of motion for just the impurity and its neighbours with the rest of the lattice assumed stationary. However, it does include the long range force constant due to the interactions between the stationary atoms and those in the ‘molecule’. It has the advantage of allowing for the inclusion of complicated effects such as long range changes and anharmonicity. On the other hand it only yields the frequencies of local and gap modes and, possibly, highly localised resonant modes and is valid only when the disturbance due to the mode is well localised. This is certainly the case for the U centre for which Jaswal introduced the model. He found very good agreement between the model predictions for the mass defect local modes and those from the Green’s function method (Jaswal and Montgomery 1964).

As in the Green’s function methods described earlier it is usual to adjust the force constant parameters to the experimental data. This is the procedure adopted by Jaswal (1965b) and Singh and Mitra (1970) for the alkali halides, Krishnamurthy (1966) for $CsI:H^-$ and Krishnamurthy and Haridasan (1966) for the zinc blende structure. Singh and Mitra (1972) have estimated the force constant changes by examining the appropriate pure crystal force constants, an idea very similar to the procedure of Caldwell and Klein (1967), as discussed in subsection 5.4. However Singh and Mitra ignored any possible relaxation around the impurity. Their calculations were quite successful for the III–V compounds and they have recently had a similar success for the alkali halides (Mitra and Singh 1973).

6. *Range of impurity disturbance*

As mentioned in subsection 3.4 no higher order approximations have been investigated numerically. However some feel for the validity of the single site approximation can be had by examining the range of disturbance around an isolated impurity. This can be done by examing $\langle \boldsymbol{u}^2(l)\rangle$ for several of the neighbours of a mass defect at the origin. Using (2.5) it is readily found that

$$\langle \boldsymbol{u}^2(l)\rangle = -(\hbar/\pi)\int_0^\infty \coth(\tfrac{1}{2}\beta\omega)\sum_\alpha \operatorname{Im} G_{\alpha\alpha}(l,l;\omega)\,\mathrm{d}\omega\,.$$

Comparisons between $\operatorname{Im} G_{xx}(l,l;\omega)$ and $\operatorname{Im} G^0_{xx}(l,l;\omega)$ for $l=0$ and $l=1$ (nearest neighbour) in an FCC crystal are shown for $\varepsilon=-2$ (Au) in fig. 14 and for $\varepsilon=0.57$ (Al) in fig. 15. The small difference at $l=1$ is remarkable. In table 4 we list the root mean square displacements at 50 K for some of the near neighbours which further emphasises the rapid fall off of the disturbance due to the presence of the impurity. The motion at the local

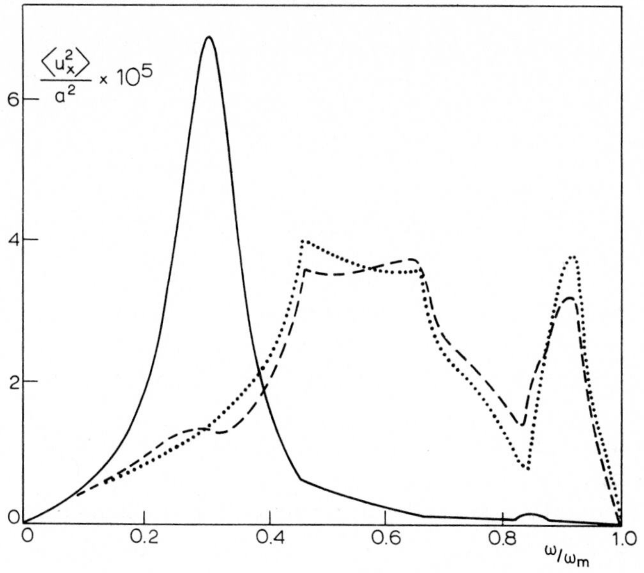

Fig. 14. $\langle u_x^2 \rangle / a^2$ for Cu as host as a function of ω/ω_m for $\varepsilon = -2$; ——— impurity atom, ----- n.n. atom, ... unperturbed atom.

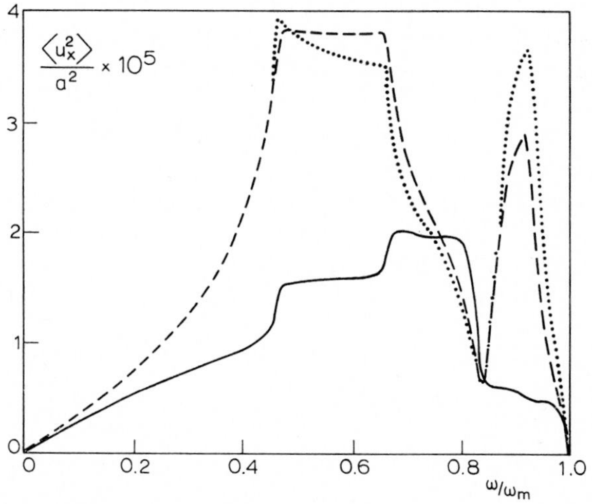

Fig. 15. $\langle u^2 \rangle / a^2$ for Cu as host as a function of ω/ω_m for $\varepsilon = 0.57$; ——— impurity atom, ----- n.n. atom, ... unperturbed crystal.

TABLE 4

Root mean square displacements in terms of the lattice constant at 50 K. Unperturbed value = −0.02225.

Lattice site	$\varepsilon=-2.1$	$\varepsilon=0.575$		
		Inband	Local mode	Total
000	0.01881	0.01736	0.01925	0.02592
110	0.02221	0.02215	0.00206	0.02224
200	0.02222	0.02223	0.00015	0.02223
211	0.02223	0.02224	0.00023	0.02224
220	0.02222	0.02222	0.00034	0.02223

mode frequency is seen to decay very rapidly away from the impurity. Calculations out to more distant neighbours by Takeno (1962) and Mozer (1968) support the exponential decay found by Maradudin (1963) in an asymptotic analysis.

Lakatos and Krumhansl (1968) have also investigated $\operatorname{Im} G_{\alpha\alpha}(l, l; \omega)$ for non-zero Δf. In fig. 16 we show their result for Mn in Al ($\varepsilon=-1$, $\alpha=x$, $l=1$, $\Delta f_L/f_L=-0.7$). The major effect due to $\Delta f_L \neq 0$ is the increase in size of the structure at 3 THz, there being very little difference for $\Delta f_L=0$ (not shown). This is characteristic of their other results in that the differences at low frequencies are enhanced as ω_R is reduced.

These results would seem to imply that the single site approximation should not be too serious providing that, on the average no impurity has

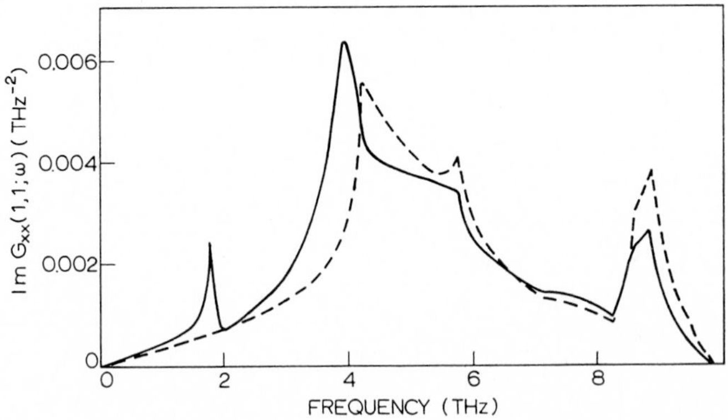

Fig. 16. n.n. Green's function as a function of frequency for $\varepsilon=-1.03$, $\Delta f_L/f_L=-0.7$; ——— n.n. atom, ----- unperturbed atom (after Lakatos and Krumhansl 1968).

another impurity as nearest neighbour. This leads to $c<0.08, 0.06$ for the BCC and FCC structures. The more stringent condition based on nearest neighbour impurity spaces barely overlapping leads to upper limits of 0.019 and 0.016. Note that we have shown the effect of a nearest neighbour mass defect impurity on the resonant peak of $\mathrm{Im}\,\boldsymbol{G}(\omega)$ in fig. 10. Further as mentioned in subsection 5.6, Takeno (1965) has investigated the splitting of the mass defect local mode due to a neighbouring impurity. Although he finds that the splitting is quite strong for a nearest neighbour impurity in a SC lattice, it is already quite small when the second impurity is a second nearest neighbour.

However, we do not wish to imply that the effects of neighbouring impurities are of no consequence at concentrations less than the above limits. Indeed in subsection 5.6 we have described situations where such effects are detectable for $c \lesssim 0.01$. Such cases, though, occur in regions of low densities of states where there is little broadening due to $\mathrm{Im}\,\boldsymbol{G}^0(\omega)$. Of course, the presence of short range order nullifies the above numerical estimates.

7. *Optical examples*

Optical spectra have been used for the last decade in detecting local, gap and resonant modes as well as the more detailed effects of impurities on the host crystal phonons. As a consequence a considerable literature has developed. Maradudin (1966) has given an early review of the subject, describing the physics of the origin of the various spectra in some detail, and several subsequent reviews are mentioned in the introduction. Consequently we will concentrate on the more recent calculations but must first indicate how the Green's functions introduced in section 2 are used to calculate the various spectra.

7.1. General formulae

The infra-red absorption is due to the coupling of the electromagnetic field to the crystal dipole moment $\boldsymbol{\mu}$. The latter is expanded in terms of atomic displacements

$$\mu_\alpha = \sum_{\beta l\kappa} \mu^{(1)}_{\alpha,\beta}(l\kappa)\, u_\beta(l\kappa) + \sum_{\substack{\beta l\kappa \\ \gamma l'\kappa'}} \mu^{(2)}_{\alpha,\beta\gamma}(l\kappa, l'\kappa')\, u_\beta(l\kappa)\, u_\gamma(l'\kappa') + \cdots ,$$

where, for the infra-red absorption, we retain the linear term as we are interested in only the one-phonon absorption. The coefficient $\mu^{(1)}_{\alpha,\beta}(lk)$ can be considered to be an effective charge. It can rise from both the ionic charge (in a polar crystal) and from atomic distortions due to wave function overlap in both polar and covalent crystals (Szigeti 1963, Leigh and Szigeti 1968). In monatomic host crystals the effective charge is zero due to either translational invariance in a Bravais structure (e.g., solid Ar) or inversion symmetry (e.g., Si). The presence of a random array of impurities removes these symmetries allowing the effective charge to be non-zero. Note this is a second role for disorder in allowing the vibrations of a disordered crystal to couple with electromagnetic radiation.

The optical absorption coefficient $\alpha(\omega)$ can be derived by examining the dielectric constant $\varepsilon(\omega)$ (Stern 1963). The latter is obtained by calculating the polarization due to the macroscopic electric field via linear response theory (Maradudin 1963). The total dielectric constant is then given by

$$\varepsilon(\omega) = \varepsilon_\infty + \frac{4\pi}{N\Omega_0}\left(\frac{\varepsilon_\infty + 2}{3}\right)^2 (\boldsymbol{\mu}^{(1)}\cdot \boldsymbol{G}(\omega)\cdot \boldsymbol{\mu}^{(1)})_{\alpha\alpha},$$

where Ω_0 is the unit cell volume and the electric field has been taken to be polarized in the direction α. This result has already been specialized to the cubic case by the introduction of the isotropic dielectric constant $\varepsilon_\infty = \varepsilon(\infty)$. Here infinity means a frequency much higher than the lattice frequencies but lower than any electronic frequency. The factor including ε_∞ in the second term is due to the Lorentz field correction (see for instance Klein 1968). Mahan (1967) has investigated how the presence of impurities affects this correction, but his result has not been evaluated in detail. The absorption coefficient is then given by

$$\alpha(\omega) = -\frac{4\pi}{N\Omega_0 v}\left(\frac{\varepsilon_\infty + 2}{3}\right)^2 \omega\,(\boldsymbol{\mu}^{(1)}\cdot \operatorname{Im} \boldsymbol{G}(\omega)\cdot \boldsymbol{\mu}^{(1)})_{\alpha\alpha}, \tag{7.2}$$

where v is the velocity of light in the crystal. The sum rule (2.16) immediately leads to a sum rule on the absorption (Alexander et al. 1970),

$$P_{\alpha\beta}(\omega) = P^0_{\alpha\beta}(\omega) + \sum_{\gamma l\kappa} P^{(1)}_{\alpha\beta,\gamma}(l\kappa,\omega)\, u_\gamma(l\kappa) + \cdots . \tag{7.3}$$

Raman scattering is due to the coupling between the electronic polarizability $\boldsymbol{P}$ and the incident radiation field. Again we expand in terms of atomic displacements

$$\int_0^\infty \alpha(\omega)\,d\omega = \frac{2\pi^2}{N\Omega_0 v}\left(\frac{\varepsilon_\infty + 2}{3}\right)^2 (\boldsymbol{\mu}^{(1)} \boldsymbol{M}^{-1} \boldsymbol{\mu}^{(1)})_{\alpha\alpha}.$$

In cubic crystals $\boldsymbol{P}^0(\omega)$ is zero and further $P^{(1)}_{\alpha\beta,\gamma}(l\kappa, \omega)$ is zero for any atom at a centre of inversion symmetry. In a disordered crystal this symmetry is lifted and first-order Raman scattering becomes possible. Born and Huang (1954) give a general formula for Raman scattering

$$I(\omega) = \frac{\omega_0^4}{2\pi v^3} \sum_{\substack{\alpha\beta \\ \gamma\lambda}} n_\alpha n_\beta E_\gamma^+ E_\lambda^- \, i_{\alpha\gamma,\beta\lambda}(\Delta\omega),$$

with

$$i_{\alpha\gamma,\beta\lambda}(\omega) = (1/2\pi) \int \langle P_{\beta\lambda}(t)\, P^*_{\alpha\gamma} \rangle_T \, e^{i\omega t}\, dt.$$

Here E^+ and E^- are the field strengths of the positive and negative frequency components of the incident radiation that has frequency ω_0. $\boldsymbol{n}$ is unit vector along the electric field of the scattered radiation which has frequency $\omega = \omega_0 + \Delta\omega$. For the one-phonon Raman process the result for the tensor $\boldsymbol{i}(\omega)$ is

$$i_{\alpha\gamma,\beta\lambda}(\omega) = -(\hbar/\pi) \sum_{\substack{l\kappa l'\kappa' \\ \mu\nu}} P^{(1)}_{\beta\lambda,\mu}(l\kappa)\, P^{(1)}_{\alpha\gamma,\nu}(l'\kappa') \frac{e^{\beta\omega}}{e^{\beta\omega} - 1} \operatorname{Im} G_{\mu\nu}(l\kappa, l'\kappa'; \omega). \tag{7.4}$$

This result was first analysed by Nguyen et al. (1965) using the single impurity result (3.6, 3.13) for $\boldsymbol{G}(\boldsymbol{w})$. As the $\boldsymbol{P}^{(1)}$ have even parity only, even phonon modes can contribute to the Raman scattering. Hence the motion of the impurity is irrelevant and so is its mass. Only force constant changes can affect (7.4). Nguyen (1968) has also evaluated this expression using the finite concentration result, (3.9), for $\boldsymbol{G}(\omega)$.

As a consequence of its high frequency the local mode of an H^- ion has large displacement. For instance Paul and Takeno (1972) suggest that the R.M.S. displacement is 10% of the nearest neighbour distance. This leads to a strong anharmonic coupling with the band modes and as a consequence sidebands have been observed. Senne (1965), and Timusk and Klein (1966) gave early treatments for these sidebands. More extensive analyses have been given by Nguyen (1966, 1967), Bilz et al. (1966), Page and Dick (1967), and Kuhner and Wagner (1967) who all took more general models for the anharmonic coupling. With the exception of Kuhner and Wagner they also included the possibility of a second order electric dipole mechanism giving rise to the absorption. The interaction term for the anharmonic coupling is taken to be

$$\mathscr{H}_{\mathrm{A}} = \sum_{\substack{\alpha\beta \\ l\kappa\gamma}} \Phi^{(3)}_{\alpha\beta\gamma}(0, 0, l\kappa)\, u_{\alpha}(0)\, u_{\beta}(0)\, u_{\gamma}(l\kappa)$$

for the U centre at the origin. The process corresponds to the decay of a local mode into a local mode plus band mode. Only the H^- ion is assumed to move at the local mode frequency, hence the $u_{\alpha}(0)u_{\beta}(0)$ factor. The range of the interaction is taken to be confined to the nearest neighbour impurity space.

The zero temperature result is of the form

$$\alpha_{\mathrm{A}}(\omega) = \frac{A\omega}{(\omega^2 - \omega_{\mathrm{L}}^2)^2} \sum_{\substack{\alpha\beta \\ l\kappa\gamma \\ l'\kappa'\gamma'}} \Phi^{(3)}_{\alpha\beta\gamma}(0,0,l\kappa)\,\mathrm{Im}\, G_{\gamma\gamma'}(l\kappa, l'\kappa'; \Omega)\,\Phi^{(3)}_{\alpha\beta\gamma'}(0,0,l'\kappa'), \tag{7.5}$$

where $\Omega = \omega - \omega_{\mathrm{L}}$ and A is a constant. Usually the frequency dependence of the first factor is approximated by Ω^{-2} although Bilz et al. (1966) suggest that there should be an anharmonic correction in this factor. Their correction is not neglible but has only been included by Bilz et al. (1967), and Page and Strauch (1968). Again assuming that only the H^- ion moves at the local mode frequency, the second-order dipole result has the form

$$\alpha_{2\mathrm{D}} = B \sum_{\substack{\alpha\beta \\ l\kappa\gamma \\ l'\kappa'\gamma'}} \mu^{(2)}_{\alpha\beta\gamma}(0, l\kappa)\,\mathrm{Im}\, G_{\gamma\gamma'}(l\kappa, l'\kappa'; \Omega)\,\mu^{(2)}_{\alpha\beta\gamma'}(0, l'\kappa'), \tag{7.6}$$

with B a constant. As the $\boldsymbol{\Phi}^{(3)}(0, 0, l\kappa)$ and the $\boldsymbol{\mu}^{(2)}(0, l\kappa)$ have similar symmetry properties and have to be parameterised to fit experiment the significant difference between $\alpha_{\mathrm{A}}(\omega)$ and $\alpha_{2\mathrm{D}}(\omega)$ is the frequency dependence of the leading factor. It should be noted that Elliott et al. (1965) using a Debye approximation to estimate $\boldsymbol{\Phi}^{(3)}$ found no frequency dependence in the leading factor of $\alpha_{\mathrm{A}}(\omega)$. However this approximation is only valid at low frequencies.

The vibronic sidebands on the electronic transitions of an impurity ion can also yield information on the lattice dynamics. The general theory has been given by Wagner (1968) for the situation where the electronic states involved do not overlap with the neighbouring ions. The interaction is then Coulombic

$$H_{\mathrm{I}} = \sum_{l\kappa\alpha} V_\alpha(l\kappa, \boldsymbol{r}_{\mathrm{e}})\, u_\alpha(l\kappa),$$

with $V_\alpha(l\kappa, \boldsymbol{r}_{\mathrm{e}})$ being the α derivative of the Coulomb interaction between the electron at $\boldsymbol{r}_{\mathrm{e}}$ and an ion at $(l\kappa)$. The final result for the emitted intensity in a cubic system is

$$I(\omega) = -\frac{\omega^4\, e^{\beta\omega}}{e^{\beta\omega} - 1} \sum_{\substack{\alpha \\ l\kappa\gamma \\ l'\kappa'\gamma'}} F_\gamma^\alpha(ab, l\kappa)\, \mathrm{Im}\, G_{\gamma\gamma'}(l\kappa, l'\kappa'; \omega)\, F_{\gamma'}^\alpha(ab, l'\kappa'), \qquad (7.7)$$

where α labels the cartesian components of the electron position, a, b the initial and final electron states and ω is measured from the frequency difference of those states. The functions $\boldsymbol{F}$ are perturbation theory matrix elements containing the coupling of the electron to the photon and to the phonons.

All these results have the form

$$f(\omega) = -\,\omega^n \sum_{\substack{\alpha l\kappa \\ \beta l'\kappa'}} M_\alpha(l\kappa)\, \mathrm{Im}\, G_{\alpha\beta}(l\kappa, l'\kappa'; \omega)\, M_\beta(l'\kappa'),$$

and it is convenient to exploit the symmetry properties of the matrix elements $\boldsymbol{M}$. These are usually confined to the impurity space so that, on defining

$$M_a(s) = -\sum_{l\kappa\alpha} \psi_\alpha^{sa\lambda}(l\kappa)\, M_\alpha(l\kappa),$$

we obtain

$$f(\omega) = -\,\omega^n \sum_a M_a(s)\, \mathrm{Im}\, G_{ab}^s(\omega)\, M_b(s).$$

It is often the case that selection rules arise in that the $\boldsymbol{M}(s)$ are non-zero for only a few of the i.r.'s (labelled by s). For instance in the alkali halides only the $T_{1\mathrm{u}}$ i.r. contributes to the infra red absorption whereas the $A_{1\mathrm{g}}$, E_{g} and $T_{2\mathrm{g}}$ contribute to the Raman and U centre sidebands. As described by Nguyen et al. (1965) and Harley et al. (1971), it is possible to separate these contributions to the Raman scattering by the appropriate choice of the incident and scattered directions and polarizations. There is not the same freedom for the U centre sidebands and the matrix elements for the different representations have to be parameterized. Alternatively a specific functional form may be adopted as was done by MacPherson and Timusk (1970) for $\boldsymbol{\Phi}^{(3)}$ in $\alpha_{\mathrm{A}}(\omega)$, (7.5).

As discussed by Wagner (1968) the selection rules for the vibronic sidebands depend upon the symmetry of the environment as well as the electronic states involved. Buchanan and Woll (1969) have investigated in detail the $A_{1g} \to A_{1g}$ electronic transition for Sm^{2+} in KCl and KBr finding, in the absence of the charge compensating vacancy, only the T_{1u} i.r. is selected. Similarly, Sangster and McCombie (1970) have investigated electronic transitions for V^{2+} and Ni^{2+} in MgO finding that the T_{1u} and T_{2u} i.r.'s are selected. The work on the effect of a neighbouring vacancy for KBr: Sm^{+} due to Kuhner and Wagner (1970) has already been referred to in subsection 5.6.

Loudon (1964) has also described the selection rules for the impurity induced infra red and sideband absorptions, restricting himself to the FCC, zinc blende and diamond structures. He arrived at some of the selection rules described above, but concentrated upon which symmetry point phonons are forbidden in these processes. In the absence of detail calculations such selection rules are useful in understanding why the spectra differ from the density of states of the host crystal.

When a number of i.r.'s contribute to any of the above processes there may be too many matrix element parameters required to adopt a sensible fitting procedure. In these cases it is common to restrict $(l\kappa)$ and $(l'\kappa')$ to the impurity site and hence compare $\omega^n \operatorname{Im} \boldsymbol{G}(0,0;\omega)$ with experiment. In other words, in this 'impurity only' approximation just the Fourier transform of $\langle \boldsymbol{u}(0)^2 \rangle$ is used.

7.2. Monatomic host crystals

For monatomic systems of simple structure, symmetry rules out the infrared one-phonon dipole absorption. Thus the dipole moments, $\boldsymbol{\mu}^{(1)}$, appearing in the optical absorption expression (7.2) have to be induced by the presence of an impurity and are usually taken to extend to only the n.n.'s of the impurity. Hence the Green's function appropriate to an impurity at the origin, (3.6), (3.13), should be substituted in (7.2).

Rare-gas atoms as impurities in rare-gas crystals constitute such a system. Elliott and Hartmann (1967) used a shell model approach to calculate an effective charge confined to the impurity, and then calculated $\alpha(\omega)$ within the mass defect approximation. Martin (1967a) has performed a similar calculation but included force constant changes whereas Davies and Healey (1968) discussed the problem from a formal symmetry point of view with $\boldsymbol{\mu}^{(1)}$ confined to the n.n. impurity space. Mannheim and Cohen (1971) have essentially repeated these calculations using the simplified model discussed in subsection 5.2.

However none of these calculations agree that well with the experiments of Jones and Woodfine (1965) whose relatively high temperature measurements were made on 1% Kr in Ar at 80 K and 0.5% Xe in Ar at 50 K. The omission of anharmonic effects in the calculations was obviously a contributing factor. However, Keeler and Batchelder (1972) have repeated the Ar:Kr experiment at 2 K and their result is shown in fig. 17. The result of a short

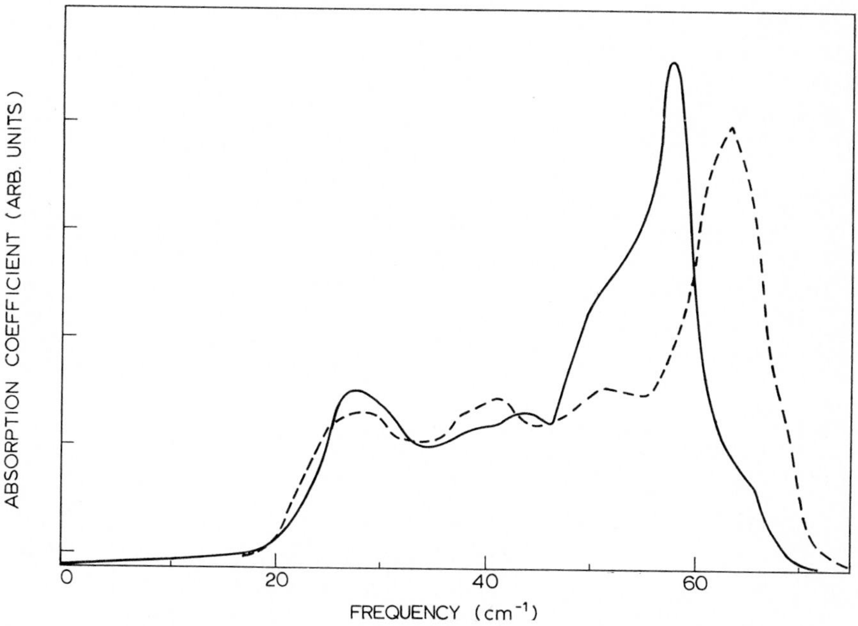

Fig. 17. Infra red absorption due to 1% of Kr in Ar; ——— calculated with $\Delta f/f = -0.06$ and 25% transverse component to effective charge, ----- experiment at 2K (Keeler and Batchelder 1972).

reinvestigation by the author using the Green's function $\boldsymbol{G}^0(\omega)$, calculated by De Remigis et al. (1971) is also shown on fig. 17. In order to fit the resonance at 30 cm^{-1} it was necessary to use a force constant change of $\Delta f/f = -0.06$ along with a transverse component for $\boldsymbol{\mu}^{(1)}$ that was 25% of the longitudinal component. However, fitting the resonance led to discrepancies in the region of the longitudinal peak, as can be seen in fig. 17. Clearly this problem requires further study.

The sidebands on a rotational–vibrational transition of H_2 in solid Ar have been discussed by Taylor and De Remigis (1973) in the light of the sum rule (2.16). Due to the experimental temperature being very close to the melting temperature and the presence of both the ortho and para species the analysis is not easy. Further Cohen (1973) has questioned the simple interpretation of the spectra being due to on-centre substitutional H_2. The temperature dependence of the local mode frequency of N_2 in solid Ar has been measured by De Remigis et al. (1971) and they were able to explain it using a model for the Ar–H_2 force constants along with the temperature dependence of the atomic spacing.

TABLE 5

Force constant changes for impurities in Si and Ge (Jain and Prabhakaran 1973a).

System	ω_L in cm^{-1}		$\Delta f/f$
	Calculated (mass defect)	Experiment	
Si:^{10}B	686	644	−0.12
^{11}B	663	620	−0.14
^{12}C	645	611	−0.08
^{13}C	624	590	−0.12
^{14}C	611	573	−0.13
Ge:Si	394	389	−0.01

Impurities in silicon form the other set of impurity systems that have a monatomic host crystal. Dawber and Elliott (1963) have given the mass defect calculation appropriate to B, Al, P, As, Sb, Bi as impurities. As reviewed by Newman (1969) the experimental local mode frequencies indicate the need for force constant changes and Jain and Prabhakaran (1973a) have recently estimated these changes. They used the nearest neighbour model discussed in subsection 5.2 but with good numerical densities of states and their results are shown in table 5. Note that different isotopes require different Δf. As will be seen in the next subsection (7.2) this does not necessarily indicate anharmonic contributions. Unfortunately, they did not consider the results of Nazarewicz and Jurkowski (1969) for $^{10,11}B$ in Ge.

Some of these systems have also been studied via Raman scattering. Feldman et al. (1966) have examined Si in Ge and Nguyen (1968) has carried through a mass defect calculation. As pure Ge is Raman active he took the $\boldsymbol{P}^{(1)}$ polarization tensor in (7.4) to be site indepencent and used the finite concentration result (3.10) for $\boldsymbol{G}(\omega)$ to obtain good qualitative agreement with experiment. Nazarewicz et al. (1971) have examined B in Si and found local mode frequencies in close agreement with the infrared results (T_1 is both infra-red and Raman active).

It has to be noted that most experiments for impurities in Si require the addition of a second impurity to remove free carrier absorption. The presence of two kinds of impurities leads to considerable complexity. The calculations for this situation due to Elliott and Pfeuty (1968) have already been discussed in subsection 5.6.

7.3. Impurities in alkali halides

Impurities in alkali halides constitute the set of systems upon which most attention has been paid. Infrared, sideband and Raman experiments have been performed with considerable precision and analysed through detailed calculations using host crystal force constants fitted to the results of inelastic coherent neutron scattering experiments. The variety of models used to explain the optical experiments have already been discussed in subsection (5.4) and so we will just consider a representative selection of comparisons between experiment and theory.

If the impurity is assumed to have the same Szigeti charge, e^*, as the host crystal atom it replaced then the linear result for $\boldsymbol{G}(\omega)$, (3.8), is simply substituted in (7.2). The incident radiation couples only with the projections of the imperfect crystal modes on a transverse optic mode and as the eigenvectors of the optic modes are easily calculated (Maradudin 1963) the final result is readily obtained,

$$\alpha(\omega) = \frac{4\pi\omega e^{*2}}{\Omega_0 v}\left(\frac{\varepsilon_\infty + 2}{3}\right)^2 \left(\frac{M_1 + M_2}{M_1 M_2}\right) \times \left[\frac{\pi}{2\omega}\,\delta(\omega - \omega_{\mathrm{TO}}) - \frac{c}{(\omega^2 - \omega_{\mathrm{TO}}^2)^2}\,\mathrm{Im}\, t_{\mathrm{TO,TO}}(\mathbf{0}, \omega)\right]. \tag{7.8}$$

The delta function is the harmonic approximation to the reststrahl and it is the second term, which contains $\boldsymbol{G}^0(\omega)$, that gives the continuum absorption seen experimentally. If the Szigeti charge of the impurity is taken to be different from the host Martin (1968) finds that a much more complicated expression results.

The simplest impurity is an isotope of one of the constituents of the pure crystal, as in a harmonic theory the force constant changes are then strictly zero. Klein and MacDonald (1968), and MacDonald et al. (1969) have presented experimental results for $Na^{35,37}Cl$ and $^{6,7}LiF$ that are in good agreement with their calculations. In these two cases the mass changes are sufficiently small that the sole effect of the presence of the impurities is to remove the translational invariance with the result that the acoustic phonons become optically active. Hence the experiments really test our knowledge of

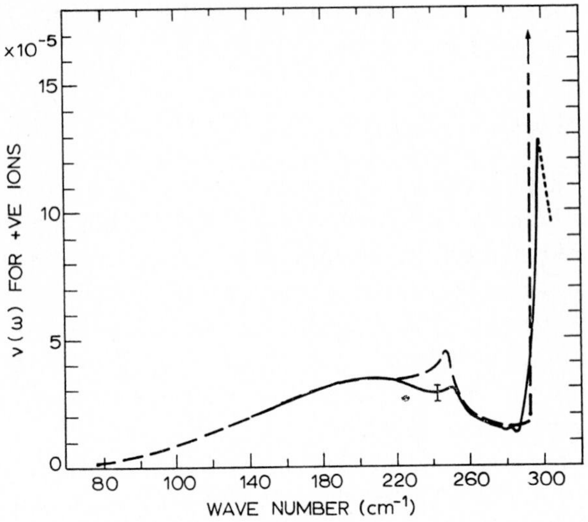

Fig. 18. Positive ion density of states $-(2M^0\omega/\pi)\,\mathrm{Im}\,G^0_{\alpha\alpha}(0.1, 0.1; \omega)$ of LiF; ----- calculation of Dolling et al. (1968), ——— deduced from infra red absorption of natural $Li^{6,7}F$ by Eldridge (1972).

the pure crystal phonons. Eldridge (1972) has examined $^{6,7}LiF$ with great care and his results are shown in fig. 18. The discrepancy around 240 cm^{-1} he identifies with inaccuracies in the pure crystal phonon eigenvectors. A somewhat stronger perturbation is caused by the isotopic substitution in LiH/D. The infrared absorption due to this system was calculated in some detail by Jaswal and Hardy (1968) using phonons derived from inelastic neutron scattering in the finite concentration result (4.3) for $\boldsymbol{G}(\omega)$. They were able to describe how the large increase in absorption below ω_{TO}, as seen by Misho (unpublished) due to the addition of small amounts of D^-, was due to the appearance of a gap mode. This work corroborated the earlier calculation of Elliott and Taylor (1967) who used a rather crude model for $\boldsymbol{G}^0(\omega)$. More recently, Wolfram et al. (1972) have determined the local mode frequency of

H^- in LiD via second-order Raman scattering to be 940 cm^{-1}. Their calculated value is 917 cm^{-1} and part of the discrepancy was put down to the use of room-temperature data. However, this system would seem to be a candidate for force constant changes arising from anharmonic effects due to the large amplitude of the H^- ion local mode.

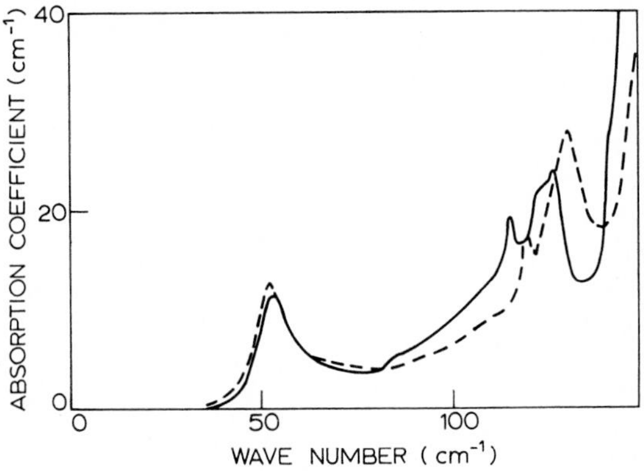

Fig. 19. Infra red absorption due to Ag^+ in NaCl ——— calculation, ----- experiment (after Montgomery et al. 1972b).

A detailed calculation of the infra-red absorption due to a range of impurities (Ag^+, Li^+, K^+, F^-, Br^-, I^-) in NaCl has been presented by MacDonald et al. (1969). They used the relaxation model employing Δf and Δg and also considered the possibility of a different Szigeti charge, e^*, for the impurity. Fig. 19 shows the excellent agreement between theory and experiments for NaCl:Ag. Note the strong T_{1u} resonance at 53 cm^{-1}. For K^+, Br^- and I^- they had to change the impurity e^* to obtain a good agreement but even with this extra parameter were not able to fit the results for Li^+. The Li^+ resonant mode at 44.5 cm^{-1} required a 96% nearest neighbour force constant reduction but the resulting calculated intensity was orders of magnitude too large. As we will see below this is a general problem with low frequency resonances. Their resulting force constant fits are collected together in table 6. Other impurities in NaCl whose infra-red absorption has been measured include Cu, Mg, Ca (Weber and Siebert 1968) but no calculations have been reported.

Another comprehensive collection of impurity calculations (and measurements) has been presented by Ward and Timusk (1972). They examined Li^+, Na^+, Tl^+, Sm^{2+}, Cl^-, F^-, OH^-, O_2^- in KBr and Li^+, Na^+, Sm^{2+},

TABLE 6

Fitted force constant changes for impurities in the alkali halides. f^* taken from Klein (1968).

Host	Impurity	Force constant changes: Δf (10^4 dyne cm^{-1})	$\Delta f/f^*$	Δg (10^4 dyne cm^{-1})	$\Delta g/f^*$	R
NaCl[a]	K^+[b]	0.30	0.19	0.0		1.40
	Ag^+	−0.85	−0.54	0.0		1.32
	F^-	−1.40	−0.91	−0.80	−0.52	0.75
	Br^-[b]	0.06	0.04	0.06[c]		1.08
	I^-[b]	0.30	0.20	0.30[c]		1.19
KCl[d]	Li^+	−1.26	−0.94	−0.59	−0.44	0.45
KCl[e]	Na^+	−0.05	−0.04	0.0		0.71
	Sm^{2+}	1.45	1.06	−0.15	−0.11	0.78
	Eu^{2+}	1.45	1.06	−0.15	−0.11	0.77
	F^-	−1.09	−0.80	−0.10	−0.07	0.75
	O_2^-	−0.10	−0.07	−0.05	−0.04	
	Br^-	−0.30	−0.22	0.15	0.11	1.08
	I^-	−0.30	−0.22	0.15	0.11	1.19
KBr[d]	Li^+	−1.21	−0.98	−0.55	−0.45	0.45
KBr[e]	Na^+	−0.75	−0.56	−0.22	−0.15	0.71
	Sm^{2+}	1.45	1.08	−0.03	−0.02	0.78
	OH^-	−1.10	−0.84	−0.80	−0.61	
	F^-	−1.10	−0.84	−0.80	−0.61	0.70
	Cl^-	−0.20	−0.15	−0.03	−0.02	0.93
	O_2^-	−0.50	−0.38	−0.06	−0.05	
	Tl^+	0.80	0.59	0.00		1.05
KBr[f]	Tl^+	−0.20	−0.16	0.0		1.05
KI	Na^+[g]	−0.53	−0.46	0.10	0.09	0.71
	Rb^+[h]	0.80	0.70			1.11
	Tl^+[f]	−0.35	−0.30			1.05
	Cl^-[d]	−0.59	−0.51	−0.46	−0.40	0.83
	Cl^-[i]	0.69	0.60			
	Cl^-[g]	−0.90	−0.78	−0.28	−0.24	
	Br^-[g]	−0.55	−0.48	−0.35	−0.30	0.90

a) MacDonald et al. (1969).
b) Effective Charge of impurity changed.
c) Next n.n. force constant change.
d) Benedek (1970).
e) Ward and Timusk (1972).
f) Benedek and Terzi (1973).
g) Ward et al. (1974).
h) Wegdam et al. (1973).
i) De Jong (1971).

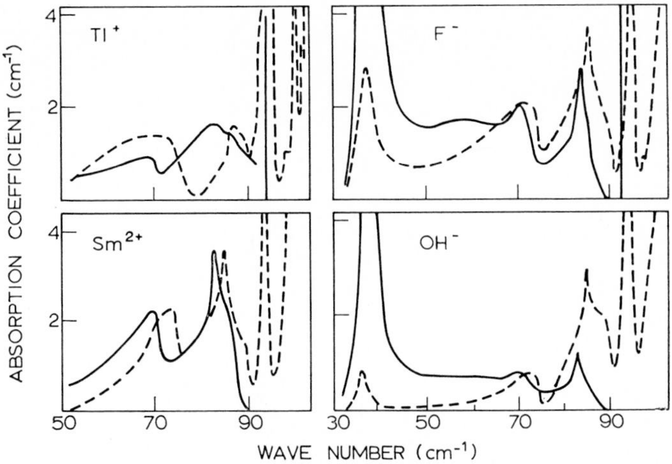

Fig. 20. Infra-red absorption due to Tl^+, Sm^{2+}, F^- and OH^- in KBr; ——— calculation, ----- experiment (after Ward and Timusk 1972).

Eu^{2+}, F^-, Br^-, I^-, O_2^- in KCl. Here we will only consider some of their KBr results which are shown in fig. 20. The relaxation model was used in the calculations but no account was taken of the possibility of the impurity having a different effective charge. In those cases where there is a low frequency resonance (OH^-, F^- and Li^+) its intensity, relative to the rest of the acoustic band, was predicted to be much too high. This is the same problem as that of MacDonald et al. (1969) and must be associated with anharmonic corrections due to the large motion predicted by the above harmonic theory. Gap modes were found and fitted for Na^+, Tl^+ and O_2^-.

A systematic frequency shift between theory and experiment can be observed in fig. 20. This can be identified with inaccuracies in the host crystal phonons. Fig. 21 shows a detail of the $KBr:Na^+$ result with the Van Hove singularities A, B, C and D indicated. Ward and Timusk (1972) find that none of these singularities correspond to high symmetry points, rather to saddle points on symmetry lines (A, C, D) and a maximum (B) on a symmetry plane. The neutron scattering experiments did not establish the phonon frequencies at these points and so the values calculated were shell model dependent.

Fig. 21 shows the experimental results at two different concentrations and there is a clear indication of a concentration dependence for these points [see also Timusk and Ward (1969)]. This is impossible to obtain in the disorder theory discussed in this chapter as the positions of discontinuities are

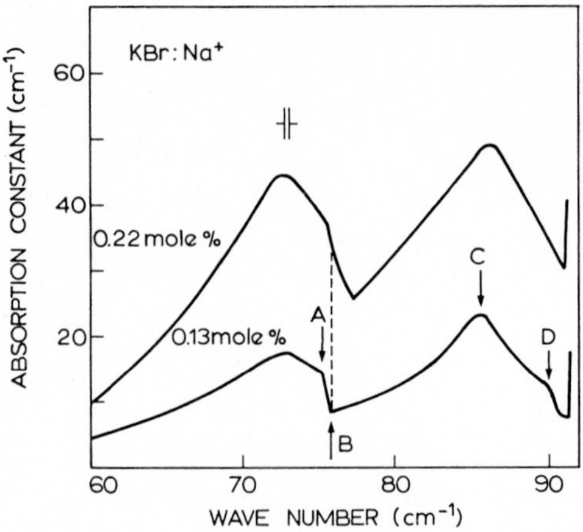

Fig. 21. Detail of experimental absorption due to Na^+ in KBr; A, B, C, D label Van Hove singularities (see text). (Ward and Timusk 1972).

preserved in perturbation theory. A self-consistent theory such as the CPA discussed in the next chapter is required to treat this problem.

There is, of course, a contribution from the volume change an alloying (see subsection 2.2). Using Vegard's law to estimate this volume change, Grüneisen parameters of more than 20 are required to account for the shift in $KBr:Na^+$ from this effect alone. We note that the volume dependence of local and low frequency resonant modes has been investigated by several authors by adding a third constituent in appreciable concentrations (Barth and Fritz 1967, Clayman and Sievers 1968, Clayman et al. 1969). Hughes (1968) has given an explanation for $KBr:Li^+$ mixed with KCl or KI, in terms of random strains in the crystal.

Returning to fig. 20, it can be seen that there is a general agreement between theory and experiment for the shape of the absorption in the region of the singularities A, B, C and D. However, a careful examination of the $KBr:Cl^-$ result indicated that the experimental step from A to B rises rather than falls but Ward and Timusk were unable to fit this feature. The possibility of different shapes (metamorphosis of the singular points) has already been mentioned in subsection 4.5.

Very recently Ward et al. (1974) have performed a similar analysis for Na^+, Cl^- and Br^- in KI. Although they were able to obtain a good fit for $KI:Na^+$ it was not possible for the other two systems. They indicate that, in part, this is due to concentration effects such as resonances due to pairs of impurities. It should be noted that Br^- produces a gap mode in KI which could not be fitted using just n.n. force constant changes (Benedek and Maradudin 1968).

The use of different isotopes of a given impurity provides a test of the models used as in a harmonic theory the same force constant changes should apply. In order to fit the local mode frequencies due to H^- and D^- in NaCl and KCl, MacDonald (1966) found a 1% difference between the required values of $\Delta f/f$. The introduction of a non-central force constant change did not help. H^- and D^- local modes have also been measured in NaI by Bauerle and Fritz (1967) but no estimate of Δf was given. In the case of gap modes neither Benedek and Maradudin (1968) nor De Jong (1971) were able to give a precise description for the isotope splitting of KI: $^{35,37}Cl^-$ using n.n. force constant changes. However, Benedek (1970), by introducing Δg, was able to fit both the gap mode and the splitting. However, as can be seen in table 6 his values are somewhat different from those of Ward et al. (1974) who attempted to fit the overall infra red spectrum along with the gap mode frequency. Part of this difference may be due to the use of different models for the KI phonons. Recently, Wegdam et al. (1973) were able to give an excellent fit using only Δf for the gap mode frequency and isotope splitting in KI: $^{85,87}Rb^+$. Low frequency resonances are difficult to treat. Kirby et al. (1968) have examined NaCl: $^{63,65}Cu^+$, KI: $^{107,109}Ag^+$, KBr: $^{6,7}Li^+$ and find that an Einstein model fits quite well as does the simple nearest neighbour model of Sievers and Takeno (1965) (see subsection 5.2). However, the deformation dipole model results of Benedek and Nardelli (1968b) give too small a splitting. Anharmonic corrections are clearly indicated and were considered by Kirby et al. However, we note that Clayman et al. (1971) using anharmonic considerations were unable to give a consistent treatment for both the electric field effects and the isotope splitting for KBr:Li^+, although they could for NaI:Cl^-. Both Benedek (1968), and Paul and Takeno (1972) have also discussed the question of anharmonic contributions to low frequency resonances (and high frequency local modes).

As discussed at the beginning of this section the presence of impurities in alkali halides can induce first order Raman scattering. As opposed to the infra-red active i.r. (T_{1u}), in the Raman active i.r.'s (A_{1g}, E_g, T_{2g}) the impurity does not move and so the spectra are independent of its mass. Further the T_{2g} spectrum is not influenced by Δf or Δg. Harley et al. (1971) have examined in detail the Raman spectra due to Tl^+ in KCl, KBr, KI, KCl and find little evidence for appreciable force constant changes (see table 2; they were unable to detect the A_{1g} spectra). This can be seen to be in contrast to the infra-red results of Ward and Timusk (1972) as well as the more recent calculations of Benedek and Terzi (1973). The latter authors have examined the comparison between the infra-red and Raman spectra in the light of their effective force constant estimates for these systems. They predict rather large changes in both Δf and Δg that are not borne out by experiment although, of the Raman spectra, only $KCl:Tl^+$ is particularly sensitive. Their fitted values for the infra red are also given in table 2. The large discrepancy between their value of Δf for $KBr:Tl^+$ and that due to Ward and Timusk (1972) is due to different criteria for fitting. Ward and Timusk fitted first to the frequency of a gap mode and then took $\Delta g = 0$ as the best fit to the remaining spectrum whereas Benedek and Terzi just fit the spectra (incorrectly placing the gap mode as a resonance at the top of the acoustic band).

A careful comparison between Raman and infra-red spectra that just aimed at fitting force constant changes but allowed for representation dependence has been given by Montgomery et al. (1972b). Their rather beautiful results for NaCl:Ag are shown in figs. 19, 22 and the fitted force constant changes are listed in table 2 (note it is the transverse force constant that is appropriate for T_{2g}). The infra-red result shows a well established T_{1u} resonance at

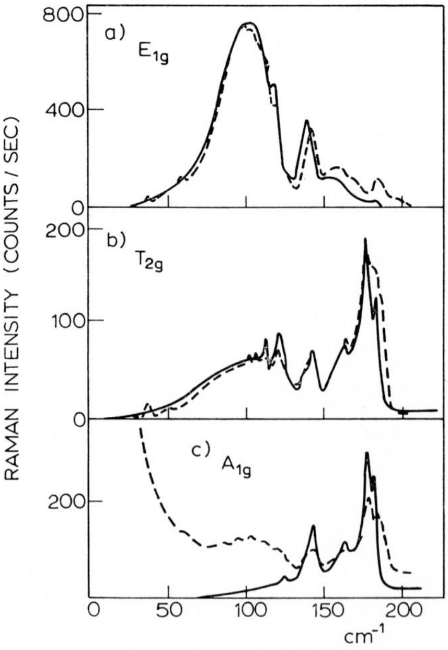

Fig. 22. First-order Raman scattering due to Ag^+ in NaCl. ——— calculation, ----- experiment (after Montogomery et al. 1972b).

53 cm^{-1} and the large peak at 96 cm^{-1} in the E_g spectrum was interpreted as being an incipient resonance. A similar analysis confined to just the Raman spectra of NaCl:Ca^{2+} has been given by Kaiser et al. (1973) and their fitted values are also given in table 2. The ambiguity for A_{ig} is a result of attempts to fit different parts of the spectrum. These results are for their quenched samples in which they assume the charge compensating vacancy is not a near neighbour of the Ca^{2+} ion. Other systems have been measured but not subjected to a detailed analysis of the above kind. They include NaCl:Br^-, I^-, Li^+, Ag^+ and KCl:I^-, Ag^+ due to Moller and Kaiser (1970, 1972) and NaCl:Cu^+ due to Ganguly et al. (1972). A rather crude analysis has been made by Jain et al. (1972) for LiF:Mn^{2+}.

The U centre has the special significance of being the only impurity to give rise to local modes in alkali halides. Benedek and Nardelli (1968b) have fitted these local modes using Δf, requiring $\Delta f/f^* \approx -0.60$ to -0.80. It might be thought that Li^+ would also produce local modes but again there is an even more dramatic force constant reduction that results in a very low frequency resonance, e.g. at 17 cm^{-1} for KBr:Li (Sievers and Takeno 1965) whereas Li^+ in KCl goes off centre (see for instance Narayanamurti and Pohl 1970). Also of interest are the far-infrared and local mode side band absorption spectra which sample, respectively, the T_{1u} and the A_{1g}, E_g, T_{2g} spectra. It has been established by several authors, including Timusk and Klein (1966), Bilz et al. (1966), and Nguyen (1967) that it is the anharmonic absorption, $\alpha_A(\omega)$, that is appropriate for these sidebands. These spectra have been analysed in some detail by MacPherson and Timusk (1970a, b) using the relaxation model along with the core–shell force constant change, Δk, introduced by Page and Strauch (1967) (see subsection 5.4). The fitted values are listed in table 7 along with the rigid ion values ($\Delta k = 0$) quoted by MacPherson and Timusk (1970a), and by Benedek and Nardelli (1968b). The effect of the non-zero Δk is seen to be quite strong. The fitting procedure adopted by MacPherson and Timusk (1970a) was to use the local mode frequency to establish a relation between Δf and Δk, then choose Δf by fitting to a common incipient E_g resonance and finally choose Δg to give a good description of the sideband structure. Page and Strauch (1968) omitted the fitting to the E_g resonance and their different fitted values given in table 7 are largely a consequence of the different criterion. MacPherson and Timusk (1970b) then found that their fitted values gave a good fit to the infra-red band absorption although they do indicate that adjustments would have lead to improvements. The case of KI:H^- is shown in figs. 23 and 24. In fig. 23, as well as the incipient E_g resonance at 31 cm^{-1}, an E_g resonance at 65 cm^{-1}

TABLE 7

Force constant changes (in 10^4 dyne cm^{-1}) used to fit local mode sidebands of U centre in alkali halides

		NaF	NaCl	NaBr	KCl	KBr	KI
$-\Delta f$	MT(1)	0.65	1.17	1.08	0.91	0.89	0.89
	MT(2)	1.22	1.23	1.01			
	PS				0.67	0.61	0.48
	BN		0.95	1.03	0.78	0.83	0.93
f^*		2.75	1.54	1.48	1.37	1.32	1.23
$\frac{1}{2}A=f$					1.22	1.07	0.94
$-\Delta g$	MT(1)	0.0	0.47	0.55	0.0	0.41	0.52
	MT(2)	0.0	0.48	0.40			
	PS				0.0	0.16	0.26
$-\Delta k$	MT(1)	96	86	4.5	0.0	0.0	0.0
	PS				0.0	0.0	22
k		114	96	77	83	78	109

MT(1) MacPherson and Timusk (1970a).
MT(2) MacPherson and Timusk (1970a), with $\Delta k=0$.
PS Page and Strauch (1968).
BN Benedek and Nardelli (1968b).

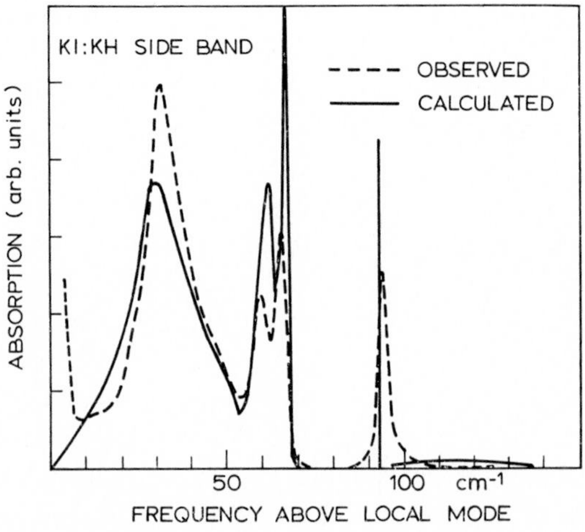

Fig. 23. Local mode side band of H^- in KI; ——— calculated, ----- experiment MacPherson and Timusk 1970a).

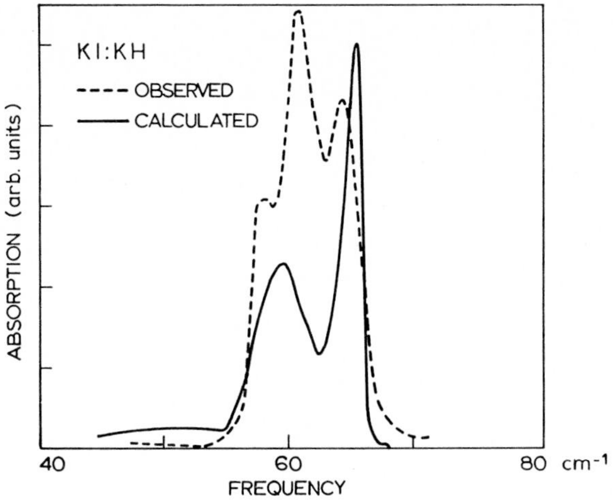

Fig. 24. Far infra-red absorption due to H^- in KI; WWW calculated, ----- experiment (MacPherson and Timusk 1970b).

and an A_{1g} gap mode at 93.5 cm^{-1} were identified. For fig. 24 they finally concluded that the high experimental peak at 60.7 cm^{-1} corresponds with an incipient T_{1u} resonance calculated to be at 65.5 cm^{-1}, that the lower frequency peaks correspond and that the experimental peak at 64 cm^{-1} has to be associated with a saddle point singularity. A similar range of properties was assigned to the other systems listed in table 7. The representations seen in the sideband should also be first order Raman active (see subsection 7.1) but, unfortunately, the scattering is extremely weak. Montgomery et al. (1972a) have managed to detect the A_{1g} gap mode for KI:H^- mentioned above as well as the second order scattering in KBr and KI. U centre sidebands have also been calculated by Bluthardt et al. (1973). However, their interest was in comparing calculations based on different shell model phonons.

Other sideband work includes the vibronic sidebands of Sm^{2+} in KBr which has already been discussed in subsection 5.6. We note, however, it was the sideband values of Δf and Δg found by Buchanan and Woll (1969) that were used to calculate the infra-red spectrum, in good agreement with experiment (fig. 20). Recently Rolfe et al. (1973) have extracted the single phonon sideband from the multiphonon sideband on an electronic transition of O_2^- in a number of alkali halides (see table 8). As the electronic transition is allowed, even parity vibrations produce the sidebands. On the whole Rolfe et al. found that the A_{1g} spectra were usually sufficient although contributions from T_{2g} were necessary for KCl and RbCl (E_g contributions are also possible in principle). Their fitted values of Δf and Δg are shown in table 8 and compared with the infra-red results where possible. Although the two results for KBr are in fair agreement, it is certainly not the case for KCl which must be interpreted as an indication of representation dependent force constant changes (see subsection 5.4).

TABLE 8

Fitted force constant changes (in 10^4 dyne cm^{-1}) for O_2^- in alkali halides

	NaCl	Kcl	KBr	KI	RbCl	RbBr	RbI
Δf(sideband)[a]	0.10	0.20	−0.55	−0.80	0	−0.40	−0.20
Δf(IR)[b]		−0.10	−0.50				
Δg(sideband)[a]	0	0.40	0	0	0	0	0
Δg(IR)[b]		−0.05	−0.38				

a) Rolf et al. (1973). b) Ward and Timusk (1972).

There have been few calculations investigating the concentration dependence of the absorption spectra. Benedek and Nardelli (1967) have presented results showing that the resonant peak due to $KBr{:}Ag^+$ moves to lower frequencies as c increases. They found a shift of -0.6 cm^{-1} as c went from 10^{-3} to 10^{-2}. Ernst and Liehl (1969) have examined the optical absorption and the density of states due to Br^- and Cl^- in KI finding that the impurity band in the gap moves to higher frequencies at c increases.

7.4. Other impurity systems

Calculations have been presented for the infra-red band absorption due to a range of impurities in the cesium halides by Martin (1971) and in series of papers by Agrawal and Ram. Their fitted force constants are shown in table 9 and compare quite well. Both groups allowed for changes in the longitudinal and transverse nearest neighbour force constants (Δf_L, Δf_T) with Martin also using the change in the longitudinal force constants (Δf_2) between the nearest neighbours themselves. Neither group considered changes of the next nearest neighbour force constants although for a BCC lattice the corresponding atomic spacings are quite similar in magnitude. [This point is taken into account in the breathing shell model used by both groups for the pure crystal phonons (Mahler and Engelhardt 1971).]

TABLE 9

Fitted force constant changes for impurities in cesium halides in 10^4 dyne/cm

	f^*			Na^+	K^+	Rb^+	In^+	Tl^+	H^-	D^-
		R		0.56	0.79	0.88	0.78	0.83		
			Ref							
		Δf_L	a		−0.10	0.50				
			b		−0.29	0.13				
CsCl	0.90(a, b)	Δf_T	a		−0.20	−0.30				
			b		−0.22	−0.20				
		Δf_2	a		0	0.70				
		Δf_L	c						−0.47	−0.50
		Δf_L	c	−0.39	−0.44	−0.33	−0.33	−0.22		
CsBr	0.88(d)	Δf_T	c	0	0	0	−0.24	−0.26		
		Δf_L	e						−0.51	
	0.79(a)	Δf_L	a	−0.20	−0.20	0	−0.75	−0.71		
CsI	0.84(c)		f		−0.24	−0.15		−0.73		
			g						−0.38	−0.45

a) Martin (1971).
b) Ram and Agrawal (1972c).
c) Ram and Agrawal (1972a).
d) Ram and Agrawal (1972d).
e) Ram and Agrawal (1972e).
f) Ram and Agrawal (1972b).
g) Agrawal and Ram (1972).

The detailed comparisons between the experimental and calculated spectra are not as successful as for the alkali halides partly due to less adequate pure crystal phonons [see Ram and Agrawal (1972d) for a comparison between theory and experiment for CsBr]. Probably the most successful comparison is that of Martin (1971) for $CsCl:K^+$ shown in fig. 25. The peak at about 40 cm^{-1} was interpreted as an incipient resonance and is common to most of these cesium halide results. Another strong resonance can be seen at 86 cm^{-1}. In^+ and Tl^+ are somewhat different in that they give rise too low frequency resonances ($\lesssim 20$ cm^{-1}) and again there are intensity problems, as with the alkali halides. It will be also noticed in table 9 that H^- and D^- require different values of Δf, presumably due to anharmonic corrections. Ram and Agrawal (1972e) have calculated the infra band absorption due to H^- from their local mode frequency fits but there are no experimental results. Like wise Martin (1972), and Ram and Agrawal (1973) have investigated the first-order Raman scattering in the light of their infra-red results, but again in the

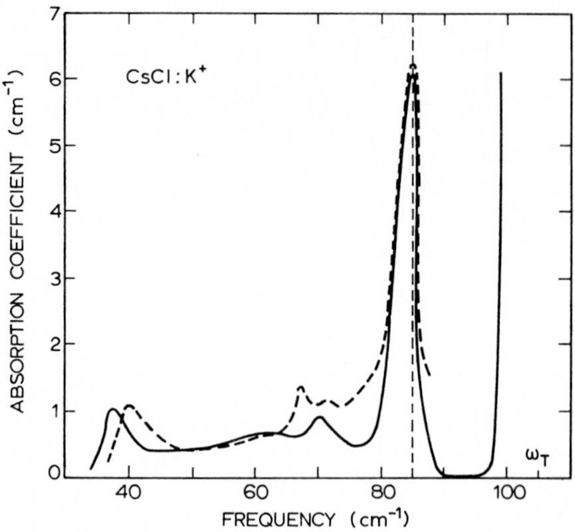

Fig. 25. Far infra-red absorption due K^+ in CsCl; ----- experiment ——— calculation (Martin 1971).

absence of experimental results. On the other hand, Olson and Lynch (1971) have measured the $CsI:H^-$ local mode sideband but there are no proper calculations, only their comparison with the density of states. Further, judging from the Raman results of Ram and Agrawal (1973), it is not clear how successful such a calculation would be.

Gaur et al. (1971) have given an extensive table comparing experimental local and gap mode frequencies with calculated mass defect values for impurities in host crystals of the zinc blende structure. They based their calculations on a modified rigid ion model for the host crystal phonons. Rather than reproduce their table here, we will give some refinements due to other work. In table 10 we compare the results of a similar calculation due to Govindarajan and Haridasan (1969) with those of Gaur et al. (1971) and note the sensitivity to the input data. Grim et al. (1972), and Jain and Prabhakaran (1973b) have investigated the force constant changes associated with these systems. The latter authors used a simple model phonon density of states within the simple nearest neighbour approximation of subsection 5.2 for a monatomic host crystal and their results are also shown in table 10. Grim et al. (1972) carried through a full calculation using a modified rigid ion model but gave only a graph from which the force constant changes are to be estimated. Their results are compatible with those of Jain and Prabkakaran.

TABLE 10

Local mode calculations for zinc blende structure, local mode frequency in cm^{-1}

		Exp	Mass defect			$\Delta f/f$	R.
	Ref.	a	b	c	d	d	
	^{10}B	540(e)		567			0.32
	^{11}B	517(e)		544			
Ga As	Al	362		369	363	0.0	0.80
	^{28}Si	384(e)	350	363	358	0.15	
	^{29}Si	379(e)		358	352	0.17	
	^{30}Si	373(e)		352	349	0.18	
As	^{28}Si	399	358	365	366	0.20	
Ga	P	355	337	351	354	0.0	0.72
In Sb	Al	296	286	307			0.62
Ga Sb	Al	317	313	333			0.80
Ga *Sb*	P	324	308	327			0.55

a) As quoted by Gaur et al. (1971), unless otherwise stated.
b) Govindarajan and Haridasan (1969).
c) Gaur et al. (1971).
d) Jain and Prabhakaran (1973b).
e) Thompson and Newman (1972).

TABLE 11

Local and gap mode frequencies (in cm^{-1}) for GaP as host crystal

		Mass defect			$\Delta f/f$
	exp.	a	b	c	c
^{10}B	593[d]	661	637	649	−0.47
^{11}B	570	635	612	625	
^{10}B	285[d]	247	289	258	>1.16
^{11}B	283	246	288	257	
^{14}N	496[e]	506	525		
^{15}N	480	491	509		

a) Hayes et al. (1969, 1970).
b) Gaur et al. (1971).
c) Kim and Yip (1972).
d) Thompson and Newman (1971).
e) Thompson and Nicklin (1972).

In table 11 we give further comparisons, this time for impurities in GaP. Hayes et al. (1969, 1970) used a simple model density of states whereas Kim and Yip (1972) used shell model phonons fitted to inelastic neutron scattering results. Although the magnitudes of the isotope splittings are well described within the mass defect calculation, Kim and Yip were not completely successful in obtaining detailed agreement for $^{10,11}B$ using nearest neighbour force constant changes. They could correctly place the local modes and their splitting, but were unable to fit the splitting of the gap modes. As can be seen from table 11, Δf's of different signs are indicated by the local and gap mode frequencies. Jain and Prabhakaran (1973b) also considered impurities in GaP but their approximations are not particularly valid for this case.

Sennett et al. (1969) have considered Be in CdTe as a mass defect using shell model phonons. This gave a value of 417 cm^{-1} for the local mode frequency, to be compared with the experimental result of 391 cm^{-1} and the rigid ion value of 426 cm^{-1} due to Gaur et al. (1971). As there are no symmetry restrictions on the band phonons contributing to the sideband of this local mode they used the 'impurity only' approximation for a mass defect. They found that the sideband was best fitted using ω^{-1} Im $G(0,0:\omega)$, a result intermediate between $\alpha_A(\omega)$ and $\alpha_{2D}(\omega)$ (subsection 7.1). Rather than indicating contributions from both $\alpha_A(\omega)$ and $\alpha_{2D}(\omega)$ this might be explainable by an appropriate weighting of the different i.r.'s contributing to the sideband. Both experiment (sideband and infra red) and the mass defect results show an incipient resonance at 61 cm^{-1} that has split off the top of the transverse peak. We note that local modes due to Li^+ and Na^+ in the silver halides have been detected by Hattori et al. (1973). However, there are no calculations with which to compare their results.

The remaining diatomic system for which calculations have been presented is MgO with V^{2+}, Ni^{2+} and Cr^{3+} as impurities. Sangster and McCombie (1970) used both longitudinal and transverse, nearest neighbour, force constant changes (Δf_L and Δf_T) to fit the vibronic sidebands of these impurities. Although both the T_{1u} and T_{2u} representations can contribute to these sidebands Sangster and McCombie found that their best fits were obtained using the T_{1u} representation with $(\Delta f/f)_L = 0.16, -0.03$ for V^{2+} and Ni^{2+} respectively and $(\Delta f/f)_T = 0.46$ for both impurities. Both these systems have a strong resonance around 210 cm^{-1}. However, for Cr^{3+} Sangster (1972) found that the best fit was obtained using just the T_{2u} representation, which does not show a resonance, using $(\Delta f/f)_T = -0.19$. $(\Delta f/f)_L$ was undetermined as it does not affect the T_{2u} representation. Manson (1971) has also examined the sideband of Ni^{2+} in MgO. He obtained as good a fit as Sangster and McCombie without the use of force constant changes but by the appropriate combination of different components of the T_{1u} representation. As Manson remarks there appear to be too many parameters required in the fitting to make precise statements as to their values.

TABLE 12

Fractional force constant changes for impurities in alkaline earth fluorides

		H^-	D^- (a)	Sm^{2+}	Co^{2+}	La^{3+} (b)	Gd^{3+}	Tm^{3+}	Y^{3+}	Ce^{3+} (c)
CaF_2	Δf	−0.32	−0.36	0.60	−0.30	0.50	0.20	−0.05	−0.25	0.45
	R			1.05	0.75	1.16	1.03	0.96	0.94	1.12
SrF_2	Δf	−0.27	−0.26							
BaF_2	Δf	−0.16	−0.13							

a) Hayes and Wiltshire (1973a).
b) Hayes and Wiltshire (1973b).
c) Hayes et al. (1973).

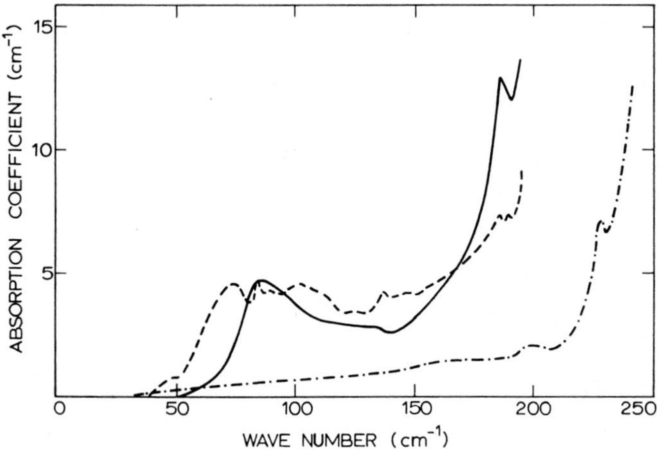

Fig. 26. Far infra-red absorption due to Tm^{3+} in CaF_2; ----- experiment ——— calculation, -·-·-·- undoped CaF_2 (Hayes and Wiltshire 1973b).

Detailed calculations for impurities in CaF_2, BaF_2 and SrF_2 have recently been presented by Hayes and coworkers. They used shell model phonons, as determined by inelastic neutron scattering, and took into account the possibility of a longitudinal force constant change, Δf. Their fitted parameters are collected together in table 12. The fitting to the infra-red spectra for all the heavy impurities was quite successful with the exception of Y^{3+} which has a low frequency resonance and again the calculated intensity is much too strong (see subsection 7.3). Most of these systems do not show resonances but another exception is Tm^{3+} shown in fig. 26. Hayes et al.

(1973) also examined a vibronic sideband of Ce^{3+} but, as all even parity modes are active, could only compare, not very successfully, with the density of states.

Vibronic sidebands of Sm^{2+} in CaF_2, $SrCl_2$ and EuF_2 have been measured by Kuhner et al. (1972). They find that they can fit their spectra using the appropriate combinations of the i.r.'s of just the unperturbed Green's functions. In fact they use their results to attempt to choose between the various shell models used to calculate the unperturbed phonons. Also, the Raman spectra due to Eu^{2+} in BaF_2 and SrF_2 have been measured by Chase et al. (1973) and analysed in terms of unperturbed Green's functions. They find evidence that the Raman coupling extends beyond the nearest neighbours of the impurity (see subsection 7.1).

The U centre work has more variety. The values of Δf in table 12 were fitted to the local mode frequencies, and Hayes and Wiltshire (1973a) employed the fitted value for $BaF_2{:}H^-$ to obtain good agreement with the experimental A_{1g} Raman spectra. As there are no symmetry restrictions for the infra-red local mode sideband they used the 'impurity only' result finding that the second-order dipole result (7.6) fitted best. However, their comparison with experiment is quite good. A strong resonance at 285 cm^{-1} can also be seen in the T_2 Raman spectra (Harrington et al. 1971). The calculated mass defect value is 272 cm^{-1} but the use of the fitted Δf, unfortunately, reduces it to 266 cm^{-1}. Clearly a more extensive force constant model is required. Harrington et al. (1971) also measured the Raman local mode sideband finding it in substantial agreement (at 300 K) with the infra-red result. Elliott et al. (1965) have calculated the $CaF_2{:}H^-$ infra-red local mode sideband and, although ignoring even the mass change, obtained fair agreement with experiment. The infra-red band absorption of these systems has been detected by Harrington and Weber (1973) but no calculations have appeared.

The work of Lacina and Pershan (1970) for $CaF_2{:}Sr$ must also be mentioned. They calculated the reflectivity and the Raman scattering using the finite concentration result for $\boldsymbol{G}(\omega)$ and estimated the force constant changes from SrF_2 data. Their nearest neighbour longitudinal and transverse changes were only -2% and -4% respectively but the F^-–F^- force constant change was -52%. Unfortunately they were at too high a concentration ($c=0.25$ and their results too insensitive to these parameters to really check these values.

Low concentration reflectivities have been measured by Harrington and Weber (1972) for $CaF_2{:}H^-$. They were interested in the Lorentz field splitting of the local mode into longitudinal and transverse local modes at ω_ℓ and ω_t, as calculated by Maradudin and Oitmaa (1969) (MO). Although MO considered the special case of just the H^- ions in motion, such a splitting is an immediate consequence of the dispersion given by (4.9). In the high-frequency limit this result becomes

$$\Delta\omega_p = \omega_p - \omega_L = (cM_0/2\omega_L M)\left[\omega_j^2(\boldsymbol{k}) - (1-\varepsilon)\,\omega_L^2\right], \tag{7.9}$$

so that

$$\Delta\omega = \omega_l - \omega_t = (cM_0/2\omega_L M)\left[\omega_{LO}^2 - \omega_{TO}^2\right]. \tag{7.10}$$

On using the approximate result that $\omega_{LO}^2 - \omega_{TO}^2$ is equal to the ion plasma frequency $4\pi e^2/M_0\Omega_0$, (7.10) reduces to the result of MO although they have different expressions for $\Delta\omega_\ell$ and $\Delta\omega_t$. For $c=0.025$ Harrington and Weber found $\Delta\omega_t = -0.6\ \text{cm}^{-1}$ and $\Delta\omega_\ell = 15\ \text{cm}^{-1}$ whereas MO predict $\Delta\omega_t = -5\ \text{cm}^{-1}$, $\Delta\omega_\ell = 10\ \text{cm}^{-1}$. Our result (7.9) predicts $\Delta\omega_t = 5\ \text{cm}^{-1}$ and $\Delta\omega_\ell = 41\ \text{cm}^{-1}$ if we use the experimental ω_{TO} and ω_{LO}. However, (7.9) applies to a monatomic host crystal. If we attempt to take into account the diatomic nature of the host crystal by using the rock salt result (4.3) then we get $\Delta\omega_t = 0.1\ \text{cm}^{-1}$ and $\Delta\omega_\ell = +25\ \text{cm}^{-1}$. Clearly, a more accurate model, including force constant changes, is required before any conclusion can be made as to whether the observed splitting can be accounted for by the above theory. Note that volume change effects (see subsection 2.2) should be included, as suggested by Harrington and Weber. We note in passing that Harrington and Walker (1971) found that the local mode in $BaF_2:H^-$ broadens according to $c^{1/2}$ which agrees with the fluctuation estimate of Dawber and Elliott (1963) and the CPA result of Taylor (1967). It is unfortunate that an experimental test of the above linear splitting is not available.

Besides the basically cubic systems discussed above the wurtzite and rutile structures have also received some attention. Beserman and Balkanski (1970) have examined CdSe:S and CdS:Se, comparing their experimental results for local and gap mode frequencies with the calculations of Nusimovici et al. (1970b). The results are shown in table 13 where it can be seen that the splitting of these modes due to the lack of cubic symmetry can be significant. In table 13 the $\parallel$ and $\perp$ symbols refer to polarization relative to the *c*-axis. They attributed the errors for the gap modes more to inaccuracies in the host crystal phonons than to force constant changes. Beserman and Balkanski also used the low-concentration results of section 4 to calculate the absorption spectra and the concentration dependence of these modes. In spite of

TABLE 13

Local and gap mode frequencies (in cm^{-1}) for the Wurtzite structure (Bederman and Balkanski 1970).

	CdS:Se Gap mode		CdSe:S Local mode	
	Exp.	Cal.	Exp.	Cal.
$\omega_{\parallel}$	182.5	191	266.5	266
$\omega_{\perp}$	187	195	269	271
R		1.45		0.69

using a cubic approximation, but with the correct wurtzite density of states due to Nusimovici et al. (1970a), they were able to obtain fair agreement with experiment.

Benson (1973) has presented calculations for the low-frequency resonances due to Eu^{2+} and Tm^{3+} in MnF_2 using the linear result for $\boldsymbol{G}(\omega)$, (3.8), in the expression for the absorption coefficient (7.2). One consequence of the reduced symmetry is that there are four infra-red active modes in the pure crystals (A_{2u} and $3E_u$) and as a consequence the cubic result (7.8) has to be generalized to include all these modes and their mixing by the presence of the impurity. Benson found little effect due to this mixing and no evidence of mode splitting. However, it has to be noted that he only considered the absorption due to unpolarized radiation. He was able to fit a 37 cm^{-1} resonance of MnF_2:Tm^{3+} with $\Delta f/f = -0.1$ and a 16 cm^{-1} resonance of MnF_2:Eu^{2+} with $\Delta f/f = -0.15$ but there remained peaks in the experimental results that he was unable to fit. The intensity comparisons were poor, partly due to inadequate statistics in calculating Im $\boldsymbol{G}^0(\omega)$ but, judging from the other low frequency resonance calculations discussed above, also due to anharmonic effects.

8. *Modifications to phonon dispersion curves*

8.1. Neutron cross sections and elastic constants

Inelastic coherent neutron scattering provides an excellent means of studying the phonon dispersion curves of both pure and impure crystals (see ch.10, vol. 1) and the measurement of elastic constants can provide complementary information. Krivoglaz (1961), and Kagan and Iosilevskii (1963) have given early discussions of neutron scattering in alloys but it was left to Elliott and Maradudin (1965) to point/out the explicit effects due to the occurrence of a resonant mode. Subsequently Elliott and Taylor (1967) have treated both the resonant and local mode behaviour on the same footing as well as including the major effects due to the different neutron scattering lengths of the host and impurity atoms.

The neutron scattering cross section is obtained from the 'golden rule' transition probability and can be separated into two parts, coherent and incoherent [see for instance Maradudin et al. (1971)]. On allowing for the scattering lengths to be site dependent the one-phonon cross section is given by

$$\left.\frac{\mathrm{d}^2\sigma}{\mathrm{d}\Omega\,\mathrm{d}\omega}\right|_{\mathrm{coh}} = \frac{k_s}{k_0}\sum_{\substack{l\kappa\\ l'\kappa'}} \exp\{-\mathrm{i}\boldsymbol{Q}\cdot[\boldsymbol{R}(l\kappa)-\boldsymbol{R}(l'\kappa')]\}\,A(l\kappa)\,A(l'\kappa') \times \sum_{\alpha\beta} Q_\alpha S_{\alpha\beta}(l\kappa, l'\kappa';\omega)\,Q_\beta\,,$$

$$\left.\frac{\mathrm{d}^2\sigma}{\mathrm{d}\Omega\,\mathrm{d}\omega}\right|_{\mathrm{incoh}} = \frac{k_s}{k_0}\sum_{l\kappa} \alpha^2(l\kappa)\sum_{\alpha\beta} Q_\alpha S_{\alpha\beta}(l\kappa, l\kappa;\omega)\,Q_\beta\,.$$

Here $\boldsymbol{k}_0$ and $\boldsymbol{k}_s = \boldsymbol{k}_0 - \boldsymbol{Q}$ are the initial and final wave vectors of the neutron and $\hbar\omega$ is the energy loss of the neutron. The scattering length $A(l\kappa)$ is the coherent scattering length of the atom at $(l\kappa)$ averaged over spin and isotope disorder, $\overline{a(l\kappa)}$, multiplied by a Debye–Waller factor,

$$A(l\kappa) = \overline{a(l\kappa)}\exp[-\tfrac{1}{2}\langle[\boldsymbol{Q}\cdot\boldsymbol{u}(l\kappa)]^2\rangle],$$

and the incoherent scattering length $\alpha^2(l\kappa)$ is similarly defined

$$\alpha^2(l\kappa) = [\overline{a(l\kappa)^2} - \overline{a(l\kappa)}^2]\exp[-\langle[\boldsymbol{Q}\cdot\boldsymbol{u}(l\kappa)^2\rangle].$$

Elliott and Taylor (1967) found rather large variations in these scattering lengths are necessary before there is any significant effect. This allows us to neglect the variations in the atomic displacements in the Debye–Waller factors.

In those cases where the impurity and host atoms have approximately the scattering lengths the final result is

$$\frac{\mathrm{d}^2\sigma}{\mathrm{d}\Omega\,\mathrm{d}\omega} = \frac{N\hbar\,\mathrm{e}^{\beta\omega}}{\mathrm{e}^{\beta\omega}-1}\sum_{\alpha\beta} Q_\alpha \tilde{S}_{\alpha\beta}(\boldsymbol{Q},\omega)\,Q_\beta\,, \tag{8.1}$$

with

$$\tilde{\boldsymbol{S}}(\boldsymbol{Q},\omega) = \tilde{\boldsymbol{S}}^{\mathrm{coh}}(\boldsymbol{Q},\omega) + \tilde{\boldsymbol{S}}^{\mathrm{incoh}}(\boldsymbol{Q},\omega),$$

and

$$\tilde{S}^{\text{coh}}_{\alpha\beta}(Q,\omega) = \text{Im}\sum_{\kappa\kappa'} A(\kappa)\,A(\kappa')\sum_{\substack{\alpha\beta\\ jj'}} \frac{w_\alpha(\kappa|Qj)\,w_\beta(\kappa'|Qj')}{[M_0(\kappa)\,M_0(\kappa')]^{1/2}}\langle G_{jj'}(Q,\omega)\rangle,$$

$$\tilde{\boldsymbol{S}}^{\text{incoh}}(Q,\omega) = \text{Im}\sum_{\kappa}\alpha^2(\kappa)\,\langle \boldsymbol{G}(l\kappa, l\kappa;\omega)\rangle.$$

When the impurity and host atom scattering lengths are different ($A_{\text{i}} \neq A_{\text{h}}$, $\alpha_{\text{i}}^2 \neq \alpha_{\text{h}}^2$) Elliott and Taylor have shown that for a cubic monatomic host crystal in the mass defect approximation the following replacements must be made in (8.1),

$$A^2 \to \left[A_{\text{h}} + \frac{c\,(A_{\text{i}} - A_{\text{h}})}{1-(1-c)\,M_0\varepsilon\omega^2\,G^0(\omega)}\right]^2,$$
$$\alpha^2 \to \alpha_{\text{h}}^2 + \frac{c\,(\alpha_{\text{i}}^2 - \alpha_{\text{h}}^2)}{1-(1-c)\,M_0\varepsilon\omega^2\,G^0(\omega)}. \tag{8.2}$$

In addition the disorder in the scattering lengths leads to an extra contribution to $\tilde{\boldsymbol{S}}^{\text{incoh}}(\boldsymbol{Q},\omega)$,

$$\text{Im}\,\frac{(A_{\text{i}} - A_{\text{h}})^2\,c\,(1-c)\,\boldsymbol{G}^0(\omega)}{1-(1-c)\,M_0\varepsilon\omega^2\,G^0(\omega)}.$$

According to the calculations of Elliott and Taylor (1967), $A_{\text{i}} - A_{\text{h}}$ has to exceed A_{h}, for there to be any significant effect on the cross sections and then only at a resonance. In none of the coherent scattering results considered in the next two subsections is this realized. Hence the extra complications of (8.2) have not been required in any of the calculations.

In general $\langle G_{jj'}(\boldsymbol{Q},\omega)\rangle$ contains off-diagonal contributions due to branch mixing. However, as discussed at the end of subsection 5.1, this Green's function becomes diagonal for $\boldsymbol{Q}$ (or rather $\boldsymbol{Q}$ reduced to the first Brillouin zone) along symmetry directions in a monatomic host crystal. Then as the scattering geometry is usually set up so that $\boldsymbol{Q}\cdot\boldsymbol{w}(\kappa|\boldsymbol{Q}j)$ projects out just one branch (see ch. 10, vol. 1) it is sufficient to examine just Im $\langle G_j(\boldsymbol{Q},\omega)\rangle$ to obtain the frequency dependence of the cross section. Further, in the on-shell approximation, we can simplify the result to the calculation of a disorder shift and width, $\Delta(\boldsymbol{Q}j)$ and $\Gamma(\boldsymbol{Q}j)$ of (5.3). In diatomic crystals this mixing remains, even for a mass defect, being at least between the acoustic and optic branches. Benedek and Nardelli (1967) have indicated that it might be dropped as it leads to a correction of $O(c^2)$.

The on-shell approximation immediately leads to expressions for the elastic constants, as demonstrated by Benedek and Nardelli (1968a). The phonon frequencies of the disordered crystal $\omega_j^2(\boldsymbol{k})$, are given by

$$\tilde{\omega}_j^2(\boldsymbol{k}) = \omega_j^2(\boldsymbol{k}) + \operatorname{Re}\Sigma_j(\boldsymbol{k}, \omega_j(\boldsymbol{k})).$$

In the limit of small $\boldsymbol{k}$, ω it can be shown that

$$\operatorname{Re}\Sigma_j(\boldsymbol{k}, \omega) = k^2 \frac{\partial \operatorname{Re}\Sigma_j(\boldsymbol{k}, 0)}{\partial k^2} + \omega^2 \frac{\partial \operatorname{Re}\Sigma_j(\boldsymbol{0}, \omega)}{\partial \omega^2},$$

where use has been made of inversion symmetry and that $\operatorname{Re}\boldsymbol{G}(\omega)$ is an even function of ω. From the definition of $\Sigma_j(\boldsymbol{k}, \omega)$, (3.10), and from

$$\sum_{l\kappa} \Delta\boldsymbol{\Phi}(l\kappa, l'\kappa') = 0,$$

it follows that

$$\frac{\partial \operatorname{Re}\Sigma_j(\boldsymbol{0}, \omega)}{\partial \omega^2} = \frac{c\varepsilon(1)}{\sum_{\kappa} M(\kappa)}$$

for an impurity on sublattice $\kappa=1$. Further, only even i.r. can contribute to $\partial[\operatorname{Re}\Sigma_j(\boldsymbol{k}, 0)]/\partial k^2$. Then, on introducing the velocity $v_j = \omega_j(\boldsymbol{k})/k$, the elastic constants in the disordered crystal, $\tilde{\rho}\tilde{v}_j$, are related to those in the pure crystal by

$$\tilde{\rho}\tilde{v}_j^2 = \rho v_j^2 \left(1 + \frac{1}{v_j^2} \frac{\partial \operatorname{Re}\Sigma_j(\boldsymbol{k}, 0)}{\partial k^2}\right). \tag{8.3}$$

The mass defect contribution from $\Sigma_j(\boldsymbol{k}, \omega)$ has cancelled against $(\tilde{\rho}-\rho)/\rho$ yielding an ω-independent result that is in agreement with that obtained by Elliott at al. (1968) using an entirely static method.

So far we have omitted the effects due to the volume change on adding the impurities. Following the approximation discussed at the end of subsection 2.2, the coherent neutron cross section should be modified by multiplying $\omega_j(\boldsymbol{k})$ in $\langle G_{jj'}(\boldsymbol{k}, \omega)\rangle$ by $1-\gamma_j(\boldsymbol{k})\,\Delta V/V$. Here $\gamma_j(\boldsymbol{k})$ is a mode Grüneisen parameter

$$\gamma_j(\boldsymbol{k}) = -\frac{\mathrm{d}\ln\omega_j(\boldsymbol{k})}{\mathrm{d}\ln V},$$

and $\Delta V/V$ is the observed volume change. The expression for the elastic constant (8.3), is modified by the addition of $-(1+2\gamma_j)\,\Delta V/V$ in the bracket.

8.2. Heavy impurities

Kesharwani and Agrawal (1972b, c) have given on-shell calculations for the $Cr_{1-c}W_c$ system in an attempt to fit the experimental results of Mackintosh and Moller (1968) for $c=0.03$ and those of Cunningham et al. (1970) for $c=0.003$, 0.008, 0.016. In figs. 27, 28 we show the experimental and calculated frequency shifts for the $T\,[00\zeta]$ and $T_2\,[0\zeta\zeta]$ branches at

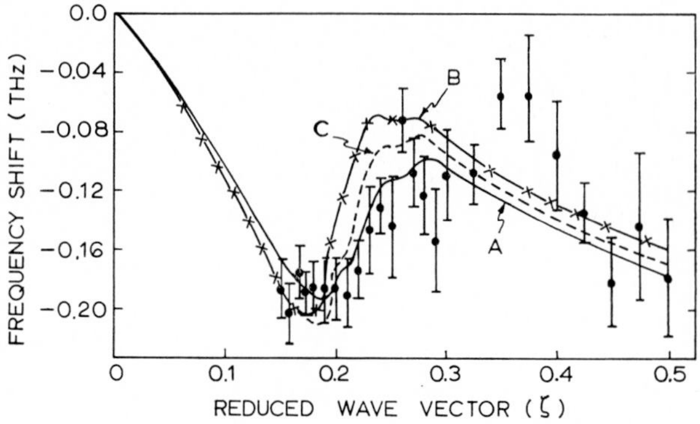

Fig. 27. Frequency shift for the $T\,[00\zeta]$ branch due to 1.6%W in Cr. Experimental points are those of Cunningham et al. (1970). The letters refer to the various parameters in Table 14 (Kesharwani and Agrawal 1972c).

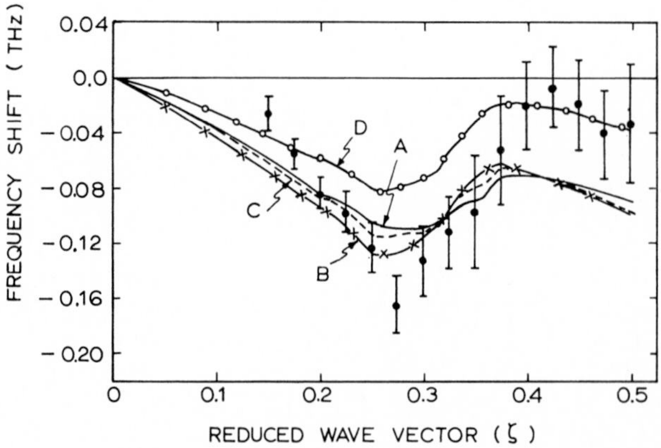

Fig. 28. Frequency shift for the $T_2\,[0\zeta\zeta]$ branch due to 1.6%W in Cr. Key as for Fig. 27.

$c=0.016$. The labelling of the various calculated curves corresponds to the parameters in table 14. In order to take into account the 0.7% volume change Kesharwani and Agrawal used $\boldsymbol{k}$-independent mode Grüneisen parameters, γ_j but concluded that a significant $\boldsymbol{k}$ dependence is required, particularly for $T[00\zeta]$, see fig. 27. Their values of γ_j were chosen to help fit to the experimental results but are considerably larger than the thermodynamic values of around 2 quoted by Gschneider (1964).

TABLE 14

Parameters used to fit Cr:W dispersion curves; $f_L=38.7\times10^4$ dyne cm^{-1}, $f_T=0.23\times10^4$ dyne cm^{-1}. Letters refer to figs. 27, 28 (Kesharwani and Agrawal 1972c).

	Mode Grüneisen γ_j		Force const. changes in 10^4 dyne cm^{-1}	
	$T\,[00\zeta]$	$T_1[0\zeta\zeta]$	Δf_L	Δf_T
A	3.5	3.5	6.04	0
B	3.0	3.5	6.04	−0.52
C	3.2	3.5	7.77	−0.52
D		2.0	7.77	−0.52

There is a definite branch dependence to these results, both in the calculations and experiment. This rules out the simpler branch independent result of Cohen and Gilat (1972) based on just the T_{1u} contribution and using the n.n. model of subsection 5.2. The agreement with experiment is quite fair with little to choose between the different fits. However, it could be said that the calculated resonance is rather too weak for $T[00\zeta]$ and this discrepancy remains in their comparisons with the $c=0.03$ results. Mackintosh and Moller also gave the widths of the cross sections as a function of ω and the calculated curves show a much weaker resonant peak as might be expected from the above shift discussion.

It should be noted that the force constant changes do have an appreciable effect on the calculations, having to move the mass defect resonance from a much lower energy. Further Kesharwani and Agrawal used only nearest neighbour longitudinal and transverse force constant changes yet, as is typical in BCC metals, their first and second nearest neighbour, longitudinal force constants, as determined via the Krebs (1965) model, are of the same magnitude being 38.76×10^4 and 35.86×10^4 dyne cm^{-1}, respectively.

Both Bruno and Taylor (1971) (BT), and Kesharwani and Agrawal (1973a) (KA) have discussed the experimental results of Svensson and Kamitakahara

(1971) for $Cu_{1-c}Au_c$, $c=0.03$, 0.093. The comparisons between the calculations and experiment for the $T[00\zeta]$ branch are shown in figs. 29, 30. The general agreement is quite good but rather different approximations were used by BT and KA. In order to take into account the volume change of

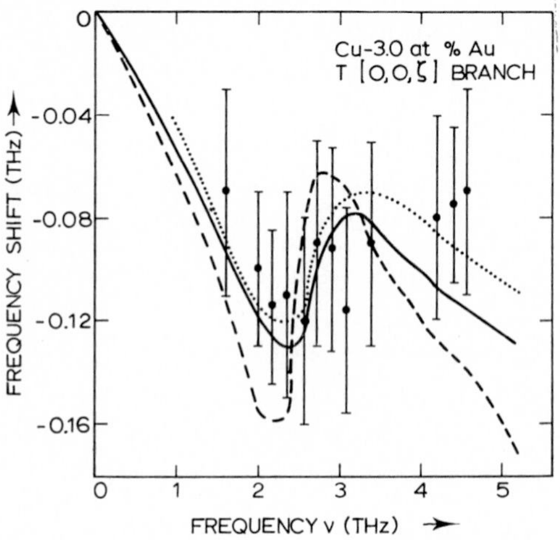

Fig. 29. Frequency shift of the $T[00\zeta]$ branch for 3% Au in Cu; ——— fit due to Kersharwani and Agrawal (1973a), ... fit due to Bruno and Taylor (1971), ----- Mass defect result (Kersharwani and Agrawal 1973a), (Effects due to volume change included). Experimental points are from Svensson and Kamitakahara (1971).

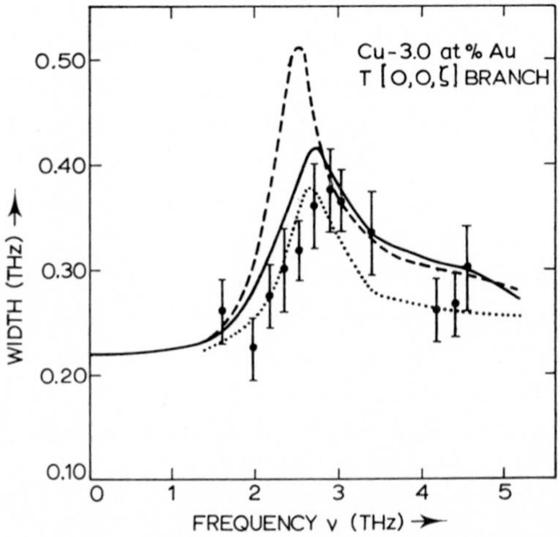

Fig. 30. FWHM for the $T[00\zeta]$ branch for 3% Au in Cu, both disorder and resolution broadening are included. Same key as for fig. 29.

TABLE 15

Comparison of force constant fits for Cu:Au. Units are 10^4 dyne cm^{-1}

	f_L	Δf_L	f_{T_1}	Δf_{T_1}	f_{T_2}	Δf_{T_2}
BT	2.56	0.68	−0.15	−0.21	−0.09	0.06
KA	3.18	1.27	−0.21	−0.03	−0.21	−0.03

BT Bruno and Taylor (1971). KA Kershawani and Agrawal (1973a).

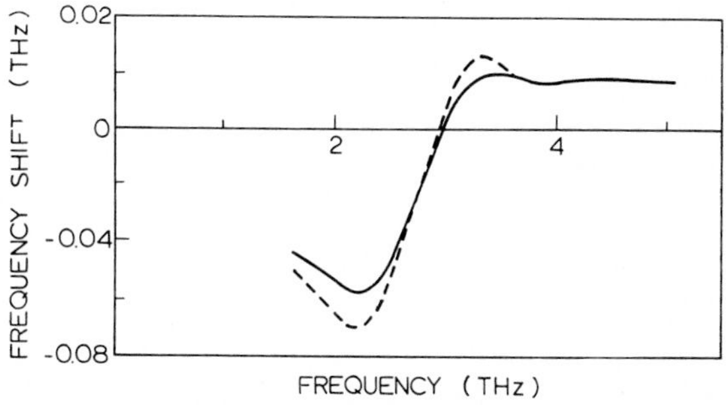

Fig. 31. Comparison of the on-shell (-----) and off-shell (———) frequency shifts of the $T\,[00\zeta]$ branch for 3% Au in Cu. The on shell shift corresponds to the fitted result of Kesharwani and Agrawal (1973a) without the volume change effect.

1.6%, BT used a Morse potential to estimate the mode Grüneisen parameters $\gamma_j(\boldsymbol{k})$ whereas KA used the experimental volume dependence of the elastic constants of Cu along with Kreb's model. The results are radically different with KA finding little $\boldsymbol{k}$ dependence whereas BT found considerable dependence but poor values for the elastic constant, Grüneisen parameters. As for Cr/W, KA used the on-shell approximation whereas BT actually calculated the cross section folded with a gaussian resolution function. (The Cu and Au scattering lengths are essentially identical). This latter procedure produces small but significant differences from the on-shell approximation. We illustrate this in fig. 31 comparing the on-shell and full calculation shifts for KA's fitted parameters. The force constant changes, have to be modified by about 20–30% to return the full calculation to the on-shell fit.

For $T_1\,[0\zeta\zeta]$ the results are quite different as is seen in fig. 32. Here BT are in much better agreement with experiment than are KA, but this is due to their, possibly dubious, strong $\boldsymbol{k}$ dependence of $\gamma_j(\boldsymbol{k})$. KA also compared their calculations with the $c=0.093$ results. In this case the theory is really being extended beyond its range of validity (see section 6) and the comparison

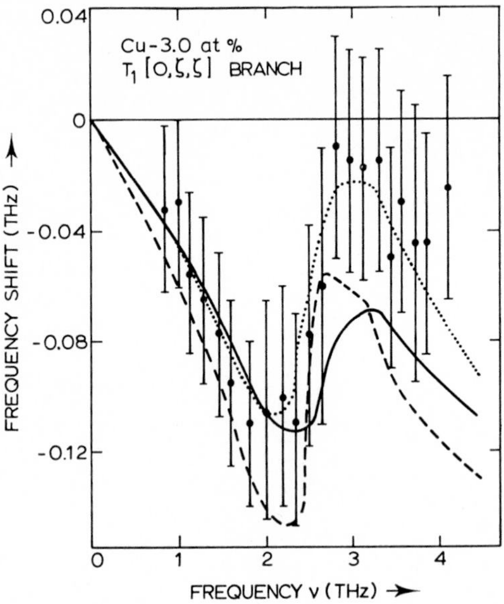

Fig. 32. Frequency shift for the $T_1[0\zeta\zeta]$ branch for 3% Au in Cu. Same key as for fig. 29.

is much worse as the experimental resonance is appreciably washed out. Svensson and Kamitakahara (1971) were able to measure the $L[00\zeta]$ shift at $c=0.093$ and it is remarkable that it shows no sign of a resonance, a fact unexplainable with the above models. Both BT and KA conjecture that this may be associated with the behaviour of conduction electrons in alloys as it is well known that electron screening has a substantially larger effect on longitudinal as opposed to transverse vibrations.

The elastic constants of low concentration Cu:Au alloys have been measured by O'Hara and Marshall (1971), their results showing a significant temperature dependence for the alloying change. Further, c_{11}, which yields the longitudinal (100) velocity, first decreases from the pure Cu value before rising as a function of Au concentration. Ignoring this behaviour which the theory of subsection 8.1 cannot explain, we have performed calculations for the transverse elastic constants, c_{12} and c_{44}. Unfortunately, we have been unable to find any combination of n.n. force constant changes to fit the experimental results (Hampson and Taylor, unpublished).

Kesherwani and Agrawal (1971, 1972a) have applied the theory of Benedek and Nardelli (1968a) for the elastic constants to impurities in CsI and to Mo:Re. In the first publication they used the force constant changes fitted to infra-red experiments (see table 9) but there were no experiments with which to compare. In the second, they fitted to the experimental results of Davidson and Brotzen (1968) for 7% Re in Mo. Subsequently, they have found that the addition of second n.n. force constant changes is of little consequence (Kesharwani and Agrawal 1973b). However, as Kesharwani and Agrawal did not include any volume change contribution the validity of these results is questionable.

8.3. Light impurities

Nicklow et al. (1968) have presented experimental results for 4% and 10% Al in Cu and compared them with the mass defect approximation. They found that the cross section at the local mode has very little dispersion, but a strong intensity dependence on $\boldsymbol{Q}$. This in fact could be explained quite well by (4.8), i.e. by the residue of the pole in $\langle G_j(\boldsymbol{Q}, \omega)\rangle$. The comparison between theory and experiment for the frequency shift $\Delta(\boldsymbol{Q}j)$ was reasonable for $c=0.04$ (but not for $c=0.10$) provided the volume change effect was included using a Grüneisen parameter $\gamma=2$. The 1% volume change shifts the calculated, local mode frequency for 8.48 THz down to 8.31 THz. As the measured value is 8.8 THz this indicates the need for an increase in the force constants. Changing just f_L we estimate $\Delta f_L/f_L=+0.14$. Unfortunately, this has an adverse effect on the agreement between theory and experiment for $\Delta(\boldsymbol{Q}j)$. The expression (4.9) suggests an impurity band dispersion of about 0.1 THz, a small value that is compatible with experiment.

The rather good agreement between theory and experiment for the $\boldsymbol{Q}$ dependence of the scattering intensity lead Nicklow et al. (1968) to use the result of Maradudin (1963) to estimate the localization of the local mode. [Maradudin was able to give an asymptotic expression for $\boldsymbol{u}(l)$ as a function of $\boldsymbol{R}(l)$ employing the dispersion of $\omega_j(\boldsymbol{k})$ at the zone boundary.] Nicklow et al. estimated a decay length of $0.38a_0$ in the $[\zeta\zeta\zeta]$ direction. This is in surprisingly good agreement with the estimate of $0.39a_0$ for the $[0\zeta\zeta]$ direction using the results of table 4.

Elastic constant measurements have been made for these alloys by Cain and Thomas (1971), but they have not been analysed in terms of the theory of this section.

Wakabayashi et al. (1971) have measured Ge:Si at the rather high Si concentration of $c=0.092$. Ignoring any volume change effect they found good agreement between the local mode dispersion formula (4.9) and experiment, see fig. 33. (The calculated local mode frequency ω_L, is 11.25 THz).

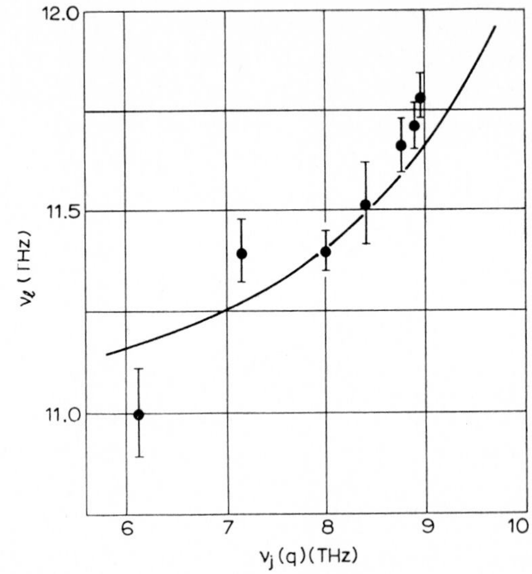

Fig. 33. Comparison of the mass defect calculation (———) with the experimental points for the dispersion of the local mode frequency in the impurity band due to 9% Si in Ge. (———). (Wakabayashi et al. 1971).

The agreement, as to the location of the local mode frequencies, may be somewhat fortuitous as it is necessary to include the volume change effect to obtain what is rather good agreement between theory and experiment for $\Delta(Qj)$. However using $\gamma=1$ and $\Delta V/V=-0.015$ the calculated curve is only moved to a little above the experimental points in fig. 33 (that is with the exception of the low point at the left of the figure). Hence the main features of the theory are well substantiated. It should be noted that there is good agreement between the Raman frequency obtained from the above study and that measured by Feldman et al. (1966), the results being 11.78 THz and 11.81 THz respectively.

9. *Frequency distributions*

In this section we will consider three properties that depend upon the frequency distributions of the disordered crystal. The first two, incoherent neutron scattering and the electron phonon function $\alpha^2 f(\omega)$, are related directly to the Green's function we have examined at length. The last property, the specific heat, is the only case where the density of states (2.15) is strictly relevant. The difference between the Green's function and the density of states is worth noting. It is easiest to demonstrate this for a mass defect using the conditional Green's functions of subsection 3.5. From (2.15) the density of states in a cubic crystal is then

$$\nu(\omega) = -(2\omega/\pi)\, M_0 \operatorname{Im}\left[c(1-\varepsilon)\, G^{\mathrm{i}}_{\alpha\alpha}(l, l; \omega) + (1-c)\, G^{\mathrm{h}}_{\alpha\alpha}(l, l; \omega)\right]. \tag{9.1}$$

For a heavy impurity $(1-\varepsilon>1)$, $\boldsymbol{G}^{\mathrm{i}}(\omega)$ has a stronger weighting in $\nu(\omega)$ than in $\langle \boldsymbol{G}(\omega)\rangle$. As a resonance will have a stronger effect on $\boldsymbol{G}^{\mathrm{i}}(\omega)$ than $\boldsymbol{G}^{\mathrm{h}}(\omega)$, we can expect resonant effects to be stronger in $\nu(\omega)$ than in $\operatorname{Im}\langle \boldsymbol{G}(\omega)\rangle$.

9.1. Inelastic incoherent neutron scattering

The main formulae for the one-phonon incoherent neutron cross section have already been given in subsection 8.1. However, no calculations have been published in the literature largely because of the absence of impurity effects, particularly resonances, in the published experiments. We note that this cross section is proportional to a combination of $\boldsymbol{G}^{\mathrm{h}}(\omega)$ and $\boldsymbol{G}^{\mathrm{i}}(\omega)$ weighted by the incoherent scattering lengths, rather than the host and impurity masses as in $\nu(\omega)$.

Mozer (1968) found no evidence of resonant modes for Ta, W, Pt in V with $c=0.05$. As the mass differences are quite appreciable ($\varepsilon \approx -2.6$) this is somewhat surprising. However, Elliott and Taylor (1967) found that the resonance due to Au in Cu ($\varepsilon = -2.1$) shows through rather weakly in the density of states and, as we have discussed above, resonances make an even weaker contribution to $\operatorname{Im}\langle \boldsymbol{G}(\omega)\rangle$. Also, the lower incoherent cross sections of the impurities, as compared to V, will further suppress any resonant mode contributions. For the much larger mass defect parameter $\varepsilon = -7.5$ for Mg:Pb Chernoplekov and Zemlyanov (1966) did see clear evidence of a low-frequency resonance at 1.0 THz.

Mozer and co-workers have been able to detect the impurity bands arising from local modes. Mozer et al. (1962) saw evidence for a local mode due to Ni in Pd whereas Mozer et al. (1966) and Mozer (1968) have investigated the well defined local mode due to Be in V. This latter local mode is well separated from the continuum, $\omega_{\mathrm{L}}/\omega_{\mathrm{m}} = 1.55$, and for $c = 0.033$ Mozer (1968) was able to detect a splitting, possibly due to clustering effects. These local mode frequencies are listed in table 16 along with the results of Natkaniec and co-workers for Mg:Li (Natkaniec et al. 1967) and Cu:Be, Cu:Mg, Pb:Na (Natkaniec et al. 1968). These authors also estimated force constant changes on the assumption that the local modes are highly localised [i.e. only changed $\Phi(0, 0)$ for an impurity at the origin]. Their results are given in table 16 and compared with our estimates using the Cu Green's functions of Bruno and Taylor (1971). Also given in table 16 are the local mode results of Zemlyanov et al. (1967) for Ni:Be.

TABLE 16

Local mode frequencies from incoherent neutron scattering.

System	Ref.	ω_L in THz Exp.	Mass defect		$\Delta f/f$	
Mg:Li	a	8.5	10.4		−0.45	
Cu:Be	b	10.2	14.0	14.0[f]	−0.56	−0.47[f]
Cu:Mg	b	8.3	9.1	8.9[f]	−0.22	−0.11[f]
Pb:Na	b	4.1	4.7		−0.25	
Pb:Mg	b	3.9	4.6		−0.33	
V:Be	c	14.0				
Pd:Ni	d	7.5				
Ni:Be	e	12.6	15.9			

a) Natkaniec et al. (1967).
b) Natkaniec et al. (1968).
c) Mozer (1968).
d) Mozer et al. (1962).
e) Zemlyanov et al. (1967).
f) from fig. 7.

9.2. Phonon distributions from superconductivity

For sufficiently strong coupling superconductors it is possible to extract a distribution $\alpha^2 f(\omega)$ from tunnelling measurements (Rowell and McMillan 1969). In terms of the formalism of this chapter this function can be written as (Taylor and Vashista 1972),

$$\alpha^2 f(\omega) = \frac{-N(0)}{8\pi^2 k_F^2 N^2} \int\limits_{k<2k_F} \frac{d^3k}{k} \sum_{\substack{ll'\\ \alpha\beta}} \bar{w}_l^*(\boldsymbol{k})\, k_\alpha \operatorname{Im} G_{\alpha\beta}(l, l'; \omega) \times \bar{w}_{l'}(\boldsymbol{k})\, k_\beta \exp\{\mathrm{i}\boldsymbol{k}\cdot[\boldsymbol{R}(l) - \boldsymbol{R}(l')]\}, \quad (9.2)$$

where $\bar{w}_l(\boldsymbol{k})$ is the screened pseudo-potential form factor for the atom at site l and $N(0)$ is the single spin electron density of states at the Fermi surface.

If the l dependence of the $\bar{w}_l(\boldsymbol{k})$ is ignored, then in the mass defect approximation this becomes

$$\alpha^2 f(\omega) = -(2/\pi) \int \mathrm{d}\omega' \, \alpha_0^2 f(\omega') \, \omega' \, \mathrm{Im}\, G(\omega', \omega).$$

Here $\alpha_0^2 f(\omega)$ is the unperturbed function and we have used the fact that $G_j(\boldsymbol{k}, \omega)$ only depends upon $(j, \boldsymbol{k})$ through $\omega_j(\boldsymbol{k})$ [see (4.2)].

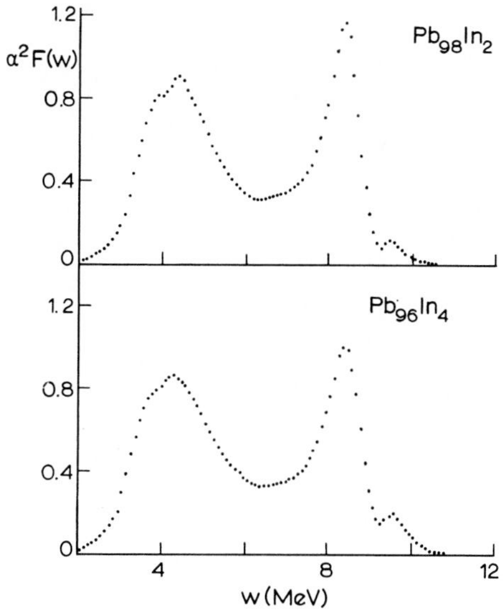

Fig. 34. Experimental values of $\alpha^2 f(\omega)$ for Pb:In (Sood 1972).

The only dilute alloy for which $\alpha^2 f(\omega)$ has been measured is Pb:In. This was first done by Rowell et al. (1965) who found an impurity band centred on 2.30 THz in good agreement with the mass defect value for ω_{L}. Sood (1972) has investigated this system for $c=0.01$ to 0.08 and we show a typical result in fig. 34. Elliott and Taylor (1967) have calculated the density of states for this system but obtained a narrow, high-impurity band in contrast to that shown in fig. 34. However, the pseudo-potential form factors, $\bar{w}_l(\boldsymbol{k})$ for Pb and In must be quite different due to their different valence and this should be included in a realistic comparison with experiment. It has to be noted that the experiment shows a significant broadening of uncertain origin.

9.3. Specific heat changes

The lattice specific heat is given by

$$C_v = 3rNk_B \int_0^{\omega_m} [\tfrac{1}{2}\beta\omega \operatorname{csch}(\tfrac{1}{2}\beta\omega)]^2 \, \nu(\omega)\, d\omega .$$

As pointed out by Lehman and De Wames (1963), and Kagan and Iosilevskii (1964) changes in the density of states, $\nu(\omega)$, due to the presence of impurities should lead to changes in C_v. Resonances at low frequencies should have a particularly strong effect at low temperatures.

Although we have indicated the general result for the density of states at finite concentrations at the beginning of this section, (9.1), it is difficult to evaluate in the presence of force constant changes. Rather it is usual to return to the basic formula (2.15) and follow the procedures described by Maradudin et al. (1971). (2.15) can be rewritten as

$$\nu(\omega) = \frac{1}{3rN\pi} \operatorname{Im} \frac{d \log \det \boldsymbol{G}(\omega)}{d\omega},$$

so that the change in the density of states on alloying is

$$\Delta\nu(\omega) = \nu(\omega) - \nu_0(\omega) = -(1/3rN\pi) \operatorname{Im}[d \log D(\omega)/d\omega],$$

where

$$D(\omega) = \det [\boldsymbol{I} - \boldsymbol{G}^0(\omega)\, \boldsymbol{C}(\omega)].$$

It appears that this expression can only be handled for one impurity in the crystal, so the final result has to be multiplied by Nc. This result is further simplified by first transforming to the irreducible representations of the impurity space (subsection 5.1) so that

$$D(\omega) = \prod_s D^s(\omega)^{d_s},$$

where d_s is the dimension of the sth i.r. Then on introducing the phase shift, $\eta_s(\omega)$, through

$$D^s(\omega) = |D^s(\omega)| \exp[i\eta_s(\omega)],$$

the final result is

$$\Delta\nu(\omega) = -(c/3r\pi) \sum_s d_s \, d\eta_s(\omega)/d\omega .$$

The change in the specific heat is finally obtained through an integration by parts and is

$$\Delta C_v = (2Nc/3r\pi)\,(\tfrac{1}{2}\beta)^2 \sum_s d_s \int_0^\infty \omega \operatorname{csch}^2(\tfrac{1}{2}\beta\omega) \times [1 - \tfrac{1}{2}\beta\omega \coth(\tfrac{1}{2}\beta\omega)]\,\eta_s(\omega)\,d\omega\,. \qquad (9.3)$$

This form for the result is due to Tiwara et al. (1973) although Hartmann et al. (1970a) obtained it for a mass defect.

ΔC_v was first detected by Panova and Samoilov (1966) for Mg:Pb and by Cape et al. (1966) for Mg:Pb and Mg:Cd. Unfortunately their results are not in good numerical agreement. Cape et al. found that the mass defect approximation accounted very well for the Mg:Pb results but gave ΔC_v too low for Mg:Cd. As moving the resonance to lower frequencies will enhance ΔC_v, this indicates the need for reduced force constants.

TABLE 17

Force constant changes from specific heat data.

		$\Delta f_L/f_L$	$\Delta f_T/f_T$
Al:Ag	a	−0.14	–
	b	0.40	–
KCl:Tl	c	−0.05	–
Mo:Re	d	0.44	3.07
Ag:Au	e	0.05	0.17

a) Tiwari et al. (1973).
b) Verbeek and Nieuwenhuys (1973).
c) Tiwari and Agrawal (1973a).
d) Tiwari and Agrawal (1973b).
e) Tiwari and Agrawal (1973c).

Calculations of C_v, including force constant changes, have now been made for a number of cubic systems, as listed in Table 17. The two very different values of $\Delta f/f$ for Al:Ag are due to fitting to two different experimental results. Tiwari et al. (1973) fitted to the earlier results of Hartmann et al. (1970a) whereas Verbeck and Nieuwenhuys (1973) fitted to their own results. These different experimental results are shown in fig. 35 along with the fitted results and the mass defect result. It can be seen that ΔC_v can be very sensitive to Δf, and because it is a small effect it is not a reliable quantity to establish values of Δf. We note that Verbeck and Nieuwenhuys (1973) used

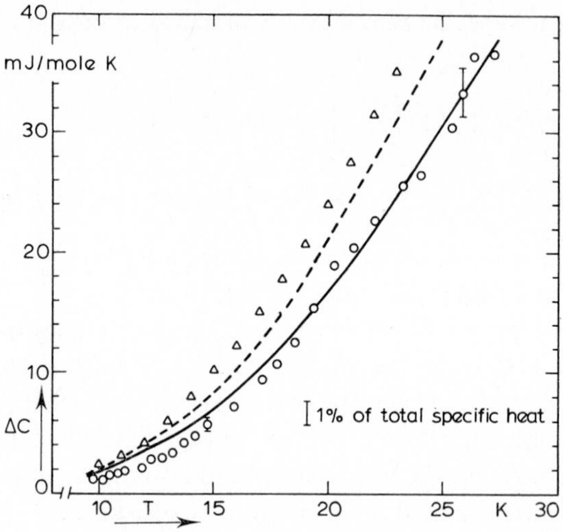

Fig. 35. ΔC_v of 0.94% Ag in Al; circles are experimental points, ——— fitted result with $\Delta f/f=0.40$, ----- mass defect result (Verbeek and Nieuwenhuys 1973). The triangles are the experimental results of Hartmann et al. (1970a).

an expression for $\Delta\nu(\omega)$ due to Mannheim (1968) appropriate to the nearest neighbour model of subsection 5.2.

In most cases it is the T_{1u} contributions which dominate ΔC_v, although the other i.r.'s are not negligible. The exception is Mo:Re where it is the even parity i.r.'s that dominate. This must be attributable to the large change in Δf_T that was required. The resulting fits are as good as those shown in fig. 35 although the results of Karlsson (1970) for KCl:Tl^+ do show a reduction in ΔC_v beyond 10 K that could not be reproduced in the calculations. The small change in Δf for KCl:Tl^+ is a little surprising as appreciable changes were required for the T_{1u} i.r. to fit the infra red absorption of KBr:Tl^+ (see table 6). Unfortunately there are no calculations for KCl:Br for which ΔC_v was measured by Karlsson and whose infra-red absorption has been fitted (table 6).

10. Conclusion

It will have been seen in the preceeding sections that the occurrence and behaviour of resonances and local modes is well described by the low concentration disorder theories presented in section 3. Further, when there is good information available on the host crystal phonons the many details of the observed spectra can be reproduced with fair precision.

However there are qualifications to this success which point the need for further investigation. These include the lack of a detailed theory for the low-frequency resonances including anharmonic corrections and a systematic method for the correct inclusion of pair effects. By the latter we mean an extension of the low-concentration theories presented in section 3, correctly allowing for the overlap of impurity spaces associated with force constant changes, and leading to calculations for comparison with observed spectra. This is to be contrasted with current calculations for just the pair mode frequencies. Another effect, so far only treated in an ad-hoc manner, is that due to the volume change on adding impurities which, as we have seen in section 8, is an important consideration in neutron scattering studies.

Besides these refinements to disorder theory, there is a need for more consideration of what basic information can be extracted from the large number of fitted force constant changes available, such as those that we have tabulated. This clearly requires more basic models for the forces and their changes that, hopefully, will come out of present investigations for the pure crystals (see for instance ch. 6, vol. 1). Such models would also seem necessary, in order to avoid numerous parameters, when detailed fits to pair effects are eventually attempted. It should be noted that one such attempt (Mostoller and Wood 1973, see subsection 5.4) at improved force constant change modelling indicates that such calculations will proceed direct to experiment rather than through fitted Δf_i.

In connection with these considerations different experiments upon the same system are always useful. In optical studies both high resolution infrared and Raman studies for the same system are becoming available and, as described in subsection 5.4, have already in one case, made a significant contribution to our knowledge of force constant changes. It is unfortunate that to date it has not been possible to have both the optical spectra and the inelastic coherent neutron scattering results on the same low-concentration impurity system.

Acknowledgements

The author wishes to thank Dr. T. Timusk and Professor R. J. Elliott for many discussions on the topic of this chapter. Thanks are also due to Professor Elliott for the hospitality of the Department of Theoretical Physics,

Oxford, where this review was completed. The assistance of Mr. D. Hampson in the numerical work of this chapter is gratefully acknowledged.

This work was supported by a research grant from the National Research Council of Canada and by the U.K. Scientific Research Council through a Senior Visiting Fellowship.

References

AGRAWAL, B.K. (1969), Phys. Rev. **186**, 712.
AGRAWAL, B.K. and P.N. RAM (1971) Phys. Rev **B4**, 2774.
AGRAWAL, B.K. and P.N. RAM (1972), Phys. Rev. **B5**, 3308.
AIYER, R.N., R.J. ELLIOTT, J.A. KRUMHANSL and P.L. LEATH (1969), Phys. Rev. **181**, 1006.
ALEXANDER, R.W., A.E. HUGHES and A.J. SIEVERS (1970), Phys Rev. **B1**, 1563.
BARTH, W. and B. FRITZ (1967), Phys. Stat. Sol. **19**, 515.
BAUERLE, D. (1973), Springer Tracts in Modern Physics **68** (Springer-Verlag).
BAUERLE, D. and B. FRITZ (1967), Phys. Stat. Sol. **24**, 207.
BECKER, C.R. and T.P. MARTIN (1972), Phys. Rev. **B5**, 1604.
BELLOMONTE, L. and M.H.L. PRYCE (1966), Proc. Phys. Soc. Lond. **89**, 967, 973.
BENEDEK, G. (1968), in *Localised excitations in solids*, ed. R.F. Wallis (Plenum, N.Y.).
BENEDEK, G. (1970), Phys. Stat. Sol. **42**, 389.
BENEDEK, G. and A.A. MARADUDIN (1968), J. Phys. Chem. Solids **29**, 423.
BENEDEK, G. and E. MULAZZI (1967), Phys. Rev. **179**, 906.
BENEDEK, G. and G.F. NARDELLI (1967), Phys. Rev. **155**, 1004.
BENEDEK, G. (1968a), Phys. Rev. **167**, 837.
BENEDEK, G. (1968b), J. Chem. Phys. **48**, 5242.
BENEDEK, G. and N. TERZI (1973), Phys. Rev. **B8**, 1746.
BENSON, H.J. (1973), Can. J. Phys. **51**, 1737.
BESERMAN, R. and M. BALKANSKI (1970), Phys. Rev. **B1**, 608.
BILZ, H., D. STRAUCH and B. FRITZ (1966), J. Physique Suppl. **27**, C2–3.
BILZ, H., R. ZEYHER and R.R. WILMER (1967), Phys. Stat. Sol. **20**, K167.
BLAESSER, G., J. PERETTI, and G. TOTH (1968), Phys. Rev. **171**, 665.
BLUTHARDT, W., W. SCHNEIDER and M. WAGNER (1973), Phys. Stat. Sol. (b) **56**, 453.
BORN, M. and K. HUANG (1954), *Dynamical theory of crystal lattices* (Oxford Univ. Press).
BRICE, D.K. (1965), Phys. Rev. **140**, A1211.
BROUT, R. and W. VISSCHER (1962), Phys. Rev. Lett. **9**, 54.
BRUNO, R. (1973), Phys. Stat. Sol. (b) **55**, 87.
BRUNO, R. and D.W. TAYLOR (1971), Can. J. Phys. **49**, 2496.
BRYKSIN, V.V. and Y.A. FIRSOV (1970), Sov. Phys. – Solid State **12**, 809.
BUCHANAN, M. and E.J. WOLL (1969), Can. J. Phys. **47**, 1757.
CAIN, L.S. and J.F. THOMAS (1971), Phys. Rev. **B4**, 4245.
CALDWELL, R.F. and M.V. KLEIN (1967), Phys. Rev. **158**, 851.
CALLAWAY, J. (1964), J. Math. Phys. **5**, 783.
CAPE, J.A., G.W. LEHMAN, W.V. JOHNSTON and R.E. DEWAMES (1966), Phys. Rev. Lett. **16**, 892.
CHASE, L., D. KUHNER and W.E. BRON (1973), Phys. Rev. **B7**, 3892.
CHERNOPLEKOV, N.A. and M.G. ZEMLYANOV (1966), Sov. Phys. – JETP **22**, 315.

CLAYMAN, B.P. and A.J. SIEVERS (1968), in *Localised excitations in solids*, ed. R.F. Wallis (Plenum, N.Y.).

CLAYMAN, B.P., I.G. NOLT and A.J. SIEVERS (1969), Solid State Comm. **7**, 7.

CLAYMAN, B.P., R.D. KIRBY and A.J. SIEVERS (1971), Phys. Rev. **B3**, 1351.

COHEN, S.S. (1973), Chem. Phys. Lett. **18**, 369.

COHEN, S.S. and G. GILAT (1972), Solid State Comm. **11**, 1269.

COWLEY, J.M. (1950), Phys. Rev. **77**, 669.

CROITORU, M. and G. GRECU (1970), Phys. Stat. Sol. **42**, 137.

CUNNINGHAM, R.M., L.D. MUHLESTEIN, W.M. SHAW and C.W. THOMPSON (1970), Phys. Rev. **B2**, 2864.

DAVIDSON, D.L. and F.R. BROTZEN (1968), J. Appl. Phys. **39**, 5768.

DAVIES, R.O. and D. HEALEY (1968), J. Phys. C. **1**, 1184.

DAWBER, P.G. and R.J. ELLIOTT (1963), Proc. Phys. Soc. Lond. **81**, 453.

DE JONG, C (1971), Solid State Comm. **9**, 527.

DE JONG, C., G.H. WEGDAM and J. VAN DER ELSKEN (1973), Phys. Rev. **B8**, 4868.

DE SOUSA, M., A.D. GONGORA, M. AEGERTER and F. LUTY (1970), Phys. Rev. Lett. **25**, 1426.

DEREMIGIS, J., H.L. WELSH, R. BRUNO and D.W. TAYLOR (1971), Can. J. Phys. **49**, 3201.

DOLLING, G., H.E. SMITH, R.M. NICKLOW, P.R. VIJAYARAGHAVAN and M.K. WILKINSON (1968), Phys. Rev. **168**, 970.

ELDRIDGE, J.E. (1972), Phys. Rev. **B6**, 3128.

ELLIOTT, R.J. (1966), in *Phonons in perfect lattices and lattices with point imperfections*, Ed. R.W.H. Stevenson (Oliver and Boyd).

ELLIOTT, R.J. and W.M. HARTMANN (1967), Proc. Phys. Soc. Lond. **91**, 187.

ELLIOTT, R.J. and A.A. MARADUDIN (1965), in *Proceedings of a symposium on neutron inelastic scattering*, Bombay (I.A.E.A.).

ELLIOTT, R.J. and P. PFEUTY (1967), J. Phys. Chem. Solids **28**, 1789.

ELLIOTT, R.J. and D.W. TAYLOR (1967), Proc. R. Soc. Lond. **A296**, 161.

ELLIOTT, R.J., W. HAYES, G.D. JONES, H.F. MACDONALD and C.T. SENNETT (1965), Proc. R. Soc. Lond. **A289**, 1.

ELLIOTT, R.J., J.A. KRUMHANSL and T.H. MERRETT (1968), in *Localised excitations in solids*, ed. R.F. Wallis (Plenum, N.Y.).

ERNST, G. and H. LIEHL (1969), Z. Physik **218**, 37.

FELDMAN, D.W., M. ASHKIN and J.H. PARKER (1966), Phys. Rev. Lett. **17**, 1209.

FETTER, A.L. and J.D. WALECKA (1971), *Quantum theory of many-particle systems* (McGraw-Hill).

GANGULY, B.N., R.D. KIRBY, M.V. KLEIN and G.P. MONTGOMERY (1972), Phys. Rev. Lett. **28**, 307.

GAUR, S.P., J.P. VETELINO and S.S. MITRA (1971), J. Phys. Chem. Solids **32**, 2737.

GETHINS, T., T. TIMUSK and E.J. WOLL (1967), Phys. Rev. **157**, 744.

GILAT, G. (1972), J. Comp. Phys. **10**, 432.

GILAT, G. and L.J. RAUBENHEIMER (1966), Phys. Rev. **144**, 390.

GOVINDARAJAM, J. and T.M. HARIDASAN (1969), Phys. Lett A **29**, 387.

GRIM, A., A.A. MARADUDIN, I.P. IPATOVA and A.V. SUBASHIEV (1972), J. Phys. Chem. Solids **33**, 775.

GSCHNEIDNER, K.A. (1964), in *Solid state physics* **16**, ed. F. Seitz and D. Turnbull (Academic Press).

Haridasan, T.M., R.K. Gupta and W. Ludwig (1973a), Solid State Comm. **12**, 1205.
Haridasan, T.M., R.K. Gupta and W. Ludwig (1973b), Chem. Phys. Lett. **23**, 217.
Harley, R.T., J.B. Page and C.T. Walker (1971), Phys. Rev. **B3**, 1365.
Harrington, J.A. and C.T. Walker (1970), Phys. Lett. A **31**, 415.
Harrington, J.A. and C.T. Walker (1971), Phys. Stat. Sol. (b) **43**, 619.
Harrington, J.A. and R. Weber (1972), Solid State Comm. **11**, 1435.
Harrington, J.A. and R. Weber (1973),Phys. Stat. Sol (b) **56**, 541.
Harrington, J.A., R.T. Harley and C.T. Walker (1971), Solid State Comm. **9**, 683.
Hartmann, W.M. (1968), Phys. Rev. **172**, 677.
Hartmann, W.M., H.V. Culbert and R.P. Huebener (1970a), Phys. Rev. **B1**, 1486.
Hartmann, W.M., T.L. Gilbert, K.A. Kaiser and A.C. Wahl (1970b), Phys. Rev. **B2**, 1140.
Hattori, T., K. Ehara, A. Mitsuishi, S. Sakuragi and H. Kanzaki (1973), Solid State Comm. **12**, 545.
Hayes, W. and M.C.K. Wiltshire (1973a), J. Phys. C **6**, 1149.
Hayes, W. and M.C.K. Wiltshire (1973b), J. Phys. C **6**, 1157.
Hayes, W., H.F. MacDonald and C.T. Sennett (1969), J. Phys. C. **2**, 2402.
Hayes, W., M.C.K. Wiltshire and P.J. Dean (1970), J. Phys. C **3**, 1762.
Hayes, W., M.C.K. Wiltshire, W.J. Manthey and D.S. McClure (1973), J. Phys. C **6**, L273.
Hughes, A.E. (1968), Solid State Comm. **6**, 61.
Izyumov, Y.A. (1965), Adv. in Phys. **14**, 569.
Izyumov, Y.A., M.V. Medvedev and I.A. Murtazin (1969), Sov. Phys. – Solid State **11**, 153.
Jain, K.P. and A.K. Prabhakaran (1973a), Phys. Lett. A **46**, 175.
Jain, K.P. and A.K. Prabhakaran (1973b), Phys. Rev. **8**, 1503.
Jain, K.P., S. Radhakrishma, and A.K. Prabhakaran (1972), Phys. Rev. **B5**, 2325.
Jaswal, S.S. (1965a), Phys. Rev **137**, A302.
Jaswal, S.S. (1965b), Phys. Rev. **140**, A 687.
Jaswal, S.S. (1966), Phys. Rev. Lett. **17**, 585.
Jaswal, S.S. (1972), Phys. Lett. A **42**, 309.
Jaswal, S.S. and J.R. Hardy (1968), Phys. Rev. **171**, 1090.
Jaswal, S.S. and D.J. Montgomery (1964), Phys. Rev. **135**, A 1257.
Jones, G.O. and J.M. Woodfine (1965), Proc. Phys. Soc. Lond. **86**, 101.
Kagan, Y. and Y. Iosilevskii (1962), Sov. Phys. – JETP **15**, 182.
Kagan, Y. and Y. Iosilevskii (1963), Sov. Phys. – JETP **17**, 926.
Kagan, Y. and Y. Iosilevskii (1964), Sov. Phys. – JETP **18**, 562.
Kaiser, R., W. Spengler and W. Moller (1973), Phys. Stat. Sol. (b) **55**, 659.
Karlsson, A. V. (1970), Phys. Rev. **B2**, 3332.
Karo, A.M. and J.R. Hardy (1963), Phys. Rev. **129**, 2024.
Keeler, G.J. and D.N. Batchelder (1972), J. Phys. C **5**, 3264.
Kesharwani, K.M. and B.K. Agrawal (1971), Phys. Rev **B4**, 4623.
Kesharwani, K.M. and B.K. Agrawal (1972a), Phys. Rev. **B5**, 2130.
Kesharwani, K.M. and B.K. Agrawal (1972b), Solid State Comm. **11**, 771.
Kesharwani, K.M. and B.K. Agrawal (1972c), Phys. Rev. **B6**, 2178.
Kesharwani, K.M. and B.K. Agrawal (1973a), Phys. Rev. **B7**, 5153.
Kesharwani, K.M. and B.K. Agrawal (1973b), Phys. Rev. **B8**, 3056.

KIM, C.H. and S. YIP (1972), J. Chem. Phys. **57**, 4055.
KIRBY, R.D., I.G. NOLT, R.W. ALEXANDER and A.J. SIEVERS (1968), Phys. Rev. **168**, 1057.
KLEIN, M.V. (1966), Phys. Rev. **141**, 716.
KLEIN, M.V. (1968), in *Physics of color centers*, ed. W.B. Fowler (Academic, N.Y.).
KREBS, K. (1965), Phys. Rev. **138**, A143.
KRISHNAMURTHY, N. (1966), Proc. Phys. Soc. Lond. **88**, 1015.
KRISHNAMURTHY, N. and T.M. HARIDASAN (1966), Phys. Lett. **A21**, 372.
KRIVOGLAZ, M.A. (1961), Sov. Phys. – JETP **13**, 397.
KUHNER, D.H. and M. WAGNER (1967), Z. Physik **207**, 111.
KUHNER, D.H. and M. WAGNER (1970), Phys. Stat. Sol. **40**, 517.
KUHNER, D.H., H.V. LAUER and W.E. BRON (1972), Phys. Rev. **B5**, 4112.
LACINA, W.B. and P.S. PERSHAN (1970), Phys. Rev. **B1**, 1765.
LAKATOS, K. and J.A. KRUMHANSL (1968), Phys. Rev. **175**, 841.
LAKATOS, K. and J.A. KRUMHANSL (1969), Phys. Rev. **180**, 729.
LANGER, J.S. (1961), J. Math. Phys. **2**, 584.
LAX, M. (1951), Rev. Mod. Phys. **23**, 287.
LAX, M. (1952), Phys. Rev. **85**, 621.
LEHMAN, G.W. and R.E. DEWAMES (1963), Phys. Rev. **131**, 1008.
LEIGH, R.S. and B. SZIGETI (1968), in *Localised excitations in solids*, ed. R.F. Wallis (Plenum Press).
LITZMAN, O. and P. ROZA (1973), Phys. Stat. Sol. (b) **58**, 451.
LOUDON, R. (1964), Proc. Phys. Soc. Lond. **84**, 379.
LUDWIG, W. (1967), Springer Tracts in Modern Physics **43** (Springer-Verlag).
MACDONALD, R.A. (1966), Phys. Rev. **150**, 597.
MACDONALD, H.F., M.V. KLEIN and T.P. MARTIN (1969), Phys. Rev. **177**, 1292.
MACKINTOSH, A.R. and H.B. MOLLER (1968), in *Localised excitations in solids*, ed. R.F. Wallis (Plenum Press).
MACPHERSON, R.W. and T. TIMUSK (1970a), Can. J. Phys. **48**, 2176.
MACPHERSON, R.W. and T. TIMUSK (1970b), Can. J. Phys. **48**, 2917.
MAHAN, G.D. (1967), Phys. Rev. **153**, 983.
MAHLER, G. and P. ENGLEHARDT (1971), Phys. Stat. Sol. (b) **45**, 543.
MANNHEIM, P.D. (1968), Phys. Rev. **165**, 1011.
MANNHEIM, P.D. and S.S. COHEN (1971), Phys. Rev. **B4**, 3748.
MANSON, N.B. (1971), Phys. Rev. **B4**, 2645.
MARADUDIN, A.A. (1963) in *Astrophysics and the many body problem* (Benjamin, N.Y.).
MARADUDIN, A.A. (1965), Rep. Prog. Phys. **28**, 331.
MARADUDIN, A.A. (1966), in *Solid state physics* **18, 19**. ed. F. Seitz and D. Turnbull (Academic, N.Y.).
MARADUDIN, A.A. and G.F. NARDELLI (1969), *Elementary excitations in solids* (Plenum).
MARADUDIN, A.A. and J. OITMAA (1969), Solid State. Comm. **7**, 1143.
MARADUDIN, A.A., E.W. MONTROLL, G.H. WEISS and I.P. IPATOVA (1971), *Theory of lattice dynamics in the harmonic approximation*, 2nd. Ed., (Academic, N.Y.)
MARTIN, T.P. (1967a), Phys. Rev. **160**, 686.
MARTIN, T.P. (1967b), Phys. Rev. **164**, 1151.
MARTIN, T.P. (1968), Phys. Rev. **170**, 779.
MARTIN, T.P. (1971), J. Phys. C **4**, 2269.
MARTIN, T.P. (1972), J. Phys. C **5**, 493.

Mazur, P., E.W. Montroll and R.B. Potts (1956), J. Wash. Acad. Sci. **46**, 2
McCombie, C.W. (1970), in *Far infrared properties of solids*, ed. S.S. Mitra and S. Nudelman (Plenum).
Mitani, Y. and S. Takeno (1965), Prog. Theo. Phys. **33**, 779.
Mitra, S.S. and R.S. Singh (1973), Solid State Comm. **12**, 867.
Moller, W. and R. Kaiser (1970), Z. Naturf. **25A**, 1024.
Moller, W. and R. Kaiser (1972), Phys. Stat. Sol. (b) **50**, 155.
Montgomery, G.P. W.R. Fenner, M.V. Klein and T. Timusk (1972a), Phys. Rev. **B5**, 3343.
Montgomery, G.P., M.V. Klein, B.N. Ganguly and R.F. Wood (1972b), Phys. Rev. **B6**, 4047.
Montroll, E.W. and R.W. Potts (1955), Phys. Rev. **100**, 525.
Mostoller, M. and R.F. Wood (1973), Phys. Rev. **B7**, 3953.
Mozer, B. (1968), in *Proceedings of a symposium on neutron inelastic scattering*, Copenhagen (IAEA), Vol. 1.
Mozer, B., V.W. Myers and K. Otnes (1962), Phys. Rev. Lett. **8**, 278.
Mozer, B., K. Otnes and C. Thaper (1966), Phys. Rev. **152**, 535.
Murtazin, I.A. (1971), Sov. Phys. – Solid State **13**, 112.
Narayanamurti, V. and R.O. Pohl (1970), Rev. Mod. Phys. **42**, 201.
Natkaniec, I., K. Parlinski, A. Bajorek and M. Sudnik-Hrynkiewicz (1967), Phys. Lett. A **24**, 517.
Natkaniec, I., K. Parlinski, J.A. Janik, A. Bajorek and M. Sudnik-Hrynkiewicz (1968), in *Proceedings of a symposium on inelastic neutron scattering*, Copenhagen (IAEA) Vol. 1.
Nazarewicz, W. and J. Jurkowski (1969), Phys. Stat. Sol. **31**, 237.
Nazarewicz, W., M. Balkanski, J.F. Morhange and C. Sebenne (1971), Solid State Comm. **9**, 1719.
Newman, R.C. (1969), Adv. in Phys. **18**, 545.
Nguyen, X.X. (1966), Solid State. Comm. **4**, 9.
Nguyen, X.X. (1967), Phys. Rev. **163**, 896.
Nguyen, X.X. (1968), in *Localized excitations in solids*, ed. R.F. Wallis (Plenum, N.Y.).
Nguyen, X.X. A.A. Maradudin and R.A. Coldwell-Horsfall (1965), J. Phys. Paris **26**, 717.
Nicklow, R.M., P.R. Vijayaraghavan, H.G. Smith, G. Dolling and M.K. Wilkinson (1968), in *Proceedings of a symposium on inelastic neutron scattering*, Copenhagen (IAEA), Vol 1.
Nusimovici, M.A., M. Balkanski and J.L. Birman (1970a), Phys. Rev. **B1**, 595.
Nusimovici, M.A., M. Balkanski and J.L. Birman (1970b), Phys. Rev. **B1**, 603.
O'Hara, S.G. and B.J. Marshall (1971), Phys. Rev. **B3**, 4002.
Oitmaa, J. (1970), Solid State Comm. **8**, 57.
Oitmaa, J. and A.A. Maradudin (1969), Solid State Comm. **7**, 1373.
Okazaki, M., M. Inoue, Y. Toyozawa, T. Inui and E. Hanamura (1967), J. Phys. Soc. Jpn. **22**, 1349.
Olson, C.G. and D.W. Lynch (1971), Phys. Rev. **B4**, 1990.
Page, J.B. and B.G. Dick (1967), Phys. Rev. **163**, 910.
Page, J.B. and D. Strauch (1967) Phys. Stat. Sol. **24**, 469.

PAGE, J.B. and D. STRAUCH (1968), in *Localized excitations in solids*, ed. R.F. Wallis. (Plenum, N.Y.).
PANOVA, G.K. and B.N. SAMOILOV (1966), Sov. Phys. – JETP **22**, 320.
PATNAIK, K. and J. MAHANTY (1967), Phys. Rev. **155**, 987.
PAUL, D. and S. TAKENO (1972), Phys. Rev. **B5** 2328.
PAULING, L. (1960), *The nature of the chemical bond*, 3rd. Ed. (Cornell Univ. Press).
RAM, P.N. and B.K. AGRAWAL (1972a), Phys. Rev. **B5**, 2335.
RAM, P.N. and B.K. AGRAWAL (1972b), J. Phys. Chem. Sol. **33**, 957.
RAM, P.N. and B.K. AGRAWAL (1972c), Solid State Comm. **10**, 1111.
RAM, P.N. and B.K. AGRAWAL (1972d), Solid State Comm. **11**, 93.
RAM, P.N. and B.K. AGRAWAL (1972e), Solid State Comm. **11**, 1719.
RAM, P.N. and B.K. AGRAWAL (1973), Phys. Stat. Sol. (b), **55**, 729.
ROLFE, J., M. IKEZAWA and T. TIMUSK (1973), Phys. Rev. **B7**, 3913.
ROWELL, J.M. and W.L. MCMILLAN (1969), in *Superconductivity*, ed. R.D. Parkes (Marcel Dekker, N.Y.).
ROWELL, J.M., W.L. MCMILLAN and P.W. ANDERSON (1965), Phys. Rev. Lett. **14**, 633.
SANGSTER, M.J.L. (1972), Phys. Rev. **B6**, 254.
SANGSTER, M.J.L. and C.W. MCCOMBIE (1970), J. Phys. C. **3**, 1498.
SCHWARTZ, L., H. KRAKAUER and H. FUKUYAMA (1973), Phys. Rev. Lett. **30**, 746.
SENNETT, C.T. (1965), J. Phys. Chem. Solids **26**, 1097.
SENNETT, C.T., D.R. BOSOMWORTH, W. HAYES and A.R.L. SPRAY (1969), J. Phys. C. **2**, 1137.
SIEVERS, A.J. and S. TAKENO (1965), Phys. Rev. **140**, A1030.
SIEVERS, A.J., A.A. MARADUDIN and S.S. JASWAL (1965), Phys. Rev. **138**, A272.
SINGH, R.S. and S.S. MITRA (1970), Phys. Rev. **B2**, 1070.
SINGH, R.S. and S.S. MITRA (1972), Phys. Rev. **B5**, 733.
SOOD, B.R. (1972), Phys. Rev. **B6**, 136.
STERN, F. (1963), in *Solid state physics* **15**, ed. F. Seitz and D. Turnbull (Academic N.Y.).
STREIFLER, M.E. and S.S. JASWAL (1969), Phys. Rev. **185**, 1194.
SVENSSON, E.C. and W. KAMITAKAHARA (1971), Can. J. Phys. **49**, 2291.
SUMI, H. (1970), J. Phys. Soc. Japan, **29**, 1273.
SZIGETI, B. (1963), J. Phys. Chem. Solids **24**, 225.
TAKENO, S. (1962), Prog. Theo. Phys. **28**, 33.
TAKENO, S. (1963) Prog. Theo. Phys. **29**, 191.
TAKENO, S. (1965), Prog. Theo. Phys. **33**, 363.
TAKENO, S. (1967), Prog. Theo. Phys. **38**, 995.
TAYLOR, D.W. (1967), Phys. Rev. **156**, 1017.
TAYLOR, D.W. and J. DEREMIGIS (1973), Can. J. Phys. **51**, 1075.
TAYLOR, D.W. and P. VASHISTA (1972), Phys. Rev. **B5**, 4410.
TEMPLETON, T.L. and B.P. CLAYMAN (1971), Solid State Comm. **9**, 697.
THOMPSON, F. and R.C. NEWMAN, (1971), J. Phys. C **4**, 3249.
THOMPSON, F. and R.C. NEWMAN, (1972), J. Phys. C **5**, 1999.
THOMPSON, F. and R. NICKLIN (1972), J. Phys. C **5**, L223.
TIMUSK, T. and M. BUCHANAN (1967), Phys. Rev. **164**, 345.
TIMUSK, T. and M.V. KLEIN (1966), Phys. Rev. **141**, 664.
TIMUSK, T. and R.W. WARD (1969), Phys. Rev. Lett. **22**, 396.
TIWARI, M.D. and B.K. AGRAWAL (1973a), Phys. Rev. **B7**, 4665.

Tiwari, M.D. and B.K. Agrawal (1973b), Phys. Rev. **B8**, 1397.
Tiwari, M.D. and B.K. Agrawal (1973c), J. Phys. F. **3**, 2051.
Tiwari, M.D., K.M. Kesharwani and B.K. Agrawal (1973), Phys. Rev. **B7**, 2378.
Toyozawa, Y., M. Inoue, T. Inui, M. Okazaki and E. Hanamura (1967), J. Phys. Soc. Jpn. **22**, 1337.
Vanamu, D. (1972), J. Phys. C **5**, 2689.
Verbeek, B.H. and G.J. Nieuwenhuys (1973), Phys. Lett. A **46**, 147.
Wagner, M. (1968), Z. Physik **214**, 78.
Wagner, M. and W.E. Bron (1965), Phys. Rev. **139**, A223.
Wakabayashi, N., R.M. Nicklow and H.G. Smith (1971), Phys. Rev. **B4**, 2558.
Wallis, R.F. (1968), *Localised excitations in solids* (Plenum).
Ward, R.W. and T. Timusk (1972), Phys. Rev. **B5**, 2351.
Ward, R.W., B.P. Clayman and T. Timusk (1974), to be published.
Weber, R. and F. Siebert (1968), Z. Physik **213**, 273.
Wegdam, G.H., J.T.E.M. Kaper and J. Van Der Elsken (1973), Solid State Comm. **13**, 1107.
Wolfram, G., S.S. Jaswal and T.P. Sharma (1972), Phys. Rev. Lett. **29**, 160.
Wood, R.F. and R.L. Gilbert (1967), Phys. Rev. **162**, 746.
Yacoby, Y. and S. Yust (1972), Solid State Comm. **11**, 1575.
Zemlyanov, M.G., V.A. Somenkov and N.A. Chernoplekov (1967), Sov. Phys. – JETP **25**, 436.
Zubarev, D.N. (1960), Sov. Phys. – Uspekhi **3**, 320.

CHAPTER 6

High Concentration Mixed Crystals and Alloys

R. J. ELLIOTT

Department of Theoretical Physics
Oxford University
Oxford
UK

P. L. LEATH

Department of Physics
Rutgers University
New Brunswick
USA

Dynamical Properties of Solids, edited by G.K. Horton and A.A. Maradudin

Contents

1. Introduction

The purpose of this chapter is to review the vibrational properties of mixed crystals and alloys. It is therefore complimentary to Taylor's chapter 5 which discusses the vibrations of isolated point defects in crystals and specifically low concentrations of substitutional impurities. The extension of this treatment to large concentration leads to mixed crystals. Such systems are an important example of randomly disordered matter and besides their intrinsic interest provide a useful testing ground for theories of this state.

The study of matter with random composition for many years received much less attention by physicists than did pure crystalline materials because the definite structure of pure crystals allowed theoretical progress due to symmetry simplifications and allowed more reproducible samples for better comparison with experiment. Nevertheless, some important results were obtained very early in certain disordered systems. The earliest significant progress seems to have been that of Rayleigh (1892) who calculated approximately the average permitivity of a heterogeneous medium. Of particular interest to the developments discussed here was the work of Foldy (1945) who showed how the effective index of wave propagation through a disordered medium could be related to the averaged forward scattering amplitudes of the disorder in the medium; this calculation was not made self-consistent. Lax (1951, 1952), extended this theory by introducing an effective medium in which scattering fluctuations were imbedded and whose scattering amplitude were obtained by an averaging process similar to that used by Foldy, but now this resulted in an implicit equation for the self-consistent determination of the effective index. This calculation by Lax provided the basis for the present averaging technique commonly now used in disordered crystals which has become known as the coherent potential approximation.

More recently, the development of such sophisticated perturbation techniques as that of Green's functions using equations of motion and the development of large computers capable of determining rather exactly some properties of reasonably large models of disordered systems has attracted many physicists into the study of disordered systems and rapid theoretical and experimental progress is now being made.

The group-theoretical methods which relied on the lattice periodicity are of course no longer applicable in disordered crystals, so the phonons are no longer characterized by wave vector $\boldsymbol{k}$ and the $\boldsymbol{k}$-selection rules are lost.

The present day, analytical understanding of high-concentration, mixed crystals has developed rapidly since the exact computer calculations on finite systems, which were begun by Dean (1959), and continued by Dean (1960, 1961) and Payton and Visscher (1967, 1968). The computer experiments, as they are sometimes called, are reviewed extensively by Dean (1972) and hence only results from these calculations will be quoted here. These calculations, for the first time, pointed out the highly spiked nature of the frequency spectrum at high frequencies in strongly disordered systems which was inexplicible via the existing theories at that time. Only very recently have analytical calculations begun to approximate with any accuracy this irregular structure. The development of the analytic theories to date as they apply to lattice dynamics calculations and as they relate to experiments is the primary purpose of this chapter which is derived mostly from the more extensive review of disordered systems by Elliott et al. (1974).

The basic formulae which are required to provide a confrontation between theory and experiment are very similar to those used by Taylor. For completeness we repeat the most important, and use a slightly simplified notation.

1.1. The harmonic model

In this chapter we shall restrict our discussion almost exclusively to that of the harmonic approximation since almost no theoretical work has been done on disordered anharmonic systems. The harmonic hamiltonian is

$$\mathscr{H} = \tfrac{1}{2} \sum_{l,\alpha} \frac{p_\alpha^2(l)}{2M_\alpha(l)} + \tfrac{1}{2} \sum_{\alpha,\alpha',l,l'} \Phi_{\alpha,\alpha'}(l,l')\, u_\alpha(l)\, u_{\alpha'}(l'), \tag{1}$$

where $P_\alpha(l)$ and $u_\alpha(l)$ are the cartesian coordinates of the momentum and displacement operators, respectively, of an atom in the unit cell at $R(l)$, coordinate, where $M_\alpha(l)$ is the mass of that atom, and Φ is the harmonic force constant as discussed in the previous chapter, for lattice-dynamical calculations, it is convenient to work with the momentum and displacement operators, rather than the phonon creation and annihilation operators.

The Heisenberg equations of motion for these operators are

$$\mathrm{i}\hbar\, \partial u_\alpha(l,t)/\partial t = [u_\alpha(l,t), \mathscr{H}] = M_\alpha^{-1}(l)\, p_\alpha(l,t), \tag{2a}$$

$$\mathrm{i}\hbar\, \partial p_\alpha(l,t)/\partial t = [p_\alpha(l,t), \mathscr{H}] = -\sum_{l',\alpha'} \Phi_{\alpha\alpha'}(l,l')\, u_{\alpha'}(l',t), \tag{2b}$$

or

$$M_\alpha(l)\, \partial^2 u_\alpha(l,t)/\partial t^2 = -\sum_{l'\alpha'} \Phi_{\alpha\alpha'}(l,l')\, u_{\alpha'}(l',t). \tag{3}$$

When Fourier transformed to frequency ω this became the equation of motion

$$\sum_{\alpha' l'} [M_\alpha(l)\, \delta_{\alpha,\alpha'}\, \delta_{l,l'}\, \omega^2 - \Phi_{\alpha\alpha'}(l,l')]\, u_{\alpha'}(l') = 0. \tag{4}$$

These equations could have, of course, been obtained classically since the system is harmonic (Messiah 1962).

In a perfect crystal the normal mode frequencies are readily obtained because of the translational symmetry. Transforming to the $(\boldsymbol{k}, j)$ representation the matrix of (4) reduces to $3\nu \times 3\nu$ matrix blocks (if there are ν atoms per unit cell) and the normal modes are found to be

$$\phi_j(\boldsymbol{k}) = \sum_{\alpha,l} \sigma_j^\alpha(\boldsymbol{k}) \exp[\mathrm{i}\boldsymbol{k}\cdot\boldsymbol{R}(l)]\, u_\alpha(l)\, (M_\alpha/N)^{1/2}. \tag{5}$$

But in the disordered crystal the translational symmetry is lost.

Nevertheless, the equation of motion (4) in the disordered crystal can be conveniently expressed in terms of that for the perfect crystal where it becomes

$$\sum_{\alpha' l'} [M_\alpha^0 \omega^2 \delta_{\alpha\alpha'}\, \delta_{ll'} - \Phi_{\alpha\alpha'}^0(l-l') - V_{\alpha\alpha'}(l,l')]\, u_{\alpha'}(l) = 0, \tag{6}$$

where M_α^0 is the mass of the αth atom in the unit cell of the perfect crystal, where Φ^0 gives the force constants of the perfect crystal, and where

$$V_{\alpha\alpha'}(l,l') = M_\alpha^0 \omega^2\, \varepsilon_\alpha(l)\, \delta_{\alpha\alpha'}\, \delta_{ll'} + \Delta\Phi_{\alpha\alpha'}(ll'), \tag{7}$$

with

$$M_\alpha(l) = M_\alpha^0 - \Delta M_\alpha(l) = M_\alpha^0[1 - \varepsilon_\alpha(l)], \tag{8a}$$

and

$$\Phi_{\alpha\alpha'}(l,l') = \Phi_{\alpha\alpha'}^0(l-l') + \Delta\Phi_{\alpha\alpha'}(l,l'). \tag{8b}$$

As discussed in detail in Elliott et al. (1974), this problem is formally identical to the problem of non-interacting electrons, magnons or excitons in disordered crystals and the theories in these various related problems have grown up together in the literature. Some of the results quoted below in the phonon problem may have first been derived in, for example, the corresponding electronic problem.

1.2. Experimental quantities

Within the harmonic approximation, the phonons are non-interacting and it is only necessary to find the frequency and spatial extent of each normal mode. This was done in the case of the translationally invariant crystal by the use of a symmetry transformation (5) which reduced the equation to a $3\nu \times 3\nu$ size. In an imperfect crystal this procedure is no longer of use and another means of attack on the equation of motion (4) is necessary. One method would be a direct numerical attack on the secular determinant of (4) for a large but finite disordered crystal. This computer method is very useful but has been reviewed by Dean (1972) and so will not be discussed in detail here. In addition special transfer matrix technique can be applied for one-dimensional chains as have been reviewed by Hori (1968); however, this method generally fails in three dimensions.

The essential requirement of a good theory is that it explains the experimental facts; thus we need to predict the various crystal properties. It is generally never possible, in an imperfect crystal, to examine a particular normal mode. It is possible, for example, by optical absorption to examine the response of all the crystal modes at a particular frequency. With inelastic neutron scattering it is possible to examine the $\boldsymbol{k}$-content of those modes; but since $\boldsymbol{k}$ is not a good quantum number all modes are still sampled. In fact, essentially all experiments simply measure a correlation or response function rather than the properties of particular modes. A well-defined formalism which leads immediately to these quantities without the necessity to solve for the normal modes is that of thermodynamic Green's functions which have been discussed in the previous chapter. The discussion here is thus very brief for the purpose only of setting the notation. We define the retarded displacement–displacement Green's function

$$\begin{aligned} G_{\alpha\alpha'}(l, l', t) &= \langle\!\langle u_\alpha(l, t); u_{\alpha'}(l', 0)\rangle\!\rangle \\ &= (2\pi/i\hbar)\,\theta(t-t')\,\langle[u_\alpha(l, t), u_{\alpha'}(l', 0)]\rangle_{\mathrm{T}}, \end{aligned} \tag{9}$$

where $\theta(t-t')$ is the Heaviside unit step function, and $[A, B]$ is the commutator of A and B. The frequency components of the displacement–displacement correlation function $\langle u(l)\, u(l')\rangle_\omega$ are simply related to those of the imaginary part of the Green's function (9) by the relation (see Zubarev, 1960)

$$\langle u_\alpha(l)\, u_\beta(l')\rangle_\omega = (\hbar/\pi)\,(\mathrm{e}^{-\hbar\beta\omega} - 1)^{-1}\,\mathrm{Im}\,[G_{\alpha\beta}(l, l'; \omega)]\,, \tag{10}$$

where $\beta = (kT)^{-1}$. From the step function $\theta(t-t')$ in eq. (9), it is clear that $G(\omega)$ is analytic in the upper half complex E plane, and thus that its real and imaginary parts are related by Kramers–Kronig relations

$$\mathrm{Re}\, G(\omega) = \frac{1}{\pi}\, \mathrm{P} \int_{-\infty}^{\infty} \frac{\mathrm{Im}\, G(\omega')}{\omega - \omega'}\, \mathrm{d}\omega'\,, \tag{11a}$$

and

$$\mathrm{Im}\, G(\omega) = \frac{-1}{\pi}\, \mathrm{P} \int_{-\infty}^{\infty} \frac{\mathrm{Re}\, G(\omega')}{\omega - \omega'}\, \mathrm{d}\omega'\,, \tag{11b}$$

where P$\int$ is the principal part of the integral. Furthermore, since the displacement operator $u_\alpha(l, t)$ is even under time reversal, we find

$$G(-\omega + \mathrm{i}\delta) = G^*(\omega + \mathrm{i}\delta)\,, \tag{12}$$

so that the Hilbert transforms (11) may be folded into integrals over only the positive frequencies

$$\mathrm{Re}\, G(\omega) = \frac{2}{\pi}\, \mathrm{P} \int_{0}^{\infty} \frac{\omega'\, \mathrm{Im}\, G(\omega')}{\omega^2 - \omega'^2}\, \mathrm{d}\omega'\,, \tag{13a}$$

and

$$\mathrm{Im}\, G(\omega) = -\frac{2\omega}{\pi}\, \mathrm{P} \int_{0}^{\infty} \frac{\mathrm{Re}\, G(\omega')}{\omega^2 - \omega'^2}\, \mathrm{d}\omega'\,. \tag{13b}$$

The equation of motion for $\boldsymbol{G}(\omega)$ can be obtained easily from the definition by taking time derivatives of (9) and using the harmonic Heisenberg equations of motion (2) for the displacement and momentum operators. The result is

$$M_\alpha(l)\, \omega^2 G_{\alpha\alpha'}(l, l', \omega) = \delta_{\alpha\alpha'}\, \delta(l, l') + \sum_{\alpha'' l''} \Phi_{\alpha\alpha''}(l, l'')\, G_{\alpha''\alpha'}(l'', l', \omega)\,. \tag{14}$$

When condensed to matrix notation, this result can be written

$$[\boldsymbol{M}\omega^2 - \boldsymbol{\Phi}]\,\boldsymbol{G}(\omega) = \boldsymbol{1}, \tag{15}$$

where **1** is the unit matrix. The transformation to normal modes will diagonalize this matrix. In the case of the perfect monatomic crystal the result is

$$G_{jj'}(\boldsymbol{k}, \boldsymbol{k}', \omega) = M_0^{-1}\,\delta_{jj'}\,\delta(\boldsymbol{k} - \boldsymbol{k}')\,[\omega^2 - \omega_j^2(\boldsymbol{k})]^{-1}, \tag{16}$$

where M_0 is the atomic mass. In the general case, $G_{ss'}(\omega)$, in the normal mode representation (s, s'), is of the form

$$G_{ss'}(\omega) = \delta_{ss'}\,u_s u_s^+\,(\omega^2 - \omega_s^2)^{-1}, \tag{17}$$

where u_s is the transformation from configuration space to the normal modes ϕ_s and would be unitary except that is is weighted by $\langle M^{-1}\rangle_s$ the average inverse mass participating in that particular mode. As a result of this mass-weighting of each mode, the frequency spectrum of the normal modes is not given directly (when the atomic mass varies from site-to-site) by $\boldsymbol{G}$, but instead by the imaginary part of a mass-weighted Green's function, namely

$$\rho(\omega) = \sum_s \delta(\omega - \omega_s) = (2\omega/\pi) \operatorname*{Im}_{\varepsilon\to 0+} \operatorname{Tr}[\boldsymbol{MG}(\omega + \mathrm{i}\varepsilon)]. \tag{18}$$

This density of states can thus be simply related to the Green's function $\langle\langle p; u\rangle\rangle$ of the two conjugate variables, according to the relation

$$\langle\langle p; u\rangle\rangle_\omega = -\,\mathrm{i}\omega\,\boldsymbol{MG}(\omega). \tag{19}$$

1.2.1. Thermal properties

The thermal properties of harmonic systems are easily obtained from these correlation functions or directly from the density of states $\rho(\omega)$. For example, the specific heat is given from eq. (18), by

$$C_v = \int_0^\infty \frac{2\hbar^2\omega^3\,\mathrm{d}\omega\,\exp(\hbar\omega/k_\mathrm{B}T)}{\pi k_\mathrm{B}T^2\,[\exp(\hbar\omega/k_\mathrm{B}T) - 1]^2}\,\operatorname{Im}\{\operatorname{Tr}(\boldsymbol{M}\cdot\boldsymbol{G})\}. \tag{20}$$

The Green's function G may also be used to calculate the mean-square atomic displacement $\langle u^2\rangle$, via eq. (10), as required for the Debye–Waller factor. Similarly the other ordinary thermal properties may be calculated directly from $\boldsymbol{G}$ and $\boldsymbol{M}\cdot\boldsymbol{G}$.

1.2.2. Neutron scattering

The most detailed information about phonon frequency spectra is given by inelastic neutron scattering experiments [see, for example, Sjölander (1964), and Lovesey and Marshall (1966, 1971)]. The one-phonon cross section for coherent scattering from the scattering length b^{c}, averaged over spin states, is given by

$$\frac{\mathrm{d}^2\sigma^{\mathrm{c}}}{\mathrm{d}\Omega\,\mathrm{d}E} = \frac{1}{2\pi\hbar}\frac{k'}{k}\int \mathrm{d}t \exp(\mathrm{i}Et/\hbar) \sum_{\alpha\alpha', ll'} B_\alpha(l)\, B_{\alpha'}(l') \times \langle [\boldsymbol{q}\cdot\boldsymbol{u}_\alpha(l,t)]\,[\boldsymbol{q}\cdot\boldsymbol{u}_{\alpha'}(l',0)]\rangle \exp\{\mathrm{i}q\cdot[\boldsymbol{R}(l)-\boldsymbol{R}(l')]\}, \quad (21)$$

where $B_\alpha(l)$ contains the Debye-Waller factor

$$B_\alpha(l) = b_\alpha^{\mathrm{c}}(l) \exp\{-\tfrac{1}{2}\langle[\boldsymbol{q}\cdot\boldsymbol{u}_\alpha(l)]^2\rangle\}. \quad (22)$$

This formula contains a correlation function which can be obtained, via eq. (10), from the appropriate Green's function

$$\frac{\mathrm{d}^2\sigma^{\mathrm{c}}(E)}{\mathrm{d}\Omega\,\mathrm{d}E} = \frac{1}{\pi}\frac{k'}{k} \sum_{\alpha\alpha', ll'} B_\alpha(l)\, B_{\alpha'}(l')\, n(E) \times \mathrm{Im}\langle\langle \boldsymbol{q}\cdot\boldsymbol{u}_\alpha(l); \boldsymbol{q}\cdot\boldsymbol{u}_{\alpha'}(l'), E\rangle\rangle \exp\{\mathrm{i}\boldsymbol{q}\cdot[\boldsymbol{R}(l)-\boldsymbol{R}(l')]\}, \quad (23)$$

where $n(E) = [\exp(E/k_{\mathrm{B}}T)-1]^{-1}$. If E is positive the cross section corresponds to phonon destruction and is proportional to the equilibrium number of phonons present. If E is negative, since $\mathrm{Im}\,G(-E) = -\mathrm{Im}\,G(E)$, there is a similar contribution proportional to $-n(-E) = n(E)+1$ corresponding to phonon emission.

The incoherent cross section involves correlations only in the motion of individual atoms

$$\frac{\mathrm{d}^2\sigma^{\mathrm{i}}}{\mathrm{d}\Omega\,\mathrm{d}E} = \frac{1}{2\pi\hbar}\frac{k'}{k} \times \int \mathrm{d}t \exp(\mathrm{i}Et/\hbar) \sum_{\alpha l} \beta_\alpha^2(l) \langle [\boldsymbol{q}\cdot\boldsymbol{u}_\alpha(l,t)]\,[\boldsymbol{q}\cdot\boldsymbol{u}_\alpha(l,0)]\rangle, \quad (24)$$

where β contains the incoherent scattering length as well as the Debye–Waller factor. Thus

$$\frac{\mathrm{d}^2\sigma^{\mathrm{i}}}{\mathrm{d}\Omega\,\mathrm{d}E} = \frac{1}{\pi}\frac{k'}{k} \sum_{\alpha\alpha', ll'} \beta_\alpha(l)\, \beta_{\alpha'}(l')\, n(E)\, \mathrm{Im}\langle\langle \boldsymbol{q}\cdot\boldsymbol{u}_\alpha(l); \boldsymbol{q}\cdot\boldsymbol{u}_\alpha(l), E\rangle\rangle. \quad (25)$$

In perfect crystals $B_\alpha(l)$ [and $\beta_\alpha(l)$] are the same in each unit cell so that the cross sections are proportional to the Fourier transform of the Green's function (9). The imaginary part is then the delta function $\delta[\omega^2 - \omega_j^2(q)]$ so that the coherent cross section (23) is sharply peaked at the phonon frequencies. In disordered crystals, of course, q is not a good quantum number so that the coherent cross section is a smooth function of frequency. Furthermore, in a crystal consisting of different atoms the scattering lengths $B_\alpha(l)$ and $\beta_\alpha(l)$ vary from site-to-site so that the neutrons interact with some atoms more strongly than with others and appropriately weighted Green's functions must be considered.

1.2.3. Optical properties

Electromagnetic waves interact with lattice vibrations primarily through the electric dipole moments produced by the vibrations, that is,

$$H_{\text{int}} = \sum_l e_\alpha(l)\, \boldsymbol{u}_\alpha(l) \cdot \mathscr{E} \exp(\mathrm{i}\omega t), \tag{26}$$

where $e_\alpha(l)$ is the effective charge of the (α, l) atom. The polarization of the medium is given by

$$\boldsymbol{P} = \left(\sum_l e_\alpha(l)\, \boldsymbol{u}_\alpha(l) \right), \tag{27}$$

thus, the one-phonon polarizability is

$$\chi(\omega) = - \sum_{\alpha\alpha', ll'} e_\alpha(l)\, e_{\alpha'}(l') \langle\langle u_\alpha(l); u_{\alpha'}(l'), \omega \rangle\rangle, \tag{28}$$

The total dielectric constant of the crystal will also contain a contribution due to the electron transitions at high frequencies. Designating this ε_∞, the general formula becomes

$$\varepsilon(\omega) = \varepsilon_\infty + \frac{4\pi}{N\Omega_0} \left(\frac{\varepsilon_\infty + 2}{3} \right)^2 \chi(\omega), \tag{29a}$$

where $N\Omega_0$ is the total volume and the optical absorption coefficient is

$$K = \frac{4\pi\omega}{N\Omega_0 c'} \operatorname{Im} \chi(\omega) \left(\frac{\varepsilon_\infty + 2}{3} \right)^2, \tag{29b}$$

where c' is the velocity of light in the medium. As for the neutron scattering case above, the optical absorption coefficient is given by a Green's function weighted, in this case, by the effective charges. The wavevector of light (in the infrared region where this effect is important) is so small that only the $q \sim 0$ response is determined. In a perfect crystal, eq. (29b) contains the delta function $\delta[\omega - \omega_j(0)]$. Two-phonon creation processes can couple the light to other than $\boldsymbol{q} = 0$ phonons.

Raman scattering by phonons is very much like neutron scattering, except that $\boldsymbol{q} \sim 0$. The one-phonon Raman cross section is

$$\frac{\mathrm{d}^2\sigma_\mathrm{R}}{\mathrm{d}\Omega\,\mathrm{d}E} \propto \sum_{\alpha\alpha', ll'} C_{\alpha\mu}(l)\, C_{\alpha'\mu'}(l')\, n(E)\, F_\mu F'_{\mu'}\, \mathrm{Im}\, \langle\!\langle u_\alpha(l)\, u_{\alpha'}(l'), E \rangle\!\rangle, \tag{30}$$

where $C_\alpha(l)$ is the Raman polarizability of the (α, l) atom. Again, in mixed crystals it is a weighted Green's function that enters. The thermal factors give the Stokes and anti-Stokes components at $\pm E$. The cross section depends on the direction of the electric field F, F' for the incoming and outgoing photons.

1.2.4. *Thermal conductivity*

The Kubo formula for thermal conductivity is of the form (cf. Mori et al. 1962)

$$\kappa_{\mu\nu}(\omega) = \lim_{\eta \to 0^+} \frac{1}{VT} \int_0^\infty \mathrm{d}t \exp(-\mathrm{i}\omega t) \exp(-\eta t) \times \int_0^\beta \mathrm{d}\lambda \, \langle J_\mu^E(0)\, J_\nu^E(t + \mathrm{i}\hbar\lambda) \rangle, \tag{31}$$

where V is the volume of the crystal, $\beta = (k_\mathrm{B} T)^{-1}$, and where the harmonic energy current density operator J^E is (see, for example, Flicker and Leath 1973).

$$\begin{aligned} J_\mu^E &= \tfrac{1}{2} \sum_{\alpha\alpha', ll'} [\boldsymbol{R}(l) - \boldsymbol{R}(l')]_\mu\, \Phi_{\alpha\alpha'}(l, l')\, u_{\alpha'}(l')\, p_\alpha(l)/M_\alpha(l) \\ &= \sum_{\alpha\alpha', ll'} A_\mu^{\alpha\alpha'}(l, l')\, u_{\alpha'}(l')\, p_\alpha(l)/M_\alpha(l). \end{aligned} \tag{32}$$

This form for the energy current operator, when put into (31) gives two-phonon correlation functions which decouple exactly into products of one-phonon correlations. The result (cf. Flicker and Leath 1973) for the dc thermal conductivity is

$$K_{\mu\nu} = \frac{-2\hbar^2}{\pi V k_B T} \times \int_{-\infty}^{\infty} d\omega \frac{\omega^2 \exp(\hbar\omega/k_B T)}{[\exp(\hbar\omega/k_B T) - 1]^2} \operatorname{Tr}[A_\mu \operatorname{Im} G(\omega) A_\nu G(\omega)]. \quad (33)$$

Each of the above experimental quantities [eqs. (20)–(33)] involves a sum over all the sites in a macroscopic sample. Thus the experiments measure sample averages of the appropriate quantities. If samples are chosen large enough that local concentration fluctuations within the sample do not cause variations in the experimental values obtained from sample to sample, then the experiments are essentially measuring (within a single, macroscopic sample) the average of the appropriate quantity over all configurations. Therefore, it is essentially exact to calculate the convenient configuration average of these experimentally useful quantities for macroscopic samples. Lifshitz (1964) first pointed out that such extensive properties are effectively 'self-averaging'. A more complete discussion of this point is given in Elliott et al. (1974). Since it is also convenient for calculation, we shall restrict our discussion below to configuration-averaged quantities.

1.3. General features

First, we consider the case of a crystal with a single defect at site l. This case has been reviewed very completely by Maradudin (1966) and was discussed in the previous chapter by Taylor.

In this case the Green's function equation of motion (15) can be solved exactly to obtain $G(\omega)$ and hence the directly related physical quantities. In this case eq. (15) becomes, in matrix form,

$$(M_0\omega^2\mathbf{1} - \boldsymbol{\Phi}^0 - \boldsymbol{V}^l)\,\boldsymbol{G}(\omega) = \mathbf{1}, \quad (34)$$

where the perturbation $\boldsymbol{V}^l$ due to the defect at site l is given by eq. (7) and consists of the mass change at, plus the force constant changes about, the site l. Multiplying through eq. (34) by $P(\omega) = (M_0\omega^2\mathbf{1} - \boldsymbol{\Phi}^0)^{-1}$, the perfect crystal Green's function, we obtain

$$\boldsymbol{G} = \boldsymbol{P} + \boldsymbol{P}\boldsymbol{V}^l\boldsymbol{G}, \quad (35)$$

which is easily iterated to give the expansion

$$\boldsymbol{G} = \boldsymbol{P} + \boldsymbol{P}\boldsymbol{V}^l\boldsymbol{P} + \boldsymbol{P}\boldsymbol{V}^l\boldsymbol{P}\boldsymbol{V}^l\boldsymbol{P} + \cdots . \tag{36}$$

This expansion is trivially summed exactly to give

$$\boldsymbol{G} = \boldsymbol{P} + \boldsymbol{P}\boldsymbol{t}^l\boldsymbol{P}, \tag{37}$$

where

$$P^l(\omega) = V^l[1 - t^l(\omega)\, V^l]^{-1}, \tag{38}$$

where P^l is the perfect lattice Green's function restricted to those sites about l where V^l is non-zero.

If $V^{(l)}$ is large enough, corresponding to a light impurity atom or to a strong harmonic coupling to the impurity, then there will be poles of $t^l(\omega)$, corresponding to the zeroes,

$$|1 - P^l(\omega)\, V^l| = 0, \tag{39}$$

at frequencies above the host frequency spectrum, corresponding to localized impurity modes. On the other hand, if the impurity is very heavy or the impurity coupling is very weak, there will be a resonance in t^l at small frequency corresponding to resonant impurity vibrations. Such a single impurity mode appears in the frequency spectrum as a sharp peak. In general, the normal modes of a crystal of atoms will be shifted in frequency by an amount of order N^{-1} by the introduction of the defect. For the simple case where the mass $M' = M^0(1-\varepsilon)$ of the impurity atom is changed and the forces are unchanged, the t-matrix (38) is site-diagonal

$$t^l(n, n') = \Delta\,[1 - \Delta P(l, l)]^{-1}\, \delta_{ln}\, \delta_{nn'}, \tag{40}$$

where $\Delta = M^0 E\omega^2$.

For the case of a pair of defects at sites l and l', the solution for G can also be carried out exactly, with the similar result,

$$G = P + Pt^{l,l'}P, \tag{41}$$

where

$$t^{l,l'}(\omega) = V^{l,l'}[1 - P^{l,l'}(\omega)\, V^{l,l'}]^{-1}, \tag{42}$$

where $P^{l,l'}(\omega)$ is restricted to those sites near l and l' where V is non-zero, where $V^{l,l'}$ represents the perturbation caused by the impurities at l and l'. If the defect hamiltonians are additive $V^{l,l'}$ is of the form

$$V^{l,l'} = V^{l} + V^{l'}, \tag{43}$$

which is rigorously true in the case of mass defects but which is sometimes assumed as a useful approximation in more general cases. For the mass defect case, the poles of $t^{l,l'}(\omega)$ occur at the zeroes,

$$1 - P(l,l) \pm \Delta P(l,l') = 0. \tag{44}$$

We note that there are now two poles of $t^{l,l'}(\omega)$, corresponding to optic and acoustic (out-of-phase and in-phase) vibrations of the two defect atoms and that as l diverges from l' that the two modes converge upon the isolated defect frequency at $1-\Delta P(l,l)=0$.

For any small number of impurities in an infinite crystal similar calculations can be carried out in detail, but for a finite concentration of defects, such a calculation becomes intractable. Thus, no exact analytic expression exists for finite concentrations although good approximate expressions exist which are valid in certain limits to be discussed below. Nevertheless, very accurate data exists for the frequency spectra models of disordered finite chains and lattices where modern day computers can essentially tackle directly the inversion of eq. (15) for the normal mode frequencies. These calculations were pioneered by Landauer and Helland (1954) were followed by Lax and Phillips (1958), Frisch and Lloyd (1960) and most successfully accomplished by Dean (1959 and later). Subsequently Payton and Visscher (1967, 1968) extended these calculations to two and three dimensions. An extensive review of these computer experiments has been given by Dean (1972); thus we review only a few important features of these numerical calculations here.

The most important feature to arise from Dean's calculations on binary mass-disordered chains was the extremely irregular (spiked) nature of the phonon frequency spectrum at high frequency outside of the heavy atom frequency band as shown in fig. 1. Each spike in the spectrum is associated with a particular isolated light atom or cluster of atoms. As is evident, from eq. (40), a single light atom will produce a delta function in the frequency spectrum at its local mode frequency. The interaction with other distant defects will broaden this delta function into an impurity band, as can be seen from eq. (44). This impurity band is represented by the histogram spike labeled A in fig. 1. The other spikes B–V correspond to the impurity bands associated with specific configurations of small clusters of light and heavy atoms in the chains. Payton and Visscher (1967), see fig. 2, found a similar high-frequency structure for simple cubic lattices at concentrations of light atoms below the region of the critical percolations concentration. Above the percolation threshold the light atoms are generally connected together in an infinite cluster so that the structure associated with isolated clusters is less important. The vibrational modes associated with these spectral spikes are localized in space, in contrast to the in-band modes which extend throughout the crystal. These dominant features first identified by Dean have only recently been approximately reproduced by analytical methods as we discuss below.

One property of the density of states about which there are exact theorems is the spectral limits (see Rayleigh 1892, Saxon and Hutner 1949, Lifshitz 1964, and most recently Thouless 1970). The simple result is that in a two-component, randomly occupied, regular lattice (in any dimension) the upper spectral limit as well as the gap limit between bands (if it is a poly-atomic crystal) is determined by the common gap regions of the two limiting pure crystalline species. This result neglects such subtleties as the relaxation of the lattice about defect atoms. An argument of Lifshitz (1964) which simply states that there is a finite probability of finding a cluster of pure A (or B) atoms of arbitrary size, means that at any frequency for which there is a mode of the infinite pure A or B atom lattice there will be a mode of the infinite mixed lattice; thus the frequency spectrum fills the region (except for sets of measure zero) out to the exact spectral limits. Furthermore, Lifshitz (1964) argued that the frequency spectrum $\rho(\omega)$ had essential singularities at its extremities ω_s and was, in fact, of the form

$$\rho(\omega) \propto \exp(\alpha|\omega - \omega_s|^{-1/2}), \tag{45}$$

for ω sufficiently near the ω_s limits. Recently Gubernatis and Taylor (1973) have numerically demonstrated using the technique developed by Schmidt (1957) that the envelope of $\rho(\omega)$ is indeed of this form (45) near ω_s for a linear chain. (Their numerical calculation was actually for the electronic case but their results surely also apply in the phonon problem.)

Finally, it has been demonstrated for linear chains and certain very special higher-dimensional systems that there are zeroes in the frequency spectrum $\rho(\omega)$ at certain special frequencies (see the review by Hori 1968). It seems

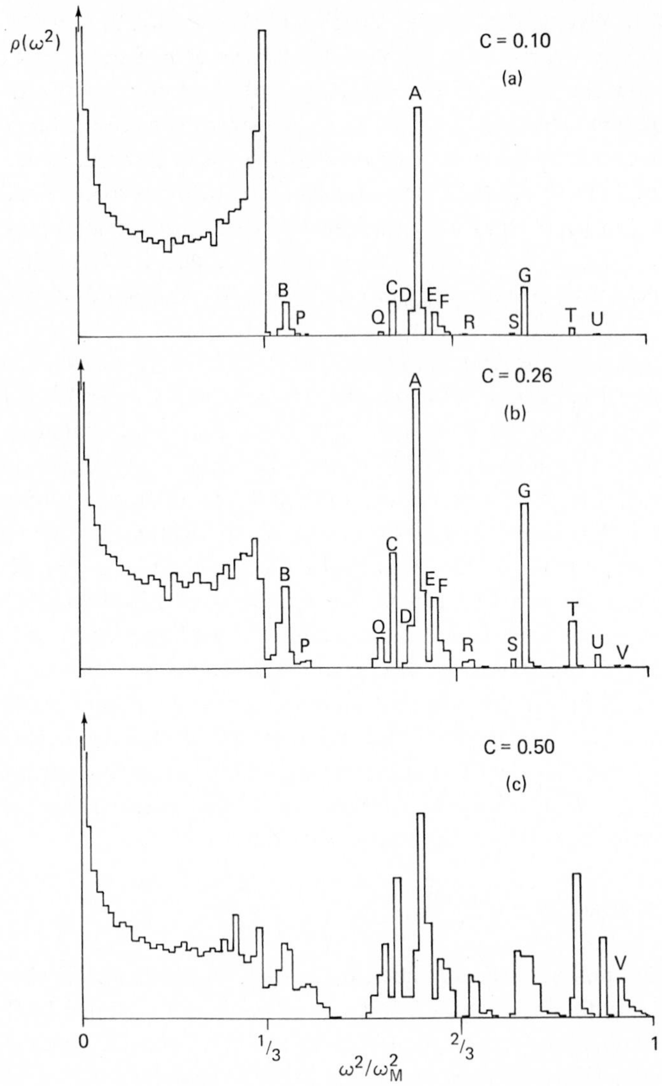

Fig. 1. The phonon density of states $\rho(\omega^2)$ versus $\omega^2/\omega^2{}_M$ for disordered linear chains of atoms of mass M_A and $M_B = \frac{1}{3}M_A$ at compositions $A_{1-c}B_c$ as given. The sharp peaks correspond to identifiable clusters of A atoms (after Dean 1961).

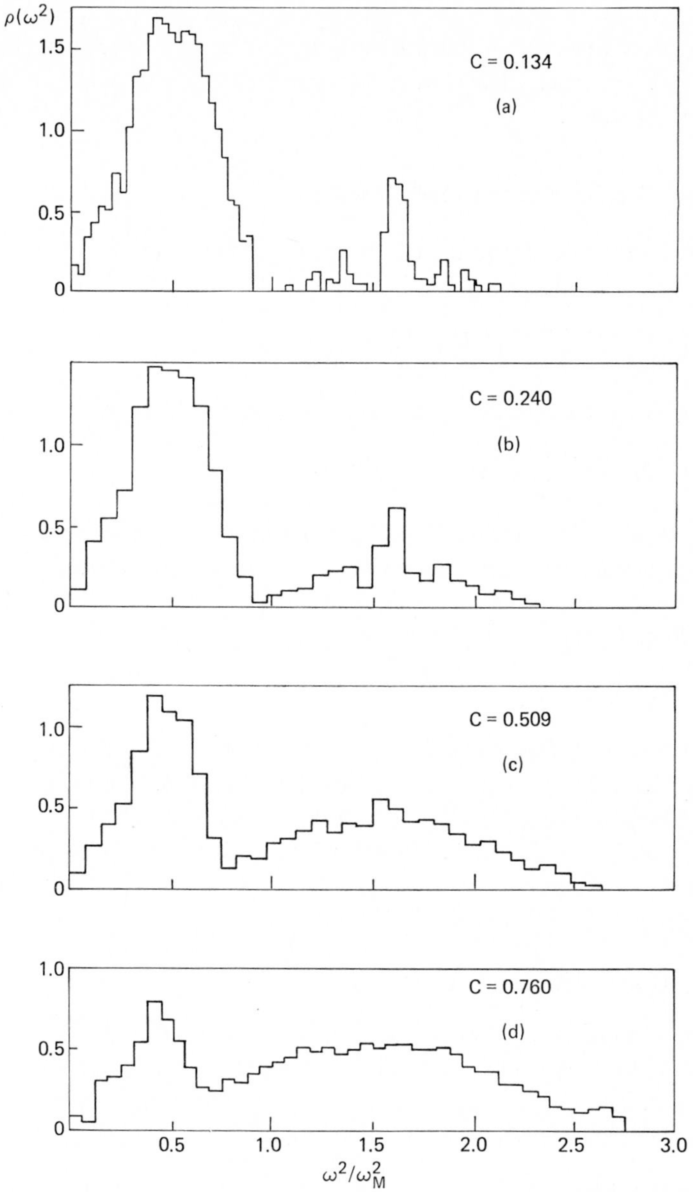

Fig. 2. The phonon censity of states $\rho(\omega^2)$ versus $\omega^2/\omega^2{}_M$ for disordered simple cubic lattices with atoms of mass M_A and $M_B=\frac{1}{3}M_A$ at compositions $A_{1-c}B_c$ as given (after Payton and Visscher 1967).

this behavior is peculiar to the special topology of these particular systems. Nevertheless the exactly known integrated frequency spectrum (Borland 1964) at these special frequencies has provided a useful check of various other calculations.

1.4. Notation for average Green's functions

As was noted in subsection 1.2 the experimental quantities are related to configurationally average Green's functions. We therefore define

$$\langle G(\boldsymbol{\delta})\rangle = N^{-1} \sum_{\boldsymbol{l}} G(\boldsymbol{l}, \boldsymbol{l}+\boldsymbol{\delta}). \tag{46}$$

where $\langle G\rangle$ has translational symmetry like P so that the Fourier transform

$$\langle G(\boldsymbol{k})\rangle = N^{-1} \sum_{\boldsymbol{\delta}} \langle G(\boldsymbol{\delta})\rangle \exp(\mathrm{i}\boldsymbol{k}\cdot\boldsymbol{\delta}). \tag{47}$$

It is convenient to define a self energy $\boldsymbol{\Sigma}$, a matrix like $\boldsymbol{\Phi}_0$, with translational symmetry which acts like an additional force constant in an effective medium which replaces the actual random one. $\boldsymbol{\Sigma}$ is in general complex and frequency dependent. Then

$$\langle \boldsymbol{G}\rangle = \boldsymbol{P} + \boldsymbol{P\Sigma}\langle \boldsymbol{G}\rangle \tag{48}$$

and $\langle \boldsymbol{G}\rangle$ can be diagonalised in $\boldsymbol{k}$. In the general case new eigenvectors $\sigma_j(\boldsymbol{k})$ as defined in (5) will have to be determined to complete the diagonalisation, if the unperturbed values are used $\Sigma_{jj'}(\boldsymbol{k}, \omega)$ and hence $\langle G_{jj'}(\boldsymbol{k}, \omega)\rangle$ will not be diagonal on j, j'. However for the simple case of a monatomic lattice where the impurity potentials are site diagonal G is diagonalised by the same transformation as P and

$$\langle G_{jj}(\boldsymbol{k})\rangle = M_0^{-1}[\omega^2\omega_j^2(\boldsymbol{k}) - \Sigma_j(\boldsymbol{k}, \omega)]^{-1}. \tag{49}$$

In this special case it is also possible to define simple relations between the weighted averages which are needed in the formulae for the experimental quantities. Defining $\boldsymbol{G}^{\mathrm{d}}$ where the first site is restricted to impurity sites, the Dyson equation for $\boldsymbol{G}$

$$\boldsymbol{G} = \boldsymbol{P} + \boldsymbol{PVG}, \tag{50}$$

can be written

$$\boldsymbol{G} = \boldsymbol{P} + \boldsymbol{PVG}^{\mathrm{d}}. \tag{51}$$

On averaging, and comparing with (48) we find

$$\langle G^{d} \rangle = V^{-1}\Sigma \langle G \rangle . \tag{52a}$$

The function where the first site is restricted to host sites

$$\langle G^{h} \rangle = \langle G \rangle - \langle G^{d} \rangle = (1 - V^{-1}\Sigma) \langle G \rangle . \tag{52b}$$

Similar manipulations lead to expressions for the Green's functions weighted for both sites

$$\langle G^{dd} \rangle = V^{-2}\Sigma \langle G \rangle \Sigma + V^{-2}(\Sigma - cV), \tag{53a}$$

$$\langle G^{dh} \rangle = (1 - V^{-1}\Sigma) \langle G \rangle \Sigma V^{-1} - V^{-2}(\Sigma - cV), \tag{53b}$$

$$\langle G^{hh} \rangle = (1 - V^{-1}\Sigma) \langle G \rangle (1 - V^{-1}\Sigma) + V^{-2}(\Sigma - cV). \tag{53c}$$

The approximation methods discussed in the next section relate the self energy to the scattering of single defects. Hence they can only be used if the perturbing hamiltonian can be written as a sum of additive terms for each impurity, as in (43). This is always rigorously true for mass defects. For a mixture of AB atoms it is only true for force constant changes in a very special case, viz. if

$$\Phi_{AB}(\boldsymbol{\delta}) = \tfrac{1}{2}[\Phi_{AA}(\boldsymbol{\delta}) + \Phi_{BB}(\boldsymbol{\delta})] \tag{54}$$

for all $\boldsymbol{\delta}$. There is however an important class of diatomic lattices where additivity is often a reasonable model, as has recently been stressed by Kaplan and Mostoller (1974a, b). In a rocksalt, blende or similar lattices, the anions and cations are interspersed, so that nearest neighbour forces always couple opposite sites. Thus if one atomic type is disordered, nearest neighbour force constant changes give additive perturbations.

2. *Approximation methods*

2.1. Virtual crystal limit

In the virtual crystal limit, when the scattering by the disorder is very weak, i.e. the mass changes and the force constant changes are small, a perturbation expansion in powers of V, as defined in (7) is valid. The virtual crystal approximation (VCA) which is valid in this limit seems first to have been used in the electronic problem by Nordheim (1931).

The perturbation expansion for $\boldsymbol{G}$ is like that for the single defect in (36) except that $\boldsymbol{V}$ is now defined as a matrix (7) extending throughout the crystal with non-zero elements on and near sites whose mass or force constants differ from those of the unperturbed lattice; namely,

$$\langle G(l, l')\rangle = P(l, l') + \sum_{m, m'} P(l, m) \langle V(m, m')\rangle P(ml') + \sum_{mm', nn'} P(l, m) \langle V(m, m') P(m', n) V(n, n')\rangle P(n'l') + \cdots, \quad (55)$$

where the equation has also been averaged over all configurations of occupation of the crystal sites by atoms of different types, and where $\langle\cdots\rangle$ denotes this ensemble configuration average. The unperturbed propagators P are independent of the configuration and can be removed from the average, leaving only averages of the form $\langle V(1, 1') V(2, 2')\cdots V(n, n')\rangle$ to be evaluated. For the case of no short-range order, the average of the product of $\boldsymbol{V}$'s factorizes into products of averages except for those terms where there is a coincidence of the specified sites 1, 2, ..., n or if two or more of these sites are close neighbors about the same defect. In the VCA, it is assumed that all the $V(m, m')$ are very small so that the higher order products of $\boldsymbol{V}$'s need only be treated approximately. Thus all such average products of $\boldsymbol{V}$'s are decoupled (a random phase approximation) into products of averages

$$\langle V(1, 1') V(2, 2') \ldots V(n, n')\rangle \simeq \langle V(1, 1')\rangle \langle V(2, 2')\rangle \ldots \langle V(n, n')\rangle . \quad (56)$$

This gives

$$\langle \boldsymbol{G}(\omega)\rangle = \boldsymbol{P}(\omega) [\mathbf{1} - \langle \boldsymbol{V}\rangle \boldsymbol{P}(\omega)]^{-1}, \quad (57a)$$

$$= (\langle M\rangle \omega^2 \mathbf{1} - \langle \boldsymbol{\Phi}\rangle)^{-1}, \quad (57b)$$

so that the Green's function is approximated by one for a perfect crystal with the atomic masses equal to the mean mass of the disordered crystal and with force constants equal to the mean force constant of the disordered crystal. Thus the frequency spectrum of the disordered crystal (in this approximation) is rigidly shifted to that of a mean or virtual crystal without broadening the states. The phonon dispersion curves in the VCA simply shift linearly with concentration throughout the entire concentration range. In this weak scattering limit, for example, if there is a single optically active mode in each perfect crystal there will also be only one such mode in the mixed crystal which will shift in frequency linearly with concentration throughout the concentration range. Also, the transition temperature T_c of any structural phase transition which is present in each pure species, in such cases, will simply shift linearly with concentration also. The VCA is clearly the crudest interpolation formula over the entire concentration range. It is valid when the mixed species are nearly identical and does not apply when there are localized modes present. In terms of this Σ, eq. (48) becomes simply

$$\Sigma(m, m') = \langle V(m, m') \rangle \tag{58}$$

or the self-energy on sites m and m' is simply the average of the perturbation on those same two sites over all occupations of the crystalline sites by the various atomic species. Clearly this Σ is purely real so that the phonon k-modes have an infinite lifetime. To find a lifetime or width of the phonon modes it is necessary to go at least to the second order of perturbation theory and consider the $\langle VPV \rangle$ term. Such a perturbation theory was carried out, for example by Maris (1965).

Use of the VCA does not require the impurity effects to be additive.

2.2. The average *t*-matrix approximation

This approximation, which was developed by Watson (1956, 1957), Korringa (1958), and Beeby and Edwards (1963) in the electronic problem was first applied to the phonon problem by Elliott and Taylor (1967). In this approach, one rearranges eq. (55) by collecting together all those terms involving repeated scattering by the same impurity, to obtain

$$\begin{aligned}\langle G(l, l') \rangle = P(l, l') &+ \sum_m P(l, m) \langle t(m, m') \rangle P(m', l) \\ &+ \sum_{m,n}{}' P(l, m) \langle t(m, m') P(m', n) t(n, n') \rangle P(n', l') \\ + \sum_{m,m,p}{}'' p(l, m) \langle t(m, m') & P(m'n) t(n, n') P(n', p) t(p, p') \rangle P(p', l') + \cdots,\end{aligned} \tag{59}$$

where $t(m, m') = t^m$ as given by eq. (38), and where the prime on the sum means that further immediately successive scatterings by the same site are excluded (i.e. $m \neq n \neq p \neq \cdots$). This equation can be formally re-written as

$$\langle \boldsymbol{G} \rangle = \boldsymbol{P} + \boldsymbol{P} \langle \boldsymbol{t} \rangle \boldsymbol{P} + \boldsymbol{P} \langle \boldsymbol{tP't} \rangle \boldsymbol{P} + \boldsymbol{P} \langle \boldsymbol{tP'tP't} \rangle \boldsymbol{Pt} \cdots, \tag{60}$$

where

$$P'(n, m) = P(n, m) - P(m', m)\, \delta_{nm'}. \tag{61}$$

The average t-matrix approximation (ATA) is now to decouple the average of the products of t's according to

$$\langle \boldsymbol{t}(1)\,\boldsymbol{t}(2)\ldots t(n)\rangle = \langle \boldsymbol{t}(1)\rangle\,\langle \boldsymbol{t}(2)\rangle \cdots \langle \boldsymbol{t}(n)\rangle\,, \tag{62}$$

which is a somewhat better approximation than the VCA [eq. (56)] because adjacent sites are restricted by $\boldsymbol{P}'$ from coinciding. Thus, we find

$$\langle \boldsymbol{G}\rangle = \boldsymbol{P} + \boldsymbol{P}[\langle \boldsymbol{t}\rangle\,(1 - \boldsymbol{P}'\langle \boldsymbol{t}\rangle)^{-1}]\,\boldsymbol{P}\,, \tag{63}$$

or $\boldsymbol{\Sigma}$ as defined in (48) and (49) is given by

$$\boldsymbol{\Sigma} = \langle \boldsymbol{t}\rangle/[1 + \langle \boldsymbol{t}\rangle\,\boldsymbol{P}]\,, \tag{64}$$

where $\boldsymbol{P}$ contains the same elements of the unperturbed Green's function as appear in $\boldsymbol{t}^m$.

For mass disorder V is diagonal in the site representation and

$$V_{\alpha\alpha'}(l, l') = \Delta M_\alpha \omega^2\,\delta_{\alpha\alpha'}\,\delta(l, l') \tag{65}$$

and so is t. Then

$$\langle t_{\alpha\alpha}\rangle = c\Delta M_\alpha \omega^2/[1 - \Delta M_\alpha \omega^2 P_{\alpha\alpha}(0)] \tag{66}$$

and

$$\Sigma_{\alpha\alpha}(\omega) = c\Delta M_\alpha \omega^2/[1 - (1 - c)\,\Delta M_\alpha \omega^2 P_{\alpha\alpha}(0)]\,. \tag{67}$$

This single-site self energy, first obtained by Elliott and Taylor (1967) is site diagonal and is equivalent to an effective mass (complex and frequency dependent) on the disordered sites. A detailed discussion of this low concentration limit is given in Taylor's chapter.

The concentration dependence at large concentrations of the average t-matrix approximation can be improved substantially by treating the virtual crystal as the unperturbed host $[P(0)=G_V(0)]$ in eq. (57). In this case $\langle t\rangle$ becomes

$$\langle t\rangle = \frac{(1 - c)\,(V_{\mathrm{A}} - \langle V\rangle)}{1 - (V_{\mathrm{A}} - \langle V\rangle)\,G_V(0)} + \frac{c\,(V_{\mathrm{B}} - \langle V\rangle)}{1 - (V_{\mathrm{B}} - \langle V\rangle)\,G_V(0)}, \tag{68}$$

where $G_V(0)$ is the site-diagonal element of eq. (57). This formula is now symmetric in A- and B-atom types and is exact at each limit of concentration. Thus the formula can be used as an interpolation formula over the entire concentration range, except at those frequencies where the high frequency structure associated with pairs and clusters is important and near frequency band edges. It is this formula (68) which has commonly become known (particularly in the electronic problem) as the ATA.

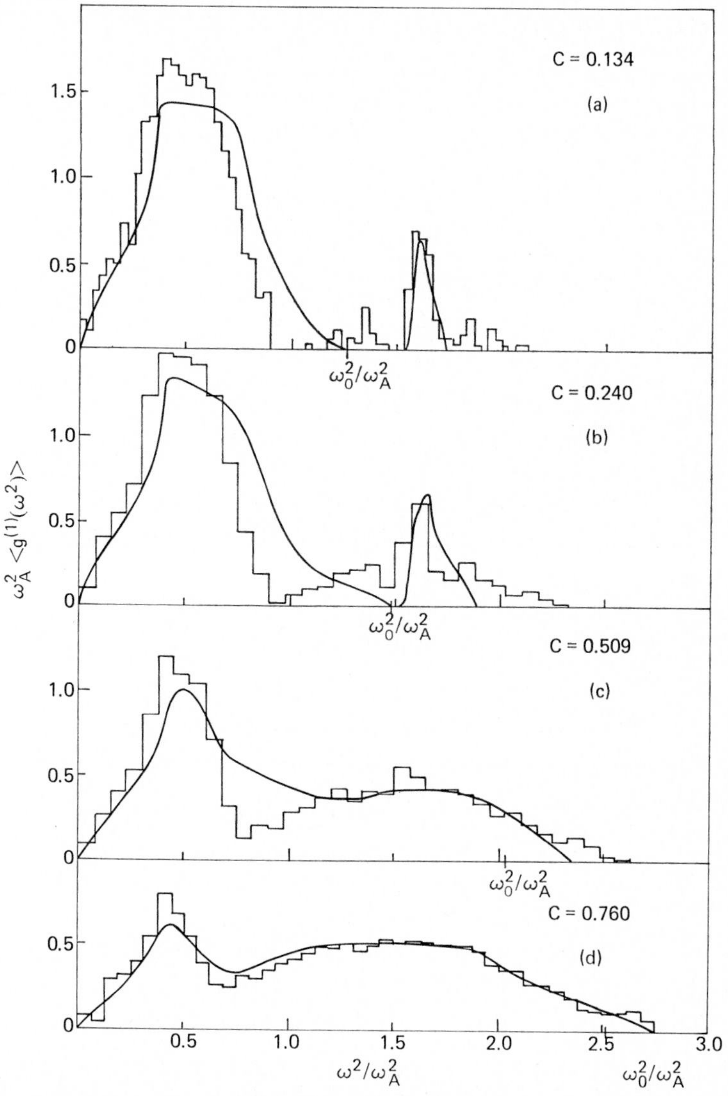

Fig. 3. Phonon density of states as in fig. 2 for a simple cubic lattice compared with the ATA (after Leath and Goodman 1969).

This formula was first derived in the phonon problem by Leath and Goodman (1969). An example is shown in fig. 3 of the application of this formula to a simple cubic lattice and of the comparison with the exact machine calculation of Payton and Visscher (1967). A similar comparison in one-dimension with the linear chain calculations of Dean is much worse because the high-frequency cluster modes dominate the spectrum in this

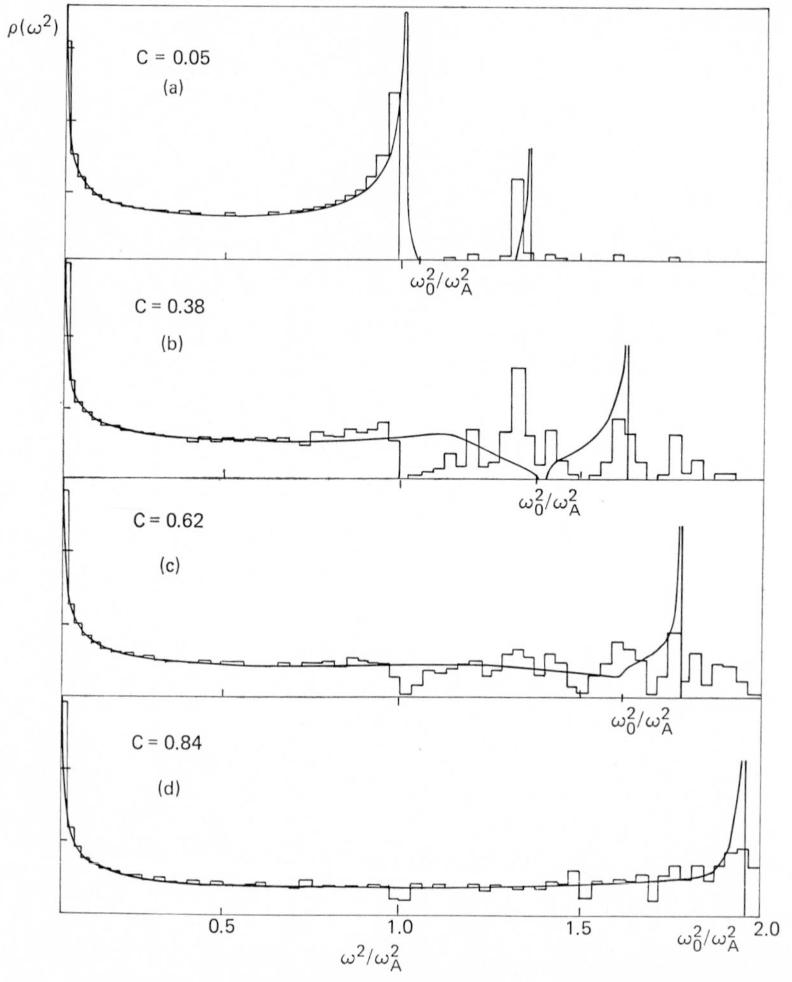

Fig. 4. The phonon density of states $\rho(\omega^2)$ versus ω^2/ω^2_M for a disordered linear chain $A_{1-c}B_c$ with $M_B/M_A=\frac{1}{2}$ for various c as calculated in the ATA compared with machine calculations of Dean (1971) (after Leath and Goodman 1969). $\omega^2{}_0$ is the mean lattice maximum frequency.

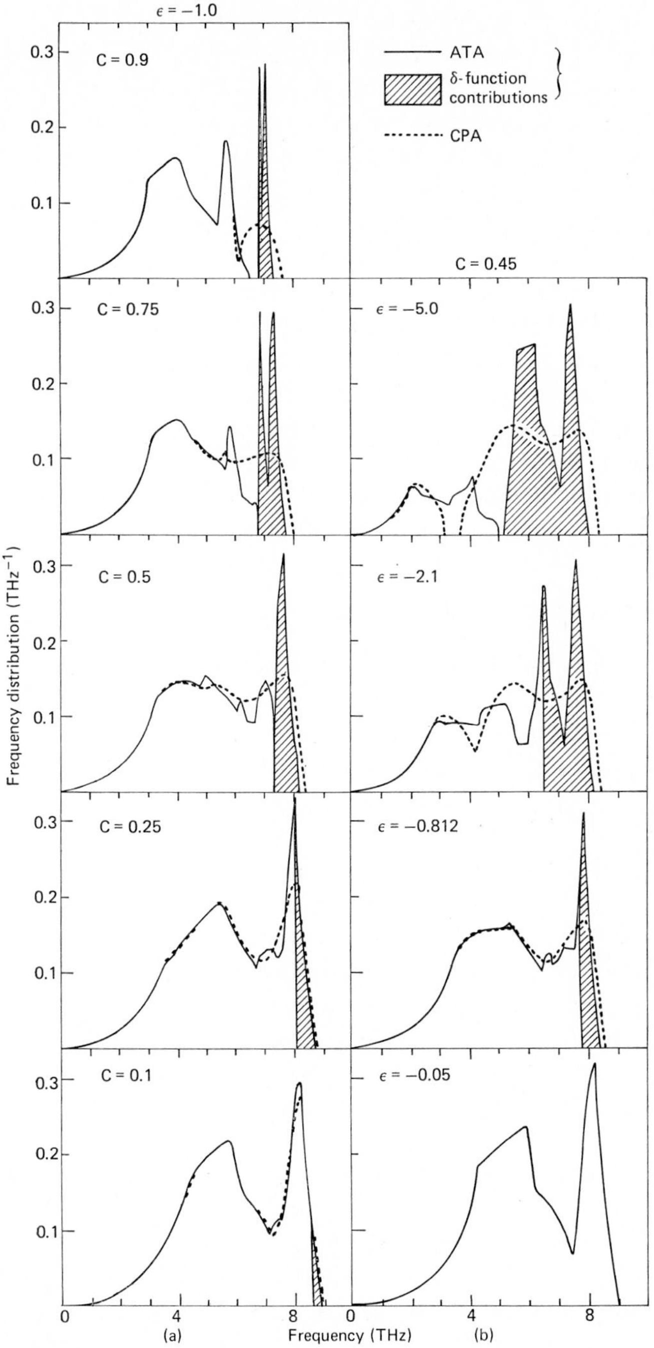

Fig. 5. (a) Phonon density of states per unit frequency in a model of f.c.c. random alloys with $M_B/M_A = 2$ and composition $A_{1-c}B_c$ comparing ATA and CPA. (b) Results for fixed concentration $c = 0.45$ and varying mass ratio $\epsilon = 1 - M_B/M_A$ (after Kamitakahara and Taylor 1974).

case (fig. 4). In three dimensions (even at 50% concentration) the approximation is surprisingly good, considering the nature of the approximation, due to the larger connectivity of three dimensional lattices whereby each atom more nearly sees an average environment.

A weak point of this approximation is its general failure to locate the band edges. To shift the band edges from those of the unperturbed lattice one must treat the scattering in a self-consistent field.

A study of a more realistic example has recently been published by Kamitakahara and Taylor (1974) using a model of a NiPd alloy. They compare the result of the ATA with the CPA (see below) and with the experiments of Kamitakahara and Brockhouse (1974). They show that the ATA gives too much structure at high frequencies and that the CPA gives much more satisfactory results (fig. 5).

Finally, this result (64) can also be obtained directly from the diagrammatic summation of all scatterings by a single site (Leath and Goodman 1969). This technique has been reviewed by Elliott et al. (1974).

2.3. The coherent potential approximation

The first attempt to treat the single-site scattering with a self-consistent field was by Klauder (1961) and Davies and Langer (1963), who merely substituted the full Green's function $\langle \boldsymbol{G} \rangle$ as the internal propagator in the single-site t-matrix (66). This formula was thus

$$\Sigma = c\Delta/(1 - \Delta \langle G(0) \rangle). \tag{69}$$

The absence of the $(1-c)$ factor as in (67), makes no qualitative difference at low c. Davies and Langer were able to solve this resulting equation for the density of states of a disordered linear chain analytically. In the case of strong impurity scattering where there were localized impurity modes, they found a broad and structureless impurity band extending well beyond the rigourously known spectral limits. On the other hand the host band did move to lower frequencies properly as the impurity states were removed. Nevertheless, the results were unphysical and quite unlike the exact machine calculations.

An enormously improved result emerged from the self-consistent calculations of Taylor (1967) in the phonon problem and of Soven (1967) on the equivalent electronic problem. Their result was based on the previous technique of Lax (1951) and the physical ideas expressed by Anderson and McMillan (1967). A review of this coherent potential method has been given by Yonezawa and Morigaki (1973). In this approach, one views the impurities as imbedded in an effective medium whose propagator G_0 has a self-energy Σ (the coherent potential) which is adjusted self-consistently so that the t-matrix for scattering off of a single impurity in this medium is zero on the average.

Specifically, it is assumed that the medium is described by a Green's function $\boldsymbol{G}_0$, which is defined in terms of the host lattice Green's function $\boldsymbol{P}$ by

$$\boldsymbol{G}_0 = \boldsymbol{P} + \boldsymbol{P}\Sigma\boldsymbol{G}_0 \,. \tag{70}$$

Thus the impurities correspond to a perturbation $(\Delta - \Sigma)$ and the host atoms to a perturbation $(-\Sigma)$ so that the average single-site t-matrix is given by

$$\langle t \rangle = \left\langle \frac{V - \Sigma}{1 - (V - \Sigma)\, G_0} \right\rangle = \frac{(1-c)(-\Sigma)}{1 + \Sigma G_0(0)} + \frac{c(\Delta - \Sigma)}{1 - (\Delta - \Sigma)\, G_0(0)} \tag{71}$$

which is set to zero. This equation is then solved simultaneously with the Dyson equation (70) to obtain the best $\boldsymbol{G}_0$ as an approximation to $\langle \boldsymbol{G} \rangle$. Eq. (71) can be manipulated algebraically into the equivalent form

$$\Sigma = c\Delta / [1 - (\Delta - \Sigma)\, G_0(0)] \,. \tag{72}$$

The most interesting and useful features of the coherent potential approximation is its invariance with respect to choice of host lattice and its correct limiting values. It can be shown (Elliott et al. 1974) that the value of $\boldsymbol{G}_0$ resulting from eq. (71) is independent of the choice of unperturbed lattice $\boldsymbol{P}$ in eq. (63). In particular, $\boldsymbol{P}$ can be chosen to be either the pure A-atom lattice or the pure B-atom lattice which illustrates that the CPA is exact in the weak scattering (virtual crystal) limit and in the opposite atomic (Einstein oscillator) limit. In fact, it was this property which led to the derivation of the CPA in the exciton calculation of Onodera and Toyozawa (1968). But, not only is the CPA exact in these extreme limits, it can also be derived independently from a diagrammatic resummation of the perturbation expansion about each of these limits as was shown by Leath (1968). The various diagrammatic approaches are reviewed by Elliott et al. (1974) as are other aspects of the CPA. In particular, they show that these results can also be obtained by considering the conditionally averaged Green's functions (52) and (53).

The CPA formulae of Taylor for the phonon spectra of a linear chain and a simple cubic lattice are compared with the corresponding exact machine calculations in figs. 6 and 7. The agreement with the machine calculations is

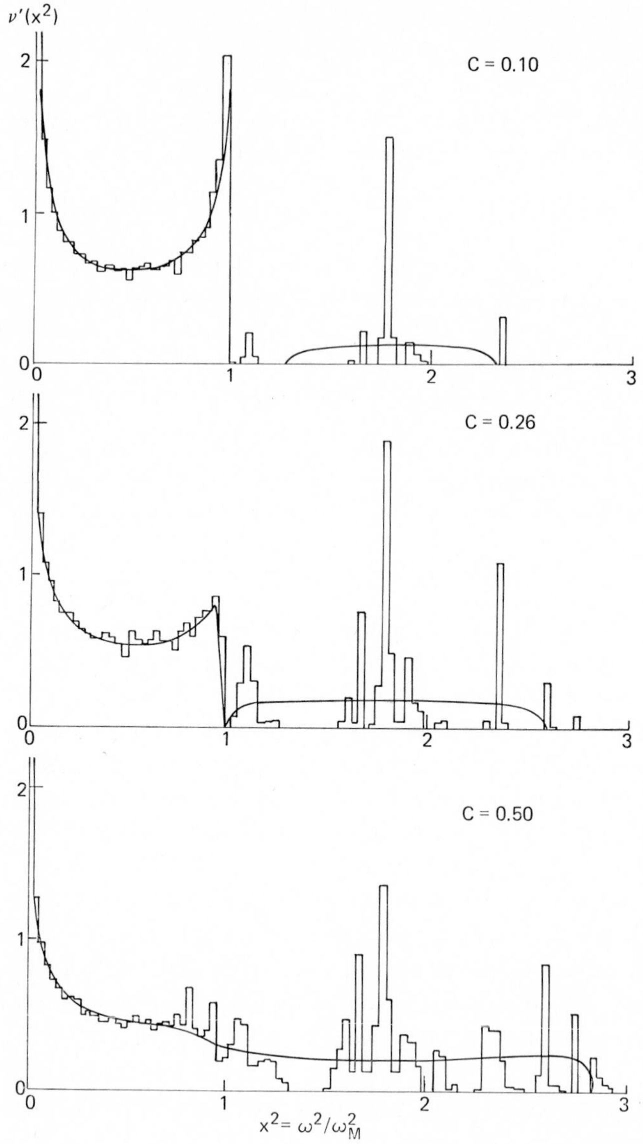

Fig. 6. Phonon density of states as in fig. 1 for a linear chain compared with CPA calculations (after Taylor 1967).

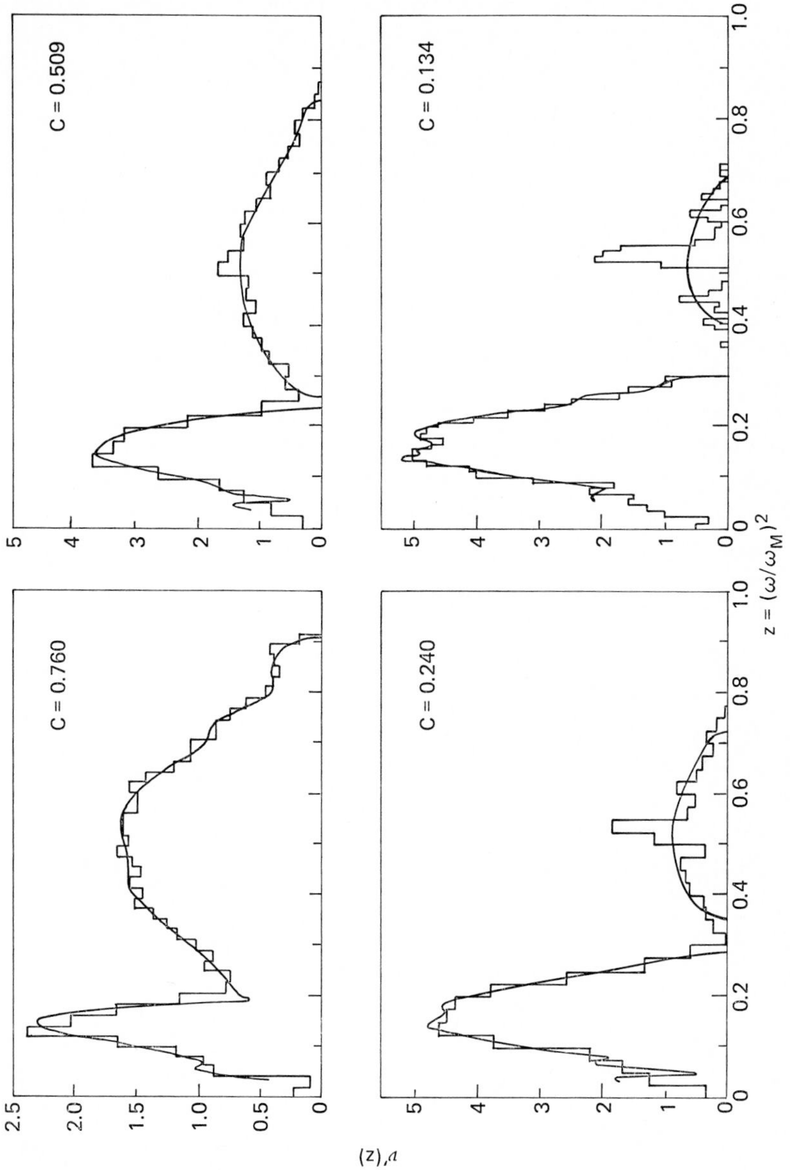

Fig. 7. Phonon density of states as in fig. 2 for a simple cubic lattice compared with CPA calculations (after Taylor 1967).

extremely good in the three-dimensional case except for the high-frequency cluster structure. In particular, the band edges are now much better located. The relationship of the CPA band edges to the exact band edges shows that the CPA always splits into host and impurity band a bit too soon which comes from the fact that the CPA does not reproduce the band tailing effects due to large clusters.

There have also been a number of calculations based on more realistic models which can be compared with experiment. Taylor in his original paper considered Si–Ge alloys and recently Srivastava and Joshi (1973) have improved the calculation of this system. Kaplan and Mostoller (1974c) have made calculations for $Al_{0.1}$ $Cu_{0.9}$ and Mostoller et al. (1974) for h.c.p. $Y_{0.9}Tb_{0.1}$; in both cases they compared their calculations with results from neutron diffraction experiments. The diatomic lattice $(NH_4)_{0.1}K_{0.9}Cl$ was also examined by Kaplan and Mostoller (1974c) while Taylor (1973) has made a more detailed study of KCl_xBr_{1-x} and $K_{1-x}Rb_xI$.

Force constant changes can only be treated by the CPA if the perturbations are additive. Then, as implied by Soven (1967), and later explicitly suggested by Takeno (1968), the theory goes through in an exactly parallel fashion. If V^l is the impurity potential we assume that $\boldsymbol{\Sigma}$ is a matrix of the same size and symmetry. Then the result (72) still holds in matrix form

$$\boldsymbol{\Sigma} = c\boldsymbol{V}/[\boldsymbol{1} - (\boldsymbol{V} - \boldsymbol{\Sigma})\,\boldsymbol{G}]. \tag{73}$$

In a polyatomic lattice $\boldsymbol{\Sigma}$ and $\boldsymbol{G}$ must maintain their appropriate site indices.

Local symmetry can be used to simplify this complex set of coupled equations since $\boldsymbol{V}$, $\boldsymbol{t}$ and $\boldsymbol{\Sigma}$ retain the same site symmetry. Detailed calculations for the single defect t matrix have been given by Lakatos and Krumhansl (1968, 1969). As an example we consider a defect at the origin (in a simple cubic lattice) with mass $M' = M_0(1-\varepsilon)$ and nearest neighbour force constant change $\Delta\Phi(0.1) = -\gamma$. Then the non-zero elements of the perturbation V^0 can be written as the matrix

$$V^0 = \begin{bmatrix} \Delta + 6\gamma & -\gamma & -\gamma & -\gamma & -\gamma & -\gamma & -\gamma \\ -\gamma & \gamma & 0 & 0 & 0 & 0 & 0 \\ -\gamma & 0 & \gamma & 0 & 0 & 0 & 0 \\ -\gamma & 0 & 0 & \gamma & 0 & 0 & 0 \\ -\gamma & 0 & 0 & 0 & \gamma & 0 & 0 \\ -\gamma & 0 & 0 & 0 & 0 & \gamma & 0 \\ -\gamma & 0 & 0 & 0 & 0 & 0 & \gamma \end{bmatrix}, \tag{74}$$

where as before $\Delta = M_0 \varepsilon \omega^2$. Using the transformation to symmetrical co-ordinates, discussed in Appendix C of Elliott et al. (1974), this matrix can be block-diagonalized into s-, p-, and d-wave parts

$$\boldsymbol{V}_{\mathrm{s}} = \begin{bmatrix} (\Delta + 6\gamma) & -\gamma\sqrt{6} \\ \gamma\sqrt{6} & \gamma \end{bmatrix}, \quad \boldsymbol{V}_{\mathrm{p}} = \gamma \begin{bmatrix} 1 & 0 & 0 \\ 0 & 1 & 0 \\ 0 & 0 & 1 \end{bmatrix}, \quad \boldsymbol{V}_{\mathrm{d}} = \gamma \begin{bmatrix} 1 & 0 \\ 0 & 1 \end{bmatrix}. \tag{75}$$

Because of the local symmetry the Green's function $G(l, l')$ can also be separated by the same transformation to give

$$\boldsymbol{G}_{\mathrm{s}} = \begin{bmatrix} G_{00} & \sqrt{6G_{01}} \\ \sqrt{6G_{01}} & G_s \end{bmatrix}, \text{ where } G_{\mathrm{s}} = G_{11} + G_{12} + 4G_{13}, \tag{76a}$$

while

$$\boldsymbol{G}_{\mathrm{p}} = G_{\mathrm{p}} \begin{bmatrix} 1 & 0 & 0 \\ 0 & 1 & 0 \\ 0 & 0 & 1 \end{bmatrix}, \text{ with } G_{\mathrm{p}} = G_{11} - G_{12}, \tag{76b}$$

and

$$\boldsymbol{G}_{\mathrm{d}} = G_{\mathrm{d}} \begin{bmatrix} 1 & 0 \\ 0 & 1 \end{bmatrix}, \text{ with } G_{\mathrm{d}} = G_{11} + G_{12} - 2G_{13}, \tag{76c}$$

where sites 1, 2, 3 are nearest neighbours of the origin (0,0,0) located at (1,0,0), (−1,1,0) and (0,0,1) respectively, $\boldsymbol{\Sigma}$ also has the same form with

$$\boldsymbol{\Sigma}_{\mathrm{s}} = \begin{bmatrix} \Sigma_{00} & \Sigma_{01} \\ \Sigma_{01} & \Sigma_{11} \end{bmatrix}, \quad \boldsymbol{\Sigma}_{\mathrm{p}} = \Sigma_{\mathrm{p}} \begin{bmatrix} 1 & 0 & 0 \\ 0 & 1 & 0 \\ 0 & 0 & 1 \end{bmatrix} \text{ and } \boldsymbol{\Sigma}_{\mathrm{d}} = \Sigma_{\mathrm{d}} \begin{bmatrix} 1 & 0 \\ 0 & 1 \end{bmatrix}. \tag{77}$$

The matrix equation (73) now gives a scalar equation for Σ_{p} and Σ_{d} and a (2×2) matrix for $\boldsymbol{\Sigma}_s$. For a given $\boldsymbol{\Sigma}$, $\boldsymbol{G}$ can be calculated and self-consistency achieved by iteration. This programme has been carried through by Kaplan and Mostoller (1974b) in a model of $(NH_4)_{1-x}K_xCl$. In this diatomic lattice there is an additional complication in that Σ_{00} acts on one sublattice while Σ_{11}, Σ_{p} and Σ_{d} act on the other and Σ_{01} connects the two. This must be included in an appropriate way to find $\langle G_{\alpha\beta}(l, l') \rangle$ for use in the self-consistent equations.

In the situation where force constant changes are important they are unlikely to be strictly additive and therefore some further approximations will be necessary. For a simple $A_{1-c}B_c$ mixture it might be possible to exploit the philosophy of the VCA and ATA in the following way. We note that while the neighbourhood of each A and B atom will fluctuate the mean environment will contain $(1-c)$ A atoms and c B atoms. We can therefore define force constants for this average environment; for A atoms it will be

$$\langle \Phi_A \rangle = (1-c)\,\Phi_{AA} + c\Phi_{AB}, \tag{78}$$

with M_A at the central site and

$$\langle M \rangle = (1-c)\,M_A + cM_B \tag{79a}$$

on the neighbours. We then prepare to do an ATA or CPA calculation on the deviations from the mean VCA lattice with mass $\langle M \rangle$ and force constant.

$$\langle \Phi \rangle = (1-c)\,\langle \Phi_A \rangle + c\,\langle \Phi_B \rangle = (1-c)^2\,\Phi_{AA} + 2c\,(1-c)\,\Phi_{AB} + c^2\Phi_{BB}. \tag{79b}$$

The CPA equation is

$$\boldsymbol{\Sigma} = (1-c)\frac{\langle \boldsymbol{\Phi}_A \rangle - \langle \boldsymbol{\Phi} \rangle}{1 - (\langle \boldsymbol{\Phi}_A \rangle - \langle \boldsymbol{\Phi} \rangle - \Sigma)\,G} + c\,\frac{\langle \boldsymbol{\Phi}_B \rangle - \langle \boldsymbol{\Phi} \rangle}{1 - (\langle \boldsymbol{\Phi}_B \rangle - \langle \boldsymbol{\Phi} \rangle - \Sigma)\,G}, \tag{80}$$

while the ATA would have no $\boldsymbol{\Sigma}$ on the R.H.S. and $\boldsymbol{G}$ replaced by $\boldsymbol{P}$ for the mean VCA lattice. Further work is planned on this proposed scheme.

The further extension of the CPA method to include pairs and clusters is an obvious generalisation which is essential for any theory of the fine structure in the density of states and particularly of the impurity bands. Such extensions have proved difficult and to date no really satisfactory theory exists – certainly none has been attempted for the vibrational problem. For further discussion and references we refer the reader to Elliott et al. (1974). A similar situation exists in the case of alloys showing short range order rather than a completely random arrangement of constituents.

2.4. Thermal conductivity

The evaluation of the configuration averaged thermal condictivity $\langle \kappa_{\mu\nu} \rangle$ as given by the average of eq. (33) involves the weighted average of a product of two one-particle Green's, $\mathrm{Tr}\langle \boldsymbol{A}_\mu \mathrm{Im}\boldsymbol{G}(\omega)\boldsymbol{A}_\nu \mathrm{Im}\boldsymbol{G}(\omega)\rangle$ which is generally evaluated in some approximate manner. In the case of mass defect scattering only, $A_\mu^{\alpha\alpha'}(l, l')$ is independent of the occupation of the lattice sites so that only the average of $\langle \mathrm{Im}\, \boldsymbol{G}(\omega)\, \mathrm{Im}\, \boldsymbol{G}(\omega)\rangle$ need be considered. Furthermore, in the case of the CPA, the irreducible scattering by only a single mass defect is included, the self-energy contains only S-wave scattering and thus, for crystals with inversion symmetry, there are no vertex correction contributions to the thermal conductivity (due to the odd parity of the energy current operator). In this case the average of the two Green's functions factorize exactly into the product of averages so that the resulting formula is

$$\langle \kappa_{\mu\nu}\rangle = -\frac{2\hbar^2}{\pi V k_{\mathrm{B}} T^2} \times \int_{-\infty}^{\infty} \mathrm{d}\omega \, \frac{\omega^2 \exp(\hbar\omega/k_{\mathrm{B}}T)}{[\exp(\hbar\omega/k_{\mathrm{B}}T) - 1]^2} \, \mathrm{Tr}\, \{\boldsymbol{A}_\mu \langle \mathrm{Im}\, \boldsymbol{G}(\omega)\rangle \, \boldsymbol{A}_\nu \langle \mathrm{Im}\, \boldsymbol{G}(\omega)\rangle\}. \tag{81}$$

This formula was studied in the dilute limit by Maradudin (1964) and Woll (1965), and in the CPA by Flicker and Leath (1973). One important physical feature of this formula is that the integrand diverges near $\omega = 0$ as ω^{-2} so that $\langle \kappa \rangle$ diverges linearly with N (the linear size of the crystal). This occurs because the phonon velocity goes to the speed of sound so that the harmonic phonons of low k are unable to reach thermal equilibrium. The inclusion of another scattering mechanism such as anharmonicity or boundaries removes this divergence so that the scattering can be calculated.

It can also be easily shown (Elliott et al. 1974) that this formula (81) reduces to the standard Boltzmann equation result

$$\langle \kappa \rangle = V^{-1} \sum_{kj} C[\omega_j(k)]\, \tau_j(k)\, |V_j(k)|^2 \cos^2\theta, \tag{82a}$$

where phonon specific heat contributions is given by

$$C(\omega) = \hbar^2\omega^2 \exp(\hbar\omega/k_{\mathrm{B}}T)/\{k_{\mathrm{B}}T^2 [\exp(\hbar\omega/k_{\mathrm{B}}T) - 1]^2\}, \tag{82b}$$

and where the phonon relaxation time is given by

$$\tau_j(k) = M\omega_j(k)/\{\mathrm{Im}\, \Sigma[\omega_j(k)]\}, \tag{82c}$$

where Σ is the phonon self-energy of eq. (49).

A more complete review of phonon thermal conductivity in disordered crystals is given by Maradudin (1966) for the dilute limit, and by Elliott et al. (1974).

3. Experimental results

3.1. Inelastic neutron scattering

As discussed in subsection 1.2, inelastic neutron scattering consists of a coherent and an incoherent part, (23) and (25). The former is related to a weighted average over the displacement correlation function, specifically

$$\frac{\mathrm{d}^2\sigma^{\mathrm{c}}}{\mathrm{d}\Omega\,\mathrm{d}E} = \frac{1}{\pi}\frac{K'}{K}\sum_{\substack{\alpha\alpha'\\ \mathrm{AA'}}} B_\alpha^{\mathrm{A}} B_{\alpha'}^{\mathrm{A'}} q_\alpha q_{\alpha'} \operatorname{Im}\langle G_{\alpha\alpha'}^{\mathrm{AA'}}(\boldsymbol{q}, E)\rangle\, n(E), \tag{83}$$

where A defines the atomic species at site α. The incoherent scattering

$$\frac{\mathrm{d}^2\sigma^{\mathrm{i}}}{\mathrm{d}\Omega\,\mathrm{d}E} = \frac{1}{\pi}\frac{K'}{K}\sum_{\alpha\mathrm{A}} \beta_\alpha^{\mathrm{A}2} q_\alpha^2 \operatorname{Im}\langle G_{\alpha\alpha}^{\mathrm{AA}}(0, 0, E)\rangle\, n(E) \tag{84}$$

is related to a weighted average of the single site Green's function and hence to the density of states. Using the expressions for the weighted Green's functions given in (52)–(53), we can write these in terms of the unweighted $\langle G\rangle$. The average in the coherent case becomes

$$\operatorname{Im}[B^h - (B^h - B^d)(\Sigma/V)]^2 \langle G(\boldsymbol{q}, E)\rangle + (B^{\mathrm{h}} - B^{\mathrm{d}})^2(\Sigma - cV)/V^2. \tag{85}$$

The first part has an effective scattering length while the latter is in some sense an incoherent contribution from the random distribution. Using the CPA it can be rewritten

$$(B^{\mathrm{h}} - B^{\mathrm{d}})^2\, \Sigma(V - \Sigma)/V^2 \operatorname{Im}\langle G(0, 0, E)\rangle.$$

Alternatively we can manipulate the whole into a different effective scattering length. For a complex crystal with several branches, the single site CPA result is

$$\frac{\mathrm{d}^2\sigma^{\mathrm{c}}}{\mathrm{d}\Omega\,\mathrm{d}E} = \frac{1}{\pi}\frac{K'}{K}\sum_{\alpha\beta j} (\sigma_j^\alpha q^\alpha)(\sigma_j^\beta q^\beta)\left(\frac{B^{\mathrm{h}} - (B^{\mathrm{h}} - B^{\mathrm{d}})}{VP_j(q, E)}\right)^2 \operatorname{Im}\langle G_j(\boldsymbol{q}, E)\rangle\, n(E). \tag{86}$$

The incoherent scattering can be written

$$\frac{\mathrm{d}^2\sigma^{\mathrm{i}}}{\mathrm{d}\Omega\,\mathrm{d}E} = \frac{1}{\pi}\frac{K'}{K}\frac{\beta^{\mathrm{h}2}(V - \Sigma) + \beta^{\mathrm{d}2}\Sigma}{Vq_\alpha^2 \operatorname{Im}\langle G(0, 0, E)\rangle\, n(E)}. \tag{87}$$

Because of difficulties of experimental resolution the incoherent cross sections have been studied little. However the coherent cross section allows a direct measurement of $\langle G(\boldsymbol{k}, E)\rangle$ and gives the most detailed experimental information about phonons in mixed crystals. There have been a number of experiments with relatively low concentrations of impurities. When the impurities are heavy such as $Cu_{1-x}Au_x$ measured by Svensson and Kamitakahara (1971) and $Cr_{1-x}W_x$ by Moller and Mackintosh (1968) a low frequency resonance is found. These results have been extensively discussed by Kesharwani and Agrawal (1972, 1973) and by Bruno and Taylor (1971) using the ATA. For a detailed review see Taylor's chapter 5. A more thorough discussion of such an alloy has been given by Mostoller et al. (1974) for the h.c.p. system $Y_{0.9}Tb_{0.1}$ where the experimental results are confronted with a CPA calculation.

A small concentration of light atoms produces localised modes. An examination of such modes has been made in a number of materials (cf. ch. 5). The most detailed results are for $Ge_{0.91}Si_{0.09}$ (Wakabayashi et al. 1971, Wakabayashi 1973) and $Cu_{0.9}Al_{0.1}$ (Nicklow et al. 1968). While ATA theory gives a good description of the intensity variation of such scattering it predicts no energy width. A CPA study has been made for CuAl by Kaplan and Mostoller (1974c) and compared with experiment (fig. 8).

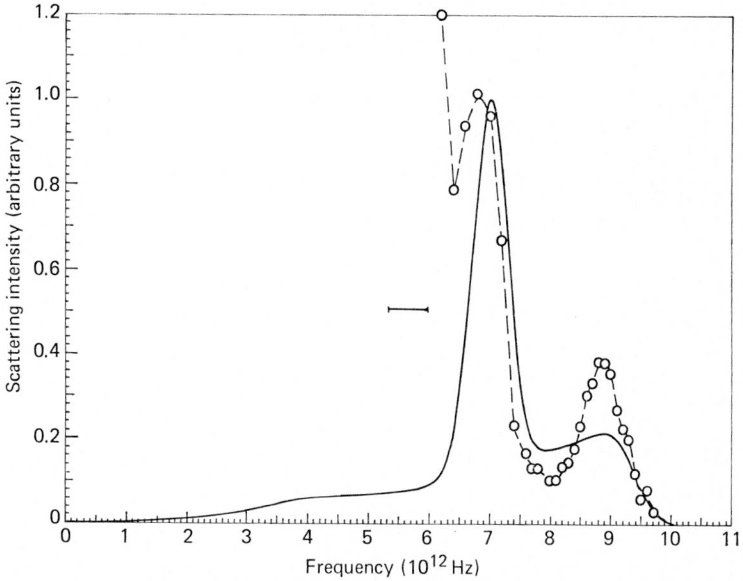

Fig. 8. Observed inelastic neutron scattering (points) from $Al_{0.1}Cu_{0.9}$ at $q=(\frac{1}{2},\frac{1}{2},\frac{1}{2})$ $(2\pi/a)$ (Nicklow et al. 1968) compared with a CPA calculation (after Kaplan and Mostoller 1974c).

There have also been a number of studies of alloys at high concentrations, notably NbMo (Woods and Powell (1965, 1968), Bl–Pb–Tl (Ng and Brockhouse 1967, Brockhouse and Roy 1970) TaNb (Als-Neilson 1968), FeNi and CuZn (Hallman and Brockhouse 1969). Here the difference in mass is small but there are considerable changes in the force constants as the Fermi surface shifts with valence. In particular the Kohn anomalies move. Since these are long range effects the VCA is the only possible method of interpretation and works satisfactorily (cf. fig. 9).

More recently Kamitakahara and Brockhouse (1974) have made a detailed

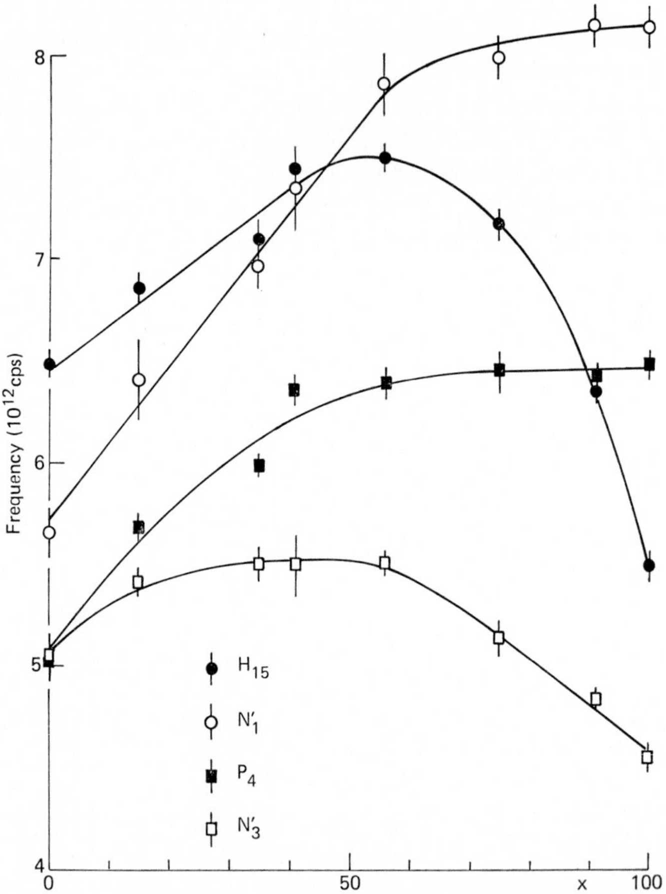

Fig. 9. Frequency variation of some zone boundary phonons as a function of composition in $Nb_{1-o_x}M_x$ (after Woods et al. 1968).

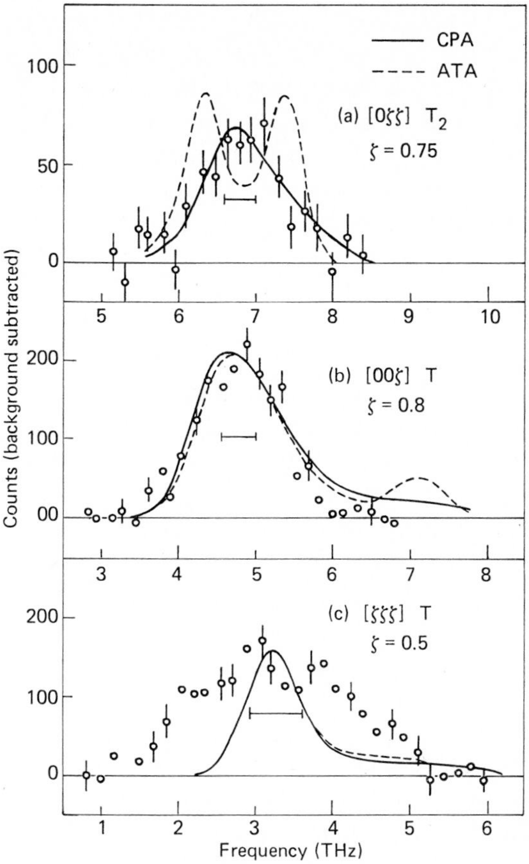

Fig. 10. Comparison of experimental neutron scattering at various $\boldsymbol{q}$ in $Ni_{0.55}Pd_{0.45}$ observed by Kamitakahara and Brockhouse (1974) with ATA and CPA calculations (after Kamitakahara and Taylor 1974).

study of $Ni_{0.55}Pd_{0.45}$ and a theoretical interpretation has been made by Kamitakahara and Taylor (1974) using CPA for the mass disorder and VCA for the force constant changes. In particular they show that the CPA gives a much better description than the ATA (fig. 10).

Mixed alkali halides have also been studied. Cowley and Buyers (1968) measured $K_{1-x}Rb_xBr$ ($x=22\%$ and 45%) and found a relatively broad and featureless spectrum. More recently with detailed results for $K_{0.9}(NH_4)_{0.1}Cl$, Kaplan and Mostoller (1974b,c) have discussed this system in the CPA using both mass disorder and force constant charges. A very interesting study has been made by Powell and Neilson (unpublished) of a mixture of deuterium and hydrogen. By using para H_2 which has a very small cross section they were able to emphasize the impurity scattering of ortho D_2 up to 11% D_2. They compare their experimental result with ATA and CPA calculations based on a simplified cubic model and get satisfactory agreement although anharmonic effects in their quantum crystals cause important changes in the intensities.

3.2. Optical properties

3.2.1. Optical absorption

The optical constants of ionic crystals in the infra-red are largely determined by the optical vibrations. For a perfect crystal χ in (28) is proportional to $1/M(\omega^2-\omega_{\mathrm{TO}}^2)$ where ω_{TO} is the frequency of the transverse optic mode. Thus the imaginary part of ε is proportional to $\delta(\omega-\omega_{\mathrm{TO}})$. The real part however becomes negative near the frequency range $\omega_{\mathrm{TO}}<\omega<\omega_{\mathrm{LO}}$ where the longitudinal optic mode frequency ω_{LO} is given by the LST relation (Born and Huang 1954)

$$\omega_{\mathrm{LO}}^2/\omega_{\mathrm{TO}}^2=\varepsilon_0/\varepsilon_\infty\,. \tag{88}$$

In this region the refractive index is imaginary and total reflection occurs. In the imperfect crystal $\langle G_{\mathrm{TO}}(\boldsymbol{k}=0)\rangle$ will have a complicated structure. However the real part will often remain large in some energy regions to give large reflection. This effect is relatively easy to measure and a great deal of experimental information has now been collected particularly for mixed alkali halides, III–V and II–VI compounds

The experimental results up to 1970 are extensively discussed in a review article by Chang and Mitra (1971). Further details can be found in Harada and Narita (1971) and in a projected review by Barker and Sievers. We shall therefore only give explicit references to more recent work. Reflection spectra are broad and detailed interpretation requires considerable analysis. Much attention has therefore been focused on the number of peaks observed. Roughly speaking the spectra fall into two types – I those showing a single peak which moves as the concentration changes, and II those showing two peaks whose relative intensity changes with composition.

The same system can show different types of behaviour at different ends of the concentration range. Specific examples shown in figs. 11–13, demonstrate that the behaviour of real systems is quite complex.

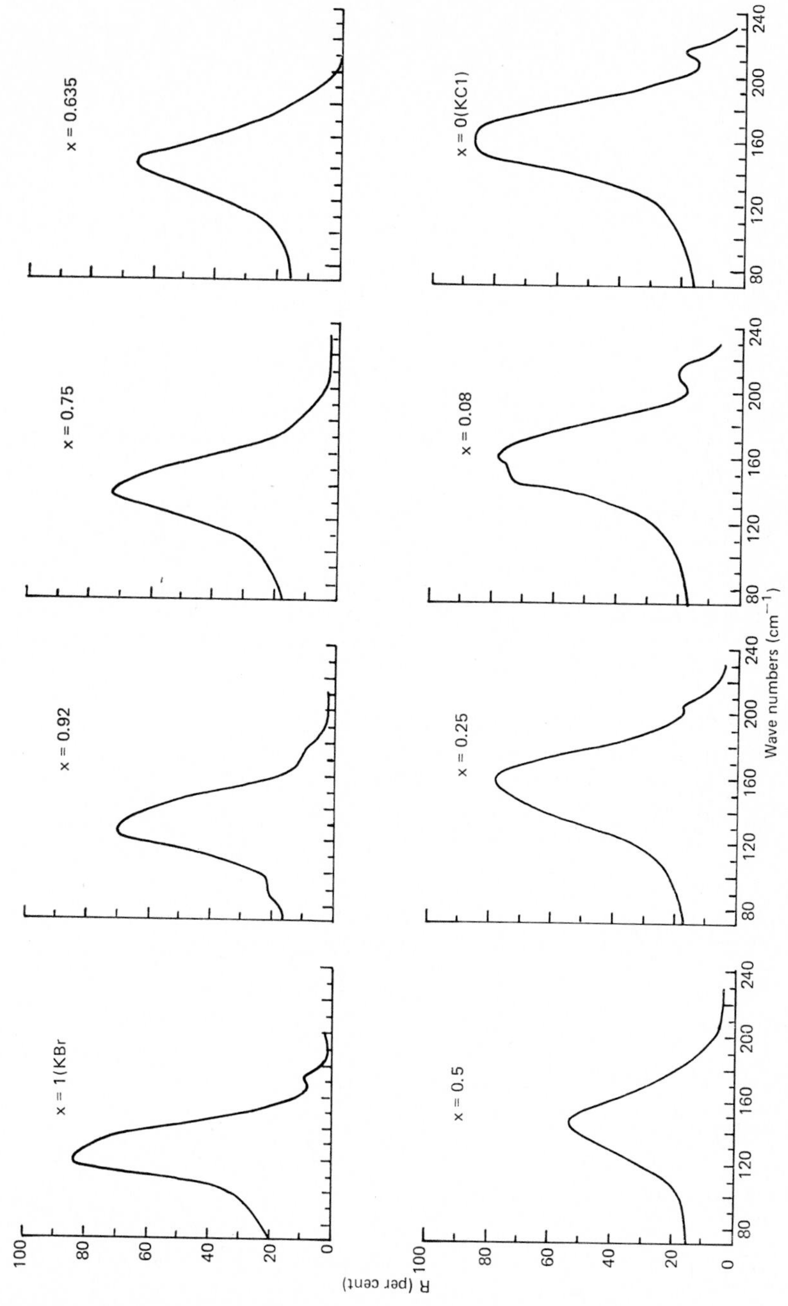

Fig. 11. Reflectivity spectra of KCl_xBr_{1-x} (type I behaviour).

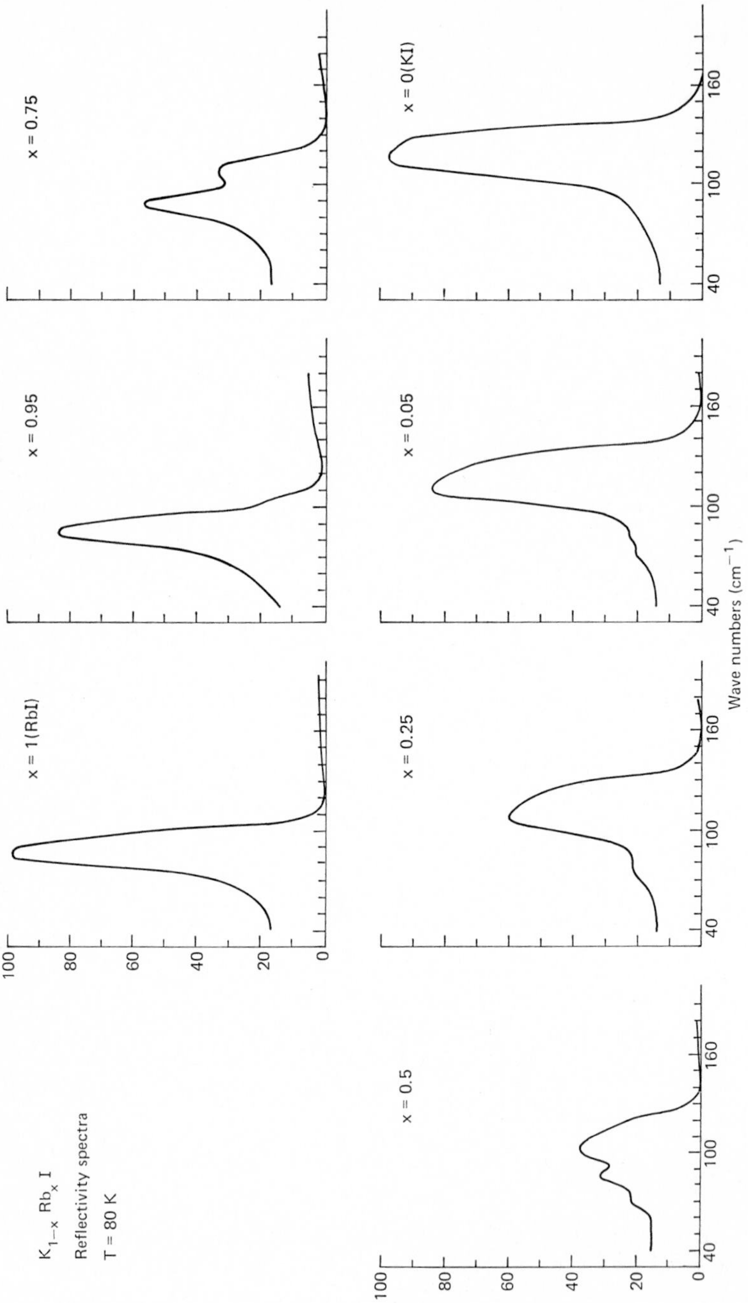

Fig. 12. Reflectivity spectra of $K_{1-x}Rb_xI$ (near type II behaviour) (after Fertel and Perry 1969).

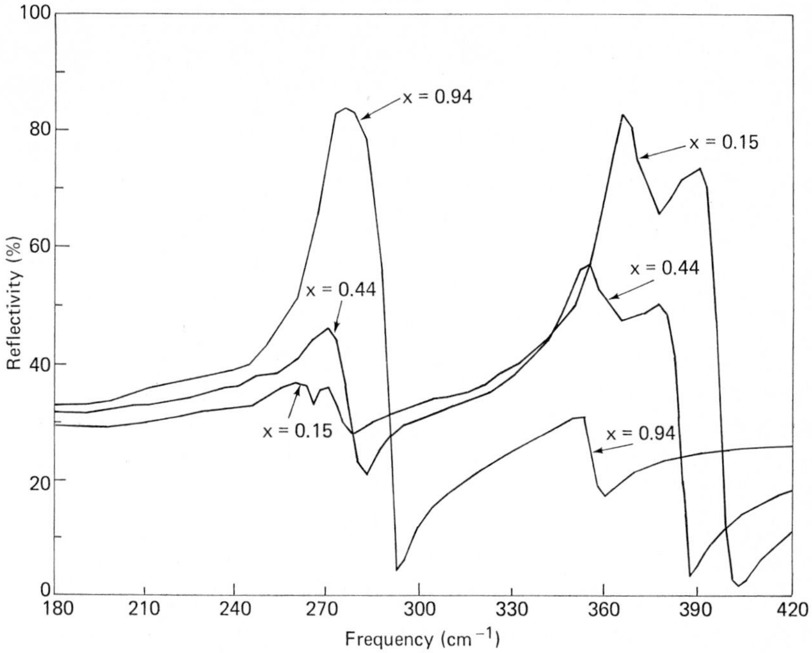

Fig. 13. Reflectivity spectra of $GaAs_xP_{1-x}$ (clear type II behaviour) (after Verleur and Barker 1966).

There has been a great deal of discussion in the literature about the criteria for these two types of behaviour. The most important necessary condition for type II behaviour to occur is that there is a local mode at the isolated defect (Chang and Mitra 1968, Brodsky et al. 1970). As the concentration increases these local modes spread into a band. If it remains distinct from the host spectral band two peaks will occur in the reflectance but if the two bands merge, one peak is likely. Thus the ratio of the restrahl band width to the local mode splitting is an important criterion as has been stressed by Fertel and Perry (1969) and others. They suggested that type I behaviour would always occur if the two restrahl bands of the constituent crystals overlap. This is too strong a condition, although it holds if the overlap is large.

The existence of localised modes above the optic branch is likely for light mass impurities. For heavy mass impurities gap modes may occur below the optic branch if the impurity is substituted on a light atom site. In other cases the heavy impurities give rise to resonances in the acoustic bands. These are often broad so that two mode behaviour is less likely, though not impossible, in this situation. If a diatomic crystal is constituted from atoms of similar mass the gap between optic and acoustic branches will be small so that heavy impurities will always give resonances, and hence are less likely to show type II behaviour.

The simple features of these spectra has led to a number of simplified theories for their interpretation. Verleur and Barker (1966) for example, made calculations with finite atomic clusters. A widely used model called the random element isolelectonic model (REI) was introduced by Chen et al. (1966) and has been extended by a number of authors e.g. Chang and Mitra (1968), and most recently by Genzel et al. (1974). In this model for a mixed crystal of composition $A_{1-x}A'_xB$ all atoms of the same type are assumed to oscillate in phase, to give two TO and two LO modes. This model clearly neglects the random nature of the crystal – it is moderately successful primarily because the mode width is often not significant in the broad restrahl phenomena.

A simple model which emphasizes the disorder has been put forward by Elliott et al. (1974). This is based on the model CPA calculations of Onodera and Toyozawa (1968) who were examining a similar phenomenon in the exciton spectra of mixed crystals. They use a simple parabolic density of states of width $2W$ and have site diagonal energies differing by Δ. Translating this into the phonon case we neglect the acoustic modes and assume the optic modes to have a parabolic density in ω^2 centred at ω_0^2. If the characteristic force constant is Φ, ω_0^2 depends on the reduced mass.

$$\omega_0^2 = \Phi\left(\frac{1}{M_A} + \frac{1}{M_B}\right) = \frac{\Phi}{\mu}. \tag{89}$$

Hence the defect gives

$$\Delta/\omega_0^2 = (1 - \mu/\mu'). \tag{90}$$

If the width of the optic branch is dominated by the electrical forces the width

$$W/\omega_0^2 = (\varepsilon_0 - \varepsilon_\infty)/(\varepsilon_0 + \varepsilon_\infty). \tag{91}$$

The condition for a local mode at small x is then

$$|1 - \mu/\mu'| > \tfrac{1}{2}(\varepsilon_0 - \varepsilon_\infty)/(\varepsilon_0 + \varepsilon_\infty). \tag{92}$$

The CPA calculations of Onodera and Toyozawa are shown in fig. 14 for various values of $\delta = \Delta/W$. For small δ the density of states $\mathrm{Im}\langle G(k=0, \omega^2)\rangle$

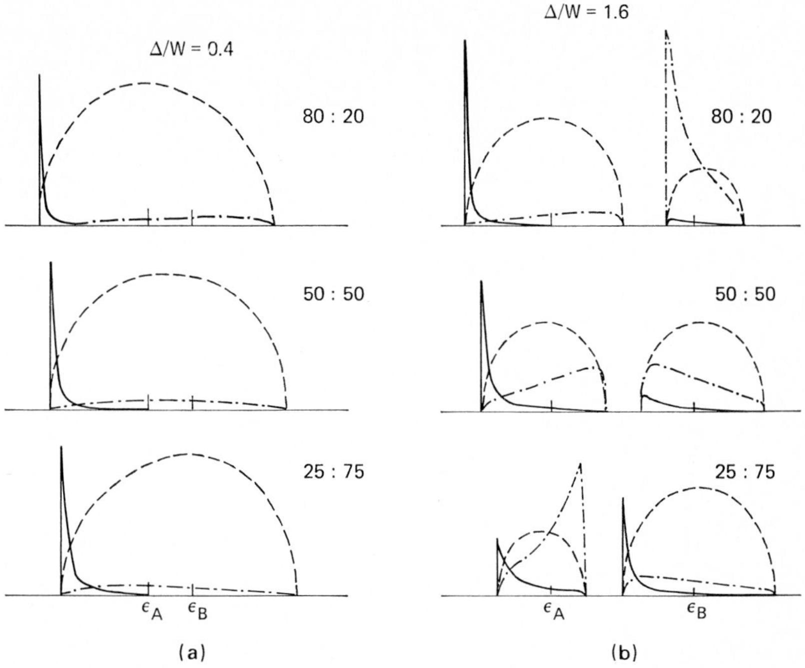

Fig. 14. CPA calculations of the uniform response functions, Im $\langle G(k=0)\rangle$ – full line, the density of states, Im $\langle G(0,0)\rangle$ – dashed line, and Im Σ – dot–dash line for a simple model showing a) type I and b) type II behaviour for different ratios of Δ/W (after Onodera and Toyozawa 1968).

and $\mathrm{Im}\,\Sigma(\omega^2)$ have a single peak while for large δ they have two peaks. For two peaks to exist over a range of x up to 50% requires a stronger condition, namely

$$|1 - \mu/\mu'| > (\varepsilon_0 - \varepsilon_\infty)/(\varepsilon_0 + \varepsilon_\infty). \qquad (93)$$

The results of this criterion are compared in table 1 with a summary of the available data on simple binary crystals. It is seen to account reasonably for most of the results. Some of the main discrepancies are due to the neglect of the acoustic branches where, as has been remarked, heavy impurities on the heavy aton site or a crystal with $M_A \simeq M_B$ will give resonances. This would account for the type I behaviour of In and Sb in GaAs. There remain, however, other discrepancies. In particular $Ga_{1-x}In_xSb$ and $InAs_{1-x}Sb_x$ are difficult to understand in the model but Brodsky et al. (1970) and Lucovsky and Chen (1970) suggest that there is no gap mode in these systems either at

TABLE 1

Crystal	x	$1-\mu/\mu'$	$\frac{\varepsilon_0-\varepsilon_\infty}{\varepsilon_0+\varepsilon_\infty}$	Expt.	Ref.
$Na_xK_{1-x}Cl$	1	0.26	0.45	I	a
	0	0.35	0.39	I	
$K_xTl_{1-x}Cl$	1	0.38	0.39	I	a, b
	0	0.61	0.72	I	
$K_xRb_{1-x}Cl$	1	0.25	0.39	I	a
	0	0.33	0.39	I	
$K_xTl_{1-x}Br$	1	0.52	0.39	II	b
	0	1.09	0.69	II	
$Na_xRb_{1-x}I$	1	0.65	0.37	II	a, c
	0	1.61	0.35	II	
$K_xRb_{1-x}I$	1	0.41	0.30	II	a, b
	0	0.72	0.35	II	
KCl_xBr_{1-x}	1	0.29	0.39	I	a, c
	0	0.40	0.39	I	
$(NH_4)Cl_xBr_{1-x}$	1	0.19	0.38	I	d
	0	0.23	0.33	I	
$AgBr_xCl_{1-x}$	1	0.72	0.48	I	e
	0	0.42	0.51	I	
$Ga_xIn_{1-x}As$	1	0.20	0.08	I	a, f
	0	0.25	0.09	II	
$Ga_xIn_{1-x}Sb$	1	0.27	0.05	I	a, g
	0	0.36	0.04	II	
$Ga_xAl_{1-x}As$	1	0.82	0.08	II	a
	0	0.45	0.09	II	
$Ga_xIn_{1-x}P$	1	0.12	0.09	I	h
	0	0.14	0.12	I	
GaP_xAs_{1-x}	1	0.040	0.09	II	a
	0	0.68	0.08	II	
InP_xAs_{1-x}	1	0.46	0.12	II	a
	0	0.85	0.09	II	
$GaAs_xSb_{1-x}$	1	0.18	0.08	I	a, f
	0	0.22	0.05	II	
$InAs_xSb_{1-x}$	1	0.22	0.09	II	a, f
	0	0.29	0.04	I	
$Zn_xCd_{1-x}S$	1	0.13	0.24	I	a
	0	0.15	0.23	I	
$Zn_xCd_{1-x}Te$	1	0.30	0.14	II	a, i
	0	0.43	0.18	I	
$Cd_xHg_{1-x}Te$	1	0.29	–	II	j
	0	0.31	0.18	II	
$ZnSe_xTe_{1-x}$	1	0.14	0.19	I	a
	0	0.16	0.14	I	

Table 1 (Continued)

Crystal	x	$1-\mu/\mu'$	$\dfrac{\varepsilon_0-\varepsilon_\infty}{\varepsilon_0+\varepsilon_\infty}$	Expt.	Ref.
ZnS_xSe_{1-x}	1	0.40	0.24	II	a
	0	0.68	0.19	II	
CdS_xSe_{1-x}	1	0.46	0.23	II	a
	0	0.88	0.18	II	
$CdSe_xTe_{1-x}$	1	0.22	0.18	II	j, k
	0	0.29	0.18	II	
$CuCl_xBr_{1-x}$	1	0.36	0.47	II	k, l
	0	0.56	0.32	II	
$Ni_xCo_{1-x}O$	1	0.002	0.30	I	a
	0	0.002	0.42	I	
$Ca_xSr_{1-x}F_2$	1	0.26	0.61	I	a
	0	0.36	0.57	I	
$Ba_xSr_{1-x}F_2$	1	0.12	0.55	I	a
	0	0.11	0.57	I	

a Chang and Mitra
b Bauhofer and Genzel (1974b), Mercier and Voichovsky (1974)
c Fertel and Perry (1969)
d Bauhofer and Genzel (1974b)
e Bootz and van der Osten (1974)
f Lucovsky and Chen (1970)
g Lucovsky et al. (1970), Gasanly et al. (1971)
h Lucovsky et al. (1971)
i Vodopyanov et al. (1972)
j Kim and Narita (1971)
k Gorska et al. (1974), Vinogradov et al. (1973)
l Murakashi et al. (1973)

low x. The model is very crude, but no cruder than other models like the REI or linear chains which are sometimes used. It emphasises that the important physical criterion is one of comparing mass defect to band widths. The most important elements which are missing are the changes in force constant and the effect of full density of states including acoustic branches.

There has been relatively little theoretical work applying the more complete theories of the disordered crystal to these systems. Important exceptions are found in the work of Pershan and Lachina (1970) and Besserman and Balkanski (1970) who applied the ATA to $Ca_{1-x}Sr_xF_2$ and $CdS_{1-x}Se_x$ respectively. Early attempts at this type of calculations made for $LiH_{1-x}D_x$ by Elliott and Taylor (1964) and by Jaswal and Hardy (1968). Recently Taylor (1973) has applied the CPA to alkali halides with mass disorder and calculated the reflectivity directly. His results for $K_{1-x}Rb_xI$ and $KBr_{1-x}Cl_x$ are shown in fig. 15. The former is clearly type II as is observed. The latter is

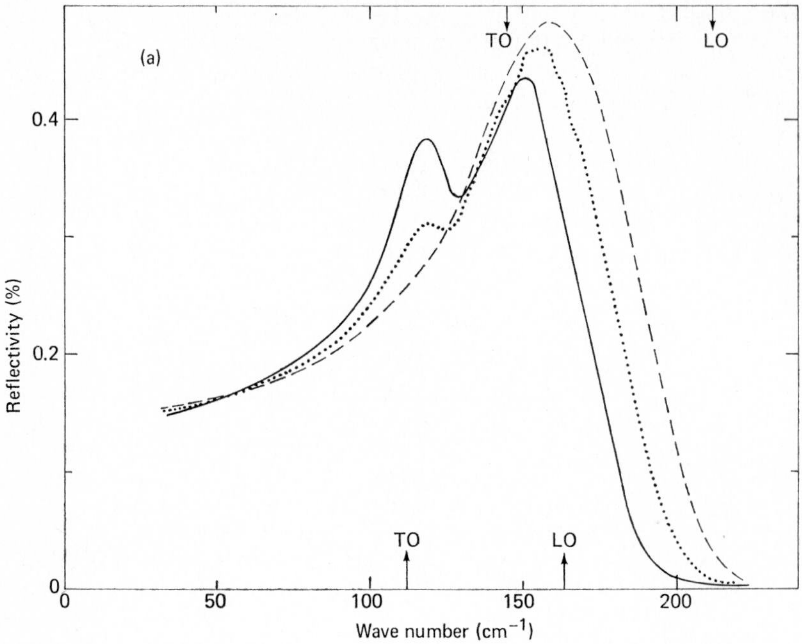

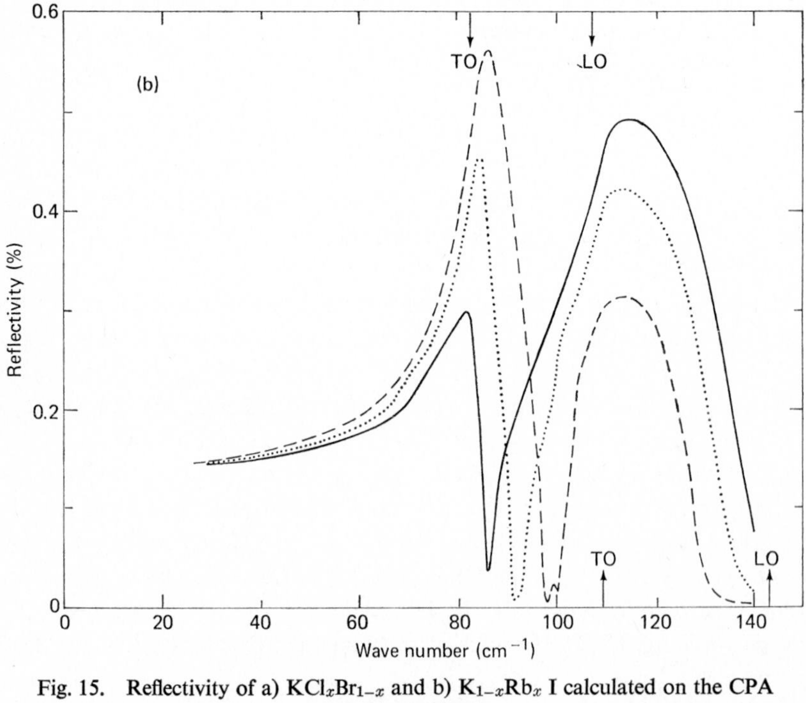

Fig. 15. Reflectivity of a) KCl_xBr_{1-x} and b) $K_{1-x}Rb_x$ I calculated on the CPA (after Taylor 1973).

usually classed as type I although the theory shows some double peaking and demonstrates how crude this simple criterion can be.

Similar reflective experiments have been made on a wide variety of more complicated crystals, which have several optically active branches. One elemental mixture with complex crystal structure is $Te_{1-x}Se_x$ studied by Geick and Hassler (1969). In the perovskite system $KNi_{1-x}Mg_xF_3$ (Barker et al. 1968) and $K_{1-x}Na_xTaO_3$ (Perry and Tronberg 1969) show type I behaviour for some modes and type II for others. In the ferroelectric perovskites the soft modes associated with the phase transitions are of particular interest. This has been studied for example in $KNaTaO_3$ by Davis (1972), and in $PbTi_{1-x}Zr_xO_3$ by Pinzuk (1973).

Optical absorption can also be observed in mixed crystals whose pure constituents have no infra-red active modes. The variation in atomic polarisability and the breakdown of the $\boldsymbol{k}$ quantum number allows absorption by all modes. This process has been studied using the shell model for small concentrations of impurities in rare gas crystals (Martin 1967, Elliott and Hartmann 1967). The far infra-red absorption induced by Kr and Ne in A has been observed by Keeler and Batchelder (1972). To date no detailed theory has been given for high concentration systems. In principle it is given by an expression like (29) with an effective charge $\xi(l)$ say which depends on the relative displacements of neighbours. Elliott and Hartmann suggested that in a simple crystal it would be proportional to ω^2. We are concerned with response to a uniform field so that the absorption coefficient is proportional to

$$(\xi^{\mathrm{h}} - \xi^{\mathrm{d}})^2 \,\mathrm{Im}\,\langle G_{\mathrm{a}}(\boldsymbol{k}=0), \omega\rangle, \tag{93}$$

where a indicates the uniform (acoustic) combination. There are experimental results in Ge_xSi_{1-x} (Braunstein 1963, Cosand and Spitzer 1971)

3.2.2. *Raman scattering*

Raman scattering has been observed in a variety of mixed crystals, again an extensive review of earlier work can be found in Chang and Mitra (1971) and in Barker and Sievers (to be published). The most detailed effects occur in mixed crystals which have Raman active modes in the pure constituents such as Ge–Si alloys and mixed III–V and II–VI compounds. The theoretical cross section (30) reduces to a result similar to the neutron cross sections (23) at $\boldsymbol{q}=0$. Here B is replaced by the Raman polarisability C

$$\sigma_{\mathrm{R}} \propto \sum_{\substack{\alpha\alpha' \\ \mathrm{AA}'}} C^{\mathrm{A}}_{\alpha\mu} C^{\mathrm{A}'}_{\alpha'\mu'} \,\mathrm{Im}\,\langle G^{\mathrm{AA}'}_{\alpha\alpha'}(q=0, E)\rangle\, n(E). \tag{94}$$

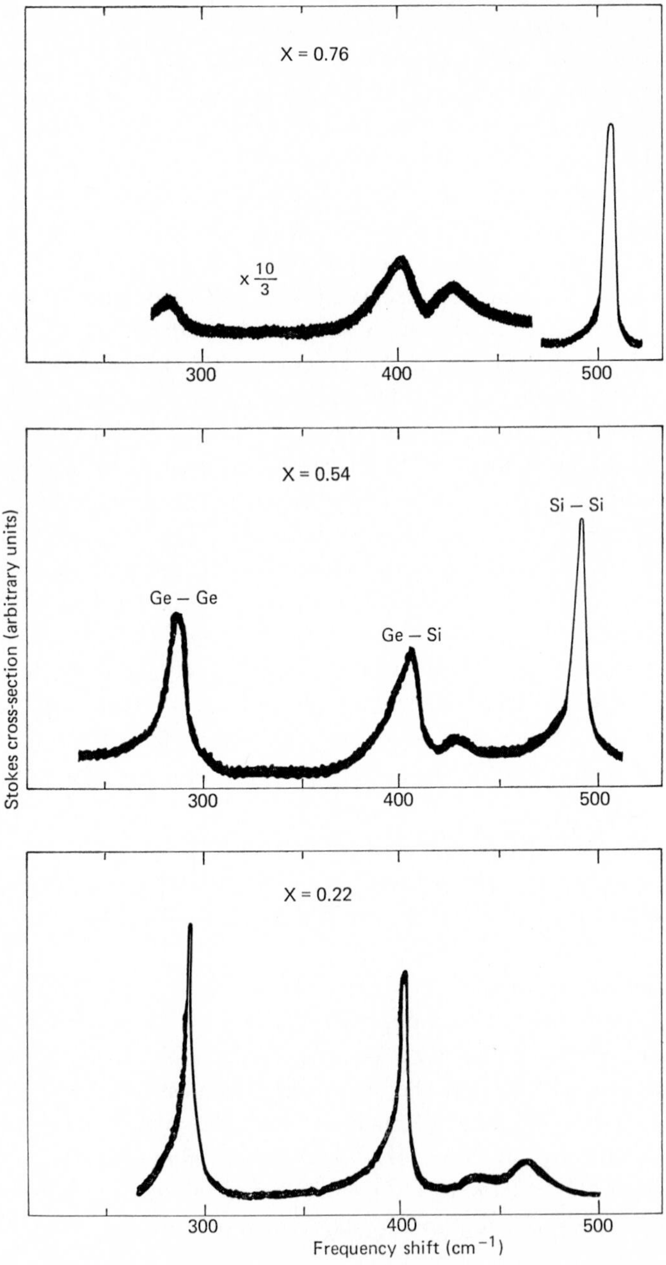

Fig. 16. Raman spectra of Si_xGe_{1-x} showing complex behaviour of type II (after Renucci et al. 1971).

Using the coherent potential results, the weighted Green's functions for appropriate sites can be written in a form analogous to (85). For crystals like Si–Ge with the same disorder on inequivalent sites it can be transformed into an equation similar to (86),

$$\sigma_{\mathrm{R}} \propto \sum_{\alpha\alpha' j} \sigma_j^{\alpha} \sigma_j^{\alpha'} \left(C_{\alpha\mu}^{\mathrm{h}} - \frac{C_{\alpha\mu}^{\mathrm{h}} - C_{\alpha\mu}^{\mathrm{d}}}{VP_j(0, E)} \right) \frac{C_{\alpha'\xi}^{\mathrm{h}} - C_{\alpha'\xi}^{\mathrm{d}}}{VP_j(0, E)} \operatorname{Im} \langle G_j(0, E) \rangle \, n(E) .$$

The symmetry properties of $C_{\alpha\mu}$ and σ_j^{α} give selection rules in the perfect crystal to restrict the Raman active modes. In the imperfect crystal these sharp peaks are shifted and broadened, and further structure may appear. For a single active mode, one or two-peak behaviour is expected as in the optical reflection experiments and with similar criteria. The most investigated simple case is $Ge_{1-x}Si_x$ but even this has a complex behaviour (fig. 16) of type II (Feldman et al. 1966, Renucci et al. 1972). The vibrations of this alloy were examined using the CPA by Taylor (1967), and the Raman response was considered in more detail by Srivastava and Joshi (1973).

In the III–V and II–VI compounds both LO and TO phonons are Raman active, so that there are two lines in the pure crystal spectra. In mixed crystals

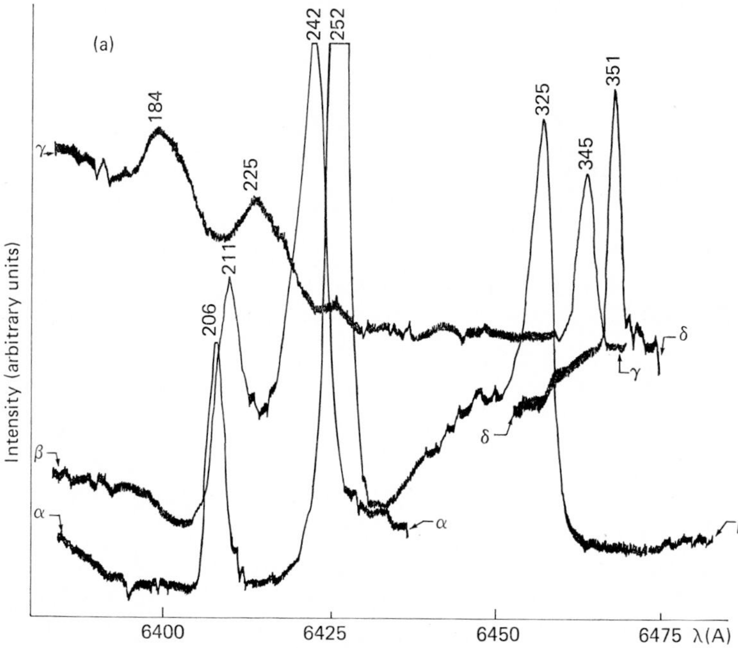

Fig. 17a. Raman spectra of ZnS_xSe_{1-x} for $x=0\alpha$; 0.33, β; 0.82γ; 1.0, δ.

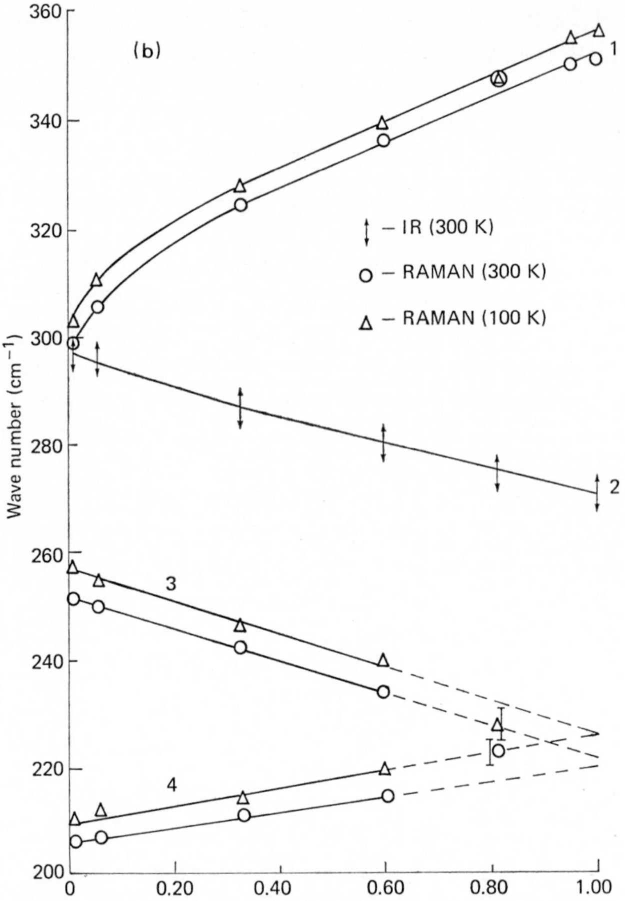

Fig. 17b. Frequencies of $q=0$ responses observed by Raman and infra-red measurements 1) LO (ZnS) 2) TO(ZnS) 3) LO(ZnSe) 4) TO(ZnSe) (after Brafman et al. 1968).

showing type II behaviour four peaks are observed (cf. fig. 17). Many experiments of this type have been performed – the information on behaviour type is given in table 1. Unfortunately no detailed theoretical analysis is available for these systems it seems in some ways a more fruitful area for comparison between theory and experiment than the reflection spectra.

More complex mixed crystals have also been investigated, notably ferroelectric crystals like $KTaO_3$ containing Li and Na (Yacoby and Yust 1974) and $PbTi_{1-x}Zr_xO_3$ (Merlin and Pinzuk 1974) and layer compounds GaS_xSe_{1-x} (Hayek et al. 1973, Mercier and Voitchovsky 1974) and

$HgBr_{2(1-x)}I_{2x}$ (Nakashima and Mishima 1974). In the alkaline earth fluorides the Raman active mode arises from F motions and show only weakly varying type I behaviour in mixed crystals (Pershan and Lachina 1969). In crystals like the alkali halides which have no first-order Raman spectrum, only a weak response is expected as has been observed by Nair and Walker (1971) in $KCl_{1-x}Br_x$. The peaks of the spectrum are correlated with peaks in the density of states and with resonant modes.

3.3. Other properties

Several other properties of mixed crystals give information about the lattice vibrations but none have such wide applicability as these discussed above. One interesting type of experiment is superconducting tunneling which can give a density of states weighted by some unknown coupling constant. Because of experimental difficulties most investigations have been confined to low concentration cases (cf. Taylor's chapter and Claeson and Grandqvist 1974). The most studied system is $Pb_{1-x}In_x$ where Adler et al. (1966) and Sood (1973) have covered a range of x.

Elastic constants can also provide detailed information about changes in the crystal they essentially measure the peak response of $G(\boldsymbol{k}, \omega)$ at very small $\boldsymbol{k}$ and ω. For mass changes the self energy $\Sigma(\omega) \sim c \Delta M \omega^2$ at low ω, i.e. the VCA result is adequate. However force constant changes lead to more interesting variations. At low concentrations the ATA provides an adequate description (Elliott et al. 1968, Kesharwani and Agrawal 1974). At high concentrations no detailed theory is available. Little experimental information has been obtained for this situation except in metals where the VCA is reasonably satisfactory.

Thermal properties usually involve an average over all crystal modes so that they yield little information about the detailed changes brought about by disorder. Karlsson (1970) has measured the specific heat of $KCl_{1-x}Br_x$ over a wide range of x. He finds that the Debye temperature of the mixed crystal is that expected by averaging the inverse square of the frequency

$$\theta_D^{-2}(x) = (1-x)\,\theta_D^{-2}(1) + x\theta_D^{-2}(0).$$

A similar situation holds in the case of thermal conductivity. While detailed studies have been made for crystals containing small concentrations of defects (Pohl 1968), high concentration mixed crystals are not expected to show easily identifiable features.

4. Conclusion

The vibrational properties of mixed crystals have been extensively studied by spectroscopic techniques and detailed information is available on a number of systems, usually with relatively simple crystal structures. The theoretical methods of the average t-matrix approximation and the coherent potential approximation provide a satisfactory framework for the interpretation of these properties. However they only deal completely with the mass disorder; changes in force constant which are not additive cannot be conveniently handled by these methods. When these are important less satisfactory approximations have to be used. One of the outstanding theoretical problems is the improvement of the approximations in these situations. Another area requiring theoretical advance lies in the interpretation of the detailed optical data available on mixed III–V and II–VI compounds. Complimentary neutron studies in these materials would be useful.

The theoretical techniques described in this paper have been applied to many forms of excitation in mixed crystals (cf. Elliott et al. 1974). In the vibrational case they can be confronted with detailed experimental results on well defined systems. Their success gives confidence in extrapolating to other systems. The general features of the vibrations of mixed crystals can now be interpreted with reasonable certainty.

Acknowledgements

We are especially indebted to Prof. J. A. Krumhansl with whom we originally explored the properties of disordered systems, for many insights. We also wish to acknowledge assistance from Prof. D. W. Taylor who showed us a copy of his chapter and advised on many details. Dr. G. Lucovsky provided many references on experimental work and Mrs. J. Martinez helped to compile table 1. To these, and many other colleagues in the field, we are grateful, and only too conscious of our inadequate treatment of their work.

References

Adler, J.G., and B.S. Chandrashekar (1968), in *Localised excitations in solids*, ed. by R.F. Wallis (Pleunum, New York), p. 694.

Als-Nielson, J. (1968), in *Neutron inelastic scattering*: Proc. of a Symp. on Neutron In-Inelastic Scattering held by the Intern. Atomic Agency in Copenhagen, May 20–25, 1968 (IAEA, Vienna), p. 60.

ANDERSON, P.W. and W.L. MCMILLAN (1967), in *Theory of magnetism in transition metals*, Proc. of the Intern. School of Physics, 'Enrico Fermi', ed. by H. Suhl (Academic, New York).
BAKER, A.S., J.A. DITZENBERGER and H.J. GUGGENHEIM (1968), Phys. Rev. **175**, 1180.
BAUHOFER, W., L. GENZEL and I.R. JAHN (1974a), Phys. Stat. Sol. **62b**, 361.
BAUHOFER, W., L. GENZEL and I.R. JAHN (1974b) Phys. Stat. Sol. **63b**, 465.
BEEBY, J. and S.F. EDWARDS (1962), Proc. R. Soc. Lond. A**274**, 395.
BESERMAN. R. and M. BALKANSKI (1970), Phys. Rev. B**1**, 608.
BOOTZ, B., W. VANDER OSTEN and N. UNLE (1974), Phys. Stat. Sol. **66b**, 169.
BORLAND, R.E. (1964), Proc. Phys. Soc. Lond. **83**, 1027.
BORN, M. and K. HUANG (1954), *Dynamical theory of crystal lattices* (Oxford U.P., London).
BRAFMAN, O., I.F. CHANG, G. LENGYEL, S.S. MITRA and E. CARNALL JR. (1968), in *Localized excitations in solids*, ed. by R.F. Wallis (Plenum, New York), p. 602.
BRAUNSTEIN, R. (1963), Phys. Rev. **130**, 869, 879.
BROCKHOUSE, B.N. and A.P. ROY (1970), Can. J. Phys. **48**, 1781.
BRODSKY, M.H., G. LUCOVSKY, M.F. Chen and T.S. PLASKETT (1970), Phys. Rev. B**2**, 3303.
BRUNO, R. and D.W. TAYLOR (1971), Can. J. Phys. **49**, 3201.
CHANG, I.F. and S.S. MITRA (1968), Phys. Rev. **172**, 924.
CHANG, I.F. and S.S. MITRA (1971), Adv. Phys. **20**, 359.
CHEN, Y.S., W. SHOCKLEY and G.L. PEARSON (1966), Phys. Rev. **151**, 648.
CLAESON, T. and C.G. GRANDQVIST (1974), Z. Physik **269**, 23.
COSAND, A.E. and W.G. SPITZER (1971), J. Appl. Phys. **42**, 5241.
COWLEY, R.A. and W.J.L. BUYERS (1968), in *Neutron inelastic scattering*: Proc. of a Symp. on Neutron Inelastic Scattering held by the Intern. Atomic Energy in Copenhagen, May 20–25, 1968 (IAEA, Vienna), p. 43.
DAVIES, R.W. and J.S. LANGER (1963), Phys. Rev. **131**, 163.
DAVIS, T.G. (1972), Phys. Rev. **B5**, 2530.
DEAN, P. (1959), Proc. Phys. Soc. Lond. **73**, 413.
DEAN, P. (1960), Proc. R. Soc. Lond. A**254**, 507.
DEAN, P. (1961), Proc. R. Soc. Lond. A**260**, 263.
DEAN, P. (1972), Rev. Mod. Phys. **44**, 127.
ELLIOTT, R.J. and D.W. TAYLOR (1967), Proc. R. Soc. London, A**296**, 161.
ELLIOTT, R. J. and W. HARTMANN (1967), Proc. Phys. Soc. Lond. **91**, 187.
ELLIOTT, R.J., J.A. KRUMHANSL and P.L. LEATH (1974), Rev. Mod. Phys. **46**, 465.
ELLIOTT, R.J., J.A. KRUMSHANSL and T. MERRETT (1968), *Localised excitations in solids* (Ed. R.F. Wallis, Plenum) p. 109.
FELDMAN, D.W., M. ASHKIN and J.H. PARKER (1966), Phys. Rev. Lett. **17**, 1209.
FERTEL, J.H. and C.H. PERRY (1969), Phys. Rev. **184**, 874.
FLICKER, J.K. and P.L. LEATH (1973), Phys. Rev. B**7**, 2296.
FOLDY, L.L. (1945), Phys. Rev. **67**, 107.
FRISCH, H.L. and S.P. LLOYD (1960), Phys. Rev. **120**, 1175.
GASANLY, N.M., V.K. SUBASHIEV, M.I. ALIEV, and A.A. KIRKHARSKII (1971), Sov. Phys. Solid State **13**, 54.
GEICK, R. and J. HASSLER (1969), Phys. Stat. Sol. **33**, 689.
GENZEL, L., T.P. MARTIN and C.H. PERRY (1974), Phys. Stat. Sol. **62b**, 83.
GORSKA, M. and W. NAZAREWICZ (1974), Phys. Stat. Sol. **65b**, 193.
GUBERNATIS, J.E. and P.L. TAYLOR (1973a), Phys. Lett. A**43**, 211.

GUBERNATIS, J.E. and P.L. TAYLOR (1973), J. Phys. C**6**, 1889.
HALLMAN, E.D. and B.N. BROCKHOUSE (1969), Canad. J. Phys. **47**, 1117.
HARADA, H. and S. NARITA (1971), J. Phys. Soc. Jap. **30**, 1628.
HAYEK, M., O. BRAFMAN and R.M.A. LIETH (1973), Phys. Rev. **B8**, 2772.
HORI, J. (1968), *Spectral properties of disordered chains and lattices* (Pergamon, London).
JASWAL S.S., and J.R. HARDY (1968), Phys. Rev. **171**, 1090.
KAMITAKAHARA, W.A. and B.N. BROCKHOUSE (1974) Phys. Rev. **B10**, 1200.
KAMITAKAHARA, W.A. and D.W. TAYLOR (1974) Phys. Rev. **B10**, 1190.
KAPLAN, T. and M. MOSTOLLER, (1974a), Phys. Rev. **B9**, 1783.
KAPLAN, T. and M. MOSTOLLER (1974b), Phys. Rev. **B10**, 3610.
KAPLAN, T. and M. MOSTOLLER (1974c), Phys. Rev. **B9**, 353.
KARLSSON, A.V. (1970), Phys. Rev. B**2**, 3332.
KEELER, G.J. and D.N. BATCHELDER, (1972), J. Phys. C**5**, 3264.
KESHARWANI, K.M. and B.K. AGRAWAL (1972) Phys. Rev. **B6**, 2178.
KESHARWANI, K.M. and B.K. AGRAWAL (1973), Phys. Rev. **B7**, 5153.
KESHARWANI, K.M. and B.K. AGRAWAL (1974), Phys. Rev. **B8**, 3056.
KIM, R. and S. NARITA (1971), J. Phys. Soc. Japan **31**, 613
KLAUDER, R. (1961), Ann. Phys. (N.Y.) **14**, 43.
KORRINGA, J. (1958), J. Phys. Chem. Solids **7**, 252.
LAKATOS, K. and J.A. KRUMHANSL (1968), Phys. Rev. **175**, 841.
LAKATOS, K. and J.A. KRUMHANSL (1969), Phys. Rev. **180**, 729.
LANDAUER, R. and J.C. HELLAND (1954), J. Chem. Phys. **22**, 1655.
LAX, M. (1951), Rev. Mod. Phys. **23**, 287.
LAX, M. (1952), Phys. Rev. **85**, 621.
LAX, M. and J.C. PHILLIPS (1958), Phys. Rev. **110**, 41.
LEATH, P.L. (1968), Phys. Rev. **171**, 725.
LEATH, P.L. and B. GOODMAN (1969), Phys. Rev. **181**, 1062.
LIFSHITZ, I.M. (1964), Adv. Phys. **13**, 483.
LORD RAYLEIGH (1892), Phil. Mag. Str. **5**, 34, 481.
LOVESEY, S.W. and W. MARSHALL (1966), Proc. Phys. Soc. Lond. **89**, 613.
LOVESEY, S.W. and W. MARSHALL (1971), *Theory of thermal neutron scattering* (Oxford U.P. London).
LUCOVSKY, G., M.H. BRODSKY, M.F. CHEN, R.J. CHICOTKA and A.T. WARD (1970), Phys. Rev. **B2**, 3303.
LUCOVSKY, G. and M.F. CHEN (1970), Solid State Comm. **8**, 1397.
MARADUDIN, A.A. (1966), in *Solid state physics*, ed. by F. Seitz and D. Turnbull (Academic, New York), Vols. 18-19.
MARIS, H.J. (1966), Phil. Mag. **13**, 465.
MARTIN, T.P. (1967), Phys. Rev. **160**, 686.
MERCIER, A. and J.P. VOITCHOVSKY (1974), Solid State Comm. **14**, 757.
MERLIN, R. and A. PINCZUK (1974), Ferroelectrics **7**, 275.
MESSIAH, A. (1962), *Quantum mechanics* (Wiley, New York).
MØLLER, H.B. and A.R. MACKINTOSH (1965), Phys. Rev. Lett. **15**, 623.
MOSTOLLER, M., T. KAPLAN, N. WAKABAYASHI and R.M. NICKLOW (1974), Phys. Rev. **B10**, 3144.
MORI, H., I. OPPENHEIM and J. ROSS (1962), in *Studies in statistical mechanics*, ed. by J. De Boer (Interscience, New York).

MURAKASHI, T., T. KODA, Y. OKA and T. KUSHIDA (1973), Solid State Comm. **13**, 307.

NAIR, T. and C.T. WALKER (1971), Phys. Rev. **B3**, 3446.

NAKASHIMA, S., H. MISHIMA and H. TAI (1974), J. Chem. Phys. Solids **35**, 531.

NG, S.C. and B.N. BROCKHOUSE, (1967), Solid State Commun. **5**, 79.

NICKLOW, R.M., P.R. VIJAYARAGHAVAN, H.G. SMITH, G. DOLLING and M.K. WILKINSON (1968), in *Neutron inelastic scattering*: Proc. of a Symp. on Neutron Inelastic Scattering held by the Intern. Atomic Energy in Copenhagen, May 20–25, 1968 (IAEA, Vienna), Vol. 1, p. 47.

NORDHEIM, L. (1931), Ann. Phys. (Leipz) **9**, 607.

ONODERA, Y. and Y. TOYOZAWA (1968), J. Phys. Soc. Jap. **24**, 341.

PAYTON III, D.N. and W.M. VISSCHER (1967), Phys. Rev. **154**, 802.

PAYTON III, D.N. and W.M. VISSCHER (1968), Phys. Rev. **175**, 1201.

PERRY, C.H. and N.E. TRONBERG (1969), Phys. Rev. **183**, 595.

PERSHAN, P.S. and W.B. LACINA (1969), Proc. Light Scatt. Conf. N.Y. (Springer-Verlag, Ed. Wright) p. 439.

PERSHAN, P.S. and W.B. LACINA (1970), Phys. Rev. **B1**, 1765.

PINZUK, A. (1973), Solid State Comm. **12**, 1035.

POHL, R. (1968), in *Localised excitations in solids* (Ed. By R. F. Wallis (Plenum, N.Y.)) p. 434.

RENUCCI, M.A., J.B. RENUCCI and M. CARDONA (1972), Proc. Light Scatt. Conf. Paris (Flammarion, Ed. Balkanski) p. 326.

SAXON, D.A. and R.A. HUTNER (1949), Philips Res. Rep. **4**, 81.

SCHMIDT, H. (1957), Phys. Rev. **105**, 425.

SJÖLANDER, A. (1964), in *Phonons and phonon interactions*, ed. by T.A. Bak (Benjamin, New York)

SOOD, B.R. (1973), Phys. Rev. **B6**, 136.

SOVEN, P. (1967), Phys. Rev. **156**, 809.

SRIVASTAVA, V. and S.K. JOSHI (1973), Phys. Rev. **B8**, 4671

SVENSSON, E.C. and W.A. KAMITAKAHARA (1971), Can. J. Phys. **49**, 2291.

TAKENO, S. (1968), Prog. Theor. Phys. **40**, 942.

TAYLOR, D.W. (1967), Phys. Rev. **156**, 1017.

TAYLOR, D.W. (1973), Solid State Comm. **13**, 117.

THOULESS, D.J. (1970), J. Phys. C **3** 1559.

VERLEUR, H.W. and A.S. BARKER (1966), Phys. Rev. **149**, 715.

VINOGRADOV, E.A., L.K. VODOPYANOV and G.S. OLEINIK (1973), Sov. Phys. Solid State **15**, 322.

VODOPYANOV, L.K., E.A. VINOGRADOV, A.M. BLINOV and V.A. RUKAVISHNIKOV (1972), Sov. Phys. Solid State **14**, 219.

WAKABAYASHI, N., R.M. NICKLOW and H.G. SMITH (1971), Phys. Rev. **B4**, 2558.

WAKABAYASHI, N. (1974), Phys. Rev. **B8**, 6016.

WATSON, K.M. (1956), Phys. Rev. **103**, 489.

WATSON, K.M. (1957), Phys. Rev. **105**, 1388.

WOODS, A.D.B. and B.M. POWELL (1965), Phys. Rev. Lett. **15**, 778.

WOODS, A.D.B., B.M. POWELL and P. MARTEL (1968), Phys. Rev. **171**, 727.

YACOBY, Y. and S. YUST (1974), Ferroelectrics **7**, 271.

YONEZAWA, F. and K. MORIGAKI (1973), Prog. Theor. Phys. Suppl. **53**, 1.

ZUBAREV, D.N. (1960), Usp. Fiz. Nauk **71**, 71 (Sov. Phys.-Usp. 3, 320 (1960)).

CHAPTER 7

Effects of Surfaces in Lattice Dynamics

R.F. WALLIS

Dept. of Physics, University of California
Irvine, California 92664
USA

Dynamical Properties of Solids, edited by
G.K. Horton and A.A. Maradudin

Contents

1. Introduction

There has been a rather remarkable increase in interest in the lattice dynamics of crystal surfaces during the last decade. This stems in large part from a number of experimental advances. Interest in surface elastic waves has been stimulated by the possibility that they may be used in practical devices such as delay lines and band-pass filters. Miniaturization is possible for surface wave devices because, for a given frequency, the wavelength of acoustic waves is much smaller than that of electromagnetic waves.

The development of commercial apparatus for low-energy electron diffraction (LEED) has made possible experimental determinations of the mean square displacements of surface atoms. Studies of inelastic scattering of low-energy electrons have recently yielded information concerning the frequencies of surface vibrational modes.

Optical investigations of surface modes have also been extensively developed. Recently, attenuated total reflection has been used to obtain experimental dispersion curves for surface polaritons associated with surface optical phonons in polar crystals. Infrared and Raman spectroscopy are also being used with increasing frequency to observe surface modes.

On the theoretical side, the development of Green's function methods has stimulated the development of the formal theory of surface effects in lattice dynamics. Detailed calculations are enormously facilitated by modern high-speed computers.

A detailed review of surface effects in lattice dynamics has recently appeared (Wallis 1973). Chapter IX of the treatise on lattice dynamics by Maradudin et al. (1971) discusses surface effects. Other reviews on more specialized topics include those of Farnell (1970) on surface elastic waves, Dransfeld and Salzmann (1970) on surface wave attenuation, and Ruppin and Englman (1970) on optical properties of small crystals.

2. Elastic surface waves

The theoretical study of elastic surface waves was initiated by Lord Rayleigh (1887) who studied an isotropic elastic continuum with a planar free surface. We shall start our discussion by considering a general elastic continuum characterized by density ρ and elastic constant tensor c_{pqrs}. The equations of motion for a material point can be written in the form

$$\rho \frac{\partial^2 u_r}{\partial t^2} = \frac{\partial \sigma_{rs}}{\partial x_s}, \quad r = 1, 2, 3, \tag{2.1}$$

where u_r is the rth cartesian component of displacement of the medium at the point whose position vector has the sth cartesian component x_s, σ_{rs} is an element of the stress tensor, and the summation convention for repeated indices is assumed. In the linear theory of elasticity the stress tensor is specified by Hooke's law

$$\sigma_{pq} = c_{pqrs} \frac{\partial u_r}{\partial x_s}. \tag{2.2}$$

If a free surface is specified by the plane $x_3 = 0$, then the boundary conditions corresponding to the vanishing of the three components of stress at this surface are

$$\sigma_{r3} = 0 \quad \text{at} \quad x_3 = 0, \quad r = 1, 2, 3. \tag{2.3}$$

We specialize now to the case of a cubic crystal with principal axes chosen parallel to the coordinate axes and adopt the Voigt notation for the elastic constants. The equations of motion can then be written as

$$\rho \frac{\partial^2 u}{\partial t^2} = c_{11} \frac{\partial^2 u}{\partial x^2} + c_{12} \frac{\partial}{\partial x}\left(\frac{\partial v}{\partial y} + \frac{\partial w}{\partial z}\right) + c_{44} \frac{\partial}{\partial y}\left(\frac{\partial u}{\partial y} + \frac{\partial v}{\partial x}\right) + c_{44} \frac{\partial}{\partial z}\left(\frac{\partial u}{\partial z} + \frac{\partial w}{\partial x}\right), \tag{2.4}$$

where u, v, w are the displacement components in the x, y, z directions, respectively, ρ is the density, c_{11}, c_{12}, and c_{44} are the elastic constants, and two additional equations are obtained by a cyclic permutation of u, v, w and of x, y, z.

Consider now a semi-infinite crystal with a (001) free surface. The boundary conditions, which state that the three components of stress at the surface are zero, have the form

$$\frac{\partial u}{\partial z}+\frac{\partial w}{\partial x}=0\,,\qquad \frac{\partial v}{\partial z}+\frac{\partial w}{\partial y}=0\,,\qquad c_{12}\left(\frac{\partial u}{\partial x}+\frac{\partial v}{\partial y}\right)+c_{11}\frac{\partial w}{\partial z}=0\,. \tag{2.5}$$

Since we are interested in waves localized at the surface $z=0$, we assume trial solutions of the form

$$(u, v, w)=(U, V, W)\exp\{k[-qz+\mathrm{i}(lx+my-ct)]\}\,. \tag{2.6}$$

which represents a plane wave propagating with speed c and wave vector magnitude k in a direction with direction cosines l, m parallel to the surface, but damped toward the interior with a decay constant q. In order for eq. (2.6) to be a non-trivial solution of the equations of motion, the following determinantal equation must be satisfied

$$\begin{vmatrix} g_1 l^2+m^2-p^2-q^2 & lm(g_2+1) & lq(g_2+1) \\ lm(g_2+1) & l^2+g_1m^2-p^2-q^2 & mq(g_2+1) \\ lq(g_2+1) & mq(g_2+1) & p^2+g_1q^2-1 \end{vmatrix}=0\,, \tag{2.7}$$

where $g_1=c_{11}/c_{44}$, $g_2=c_{12}/c_{44}$, and $p^2=\rho c^2/c_{44}$.

For given p, there are in general three values of q, with positive real part, denoted by q_1, q_2, q_3, which satisfy eq. (2.7). The amplitudes for any q_j satisfy the equation

$$U_j/\xi_j=V_j/\eta_j=\mathrm{i}W_j/\zeta_j=K_j\,,\quad j=1,2,3\,, \tag{2.8}$$

where the K_j are constants and ξ_j, η_j, ζ_j are cofactors of the determinant in eq. (2.7) given by

$$\begin{aligned} \xi_j &= (l^2+g_1m^2-p^2-q_j^2)(p^2+g_1q_j^2-1)-m^2q_j^2(g_2+1)^2\,,\\ \eta_j &= lm(g_2+1)\left[q_j^2(g_2+1-g_1)+1-p^2\right],\\ \zeta_j &= lq_j(g_2+1)\left[m^2(g_2+1-g_1)-l^2+p^2+q_j^2\right]. \end{aligned} \tag{2.9}$$

To satisfy the boundary conditions, we superpose the particular solutions corresponding to the various q_j to give

$$(u, v, \mathrm{i}w)=\sum_{j=1}^{3}(\xi_j, \eta_j, \zeta_j)\,K_j\exp\{k[-q_jz+\mathrm{i}(lx+my-ct)]\}\,. \tag{2.10}$$

Substitution of this form into eqs. (2.5) leads to a set of linear equations in the K_j. A non-trivial solution is obtainable if we set the determinant of the K_j to zero,

$$D(p) \equiv |f_{ij}| = 0\,, \tag{2.11}$$

where

$$f_{1j} = l\zeta_j - q_j\xi_j,\ f_{2j} = m\zeta_j - q_j\eta_j,\ f_{3j} = l\xi_j + m\eta_j + \frac{c_{11}}{c_{12}}q_j\zeta_j\,. \tag{2.12}$$

Eq. (2.11) is the frequency equation which must be solved simultaneously with eq. (2.7). This can be done (Stoneley 1955) by solving eq. (2.7) for the q_j in terms of p and then substituting into eq. (2.11) and solving the latter for p. There are two types of solutions corresponding to surface waves: 1. All q_j real and positive–*ordinary Rayleigh waves*. 2. Some q_j complex–*generalized Rayleigh waves*. The type of surface wave which appears depends on the elastic constants, the kind of surface, and to some extent, on the direction of propagation.

2.1. Isotropic materials

An isotropic elastic solid is characterized by the relation $c_{11}=c_{12}+2c_{44}$. Since the surface wave characteristics are independent of direction, we can choose $l=1$, $m=0$ in eq. (2.7) and obtain

$$q_1 = (1 - p^2/g_1)^{1/2}\,, \quad q_2 = q_3 = (1 - p^2)^{1/2}\,. \tag{2.13}$$

We note that p and $p/g_1^{1/2}$ are the ratios of the surface wave speed to the speeds of transverse and longitudinal bulk waves, respectively. Both p and $p/g_1^{1/2}$ must be less than unity in order to have real decay constants. Utilizing eq. (2.13), we can express the frequency equation in the form (Love 1944)

$$g_1(p^6 - 8p^4 + 24p^2 - 16) - 16(p^2 - 1) = 0\,. \tag{2.14}$$

The solutions for the quantity p range from 0.96 for $g_1=\infty$, the incompressible case, to 0.69 for $g_1=1.333\cdots$, the smallest value of g_1 consistent with crystal stability. The displacements can be written in the form

$$\begin{aligned} u &= K[\exp(-kq_1z) - (1 - \tfrac{1}{2}p^2)\exp(-kq_2z)]\exp[\mathrm{i}k(x - ct)]\,,\\ v &= 0\,,\\ w &= \mathrm{i}K[1 - (p^2/g_1)]^{1/2}\\ &\quad \times [\exp(-kq_1z) - (1 - \tfrac{1}{2}p^2)^{-1}\exp(-kq_2z)]\exp[\mathrm{i}k(x - ct)]\,. \end{aligned} \tag{2.15}$$

We note that the particle displacements generate ellipses in the sagittal plane, i.e., the plane containing both the surface normal and the direction of propagation. Two decay constants, q_1 and q_2, are required to characterize the Rayleigh surface waves in isotropic materials. A diagram showing the displacements for $g_1 = 4$ is given in fig. 1.

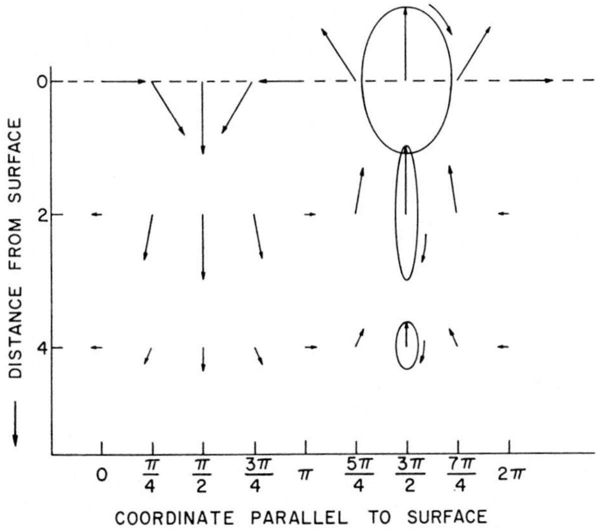

Fig. 1. Particle displacements (arrows) of a surface wave at a fixed instant of time for $g_1 = 4$. The ellipses show the time evolution of particle displacements at fixed positions.

2.2. Cubic materials

For the (001) surface, we can obtain (Stoneley 1955) explicit equations analogous to eq. (2.14) for the determination of p only for directions of propagation of high symmetry such as the [100] and [110] directions. For other directions, we must solve eqs. (2.7) and (2.11) numerically using a computer. The displacement patterns for surface waves propagating in the two directions of high symmetry are qualitatively similar to the isotropic case. The displacements are superpositions of two attenuated terms and trace out ellipses lying in the sagittal plane. For other directions of propagation, however, the displacements correspond to superpositions of three attenuated terms and trace out ellipses whose planes are in general inclined to the sagittal plane.

The distinction between crystals which exhibit ordinary Rayleigh waves and those which exhibit generalized Rayleigh waves can be illustrated graphically using a plot (Gazis et al. 1960) of the elastic constant ratios g_1 and g_2. The case of propagation in the [100] direction is given in fig. 2. The region of crystal stability lies to the right of the lines $g_1 = g_2$ and $g_1 + 2g_2 = 0$. Crystals to the right of the line labeled 'bound 1' have ordinary Rayleigh waves while those to the left of bound 1 have generalized Rayleigh waves. The line of isotropy $g_1 = g_2 + 2$ is seen to lie entirely in the ordinary Rayleigh wave region.

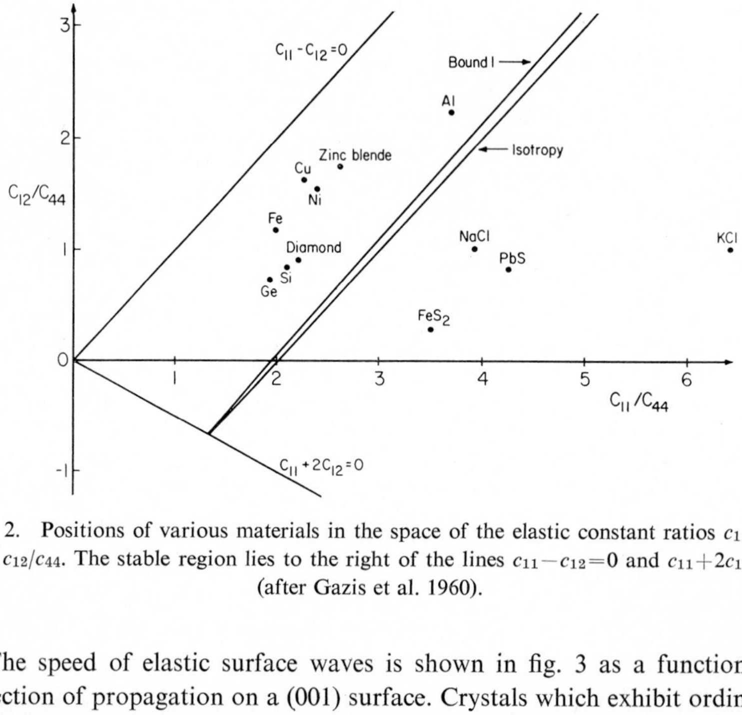

Fig. 2. Positions of various materials in the space of the elastic constant ratios c_{11}/c_{44} and c_{12}/c_{44}. The stable region lies to the right of the lines $c_{11} - c_{12} = 0$ and $c_{11} + 2c_{12} = 0$ (after Gazis et al. 1960).

The speed of elastic surface waves is shown in fig. 3 as a function of direction of propagation on a (001) surface. Crystals which exhibit ordinary Rayleigh waves show little dependence of speed on direction, while materials which exhibit generalized Rayleigh waves show a much more marked variation, including a maximum at an intermediate direction.

Copper may be considered as a typical generalized Rayleigh wave material. The decay constants are plotted as functions or propagation direction in fig. 4. Two of the decay constants form a complex conjugate pair whose real and imaginary part are plotted in fig. 4. The third decay constant is real and decreases rapidly as the [110] direction is approached. In the [110] direction itself, this decay constant vanishes and the wave becomes a transverse bulk

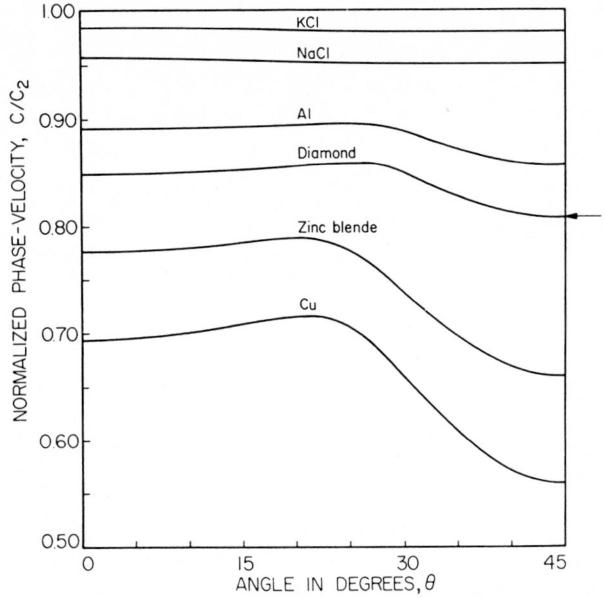

Fig. 3. Reduced surface wave speed plotted against the angle between the direction of propagation and the [100] direction on a (001) surface (after Gazis et al. 1960).

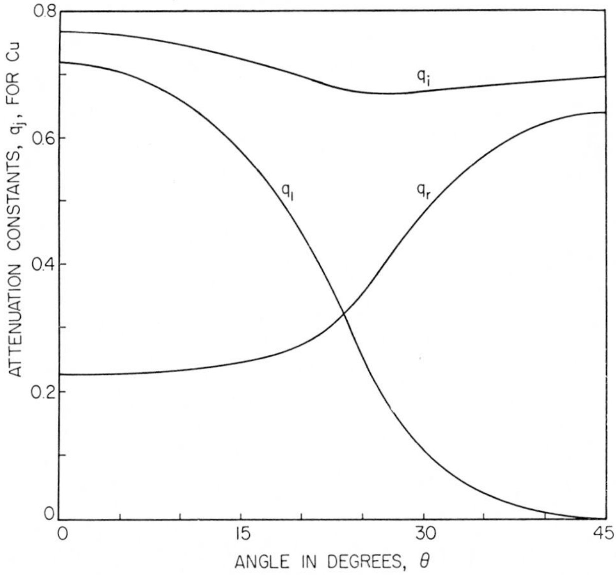

Fig. 4. Attenuation constants plotted against the angle between the direction of propagation and the [100] direction on a (001) surface for Cu (after Gazis et al. 1960).

wave. There is a surface wave in the [110] direction; however, its speed is greater than that of the lower transverse bulk wave and is indicated by the arrow in fig. 3. Away from the [110] direction, the surface wave degenerates into a *pseudosurface wave* (Lim and Farnell 1968), i.e., a superposition of bulk and surface components.

Rayleigh waves also exist on the (110) and (111) surfaces of cubic crystals. Crystals which exhibit ordinary Rayleigh waves on the (001) surface frequently have generalized Rayleigh waves on the (110) surface and vice-versa. On the (111) surface, the surface waves are usually of the generalized Rayleigh type. Pseudosurface waves can exist on both (110) and (111) surfaces. For further information concerning surface waves on various surfaces of both cubic and non-cubic materials, the reader may consult the recent review article by Farnell (1970).

So far we have considered surface waves localized at the planar interface between a crystal and vacuum. Localized waves, called Stoneley waves (Stoneley 1924), may exist at the planar interface between two contiguous crystals, which may be the same material but differently oriented, or different materials. For the case of two isotropic materials, the displacements in both materials lie in the sagittal plane, and the conditions for the existence of these Stoneley waves have been determined by Scholte (1947). Another type of localized wave is the Love wave (Love 1911) which occurs when a thin plate is contiguous to a semi-infinite substrate of another material. For isotropic materials, the displacements in both media are parallel to the interface, decay exponentially away from the interface in the substrate, and vary sinusoidally within the layer. A recent discussion of Stoneley and Love waves has been given by Farnell and Adler (1972).

2.3. Piezoelectric materials

In a piezoelectric crystal one finds a contribution to the stress arising from the electric potential φ (Cady 1964). The equations of motion then have the form

$$\rho \frac{\partial^2 u_r}{\partial t^2} = \frac{\partial}{\partial x_s}\left(c_{rspq} \frac{\partial u_p}{\partial x_q} + e_{prs} \frac{\partial \varphi}{\partial x_p}\right), \tag{2.16}$$

where u_p and x_p are the pth cartesian components of displacement and position, c_{rspq} is an element of the fourth-rank elastic constant tensor, and e_{prs} is an element of the third-rank piezoelectric tensor. The constitutive relation involving the electric displacement $\boldsymbol{D}$ and the second-rank dielectric tensor ε_{pr}

$$D_p = 4\pi e_{prs} \frac{\partial u_r}{\partial x_s} - \varepsilon_{pr} \frac{\partial \varphi}{\partial x_r}, \tag{2.17}$$

together with the Maxwell equation

$$\nabla \cdot \boldsymbol{D} = 0, \tag{2.18}$$

yields the equation

$$\frac{\partial}{\partial x_p} \left(4\pi e_{prs} \frac{\partial u_r}{\partial x_s} - \varepsilon_{pr} \frac{\partial \varphi}{\partial x_r} \right) = 0, \tag{2.19}$$

which is to be solved simultaneously with eq. (2.16).

The boundary conditions for a surface defined by the plane $x_3 = 0$ can be written as

$$c_{3spq} \frac{\partial u_p}{\partial x_q} + e_{p3s} \frac{\partial \varphi}{\partial x_p} = 0, \quad s = 1, 2, 3, \tag{2.20}$$

corresponding to the vanishing of the three components of stress at $x_3 = 0$, and

$$-\frac{\partial \hat{\varphi}}{\partial x_3} = 4\pi e_{3rs} \frac{\partial u_r}{\partial x_s} - \varepsilon_{3r} \frac{\partial \varphi}{\partial x_r} \tag{2.21}$$

corresponding to the continuity of the normal component of $\boldsymbol{D}$ at $x_3 = 0$. In eq. (2.21), $\hat{\varphi}$ is the electric potential outside the crystal which must satisfy Laplace's equation and approach zero as $x_3 \to -\infty$.

For a general direction of propagation, one has 4×4 determinants in the analogues of eqs. (2.7) and (2.11) rather than 3×3 determinants as in the non-piezoelectric case. Surface wave solutions have been determined (Tseng and White 1967, Tseng 1967) for a number of piezoelectric materials. In an approximate sense one can express the surface wave speed in terms of elastic constants 'stiffened' by the piezoelectric coupling. Another consequence of the piezoelectric coupling is the existence of a new type of surface wave, the Bleustein–Gulyaev wave (Bleustein 1968, Gulyaev 1969), which we now discuss.

The Bleustein–Gulyaev surface wave involves displacements parallel to the surface and has no analogue in ordinary elastic materials. Consider a crystal such as CdS belonging to class C_{6v} and having its six-fold axis parallel to the x_3 direction. If we consider a surface defined by $x_2=0$ and restrict ourselves to displacements only in the 3-direction which are functions only of x_1 and x_2, then eqs. (2.16) and (2.19) reduce to the form

$$\rho \frac{\partial^2 u_3}{\partial t^2} = c_{44}\nabla^2 u_3 + e_{15}\nabla^2\varphi, \quad 0 = 4\pi e_{15}\nabla^2 u_3 - \varepsilon_{11}\nabla^2\varphi, \tag{2.22a, b}$$

where ∇^2 is the laplacian in the variables x_1, x_2 and the Voigt notation has been used for the elastic and piezoelectric constants.

The non-trivial boundary conditions at $x_2=0$ can be written as

$$\varphi = \hat{\varphi}, \tag{2.23a}$$

$$\bar{c}_{44}\frac{\partial u_3}{\partial x_2} + e_{15}\frac{\partial \psi}{\partial x_2} = 0, \quad -\frac{\partial \hat{\varphi}}{\partial x_2} = 4\pi e_{15}\frac{\partial u_3}{\partial x_2} - \varepsilon_{11}\frac{\partial \varphi}{\partial x_2}, \tag{2.23b, c}$$

where $\psi = \varphi - 4\pi(e_{15}/\varepsilon_{11})\,u_3$ and $\bar{c}_{44} = c_{44} + 4\pi e_{15}^2/\varepsilon_{11}$.
If we take

$$u_3 = A\cos(kx_1 - \omega t)\exp(-qx_2), \quad x_2 > 0, \tag{2.24a}$$

$$\psi = B\cos(kx_1 - \omega t)\exp(-kx_2), \quad x_2 > 0, \tag{2.24b}$$

$$\hat{\varphi} = C\cos(kx_1 - \omega t)\exp(kx_2), \quad x_2 < 0, \tag{2.24c}$$

and substitute into eqs. (2.22), we find for a non-trivial solution that

$$\rho\omega^2 = \bar{c}_{44}(k^2 - q^2). \tag{2.25}$$

Substituting eqs. (2.24) into eqs. (2.23) we obtain the relation

$$q = \frac{4\pi e_{15}^2}{\varepsilon_{11}\bar{c}_{44}(1 + \varepsilon_{11})}k. \tag{2.26}$$

Combining eqs. (2.25) and (2.26), we find for the speed of the Bleustein–Gulyaev wave

$$v^2 = \frac{\bar{c}_{44}}{\rho}\left(1 - \frac{16\pi^2 e_{15}^4}{\varepsilon_{11}^2\bar{c}_{44}^2(1 + \varepsilon_{11})^2}\right). \tag{2.27}$$

It can be seen that the speed is somewhat less than the transverse bulk wave speed calculated with the piezoelectrically stiffened elastic constant $\bar{c}_{44}$. For CdS, $v^2 = 0.9999875\ \bar{c}_{44}/\rho$.

3. Lattice dynamical theory of surface vibrational modes

3.1. Static displacements near a surface

In the lattice dynamical theory, one assumes that the material under consideration is made up of discrete atoms or ions which vibrate about their equilibrium positions. For an infinite crystal these equilibrium positions are associated with the sites of a crystal lattice periodic in three dimensions. The crystal can be considered as made up of unit cells, each cell containing a given number of atoms. The position vector $\boldsymbol{r}\,(l\kappa)$ of the κth atom in the lth unit cell may be written in the form $\boldsymbol{r}(l\kappa)=\boldsymbol{R}^{(0)}(l\kappa)+\boldsymbol{u}(l\kappa)$, where $\boldsymbol{R}^{(0)}(l\kappa)$ is the position vector of the equilibrium site and $\boldsymbol{u}(l\kappa)$ is the displacement vector from equilibrium. In terms of the primitive translation vectors of the lattice $\boldsymbol{a}_1$, $\boldsymbol{a}_2$, $\boldsymbol{a}_3$, we can write $\boldsymbol{R}^{(0)}(l\kappa)$ in the form

$$\boldsymbol{R}^{(0)}(l\kappa) = l_1\boldsymbol{a}_1 + l_2\boldsymbol{a}_2 + l_3\boldsymbol{a}_3 + \boldsymbol{R}(\kappa), \tag{3.1}$$

where l_1, l_2, l_3 are integers and $\boldsymbol{R}(\kappa)$ is the position vector of the κth atom relative to the origin of the unit cell.

We consider semi-infinite crystals with a free surface parallel to some lattice plane. The crystal is periodic in the two directions parallel to the surface but not in the direction which is normal to the surface. Two basis vectors $\boldsymbol{a}_1$ and $\boldsymbol{a}_2$ are chosen parallel to the surface, while the third basis vector $\boldsymbol{a}_3$ is chosen not parallel to the surface. These basis vectors may differ from the primitive translation vectors of the infinite lattice. The equilibrium position vector $\boldsymbol{R}(l\kappa)$ for an atom in the semi-infinite lattice can be written as

$$\boldsymbol{R}(l\kappa) = \boldsymbol{R}^{(0)}(l\kappa) + \boldsymbol{S}(l\kappa), \tag{3.2}$$

where the vector $\boldsymbol{S}(l\kappa)$ takes into account the 'relaxation' of the equilibrium atomic sites in the semi-infinite crystal away from the corresponding sites of the infinite crystal.

The static displacements $\boldsymbol{S}(l\kappa)$ are determined by the equilibrium conditions

$$F_\alpha(l\kappa) \equiv -\left.\frac{\partial\Phi}{\partial r_\alpha(l\kappa)}\right|_{\boldsymbol{r}(l\kappa)=\boldsymbol{R}(l\kappa)} = 0, \tag{3.3}$$

$$l_{1,2} = 0, \pm 1, \pm 2, \ldots;\ l_3 = 0, 1, 2, \ldots;\ \kappa = 1, 2, \ldots, s;\ \alpha = 1, 2, 3,$$

where Φ is the potential energy of the crystal as a function of the atomic positions and s is the number of atoms in a unit cell. If the static displacements are small, they may be calculated by expanding the forces appearing on the left in eq. (3.3) in power series about the configuration the atoms would have at equilibrium in the infinite lattice (Gazis and Wallis 1965, Feuchtwang 1967):

$$F_\alpha(l\kappa) = F_\alpha^{(0)}(l\kappa) - \sum_{l'\kappa'\beta} \Phi_{\alpha\beta}^{(0)}(l\kappa; l'\kappa')\, S_\beta(l'\kappa') + \cdots, \tag{3.4}$$

where

$$F_\alpha^{(0)}(l\kappa) = -\left.\frac{\partial \Phi}{\partial r_\alpha(l\kappa)}\right|_{S(l\kappa)=0}, \tag{3.5}$$

$$\Phi_{\alpha\beta}^{(0)}(l\kappa; l'\kappa') = \left.\frac{\partial^2 \Phi}{\partial r_\alpha(l\kappa)\, \partial r_\beta(l'\kappa')}\right|_{S(l\kappa),\, S(l'\kappa')=0}, \tag{3.6}$$

and higher terms in the series expansion are neglected. We note that the forces $F_\alpha^{(0)}(l\kappa)$ are not all zero because Φ is the potential energy for the *semi-infinite* lattice; in fact, the $F_\alpha^{(0)}(l\kappa)$ are non-zero for those atoms whose distance from the surface is less than the range of the interatomic forces. The quantities $\Phi_{\alpha\beta}^{(0)}(l\kappa; l'\kappa')$ are the harmonic force constants when the atoms are in the configuration appropriate to the infinite lattice. For some assumed set of interatomic interactions, the static displacements can be calculated by solving eqs. (3.3) and (3.4).

Physically, the semi-infinite lattice may be considered as arising from the infinite lattice by the removal of all atoms beyond the bounding plane defining the free surface. Atoms near the surface are acted upon by unbalanced forces, $F_\alpha^{(0)}(l\kappa)$, due to the removal of the interactions with atoms across the bounding plane and therefore relax to new equilibrium positions. Symmetry may require that the static displacements be normal to the surface, but this is not always the case.

We now calculate the static displacements for a monoatomic body-centered cubic lattice with a free (001) surface (Clark et al. 1967). We assume that each particle of the lattice interacts with its nearest and next-nearest neighbors through interaction potentials of the Lennard–Jones 6–12 type,

$$\varphi_1(r) = \frac{A_1}{r^{12}} - \frac{B_1}{r^6}, \quad \varphi_2(r) = \frac{A_2}{r^{12}} - \frac{B_2}{r^6}, \tag{3.7a, b}$$

where the subscripts 1 and 2 refer to nearest and next-nearest neighbor interactions, respectively, and r is the distance between the interacting particles.

The total potential energy Φ for the model under consideration can be written in the form

$$\Phi = \tfrac{1}{2}\sum_{i,j}{}' \varphi_1(r_{ij}) + \tfrac{1}{2}\sum_{i,j}{}'' \varphi_2(r_{ij}), \tag{3.8}$$

where the prime on the first sum on the right means that only nearest neighbors are summed over and the double prime on the second sum means that only next-nearest neighbors are summed over. If we consider a body-centered cubic lattice of N particles where N is large and if we neglect surface effects, then Φ can be reduced to

$$\Phi = N\{4\varphi_1(r) + 3\varphi_2(2r/\sqrt{3})\}, \tag{3.9}$$

where r is the nearest neighbor separation. At equilibrium,

$$\left.\frac{\partial\Phi}{\partial r}\right|_{r=r_0} = 0, \tag{3.10}$$

and so,

$$4\,\varphi_1'(r_0) = -\,2\sqrt{3}\,\varphi_2'(2r_0/\sqrt{3}), \tag{3.11}$$

where primes denote derivatives with respect to arguments. Substitution of eqs. (3.7) into eq. (3.11) yields

$$-\,2A_1' + B_1' = 2A_2' - B_2', \tag{3.12}$$

where

$$A_1' = A_1\, r_0^{-14}, \quad A_2' = A_2(2r_0/\sqrt{3})^{-14}, \tag{3.13a, b}$$

$$B_1' = B_1\, r_0^{-8}, \quad B_2' = B_2(2r_0/\sqrt{3})^{-8}. \tag{3.13c, d}$$

Let $\boldsymbol{u}_i$ denote the displacement vector of particle i from its equilibrium position. For a central-potential model, the potential energy in a non-equilibrium configuration can be written in the form

$$\begin{aligned}\Phi = \Phi_0 &+ \tfrac{1}{4}\sum_{i,j}\sum_{x,y} \varphi_{xy}(i-j)(u_{ix}-u_{jx})(u_{iy}-u_{jy}) \\ &+ \tfrac{1}{12}\sum_{i,j}\sum_{x,y,z} \varphi_{xyz}(i-j)(u_{ix}-u_{jx})(u_{iy}-u_{jy})(u_{iz}-u_{jz}) \\ &+ \cdots,\end{aligned} \tag{3.14}$$

where the force constants $\varphi_{xy}(i-j)$ and $\varphi_{xyz}(i-j)$ are defined by

$$\varphi_{xy}(i-j) = \frac{\partial^2 \varphi(r_{ij})}{\partial p_x \partial p_y}, \quad \varphi_{xyz}(i-j) = \frac{\partial^3 \varphi(r_{ij})}{\partial p_x \partial p_y \partial p_z}, \tag{3.15a, b}$$

$$\boldsymbol{p} = \boldsymbol{u}_i - \boldsymbol{u}_j. \tag{3.16}$$

The central force character of the two-particle interactions can be exploited to write the force constants in the form

$$\varphi_{xy}(i-j) = \left\{ \frac{xy}{r^2} \left[\varphi''(r) - \frac{1}{r}\varphi'(r) \right] + \frac{\delta_{xy}}{r}\varphi'(r) \right\} \Bigg|_{r=r_0(ij)}, \tag{3.17a}$$

$$\begin{aligned} \varphi_{xyz}(i-j) = &\left\{ \frac{xyz}{r^3} \left[\varphi'''(r) - \frac{3}{r}\varphi''(r) + \frac{3}{r^2}\varphi'(r) \right] \right. \\ &\left. + \left(\delta_{xy}\frac{z}{r^2} + \delta_{yz}\frac{x}{r^2} + \delta_{zx}\frac{y}{r^2} \right) \left[\varphi''(r) - \frac{1}{r}\varphi'(r) \right] \right\} \Bigg|_{r=r_0(ij)}, \end{aligned} \tag{3.17b}$$

where primes denote derivatives with respect to the arguments, $\delta_{\alpha\beta}$ is the Kronecker delta,

$$r = |\boldsymbol{r}(ij)| = |\boldsymbol{r}_i - \boldsymbol{r}_j|, \tag{3.18a}$$

$$\boldsymbol{r}(ij) = (r_{ix} - r_{jx}, r_{iy} - r_{jy}, r_{iz} - r_{jz}) \equiv (x, y, z), \tag{3.18b}$$

and $r_0(ij)$ is the equilibrium separation of particles i and j in the infinite lattice.

The equations of motion of the particles can be derived from the potential energy given by eq. (3.14). Neglecting surface effects, the x-component of acceleration of the particle identified by integers l, m, n can be written in the harmonic approximation for our model of a body-centered cubic lattice as follows:

$$\begin{aligned} M\ddot{u}_{l,m,n} = &\alpha_1 \sum_{\lambda\mu\nu=\pm 1} (u_{l+\lambda, m+\mu, n+\nu} - u_{l,m,n}) \\ &+ \alpha_2 \sum_{\lambda\mu\nu=\pm 1} (\lambda\mu v_{l+\lambda, m+\mu, n+\nu} + \lambda\nu w_{l+\lambda, m+\mu, n+\nu}) \\ &+ \beta_1 \sum_{\lambda=\pm 2} (u_{l+\lambda, m, n} - u_{l,m,n}) \\ &+ \beta_2 \sum_{\lambda=\pm 2} (u_{l, m+\lambda, n} + u_{l, m, n+\lambda} - 2u_{l,m,n}). \end{aligned} \tag{3.19}$$

Here, M is the particle mass, u, v, and w are the x, y, and z components of displacement, the double dot indicates a second partial derivative with respect to time,

$$\alpha_1 = \varphi_{xx}(a, a, a) = \tfrac{1}{3}[\varphi_1''(r_0) + (2/r_0)\varphi_1'(r_0)], \tag{3.20a}$$

$$\alpha_2 = \varphi_{xy}(a, a, a) = \tfrac{1}{3}[\varphi_1''(r_0) - (1/r_0)\varphi_1'(r_0)], \tag{3.20b}$$

$$\beta_1 = \varphi_{zz}(0, 0, 2a) = \varphi_2''(2r_0/\sqrt{3}), \tag{3.20c}$$

$$\beta_2 = \varphi_{xx}(0, 0, 2a) = (\sqrt{3}/2r_0)\varphi_2'(2r_0/\sqrt{3}), \tag{3.20d}$$

$$a = r_0/\sqrt{3}. \tag{3.20e}$$

Corresponding equations for $\ddot{v}_{l,m,n}$ and $\ddot{w}_{l,m,n}$ may be obtained from eq. (3.19) by suitable permutations of the symbols.

The force constants α_1, α_2 and β_1 can be related to the elastic constants c_{11}, c_{12} and c_{44} by taking the continuum limit of eq. (3.19). The results are found to be

$$ac_{11} = \alpha_1 + \beta_1, \quad ac_{12} = \alpha_2, \quad ac_{44} = \alpha_2. \tag{3.21a, b, c}$$

Utilizing eqs. (3.7), (3.12), (3.13), (3.17a), (3.20), and (3.21), we can relate the experimentally measurable elastic constants to the quantities A_1', A_2', B_1' and B_2' characterizing the Lennard–Jones potentials. The fourth relation required to specify these quantities is obtained from the phonon frequency $\omega(\pi, 0, 0) = 4(\alpha_1/M)^{1/2}$.

We are now in a position to calculate the static displacements. Let $\boldsymbol{F}_0$ and $\boldsymbol{F}_1$ be the unbalanced forces $\boldsymbol{F}^{(0)}(000)$ and $\boldsymbol{F}^{(0)}(001)$ acting on atoms in the surface layer and in the next-to-surface layer, respectively, when the particles of the semi-infinite lattice are situated in the equilibrium sites they would occupy in the infinite lattice. From symmetry we note that the forces $\boldsymbol{F}_0$ and $\boldsymbol{F}_1$ and the static displacements are normal to the surface. In the harmonic approximation the equations which determine the displacements $w(j)$ are

$$-F_0 = 4\alpha_1[w(1) - w(0)] + \beta_1[w(2) - w(0)], \tag{3.22a}$$

$$-F_1 = 4\alpha_1[w(2) + w(0) - 2w(1)] + \beta_1[w(3) - w(1)], \tag{3.22b}$$

$$\begin{aligned} 0 = 4\alpha_1&[w(j+1) + w(j-1) - 2w(j)] \\ &+ \beta_1[w(j+2) + w(j-2) - 2w(j)], \quad j \geqq 2. \end{aligned} \tag{3.22c}$$

The forces F_0 and F_1 for our model can be written as

$$F_0 = \sum_{\mathrm{nn}}{}' \frac{\partial}{\partial w(0)} \varphi_1 [r(0, \mathrm{nn})]|_0 + \sum_{\mathrm{nnn}}{}' \frac{\partial}{\partial w(0)} \varphi_2 [r(0, \mathrm{nnn})]|_0, \tag{3.23a}$$

$$F_1 = \sum_{\mathrm{nnn}}{}' \frac{\partial}{\partial w(1)} \varphi_2 [r(1, \mathrm{nnn})]|_0, \tag{3.23b}$$

where $w(0)$ and $w(1)$ are the z-components (normal to the surface) of particles in the surface and next-to-surface layers, respectively, 'nn' and 'nnn' refer to the nearest and next-nearest neighbors of the appropriate particles, the derivatives are evaluated at the equilibrium positions of the infinite lattice and the primes on the sums mean that the latter are carried out only over particles in the semi-infinite lattice which interact with the atoms of interest.

For the body-centered cubic lattice we obtain

$$F_0 = \tfrac{4}{3}\sqrt{3}\, \varphi_1'(r_0) + \varphi_2'(2r_0/\sqrt{3}), \quad F_1 = \varphi_2'(2r_0/\sqrt{3}). \tag{3.24a, b}$$

Adding eqs. (3.24a) and (3.24b) we see that

$$F_0 + F_1 = \tfrac{4}{3}\sqrt{3}\, \varphi_1'(r_0) + 2\varphi_2'(2r_0/\sqrt{3}). \tag{3.25}$$

From the equation of equilibrium for the infinite lattice, eq. (3.11), we obtain

$$F_0 + F_1 = 0. \tag{3.26}$$

The desired solutions to eqs. (3.22) can be written in the form

$$w(j) = A e^{-qj}, \tag{3.27}$$

where q and A are specified by

$$\cosh q = -(2\alpha_1 + \beta_1)/\beta_1, \tag{3.28a}$$

$$A = \frac{\beta_1 F_0 - (2\alpha_1 + \beta_1) F_1}{4\beta_1 (\alpha_1 + \beta_1) \sinh q} = \frac{F_0}{2\beta_1 \sinh q}. \tag{3.28b}$$

If the quantity $(2\alpha_1 + \beta_1)/\beta_1$ is positive, it is convenient to let $q = q_0 + i\pi$. Then eq. (3.25a) becomes

$$\cosh q_0 = (2\alpha_1 + \beta_1)/\beta_1, \tag{3.29}$$

where q_0 is real.

We now make an explicit calculation for iron. The elastic constants and phonon frequency, which are given in the work of Low (1962), have the following values at 16 °C:

$$c_{11} = 2.332, \quad c_{12} = 1.355, \quad c_{44} = 1.180 \; (\times 10^{12} \text{ dyn/cm}^2), \qquad (3.30\text{a, b, c})$$

$$\hbar\omega(\pi, 0, 0) = 0.035 \text{ eV}. \qquad (3.31)$$

The value of the unit cube edge, $2a$, is 2.866 Å. We take the force constant α_2 to be given by

$$\alpha_2 = \tfrac{1}{2}a\,(c_{12} + c_{44}). \qquad (3.32)$$

Using these data we obtain the following values for A_1', B_1', A_2' and B_2' in units of 10^3 dyn/cm: $A_1'=0.57$, $B_1'=0.87$, $A_2'=0.39$, $B_2'=1.06$.

From the values of α_1 and β_1 given by eqs. (3.21), (3.30) and (3.31), we find that for iron, $q_0=1.74$. The values of A_1', B_1', A_2', and B_2' are used to calculate F_0 by means of eqs. (3.7), (3.13) and (3.24). When the result is substituted into eq. (3.28b) the value of A turns out to be

$$A = -\,0.051 \times 10^{-8} \text{ cm} = -\,0.036a\,, \qquad (3.33)$$

and the first few values of $w(j)$ are found to be

$$w(0) = -\,0.036a, \quad w(1) = +\,0.006a, \quad w(2) = -\,0.001a. \qquad (3.34\text{a, b, c})$$

We see that the surface layer is displaced outward approximately four per cent of the interlayer spacing. The displacements of successive layers are alternately outward and inward; their magnitude approaches zero exponentially. The exponential behavior in eq. (3.27) and the alternation of sign turn out to be functions of the model employed. If the model involves interaction potentials varying as $1/r^p$ where r is the separation of a pair of atoms and $p>3$, then the increase in interlayer spacing is found (Allen and De Wette 1969) to vary at large distances d from the surface as $1/d^{p-3}$. Hence for a 6–12 Lennard–Jones potential, the spacing varies as $1/d^3$.

3.2. Changes in surface force constants

The change in the interlayer spacing near the surface produces a change in the harmonic force constants coupling particles near the surface. Expanding the harmonic force constants about the equilibrium configuration of the infinite lattice, we find for the central-potential model,

$$\varphi_{xy}(ij) = \varphi_{xy}^{(0)}(ij) + \sum_z \varphi_{xyz}^{(0)}(ij)\,(u_{iz} - u_{jz}) + \cdots, \tag{3.35a}$$

or

$$\Delta\varphi_{xy}(ij) = \sum_z \varphi_{xyz}^{(0)}(ij)\,(u_{iz} - u_{jz}) + \cdots. \tag{3.35b}$$

In eqs. (3.35) the subscripts x and y may each take on the values x, y or z. The changes in the harmonic force constants are given correctly to lowest order in the cubic anharmonic coefficients if the displacements are determined in the harmonic approximation.

We now evaluate the changes in the surface force constants for the nearest and next-nearest neighbor model. The cubic anharmonic force constants are specified by eq. (3.17b) and lead to the following expressions for the surface force constant changes:

$$\Delta\alpha_1(\parallel) = \Delta\varphi_{xx}(a, a, a) = \frac{1}{3\sqrt{3}}\,\varphi_1'''(r_0)\,[w(1) - w(0)], \tag{3.36a}$$

$$\begin{aligned}\Delta\alpha_1(\perp) &= \Delta\varphi_{zz}(a, a, a)\\ &= \left(\frac{1}{3\sqrt{3}}\,\varphi_1'''(r_0) + \frac{2}{r_0\sqrt{3}}\left[\varphi_1''(r_0) - \frac{1}{r_0}\,\varphi_1'(r_0)\right]\right)\\ &\qquad\times [w(1) - w(0)],\end{aligned} \tag{3.36b}$$

$$\begin{aligned}\Delta\alpha_2(\parallel) &= \Delta\varphi_{xy}(a, a, a)\\ &= \left(\frac{1}{3\sqrt{3}}\,\varphi_1'''(r_0) - \frac{1}{r_0\sqrt{3}}\left[\varphi_1''(r_0) - \frac{1}{r_0}\,\varphi_1'(r_0)\right]\right)\\ &\qquad\times [w(1) - w(0)],\end{aligned} \tag{3.36c}$$

$$\Delta\alpha_2(\perp) = \Delta\varphi_{xz}(a, a, a) = \Delta\varphi_{xx}(a, a, a), \tag{3.36d}$$

$$\Delta\beta_1(\parallel) = \Delta\beta_2(\parallel) = 0, \tag{3.36e}$$

$$\Delta\beta_1(\perp) = \Delta\varphi_{zz}(0, 0, 2a) = \varphi_2'''(2r_0/\sqrt{3})\,[w(2) - w(0)], \tag{3.36f}$$

$$\begin{aligned}\Delta\beta_2(\perp) &= \Delta\varphi_{xx}(0, 0, 2a)\\ &= (\sqrt{3}/2r_0)\,[\varphi_2''(2r_0/\sqrt{3}) - (\sqrt{3}/2r_0)\,\varphi_2'(2r_0/\sqrt{3})]\\ &\qquad\times [w(2) - w(0)].\end{aligned} \tag{3.36g}$$

A numerical calculation can now be carried out for iron. Using the values of A'_1, B'_1, A'_2, and B'_2 and the static displacements given by eq. (3.34), we find for iron:

$$\begin{aligned} &\Delta\alpha_1(\|) = -0.34\alpha_1, && \Delta\alpha_1(\perp) = -0.25\alpha_1, && \Delta\alpha_2(\|) = -0.35\alpha_2, \\ &\Delta\beta_1(\|) = \Delta\beta_2(\|) = 0, && \Delta\beta_1(\perp) = -0.51\beta_1, && \Delta\beta_2(\perp) = 0.016\beta_1. \end{aligned} \tag{3.37}$$

From these results we see that the relative change in the force constants at the surface can be quite large, i.e., 30 or 40 per cent. This suggests that quartic and possible higher anharmonic terms may make a significant contribution. The change at the surface is typically a decrease, although increases may also occur. Another result is that the nearest-neighbor force constants acquire an anisotropy at the surface. This anisotropy arises because the expressions for the changes in the force constants involve not only third derivatives of the interaction potentials but also second derivatives and first derivatives.

The foregoing calculation is deficient in that a universal interaction potential has been assumed between atom pairs of a given type such as nearest neighbors, regardless of the distance of the atom pair from the surface. This assumption is not necessarily valid. A more fundamental approach would be to calculate the ground-state electronic energy of the crystal with a free surface for arbitrary positions of the nuclei. Expansion of the ground-state energy in powers of the displacements of the nuclei from equilibrium would then yield the force constants both at the surface and in the bulk.

3.3. Equations of motion for a crystal with a surface

The vibrations of the atoms in a crystal may be analyzed by expanding the potential energy in power series in the components of the displacements of the nuclei from their equilibrium sites in the slab or semi-infinite lattice,

$$\begin{aligned} \Phi = \Phi_0 &+ \tfrac{1}{2} \sum_{l\kappa\alpha} \sum_{l'\kappa'\beta} \Phi_{\alpha\beta}(l\kappa, l'\kappa')\, u_\alpha(l\kappa)\, u_\beta(l'\kappa') \\ &+ \tfrac{1}{6} \sum_{l\kappa\alpha} \sum_{l'\kappa'\beta} \sum_{l''\kappa''\gamma} \Phi_{\alpha\beta\gamma}(l\kappa, l'\kappa', l''\kappa'')\, u_\alpha(l\kappa)\, u_\beta(l'\kappa')\, u_\gamma(l''\kappa'') \\ &+ \cdots, \end{aligned} \tag{3.38a}$$

where $\boldsymbol{u}(l\kappa) = \boldsymbol{r}(l\kappa) - \boldsymbol{R}(l\kappa)$,

$$\Phi_{\alpha\beta}(l\kappa, l'\kappa') = \left. \frac{\partial^2 \Phi}{\partial r_\alpha(l\kappa)\, \partial r_\beta(l'\kappa')} \right|_{\{\boldsymbol{u}(l\kappa)\}=0}, \tag{3.38b}$$

$$\Phi_{\alpha\beta\gamma}(l\kappa, l'\kappa', l''\kappa'') = \left.\frac{\partial^3 \Phi}{\partial r_\alpha(l\kappa)\, \partial r_\beta(l'\kappa')\, \partial r_\gamma(l''\kappa'')}\right|_{\{u(l\kappa)\}=0}, \tag{3.38c}$$

and $\{u(l\kappa)\}$ stands for the entire set of displacements $u(l\kappa)$. The coefficients $\Phi_{\alpha\beta}(l\kappa, l'\kappa')$, $\Phi_{\alpha\beta\gamma}(l\kappa, l'\kappa', l''\kappa'')$, etc., are the harmonic, cubic anharmonic, etc., coupling constants.

The coupling constants satisfy certain invariance conditions. The periodicity of the lattice parallel to the surface (specified by $l_3=0$) requires that the coupling coefficients be functions only of the differences l_1-l_1', l_2-l_2', l_1-l_1'', l_2-l_2'', etc.; however, they are, in general, functions of l_3, l_3', l_3'', $\cdots$ separately. Infinitesimal translational invariance imposes the requirement that

$$\sum_{l'\kappa'} \Phi_{\alpha\beta}(l\kappa, l'\kappa') = 0, \quad \sum_{l'\kappa'} \sum_{l''\kappa''} \Phi_{\alpha\beta\gamma}(l\kappa, l'\kappa', l''\kappa'') = 0, \text{ etc.}, \tag{3.39}$$

while infinitesimal rotational invariance requires that

$$\sum_{l'\kappa'} \{\Phi_{\alpha\beta}(l\kappa, l'\kappa') [R_\gamma(l\kappa) - R_\gamma(l'\kappa')] - \Phi_{\alpha\gamma}(l\kappa, l'\kappa') [R_\beta(l\kappa) - R_\beta(l'\kappa')]\} = 0 \tag{3.40}$$

with corresponding equations for the anharmonic coupling coefficients. The constraints imposed on the coupling coefficients by rotational invariance are especially important for surface problems.

The normal modes of vibration for the crystal with a surface may be found by solving the harmonic equations of motion for the displacements. Using eq. (3.38a) these equations can be written in the form

$$M_\kappa \ddot{u}_\alpha(l\kappa) = -\frac{\partial \Phi}{\partial u_\alpha(l\kappa)} = -\sum_{l'\kappa'\beta} \Phi_{\alpha\beta}(l\kappa, l'\kappa')\, u_\beta(l'\kappa'), \tag{3.41}$$

where we have used the symmetry property $\Phi_{\alpha\beta}(l\kappa, l', \kappa') = \Phi_{\beta\alpha}(l'\kappa', l\kappa)$. The solution of eq. (3.41) is difficult for two reasons. First, there is no periodicity of the atomic sites in the direction normal to the surface; second, the coupling coefficients $\Phi_{\alpha\beta}(l\kappa; l'\kappa')$ are not necessarily the same as the corresponding coefficients for the infinite lattice as discussed in subsection 3.2. We exploit the translational periodicity parallel to the surface by seeking solutions to eq. (3.41) having the form

$$u_\alpha(l\kappa) = M_\kappa^{-1/2}\, v_\alpha(l_3\kappa, \boldsymbol{k}_p) \exp[\mathrm{i}(k_1 l_1 + k_2 l_2 - \omega t)], \tag{3.42}$$

where ω is the circular frequency and $\boldsymbol{k}_p$ is a dimensionless two-dimensional wave vector parallel to the surface with components k_1 and k_2. Substitution of eq. (3.42) into eq. (3.41) yields a set of linear difference equations in the amplitudes $v_\alpha(l_3\kappa, \boldsymbol{k}_p)$,

$$\omega^2 v_\alpha(l_3\kappa, \boldsymbol{k}_p) = \sum_{l'_3\kappa'\beta} D_{\alpha\beta}(l_3\kappa, l'_3\kappa', \boldsymbol{k}_p)\, v_\beta(l'_3\kappa', \boldsymbol{k}_p), \tag{3.43}$$

where the quantities

$$D_{\alpha\beta}(l_3\kappa, l'_3\kappa', \boldsymbol{k}_p) = (M_\kappa M_{\kappa'})^{-1/2} \sum_{l'_1 l'_2} \Phi_{\alpha\beta}(l\kappa, l'\kappa') \times \exp i\left[k_1(l'_1 - l_1) + k_2(l'_2 - l_2)\right] \tag{3.44}$$

are the elements of the reduced dynamical matrix of the slab or semi-infinite crystal. The normal mode frequencies of the crystal are obtained by setting the determinant of the coefficients of the amplitudes in eq. (3.43) equal to zero:

$$|D_{\alpha\beta}(l_3\kappa, l'_3\kappa', \boldsymbol{k}_p) - \omega^2 \delta_{l_3 l'_3} \delta_{\kappa\kappa'} \delta_{\alpha\beta}| = 0\,. \tag{3.45}$$

For a semi-infinite crystal, the determinant is infinite in size. For a slab L_3 atomic layers thick, the size of the determinant is $3sL_3 \times 3sL_3$ where s is the number of atoms in a unit cell. Results that are reasonably representative of real crystals are obtained if L_3 is as small as 20 or 30. For simple crystals one then must work with 60×60 or 90×90 determinants, which can easily be handled using high speed computers.

An alternative approach, particularly useful with short-range forces, is to treat all atoms as having the same equations of motion. They are to be augmented by boundary conditions, which are constraints that restore the effect of the surface on the equations of motion. The procedure is entirely analogous to that employed in the continuum theory of surface elastic waves. The determinants which occur in the secular equation and the frequency equation are generally on the order of $3s \times 3s$ in size. This is relatively small and easily handled on a computer.

The solutions to the equations of motion, eqs. (3.43), may be 'bulk' solutions where the displacements do not approach zero at large distances from the boundaries and 'surface' solutions where the displacements do approach zero at large distances from the boundaries. In addition there may be combinations of these solutions or 'mixed' solutions. We now consider the surface solutions for a variety of cases.

3.4. Acoustical surface modes

For illustrative purposes we start with a discussion of the semi-infinite monoatomic linear chain with nearest neighbor interactions. No surface mode exists for this case unless the mass of the end atom or the force constant coupling this atom to its neighbor is different from the bulk value. We therefore allow for such changes by writing the equations of motion in the form

$$M'\ddot{u}_0 = \alpha'(u_1 - u_0), \tag{3.46a}$$

$$M\ddot{u}_1 = \alpha(u_2 - u_1) + \alpha'(u_0 - u_1), \tag{3.46b}$$

$$M\ddot{u}_n = \alpha(u_{n+1} + u_{n-1} - 2u_n), \quad n \geqslant 2. \tag{3.46c}$$

For a surface mode, the displacements can be taken to be

$$u_0 = U_0\, e^{i\omega t}, \quad u_n = U(-1)^n\, e^{-qn}\, e^{i\omega t}, \quad n \geqslant 1, \tag{3.47a, b}$$

where U_0 and U are constant amplitudes. In order for eqs. (3.47) to be solutions of eqs. (3.46), it is necessary that the frequency ω be related to the decay constant q by

$$M\omega^2 = 2\alpha(1 + \cosh q), \tag{3.48}$$

and that q be a solution of the equation

$$[\alpha' - \alpha(1 + e^q)]\,[\alpha' - 2(M'/M)\,\alpha(1 + \cosh q)] - \alpha'^2 = 0. \tag{3.49}$$

The value of q obtained from eq. (3.49) must be real and positive, a condition which requires that the following inequality be satisfied,

$$\frac{\alpha'}{\alpha} > \frac{4M'/M}{2(M'/M) + 1}. \tag{3.50}$$

It is clear from eq. (3.48) that the surface mode frequency, when it exists, lies above the maximum frequency of the infinite chain given by $\omega_m^2 = 4\alpha/M$. A surface mode can exist in the monoatomic linear chain only if the surface force constant is sufficiently large or the surface atom mass is sufficiently small compared to the corresponding bulk values. In accordance with Rayleigh's theorem (Maradudin et al. 1971, section VIII.2) changes in parameters of this sort lead to an increase in normal mode frequencies and hence the possibility of the surface mode frequency appearing in the 'forbidden' region above ω_m.

One must consider the two- or three-dimensional case in order to exhibit the lattice dynamical analogue of Rayleigh waves. The creation of a free surface can be viewed as a consequence of setting to zero the force constants coupling atoms on opposite sides of a plane defining the boundary. A reduction of force constants in this way will depress the normal mode frequencies, and a surface mode can arise if the lowest normal mode frequency drops into a gap in the bulk mode spectrum just above zero frequency. In the one-dimensional case, no such gap exists and hence there is no Rayleigh wave, but in the two- and three-dimensional cases for non-zero values of the wave vector parallel to the surface, such a gap does exist and Rayleigh waves are possible.

As an illustration we consider a monoatomic simple cubic lattice with nearest and next-nearest neighbor central forces plus angle-bending interactions involving pairs of nearest neighbors. The equations of motion of a bulk atom can be written as (Gazis et al. 1960)

$$\begin{aligned} M\ddot{u}_{l,m,n} = {} & \alpha\Big\{\sum_{\delta=\pm1}(u_{l+\delta,m,n} - u_{l,m,n})\Big\} \\ & + \beta\Big\{\sum_{\varepsilon=\pm1}\sum_{\delta=\pm1}(u_{l+\delta,m+\varepsilon,n} + u_{l+\delta,m,n+\varepsilon} - 2u_{l,m,n})\Big\} \\ & + (\beta+\gamma)\Big\{\sum_{\varepsilon=\pm1}\sum_{\delta=\pm1}[\varepsilon\delta(v_{l+\delta,m+\varepsilon,n} + w_{l+\delta,m,n+\varepsilon})]\Big\} \\ & + 4\gamma\Big\{\sum_{\delta=\pm1}(u_{l,m+\delta,n} + u_{l,m,n+\delta} - 2u_{l,m,n})\Big\}, \end{aligned} \tag{3.51}$$

where α and β are the central coupling constants, γ is the angle-bending coupling constant, and the other equations arise by cyclically permuting the displacement components u, v, w and the increments δ, ε on the indices l, m, n which identify a lattice site.

The equations of motion must be augmented by boundary conditions in order to include the effect of the surface. For a (001) surface characterized by $n=0$, the boundary conditions can be written as

$$\begin{aligned} & \sum_{\delta=\pm1}\{\beta(u_{l+\delta,m,-1} - u_{l,m,0} - \delta w_{l+\delta,m,-1}) \\ & \qquad + \gamma[2(u_{l,m,-1} - u_{l,m,0}) - \delta(w_{l+\delta,m,0} + w_{l+\delta,m,-1})]\} = 0, \\ & \sum_{\delta=\pm1}\{\beta(v_{l,m+\delta,-1} - v_{l,m,0} - \delta w_{l,m+\delta,-1}) \\ & \qquad + \gamma[2(v_{l,m,-1} - v_{l,m,0}) - \delta(w_{l,m+\delta,0} + w_{l,m+\delta,-1})]\} = 0, \\ & \sum_{\delta=\pm1}\{\tfrac{1}{2}\alpha(w_{l,m,-1} - w_{l,m,0}) \\ & \qquad + \beta(w_{l+\delta,m,-1} + w_{l,m+\delta,-1} - 2w_{l,m,0}) \\ & \qquad - \beta\delta(u_{l+\delta,m,-1} + v_{l,m+\delta,-1}) \\ & \qquad + 2\gamma(w_{l+\delta,m,0} + w_{l,m+\delta,0} - 2w_{l,m,0}) \\ & \qquad + \gamma\delta(u_{l+\delta,m,0} - u_{l+\delta,m,-1} + v_{l,m+\delta,0} - v_{l,m+\delta,-1})\} = 0. \end{aligned} \tag{3.52}$$

We solve eqs. (3.51) and (3.52) in a manner analogous to that employed with the cubic continuum. If we assume a solution having the form

$$(u, v, w)_{l,m,n} = (U, V, W) \exp[-qn + \mathrm{i}(\varphi_1 l + \varphi_2 m + \omega t)] \tag{3.53}$$

and substitute this expression into eqs. (3.51), we get a set of linear equations in U, V, W whose determinant of coefficients must vanish in order to have a nontrivial solution:

$$|d_{ij}(\varphi_1, \varphi_2, \omega^2, q)| = 0. \tag{3.54}$$

For a given set of force constants and wave number components, eq. (3.54) constitutes a relation between the frequency ω and the attenuation constant q. Since it is a cubic equation in cosh q, we can solve for three values of q for given ω and use these to form a solution which satisfies the boundary conditions. A surface wave results only if the real part of each q_j required is greater than zero.

We now seek to satisfy the boundary conditions by means of a solution having the form

$$(u, v, \mathrm{i}w)_{l,m,n} = \sum_{j=1}^{3} (\xi_j, \eta_j, \zeta_j) K_j \times \exp[-q_j n + \mathrm{i}(\varphi_1 l + \varphi_2 m + \omega t)], \tag{3.55}$$

where ξ_j, η_j, ζ_j are the appropriate cofactors of $|d_{ij}|$. Substitution of eq. (3.55) into eqs. (3.52) yields a set of linear equations in the amplitudes K_j. A non-trivial solution requires that a determinantal equation be satisfied,

$$|T_{ij}| = 0, \tag{3.56}$$

whose solution determines the frequency ω or phase velocity $c = \omega a/\varphi$, where a is the lattice constant.

The force constants α, β, γ can be determined by fitting the elastic constants. This procedure can be accomplished by expanding the displacement components in power series in the lattice parameter a about $u_{l,m,n}$. Substitution of these expansions into eqs. (3.51) and (3.52) and retention of terms only through a^2 yields partial differential equations which are analogous to the continuum equations of motion and continuum boundaıy conditions, respectively. Comparison of the coefficients of corresponding terms then yields the following identification of the elastic constants

$$c_{11} = (\alpha + 4\beta)/a, \quad c_{12} = 2\beta/a, \quad c_{44} = (2\beta + 4\gamma)/a. \tag{3.57}$$

A calculation has been made with the above model for surface waves propagating in the [100] direction on a (001) surface of KCl (considered monoatomic). The results, given in fig. 5 show the dispersion of the Rayleigh waves expected in a lattice theory. Another interesting feature is the divergence of one of the attenuation constants at a critical value of $\varphi = \varphi_c = 1.75$. At φ_c this attenuation constant changes from a real value to a complex value of the form $q_0 + i\pi$. Consequently, for $\varphi > \varphi_c$, the surface wave is a special type of generalized Rayleigh wave.

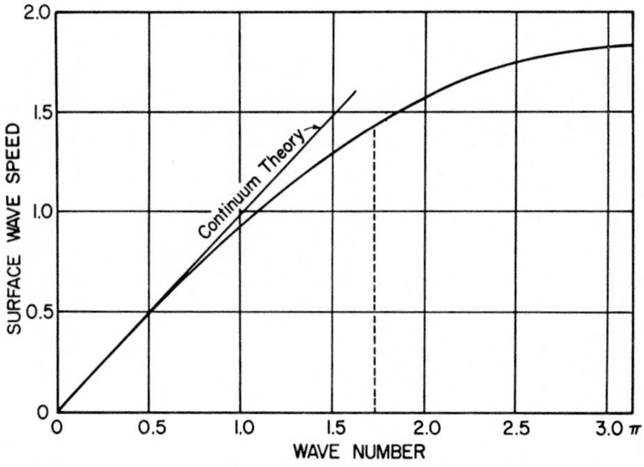

Fig. 5. Dispersion curve of surface waves propagating in the [100] direction on the (001) surface of KCl. The Surface wave is an ordinary surface wave to the left of the dashed line and a generalized surface wave to the right of this line (after Gazis et al. 1960).

Many calculations of surface wave dispersion curves for monoatomic face-centered cubic lattices have been made by De Wette and collaborators (see, for example, Allen et al. 1971). Among their interesting results are surface modes of non-Rayleigh type whose frequencies lie in gaps in the spectrum of bulk modes.

3.5. Optical surface modes

A simple illustration of optical surface modes is provided by the diatomic linear chain with nearest neighbor interactions and free ends (Wallis 1957). Denoting the masses of the lighter and heavier atoms by m and M, respectively, we can write the equations of motion as

$$m \frac{\partial^2 u_1}{\partial t^2} = \alpha(u_2 - u_1),$$

$$M \frac{\partial^2 u_{2j}}{\partial t^2} = \alpha(u_{2j+1} + u_{2j-1} - 2u_{2j}), \quad N-1 \geqslant j \geqslant 1$$

$$m \frac{\partial^2 u_{2j-1}}{\partial t^2} = \alpha(u_{2j} + u_{2j-2} - 2u_{2j-1}), \quad N \geqslant j \geqslant 2, \tag{3.58}$$

$$M \frac{\partial^2 u_{2N}}{\partial t^2} = \alpha(u_{2N-1} - u_{2N}),$$

where the number of each type of atom is N and α is the nearest-neighbor force constant. The normal modes of vibration corresponding to the solutions of eqs. (3.58) comprise N acoustical modes and $N-1$ optical modes, all of which are bulk modes, and one optical surface mode. The displacements for the optical surface mode can be written in the form

$$u_{2j-1} = U(-1)^{j-1}(m/M)^{j-1}\exp(i\omega t), \tag{3.59a}$$

$$u_{2j} = U(-1)^{j}(m/M)^{j}\exp(i\omega t), \tag{3.59b}$$

where the frequency ω is specified by

$$\omega^2 = \alpha(m+M)/mM. \tag{3.60}$$

The displacement amplitudes for the optical surface mode are plotted as a function of position in the lattice in fig. 6. One sees the exponential decrease of the displacement amplitudes from the end having the lighter atom. The squared normal mode frequencies are displayed in fig. 7. The frequency of the surface mode lies in the gap between the acoustical and optical branches whose upper and lower boundaries are given by $(2\alpha/M)^{1/2}$, and $(2\alpha/M)^{1/2}$, respectively. This is in accord with Rayleigh's theorem. The free end arises by reducing a force constant of the cyclic chain to zero. This decreases normal mode frequencies and causes the lowest optical mode of the cyclic chain to drop down into the gap and become the optical surface mode.

The example just considered involves short-range forces. The surface mode is microscopic in the sense that the displacement amplitude decays essentially to zero within a few lattice spacings of the surface. In ionic crystals with long-range Coulomb interactions a macroscopic type of surface mode is possible in which the displacement amplitude penetrates deeply into the crystal. This type of surface mode was first studied extensively by Fuchs

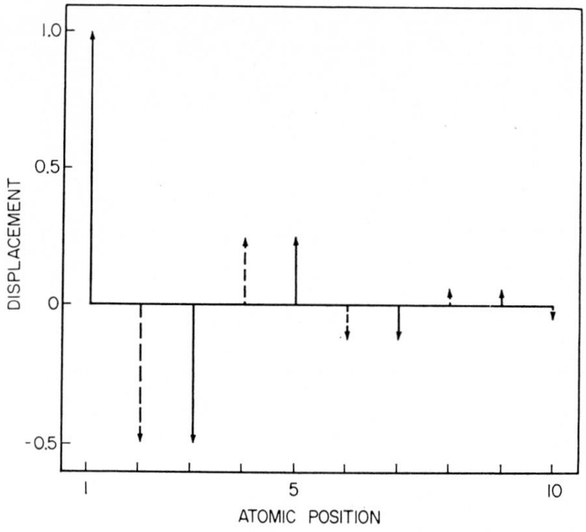

Fig. 6. Displacement amplitudes versus position in the lattice for the surface mode of a diatomic linear chain of ten atoms (after Wallis 1957).

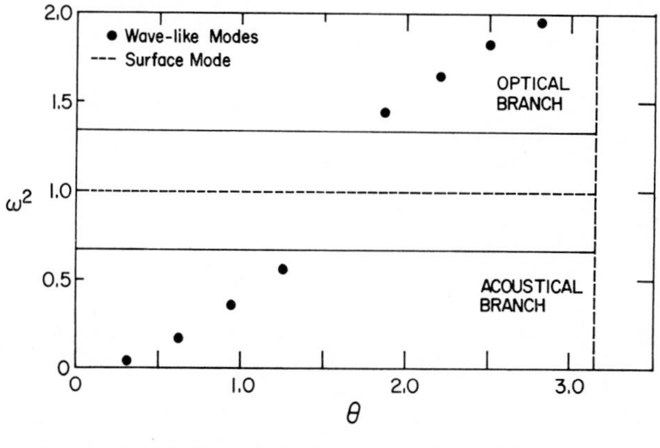

Fig. 7. Squared normal mode frequencies in units of $\alpha(m+M)/mM$ plotted against mode index θ for a diatomic linear chain of ten atoms (after Wallis 1957).

and Kliewer (1965), and Kliewer and Fuchs (1966). The ionic displacements are coupled to the electromagnetic field through the Coulomb interactions, and the coupled surface phonon–photon modes are called surface polaritons.

A simple treatment of surface polaritons can be given by considering Maxwell's equations for a dielectric medium and the electromagnetic boundary conditions at the interface with the vacuum. We assume that the dielectric medium possesses an isotropic, frequency-dependent dielectric constant $\varepsilon(\omega)$ of the form (Born and Huang 1954)

$$\varepsilon(\omega) = \varepsilon_\infty \frac{\omega_L^2 - \omega^2}{\omega_T^2 - \omega^2}, \tag{3.61}$$

where ε_∞ is the background dielectric constant, and ω_L and ω_T are the frequencies of long-wavelength longitudinal and transverse optical phonons, respectively. We take the surface to be specified by $z=0$ with the dielectric medium in the half space $z>0$ and vacuum in the half space $z>0$. The magnetic permeability is assumed to be unity everywhere.

We seek solutions of Maxwell's equations for the electric field components E_α of the form

$$E_\alpha(\boldsymbol{r}, t) = E_\alpha(z)\, \mathrm{e}^{ikx - i\omega t}, \tag{3.62}$$

where k is the wave vector and the direction of propagation has been chosen in the x-direction. After eliminating the magnetic field components, one obtains for the equations determining the electric field components

$$-\left(\frac{\mathrm{d}^2}{\mathrm{d}z^2} + \varepsilon \frac{\omega^2}{c^2}\right) E_x + ik \frac{\mathrm{d}E_z}{\mathrm{d}z} = 0, \tag{3.63a}$$

$$-\left(\frac{\mathrm{d}^2}{\mathrm{d}z^2} - k^2 + \varepsilon \frac{\omega^2}{c^2}\right) E_y = 0, \tag{3.63b}$$

$$ik \frac{\mathrm{d}E_x}{\mathrm{d}z} + \left(k^2 - \varepsilon \frac{\omega^2}{c^2}\right) E_z = 0, \tag{3.63c}$$

where $\varepsilon = \varepsilon(\omega)$ for $z>0$ and $\varepsilon=1$ for $z<0$. Surface wave solutions corresponding to exponential decay of the field amplitude with increasing distance from the vacuum–medium interface are

$$\boldsymbol{E}(\boldsymbol{r}, t) = \left(E_1^{\mathrm{m}}, E_2^{\mathrm{m}}, \frac{ik}{\alpha} E_1^{\mathrm{m}}\right) \exp(-\alpha z + ikx - i\omega t), \quad z > 0, \tag{3.64a}$$

$$= \left(E_1^{\mathrm{v}}, E_2^{\mathrm{v}}, -\frac{ik}{\alpha_0} E_1^{\mathrm{v}}\right) \exp(\alpha_0 z + ikx - i\omega t), \quad z < 0, \tag{3.64b}$$

where E_i^{m} and E_i^{v} are arbitrary amplitudes ($i = 1,2$), and

$$\alpha^2 = k^2 - \varepsilon(\omega)\, \omega^2/c^2 > 0, \quad \alpha_0^2 = k^2 - \omega^2/c^2 > 0. \tag{3.65}$$

The magnetic field components are given by

$$H(r, t) = \frac{c}{i\omega}\left(\alpha E_2^m, \frac{\omega^2}{\alpha c^2}\varepsilon(\omega) E_1^m, ikE_2^m\right) \exp(-\alpha z + ikx - i\omega t), \qquad z > 0; \tag{3.66a}$$

$$= \frac{c}{i\omega}\left(\alpha_0 E_2^v, -\frac{\omega^2}{\alpha_0 c^2} E_1^v, ikE_2^v\right) \exp(\alpha_0 z + ikx - i\omega t), \qquad z < 0. \tag{3.66b}$$

We now consider the boundary conditions. The continuity of the tangential components of $\boldsymbol{E}$ at $z=0$ yields the relations

$$E_1^m = E_1^v, \quad E_2^m = E_2^v. \tag{3.67}$$

The continuity of the normal component of $\boldsymbol{D}$ yields

$$\varepsilon(\omega) = -\alpha/\alpha_0. \tag{3.68}$$

From the continuity of the tangential components of $\boldsymbol{H}$, we obtain, in addition to eq. (3.68), the relation

$$(\alpha_0 + \alpha) E_2^m = 0. \tag{3.69}$$

Since α_0 and α must be positive quantities, we see that $E_2^m = E_2^v = 0$; hence, the electric field of the surface excitation lies in the sagittal plane.

The dispersion relation for surface polaritons is given by eq. (3.68). Utilizing eqs. (3.65), we can re-express the dispersion relation in the form

$$c^2k^2/\omega^2 = \varepsilon(\omega)/[\varepsilon(\omega) + 1]. \tag{3.70}$$

This is to be compared with the corresponding relation for bulk polaritons $c^2k^2/\omega^2 = \varepsilon(\omega)$. If we make use of eq. (3.61), we can solve eq. (3.70) and obtain the following explicit dispersion relation for surface polaritons

$$\omega^2 = \frac{c^2}{2\varepsilon_\infty}\left\{(\varepsilon_\infty + 1)k^2 + \varepsilon_\infty \frac{\omega_L^2}{c^2} - \left|\left((\varepsilon_\infty + 1)k^2 + \varepsilon_\infty \frac{\omega_L^2}{c^2}\right)^2 - \frac{4\varepsilon_\infty}{c^2}(\varepsilon_\infty \omega_L^2 + \omega_T^2)k^2\right|^{1/2}\right\}. \tag{3.71}$$

The dispersion curve for InSb is plotted in fig. 8. The curve starts at the light line at $\omega = \omega_T$, rises monotonically, and approaches the value

$$\omega = \left(\frac{\varepsilon_\infty \omega_L^2 + \omega_T^2}{\varepsilon_\infty + 1}\right)^{1/2} \tag{3.72}$$

as $k \to \infty$. To the left of the light line, α_0 is imaginary and no surface polariton exists.

Surface optical phonons can be studied experimentally in various ways. The loss of energy by high energy ($\sim$50 keV) electrons upon transmission through a thin film has been used by Boersch et al. (1966) to verify the surface phonon frequency of LiF. Low-energy ($\sim$10 eV) electron loss upon reflection has been utilized by Ibach (1970) to determine the surface phonon frequency of the (1$\bar{1}$00) surface of ZnO.

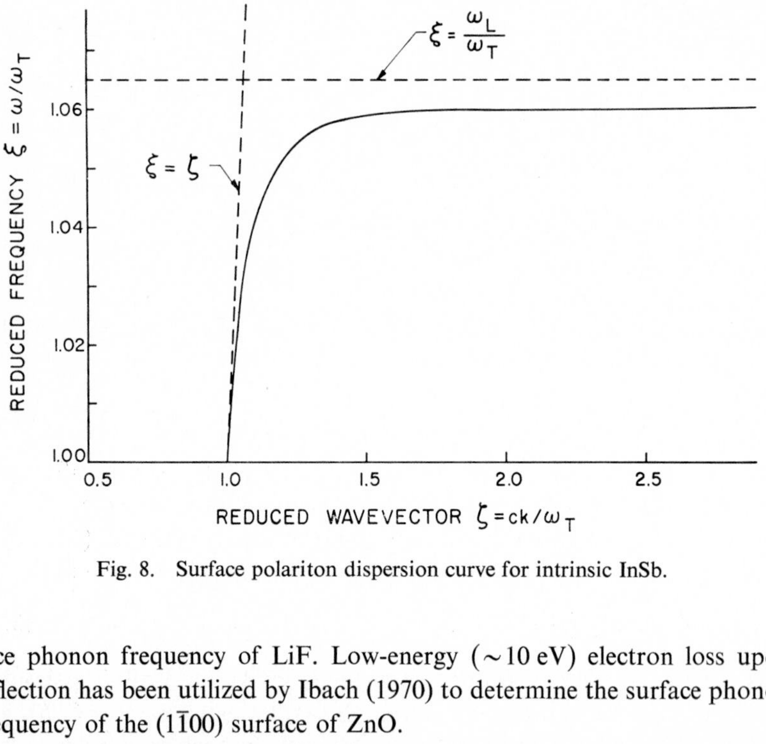

Fig. 8. Surface polariton dispersion curve for intrinsic InSb.

The electron energy loss technique gives the surface phonon frequency ω_s only for large values of the wave vector k, $k \gg \omega_s/c$. The full surface polariton dispersion curve can be determined by optical techniques such as attenuated total reflection (ATR) as developed by Otto (1968). This method has been employed, for example, by Marschall and Fischer (1972) to study GaP and by Bryksin et al. (1972) to study NaCl and CaF_2. Another optical means of studying surface polaritons is by Raman scattering (Evans et al. 1973).

The question of developing a unified treatment of both the microscopic and macroscopic surface optical modes of an ionic crystal has received attention from a number of workers. Tong and Maradudin (1969) considered a slab of NaCl with (100) surfaces 15 atomic layers thick and calculated the normal mode frequencies numerically. Their results were extended by Jones and Fuchs (1971) and Chen et al. (1971a). Both the microscopic and macroscopic surface modes are found. The macroscopic modes may appear as true surface modes or as pseudosurface modes where they have become hybridized with bulk modes.

4. *Surface specific heat*

Within the harmonic approximation, the mean vibrational energy of a crystal can be expressed in the form

$$\langle E\rangle = \sum_s \bar{\varepsilon}(\omega_s), \tag{4.1}$$

where ω_s is the frequency of the sth normal mode of vibration and the mean energy of a normal mode $\bar{\varepsilon}(\omega_s)$ is given by

$$\bar{\varepsilon}(\omega_s) = \hbar\omega_s [n(\omega_s) + \tfrac{1}{2}] \tag{4.2}$$

and

$$n(\omega_s) = [\exp(\hbar\omega_s/k_B T) - 1]^{-1}. \tag{4.3}$$

The specific heat is related to $\langle E\rangle$ by

$$C_V = \frac{\partial\langle E\rangle}{\partial T} = k_B \sum_s \left(\frac{\hbar\omega_s}{2k_B T}\right)^2 \operatorname{csch}^2\left(\frac{\hbar\omega_s}{2k_B T}\right). \tag{4.5}$$

One way of evaluating the surface specific heat is to calculate the normal mode frequencies ω_s for both the periodic crystal and the crystal with free surfaces and then substitute the results in eq. (4.5). An alternative procedure is to use the continuum approximation and write the mean vibrational energy as

$$\langle E\rangle = \int_0^{\omega_m} g(\omega)\,\bar{\varepsilon}(\omega)\,d\omega, \tag{4.6}$$

where $g(\omega)d\omega$ is the number of normal mode frequencies in the range ω to $\omega+d\omega$. The basic problem is then to calculate the change in the frequency distribution produced by the surface. We shall present a discussion of the continuum theory of the surface specific heat for an isotropic medium based upon the work of Stratton (1953, 1962).

The enumeration of the normal modes is facilitated if we treat a slab of material bounded by parallel planes of area $4L_xL_y$ and separated by a distance $2L_z$. The normal modes for the isotropic elastic slab may be classified as either symmetric or antisymmetric with respect to reflection in the mid-plane of the slab. A further classification can be made in terms of the values of the decay constants q_1, q_2 of subsection 2.1. For q_1, q_2 both real, one has Rayleigh waves; for q_1 real and q_2 imaginary, one has mixed waves; for q_1, q_2 both imaginary, one has pure bulk waves with a longitudinal component. In addition to these types of modes, there are pure transverse bulk waves.

The wave-vector magnitude k, the constants q_1, q_2 and the frequency $\omega = kc$ are related by equations which follow from eq. (2.4), namely,

$$1 = [(1 + 2K)\, q_1^2 - Kq_2^2]/(1 + K), \tag{4.7}$$

$$\omega^2 = k^2 c_t^2 \,(q_1^2 - q_2^2)\,(1 + 2K)/(1 + K), \tag{4.8}$$

where $K = \mu/\lambda$, $c_t = (\rho/\mu)^{1/2}$ is the speed of transverse bulk waves, and λ, μ are the Lamé constants. The wave-vector components $k_x = kl$ and $k_y = km$ are specified by cyclic boundary conditions

$$k_x = n_x\pi/L_x, \quad n_x = 0, \pm 1, \pm 2, \cdots; \tag{4.9}$$

$$k_y = n_y\pi/L_y, \quad n_y = 0, \pm 1, \pm 2, \cdots. \tag{4.10}$$

The specification of the Rayleigh waves is completed by the boundary conditions at $z = \pm L_z$ which can be expressed in the form

$$\frac{\tanh kq_2L_z}{\tanh kq_1L_z} = \left[\frac{4\,(1 + K)\,(1 + 2K - \alpha^2 K)\,\alpha}{(1 + 2K + \alpha^2)^2}\right]^{\pm 1} \equiv -\,[g_K(\alpha)]^{\pm 1}, \tag{4.11}$$

where $\alpha = q_2/q_1$ and the exponents $+1$, -1 refer to the symmetric and antisymmetric modes, respectively. We now need to calculate the number of Rayleigh modes with frequencies less than or equal to ω. From eqs. (4.9) and (4.10), we see that the number of modes of a given type (symmetric or antisymmetric) is

$$\begin{aligned} G_R(\omega) &= \Delta n_x\, \Delta n_y \\ &= \frac{L_xL_y}{\pi^2}\,\Delta k_x\, \Delta k_y = \frac{L_xL_y}{\pi}\,\Delta(k^2) = \frac{L_xL_y}{\pi}\,[k^2(\omega) - k_{\min}^2]. \end{aligned} \tag{4.12}$$

For ω not too small, we can take α to be the solution, α_0, of the limiting form of eq. (4.11) as $q_1 \to \infty$, namely,

$$g_K(\alpha) + 1 = 0 \tag{4.13}$$

for both the symmetric and antisymmetric solutions. From eqs. (4.7) and (4.8), we obtain

$$k^2(\omega) = (\omega^2/c_t^2)\, Y_0^2\,, \tag{4.14}$$

where

$$Y_0^2 = \frac{1 + 2K - K\alpha_0^2}{(1 - \alpha_0^2)(1 + 2K)}\,. \tag{4.15}$$

The value of $k_{\min}^2$ is negligible for slabs which are not too thin. The result for $G_R(\omega)$ is then

$$G_R(\omega) = \frac{V\omega^2}{4\pi L_z c_t^2}\, Y_0^2\,, \tag{4.16}$$

where V is the volume of the crystal.

The mixed modes have one decay constant replaced by a pure imaginary constant $q_2' = iq_2$. For large k, the solution of eq. (4.11) can be written as

$$q_2' = (\pi n_z/2L_z) + \delta_M\,, \tag{4.17}$$

where $\delta_M = \tan^{-1}[-ig_K(\alpha)]$, $n_z = 0, 2, 4, 6, \ldots$ for the symmetric modes, and $n_z = 1, 3, 5, 7, \ldots$ for the antisymmetric modes. The number of mixed modes $G_M(\omega)$ can be calculated and is found to be

$$G_M(\omega) = \frac{V}{\pi^2}\left[\frac{\omega^3}{6c_t^3}\left(\frac{1 + K}{1 + 2K}\right)^{1/2} - \frac{\pi\omega^2}{L_z c_t^2}\left(\tfrac{1}{16} + \tfrac{1}{4}I\right)\right], \tag{4.18}$$

where

$$I = \frac{1}{\pi}\int_0^{\pi/2}\left(1 + \frac{K}{1 + 2K}\tan^2\varphi\right)\delta_M'(\tan\varphi)\,\mathrm{d}\varphi\,, \tag{4.19}$$

$\tan\varphi = \alpha' = i\alpha$, and $\delta_M'(\tan\varphi) = \partial\delta_M/\partial\alpha'$. The integral I can be evaluated by contour integration yielding the result

$$I = \frac{1 + K}{1 + 2K}\left(\frac{(1 + 2K)^2}{(1 + \alpha_0)\left[(1 + 2K)^2 + \alpha_0\right]} - \frac{1}{4}\right). \tag{4.20}$$

The bulk modes have both decay constants replaced by imaginary quantities, $q_1' = iq_1$ and $q_2' = iq_2$. For large k, the solution of eq. (4.11) can be written in the form

$$q_2' = (\pi n_z/L_z) - \delta_B, \tag{4.21}$$

where $\delta_B = \tan^{-1}[g_K(\alpha)\tan(kq_1'L_z)]$ and n_z is a non-negative integer. For the number of bulk modes $G_B(\omega)$, we obtain

$$G_B(\omega) = \frac{V}{\pi^2}\left\{\frac{\omega^3}{6c_t^3}\left[\left(\frac{K}{1+2K}\right)^{3/2} - \left(\frac{1+K}{1+2K}\right)^{1/2} + 1\right] - \frac{\pi\omega^2}{16L_z c_t^2}\left(\frac{K}{1+2K}\right)\right\}. \tag{4.22}$$

Finally, the values of q_2' for the pure transverse bulk waves are given by

$$q_2' = \pi n_z/2L_z, \qquad n = 0, 1, 2, 3, \ldots. \tag{4.23}$$

The number of transverse modes with frequencies less than or equal to ω is specified by

$$G_T(\omega) = \frac{V}{\pi^2}\left(\frac{\omega^3}{6c_t^3} + \frac{\pi\omega^2}{16L_z c_t^2}\right). \tag{4.24}$$

The total number of modes with frequencies less than or equal to ω is

$$G(\omega) = G_R(\omega) + G_M(\omega) + G_B(\omega) + G_T(\omega). \tag{4.25}$$

The part of $G(\omega)$ involving ω^3 gives the bulk contribution to the specific heat; the part involving ω^2 gives the surface contribution. The total number of modes is $3N$ for a crystal consisting of N atoms. If ω_m is the maximum frequency of the crystal, then we have

$$3N = G(\omega_m). \tag{4.26}$$

Utilizing the above expressions for the contributions to $G(\omega)$, we obtain from eq. (4.26) an expression for ω_m,

$$\omega_m = \omega_{mB} + \Delta\omega_{mS}, \tag{4.27}$$

where ω_{mB} is the maximum frequency of the bulk crystal given by

$$\frac{c_t[18\pi^2 N/V]^{1/3}}{\{2 + [K/(1+2K)]^{3/2}\}^{1/3}}$$

and $\Delta\omega_{\mathrm{mS}}$ is the change in ω_{m} produced by the surface,

$$\Delta\omega_{\mathrm{mS}} = -\frac{\pi\{Y_0^2 - I - [K/4(1+2K)]\}}{2(18\pi^2)^{1/3}\{2+[K/(1+2K)]^{3/2}\}^{2/3}}\frac{A\omega_{\mathrm{mB}}}{n^{1/3}V}, \tag{4.28}$$

where A is the area of the crystal and $n = N/V$.

The differential frequency distribution $g(\omega)$ is specified by $g(\omega) = \mathrm{d}G(\omega)/\mathrm{d}\omega$. The internal energy, neglecting the zero-point contribution, can be written as

$$\langle E\rangle = \int_0^{\omega_{\mathrm{m}}} \frac{\mathrm{d}G}{\mathrm{d}\omega}\frac{\hbar\omega}{\exp(\hbar\omega/k_{\mathrm{B}}T) - 1}\,\mathrm{d}\omega\,. \tag{4.29}$$

From eq. (4.4), the specific heat then takes the form

$$C_v = k_{\mathrm{B}}\int_0^{\omega_{\mathrm{m}}} \frac{\mathrm{d}G}{\mathrm{d}\omega}\left(\frac{\hbar\omega}{k_{\mathrm{B}}T}\right)^2 \frac{\exp(\hbar\omega/k_{\mathrm{B}}T)}{[\exp(\hbar\omega/k_{\mathrm{B}}T) - 1]^2}\,\mathrm{d}\omega\,. \tag{4.30}$$

Breaking up both ω_{m} and $\mathrm{d}G/\mathrm{d}\omega$ into their bulk and surface parts, we can write the surface contribution to the specific heat, $C_{v\mathrm{S}}$, as

$$C_{v\mathrm{S}} = kAF(K)\,n^{2/3}[D(x) - E(x)], \tag{4.31}$$

where

$$F(K) = \tfrac{3}{2}(\tfrac{3}{4}\pi)^{1/3}\frac{Y_0^2 - I - [K/(1+2K)]}{\{2+[K/(1+2K)]^{3/2}\}^{2/3}}, \tag{4.32}$$

$$D(x) = \frac{2}{x^2}\int_0^x \frac{u^3 \mathrm{e}^u}{(\mathrm{e}^u - 1)^2}\,\mathrm{d}u\,, \tag{4.33}$$

$$E(x) = \frac{x^2 \mathrm{e}^x}{(\mathrm{e}^x - 1)^2}, \tag{4.34}$$

and $x = \hbar\omega_{\mathrm{mB}}/kT$.

In the low-temperature limit, one finds with the aid of the explicit expressions for Y_0 and I given by eqs. (4.15) and (4.20) that

$$C_{v\mathrm{S}} = 3\pi\zeta(3)\frac{k^3}{h^2}\frac{2c_{\mathrm{t}}^4 - 3c_{\mathrm{t}}^2 c_\ell^2 + 3c_\ell^4}{c_{\mathrm{t}}^2 c_\ell^2 (c_\ell^2 - c_{\mathrm{t}}^2)}AT^2\,, \tag{4.35}$$

where c_ℓ is the speed of longitudinal bulk waves specified by $c_\ell^2 = (\lambda + 2\mu)/\rho$ and $\zeta(3)$ is the Riemann zeta function of argument 3. Eq. (4.35) was first obtained by Dupuis et al. (1960) using a contour integral representation for C_v. A comparable result was obtained by Maradudin and Wallis (1966) using a lattice dynamical approach based on Green's functions.

The surface specific heat is proportional to the surface area and to the square of the absolute temperature at low temperatures. For fine powders at sufficiently low temperatures, the surface specific heat can become comparable to the bulk T^3 contribution. A recent experimental observation of the surface T^2 term is that of Barkman et al. (1965) for NaCl powder. Their results are in rather good agreement with numerical calculations by Chen et al. (1971b) using a high-speed computer and based on eq. (4.5).

At high temperatures, the surface specific heat approaches zero, since the specific heat has the value k_B per normal mode, independent of the presence of a free surface. Consequently, the surface specific heat must pass through a maximum. This is revealed quite clearly by calculations based on a simple model by Dobrzynski and Leman (1969) and illustrated in fig. 9.

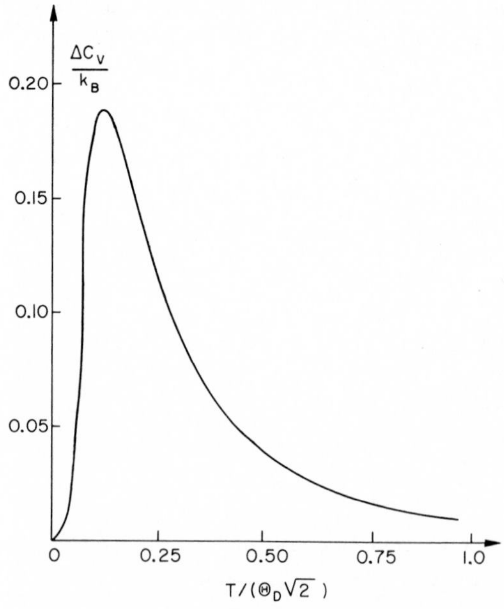

Fig. 9. Surface specific heat as a function of temperature for the (100) surface of a simple cubic lattice (after Dobrzynski and Leman 1969).

5. Surface wave attenuation

Various mechanisms can contribute to the damping of surface waves; for example, the anharmonic interaction between phonons, the interaction of the surface phonon with impurities and imperfections in the crystal, and the interaction of surface phonons with conduction electrons in metals or semiconductors.

Since long-wavelength surface waves penetrate deeply into the crystal, it may be expected that the damping constant for such surface waves can be related to the damping constants for bulk waves. Press and Healy (1957) have considered the isotropic continuum case where the Rayleigh wave velocity c_R is specified by eq. (2.11) or by the equivalent form

$$\left(2-\frac{c_R^2}{c_t^2}\right)^4 - 16\left(1-\frac{c_R^2}{c_\ell^2}\right)\left(1-\frac{c_R^2}{c_t^2}\right)=0, \tag{5.1}$$

where c_ℓ and c_t are the velocities of longitudinal and transverse bulk waves, respectively. Dissipation can be incorporated by letting each velocity become a complex quantity:

$$\begin{aligned} c_\ell \to v_\ell &= c_\ell(1+\mathrm{i}\delta_\ell)^{1/2}, \\ c_t \to v_t &= c_t(1+\mathrm{i}\delta_t)^{1/2}, \\ c_R \to v_R &= c_R(1+\mathrm{i}\delta_R)^{1/2}. \end{aligned} \tag{5.2}$$

If one takes the total differential of eq. (5.1) and solves for the increment δ_R in terms of δ_t and δ_ℓ, one obtains

$$\delta_R = \frac{\left[4\left(1-\frac{c_R^2}{c_\ell^2}\right)-\left(2-\frac{c_R^2}{c_t^2}\right)^3\right]\delta_t + \left[4\left(1-\frac{c_R^2}{c_t^2}\right)\frac{c_t^2}{c_\ell^2}\right]\delta_\ell}{4\left(1-\frac{c_R^2}{c_t^2}\right)\frac{c_t^2}{c_\ell^2}+4\left(1-\frac{c_R^2}{c_\ell^2}\right)-\left(2-\frac{c_R^2}{c_t^2}\right)^3}. \tag{5.3}$$

The damping constant is proportional to the imaginary part of the wave vector which is given by

$$k=\frac{\omega}{v}=\frac{\omega}{c}-\mathrm{i}\alpha. \tag{5.4}$$

Using eqs. (5.2), we obtain for α

$$\alpha=\tfrac{1}{2}\omega\delta/c. \tag{5.5}$$

The damping constant for the Rayleigh waves α_R can now be written in terms of the damping constants α_ℓ and α_t for longitudinal and transverse bulk waves, respectively, as

$$\alpha_R = \frac{\left[4\left(1-\frac{c_R^2}{c_\ell^2}\right)-\left(2-\frac{c_R^2}{c_t^2}\right)^3\right]\frac{c_t}{c_R}\alpha_t + \left[4\left(1-\frac{c_R^2}{c_t^2}\right)\frac{c_t^2}{c_\ell^2}\right]\frac{c_\ell}{c_R}\alpha_\ell}{4\left(1-\frac{c_R^2}{c_t^2}\right)\frac{c_t^2}{c_\ell^2}+4\left(1-\frac{c_R^2}{c_\ell^2}\right)-\left(2-\frac{c_R^2}{c_t^2}\right)^3}. \tag{5.6}$$

The theoretical prediction contained in eq. (5.6) has been found to be in good agreement with experimental data (Press and Healy 1957).

A specific expression for the surface wave attenuation constant in the high-temperature region can be obtained from the Rayleigh dissipation function Ψ given by

$$\Psi = \tfrac{1}{2}\sum_{ijkl} \eta_{ijkl}\dot{e}_{ij}\dot{e}_{kl}, \tag{5.7}$$

where η_{ijkl} is the viscosity tensor and e_{ij} is an element of the strain tensor

$$e_{ij} = \tfrac{1}{2}\left(\frac{\partial u_i}{\partial x_j}+\frac{\partial u_j}{\partial x_i}\right). \tag{5.8}$$

The attenuation constants for bulk waves in an isotropic solid have been calculated by Landau and Lifschitz (1970). An analogous calculation for surface waves in an anisotropic solid has been carried out by King and Sheard (1969). If one rewrites eq. (2.7) in the form

$$\boldsymbol{u} = \sum_{J=1}^{3} \boldsymbol{B}_J K_J \exp\left[\mathrm{i}(\boldsymbol{k}_J\cdot\boldsymbol{r}-\omega t)\right], \tag{5.9}$$

where $\boldsymbol{B}_J$ and $\boldsymbol{k}_J$ have cartesian components whose analogues in eq. (2.7) are ξ_j, η_j, $-\mathrm{i}\zeta_j$ and kl, km, and $\mathrm{i}kq_j$, respectively, one can express the attenuation constant γ in the form

$$\gamma = 8.7\eta_{\text{eff}}\omega^2/2\rho c_S^2, \tag{5.10}$$

where

$$\boldsymbol{k}_J\cdot\boldsymbol{r} = k_s(\alpha_1 x_1+\alpha_2 x_2+\alpha_3^J x_3) \equiv k_s\sum_i \alpha_i^J x_i, \quad \alpha_3^J = \mathrm{i}q_J,$$

c_S is the surface wave speed, and

$$\eta_{\text{eff}} = \frac{\sum_{ijklJJ'} \eta_{ijkl}K_{J'}B_{iJ'}\alpha_j^{J'}K_J^*B_{kJ}^*\alpha_l^J/(q_{J'}+q_J^*)}{\sum_{iJJ'} K_{J'}B_{iJ'}K_J^*B_{iJ}^*/(q_{J'}+q_J^*)}. \tag{5.11}$$

We see from eq. (5.10) that the attenuation constant has no explicit dependence on temperature and that it varies as the square of the frequency ω.

Several treatments of surface wave attenuation have appeared for the low-temperature region. Maradudin and Mills (1968) carried out a lattice dynamical calculation for a simple model using a Green's function method and found that the attenuation constant has the form

$$\gamma \sim \omega T^4, \tag{5.12}$$

similar to the result of Landau and Rumer (1937) for transverse bulk waves. King and Sheard (1970) treated a general anisotropic solid in the continuum approximation and obtained a result corresponding to eq. (5.12). We shall present the essence of King and Sheard's method.

The calculations can be simplified with the aid of several approximations. The effect of the free surface will be taken into account for the surface modes but will be ignored for the bulk modes. Even at liquid helium temperatures, the wavelength of typical thermal phonons is much less than that of the ultrasonic surface phonon. Consequently, thermal surface phonons are much more localized near the surface than the ultrasonic surface phonon, and the principal scattering of the latter is by bulk phonons. In particular, the dominant process is

$$\Sigma + \mathrm{T} \to \mathrm{T},$$

where Σ stands for the ultrasonic surface phonon and T stands for a thermal transverse bulk phonon.

The displacement vector $\boldsymbol{u}$ which satisfies the boundary conditions may be written in the form given by eq. (5.9). Since the attenuation constant is calculated quantum mechanically using perturbation theory, it is convenient to quantize the displacement field due to surface modes by writing

$$\boldsymbol{u} = \sum_J \sum_{\boldsymbol{k}} \left(\frac{\hbar}{2\rho S c_S \Xi} \right)^{1/2} [\boldsymbol{B}_J K_J b_{\boldsymbol{k}s} \exp(\mathrm{i}\boldsymbol{k}_J \cdot \boldsymbol{r}) + \boldsymbol{B}_J^* K_J^* b_{\boldsymbol{k}s}^+ \exp(-\mathrm{i}\boldsymbol{k}_J \cdot \boldsymbol{r})], \tag{5.13}$$

where $b_{\boldsymbol{k}s}$ and $b_{\boldsymbol{k}s}^+$ are the annihilation and creation operators for the mode $\boldsymbol{k}_s$, $k_S = (k_S\alpha_1, k_S\alpha_2, 0)$, S is the surface area, and Ξ is a normalization constant that can be calculated from the kinetic energy (half the total energy) and is given by

$$\Xi = \sum_{J, J', i} B_{iJ}^* B_{iJ'} K_J^* K_{J'} / (q_J^* + q_{J'}). \tag{5.14}$$

The corresponding quantization condition for bulk modes of wave vector $\boldsymbol{k}$ and polarization p can be written as (neglecting the effect of the free surface)

$$\boldsymbol{u} = \sum_{\boldsymbol{k},p} \left(\frac{\hbar}{2\rho V \omega_{\boldsymbol{k}p}}\right)^{1/2} \boldsymbol{e}_{\boldsymbol{k}p} \left[a_{\boldsymbol{k}p} \exp(\mathrm{i}\boldsymbol{k}\cdot\boldsymbol{r}) + a_{\boldsymbol{k}p}^{+} \exp(-\mathrm{i}\boldsymbol{k}\cdot\boldsymbol{r})\right], \tag{5.15}$$

where $\boldsymbol{e}_{\boldsymbol{k}p}$ is the polarization vector and $a_{\boldsymbol{k}p}$, $a_{\boldsymbol{k}p}^{+}$ are the annihilation and creation operators.

The cubic anharmonic interaction in the continuum approximation is expressable as

$$H_3 = \frac{1}{3!} \int \sum_{ijklmn} A_{ijklmn} \frac{\partial u_i}{\partial x_j} \frac{\partial u_k}{\partial x_l} \frac{\partial u_m}{\partial x_n} \,\mathrm{d}\boldsymbol{r}, \tag{5.16}$$

where the coefficients A_{ijklmn} are related to the second and third order elastic constants. Considering only interactions between a surface phonon and a bulk phonon to produce another bulk phonon,

$$\boldsymbol{k}_{\mathrm{S}} + (\boldsymbol{k}_1, p_1) \rightleftharpoons (\boldsymbol{k}_2, p_2),$$

one obtains for the matrix element of H_3 for this process

$$M(k_{\mathrm{S}}, \boldsymbol{k}_1 p_1, \boldsymbol{k}_2 p_2) = S\left(\frac{\hbar}{2\rho V}\right)\left(\frac{\hbar}{2\rho S c_{\mathrm{S}} \Xi}\right)^{1/2} k_{\mathrm{S}} \left(\frac{k_1 k_2}{c_1 c_2}\right)^{1/2}$$
$$\times\, \delta(k_{\mathrm{S}x} + k_{1x}, k_{2x})\, \delta(k_{\mathrm{S}y} + k_{1y}, k_{2y}) \left[n_{\mathrm{S}} n_1 (n_2 + 1)\right]^{1/2}$$
$$\times \sum_J \frac{F_J}{\mathrm{i} k_{\mathrm{S}} q_J + k_{1z} - k_{2z}}. \tag{5.17}$$

where c_1, c_2 are the bulk mode velocities, n_{S}, n_1, and n_2 are the mode occupation numbers, and

$$F_J = (1/3!) \sum_{ijklmn} \sum_P A_{ijklmn} B_{iJ} K_J \alpha_j^J e_{1k} \hat{k}_{1l} e_{2m} \hat{k}_{2n}. \tag{5.18}$$

Here, P denotes the six permutations of the pairs (ij), (kl), (mn), and $\hat{\boldsymbol{k}}_1$ and $\hat{\boldsymbol{k}}_2$ are unit vectors in the directions of $\boldsymbol{k}_1$ and $\boldsymbol{k}_2$. Using perturbation theory, the transition rate and the relaxation time τ_{S} for surface phonons can be calculated. The result can be written as

$$\frac{1}{\tau_{\mathrm{S}}} = \sum_{p_1 p_2} \iint \frac{\hbar k_{\mathrm{S}}^2 k_1 k_2}{64\pi^3 \rho^3 c_{\mathrm{S}} \Xi c_1 c_2} (\bar{n}_1 - \bar{n}_2)$$
$$\times \left| \sum_J \frac{F_J}{\mathrm{i} k_{\mathrm{S}} q_J + k_{1z} - k_{2z}} \right|^2 \delta(\omega_{\mathrm{S}} + \omega_1 - \omega_2)\, \mathrm{d}\boldsymbol{k}_1\, \mathrm{d}k_{2z}, \tag{5.19}$$

where $\bar{n}_1$ and $\bar{n}_2$ are the mean occupation numbers of the bulk phonons, and ω_S, ω_1, ω_2 are the frequencies of surface and bulk phonons, respectively. It should be noted that the dominant processes attenuating surface waves are energy conserving so no relaxation time for the thermal bulk phonons appears in eq. (5.19).

The integrals in eq. (5.19) may be simplified if we introduce the new variable $\boldsymbol{K}=\boldsymbol{k}_2-\boldsymbol{k}_1$ and use polar coordinates k_1, θ, φ for $\boldsymbol{k}_1$ with $\boldsymbol{K}$ as axis. Only small $\boldsymbol{K}$ are important, so both bulk phonons may be taken in the same branch, $k_1k_2 \approx k_1^2$, $v_1v_1^2 \approx v^2$. Evaluating the integral over k_1 in eq. (5.19) we get

$$\frac{1}{\tau_S} = \frac{\hbar\omega_S}{64\pi^3\rho^3c_S^3\Xi}\left(\frac{kT}{\hbar}\right)^4 \times \sum_{p_1}\int D_4 \frac{1}{c_1^7}\left|\sum_J \frac{F_J}{\mathrm{i}q_J-\lambda}\right|^2 \delta(\Delta)\sin\theta\,\mathrm{d}\theta\,\mathrm{d}\varphi\,\mathrm{d}\lambda\,, \tag{5.20}$$

where

$$\Delta = 1 - \frac{c_1K}{c_Sk_S}\cos\theta + \frac{K}{c_Sk_S}\sin\theta\,\frac{\partial c_1}{\partial\theta}, \qquad D_4 = \int_0^{x_m}\frac{x^4\mathrm{e}^x}{(\mathrm{e}^x-1)^2}\,\mathrm{d}x\,, \tag{5.21, 22}$$

$x_m=\hbar c_1k_1/k_BT$, and $\lambda=K_z/k_S$. In the low-temperature limit, $D_4=4\pi^4/15$, so we obtain

$$1/\tau_S \propto \omega_S T^4 \tag{5.23}$$

which is equivalent to eq. (5.12). The evaluation of the remaining integrals in eq. (5.20) is difficult and will not be considered here.

The frequency and temperature dependences indicated by eqs. (5.12) and (5.23) have been verified experimentally for quartz by Salzmann et al. (1968). The ω^2 dependence in the high-temperature region as specified by eq. (5.10) has been verified for quartz by Budreau and Carr (1971).

Besides anharmonicity, surface waves can be damped through their interaction with impurities and other imperfections. Steg and Klemens (1970) have calculated the surface wave attenuation constant for impurity scattering using the isotropic continuum model and obtained an ω^5 dependence but no explicit temperature dependence.

6. *Mean square displacements and velocities of surface atoms*

Low-energy electron diffraction (LEED) from a crystal provides a means of gaining information about the mean square displacements of surface atoms. The thermal vibrations of the atoms cause the peak intensity of a diffraction spot to decrease as the temperature increases. The decrease in intensity is described in the kinematic approximation by the Debye–Waller factor $\exp[-2M(l\kappa)]$ where

$$M(\boldsymbol{l}\kappa) = \tfrac{1}{2}\langle[\boldsymbol{Q}\cdot\boldsymbol{u}(l\kappa)]^2\rangle, \tag{6.1}$$

$\boldsymbol{u}(l\kappa)$ is the displacement of atom $l\kappa$, $\boldsymbol{Q}=\boldsymbol{K}'-\boldsymbol{K}$, and $\boldsymbol{K}$ and $\boldsymbol{K}'$ are the wave vectors of the incident and scattered electron. Sufficiently low energy electrons ($\sim$10–50 eV) are scattered primarily from the surface atoms; consequently, measurements of the Debye–Waller factor for such electrons can give experimental information about surface atom mean square displacements.

The kinematic approximation just mentioned corresponds to single scattering processes. Since very low energy electrons are strongly scattered by the crystal, one must consider the effects of multiple scattering. This has been done by Duke and Laramore (1970) who show that lattice vibrations enter the theory in the form of a Debye–Waller type factor multiplying the electron–ion core scattering amplitude. The extraction of the mean square displacements of surface atoms from LEED data is a complicated problem when multiple scattering is significant. An attempt to gain some insight into this problem has been initiated by Jepsen et al. (1973) who calculated the LEED spectrum for the (111) surface of silver from dynamical theory and compared the results to those of kinematic theory. They found that for electron energies in the 40–50 eV range, the surface mean square displacements are deduced reasonably well from kinematic theory, but for energies above and below this range, significant deviations appear.

We turn now to the actual calculation of mean square displacements at a surface. Qualitatively, we can visualize several effects arising from a free surface. The mean square displacements of atoms are determined by the interatomic forces acting upon them. A surface atom is acted upon by fewer neighbors than an interior atom, so this will generally cause the mean square displacement to be larger for the surface atom. Furthermore, the interatomic coupling constants may have different values at the surface than in the bulk. The environment of a surface atom has symmetry different from that of an interior atom, and this may lead to an anisotropy of the mean square displacements at the surface even in cubic crystals.

In discussing mean square displacements, one finds it convenient to introduce an effective Debye temperature Θ which is defined by

$$\langle u^2 \rangle = (3\hbar^2 T / m k_B \Theta^2)\, \Phi(\Theta/T), \tag{6.2}$$

where

$$\Phi(x) = \tfrac{1}{4}x + \frac{1}{x}\int_0^x \frac{u\,du}{e^u - 1}. \tag{6.3}$$

For $T \gg \Theta$, $\Phi(\Theta/T) \to 1$, and $\langle u^2 \rangle$ becomes proportional to the temperature T.

To calculate the mean square displacements, we assume that the displacement components satisfy harmonic equations of motion as given by eq. (3.41). Making the transformation $v_\alpha(l\kappa) = M_\kappa^{1/2} u_\alpha(l\kappa)$, we find that

$$\ddot{v}_\alpha(l\kappa) = -\sum_{l'\kappa'\beta} D_{\alpha\beta}(l\kappa; l'\kappa')\, v_\beta(l'\kappa'), \tag{6.4}$$

where the quantities $D_{\alpha\beta}(l\kappa; l'\kappa')$ are the elements of the dynamical matrix defined by

$$D_{\alpha\beta}(l\kappa; l'\kappa') = (M_\kappa M_{\kappa'})^{-1/2}\, \Phi_{\alpha\beta}(l\kappa; l'\kappa').$$

The presence of the free surface is manifested in the values of appropriate elements of either the coupling-constant matrix or the dynamical matrix.

The dynamical matrix can be diagonalized with the aid of the normal coordinate transformation

$$v_\alpha(l\kappa) = \sum_p e_{p\alpha}(l\kappa)\, Q_p, \tag{6.5}$$

where $e_{p\alpha}(l\kappa)$ is the $l\kappa\alpha$th component of the eigenvector of the dynamical matrix for the pth normal mode and Q_p is the normal coordinate for that mode. Then we obtain

$$\langle u_\alpha^2(l\kappa) \rangle = (1/M_\kappa) \sum_p |e_{p\alpha}(l\kappa)|^2 \langle |Q_p|^2 \rangle, \tag{6.6}$$

where we have used the fact that

$$\langle Q_p^* Q_{p'} \rangle = \langle |Q_p|^2 \rangle\, \delta_{pp'}. \tag{6.7}$$

Now from statistical mechanics

$$\langle |Q_p|^2 \rangle = \bar{\varepsilon}(\omega_p)/\omega_p^2\,, \tag{6.8}$$

where ω_p is the frequency of normal mode p and $\bar{\varepsilon}(\omega_p)$ is the mean energy of the mode given by

$$\bar{\varepsilon}(\omega_p) = \tfrac{1}{2}\hbar\omega_p \coth(\hbar\omega_p/2k_B T)\,. \tag{6.9}$$

The mean square displacement component now takes the form

$$\langle u_\alpha^2(l\kappa)\rangle = (1/M_\kappa)\sum_p |e_{p\alpha}(l\kappa)|^2\,\bar{\varepsilon}(\omega_p)/\omega_p^2\,. \tag{6.10}$$

Alternatively, using a well-known theorem of matrices (Born 1942)

$$\sum_p f(\omega_p^2)\, e_{p\alpha}(l\kappa)\, e_{p\beta}(l'\kappa') = [f(D)]_{l\kappa\alpha,\, l'\kappa'\beta}\,, \tag{6.11}$$

and eq. (6.9), we can rewrite eq. (6.10) directly in terms of the dynamical matrix

$$\langle u_\alpha^2(l\kappa)\rangle = (\hbar/2M_\kappa)\,[D^{-1/2}\coth(\hbar D^{1/2}/2k_B T)]_{l\kappa\alpha,\, l\kappa\alpha}\,. \tag{6.12}$$

At high and low temperatures, we find the limiting results

$$\langle u_\alpha^2(l\kappa)\rangle \approx (k_B T/M_\kappa)\,[D^{-1}]_{l\kappa\alpha,\, l\kappa\alpha}\,, \qquad T > \Theta_D\,, \tag{6.13a}$$

$$\langle u_\alpha^2(l\kappa)\rangle \approx (\hbar/2M_\kappa)\,[D^{-1/2}]_{l\kappa\alpha,\, l\kappa\alpha}\,, \qquad T = 0\,\mathrm{K}\,. \tag{6.13b}$$

For a monoatomic crystal, the mean square displacement is independent of the atomic mass and is proportional to the temperature at high temperatures. It varies as $M^{-1/2}$ and acquires its zero point value as $T \to 0$.

In the simplest approximation, one ignores the off-diagonal terms of D and simply takes the appropriate function of the diagonal element of D in eqs. (6.12) and (6.13). This approximation shows that the mean square displacement of a surface atom will generally be larger than that of a bulk atom unless the surface coupling constants are exceptionally large. Correction terms can be obtained by expanding out eqs. (6.12) and (6.13) in powers of the off-diagonal part of D (Masri and Dobrzynski 1972).

In actual calculations, it is convenient to introduce periodic boundary conditions in the two directions parallel to the surface and an associated two-dimensional wave vector $\boldsymbol{q} = (q_1, q_2)$. The eigenvectors then take the form

$$e_{p\alpha}(l\kappa) = (1/\sqrt{N_S})\exp[\mathrm{i}(q_1 l_1 + q_2 l_2)]\, e_{j\alpha}(l_3\kappa;\, q_1 q_2)\,, \tag{6.14}$$

were N_S is the number of unit cells in a surface layer and j identifies the normal modes for given q_1, q_2. A reduced dynamical matrix can be introduced whose elements are given by

$$[D(q_1 q_2)]_{l_3\kappa\alpha,\, l_3'\kappa'\beta} = \sum_{l_1, l_2} D_{\alpha\beta}(l\kappa; l'\kappa') \exp\{\mathrm{i}[q_1(l_1' - l_1) + q_2(l_2' - l_2)]\}. \tag{6.15}$$

Alternative expressions for $\langle u_\alpha^2(l\kappa)\rangle$ can now be written as

$$\langle u_\alpha^2(l\kappa)\rangle = (1/M_\kappa N_S) \sum_{\boldsymbol{q}} \sum_{j} |e_{j\alpha}(l_3\kappa; \boldsymbol{q})|^2 \,\bar{\varepsilon}[\omega(\boldsymbol{q}j)]/\omega^2(\boldsymbol{q}j) \tag{6.16}$$

and

$$\langle u_\alpha^2(l\kappa)\rangle = (\hbar/2M_\kappa N_S) \times \sum_{\boldsymbol{q}} [D^{-1/2}(\boldsymbol{q}) \coth\{\hbar D^{1/2}(\boldsymbol{q})/2k_B T\}]_{l_3\kappa\alpha,\, l_3\kappa\alpha}. \tag{6.17}$$

If the crystal is L layers thick, the size of the reduced dynamical matrix is $3rL \times 3rL$, where r is the number of atoms per unit cell. In contrast, the original dynamical matrix is $3rLN_S \times 3rLN_S$, so for a crystal 20 atomic layers on each edge, the reduced dynamical matrix is smaller by a factor of 400 than the unreduced dynamical matrix. Working with the reduced matrix enables one to save considerable computer time.

Computer calculations can be avoided only if very simple models are used. Rich (1963) studied the Rosenstock and Newell (1953) model of a monoatomic simple cubic crystal with a (100) surface and found a larger mean square displacement at the surface than in the bulk. Maradudin and Melngailis (1964) used a Green's function technique to investigate the (100) surface of a simple cubic lattice with nearest and next-nearest neighbor central forces and obtained an anisotropy of the mean square displacements at the surface, in contrast to the isotropy in the bulk. The normal component was found to be approximately twice as large as the bulk value, whereas the parallel component was found to be only 50% larger than the bulk value.

A large number of computer calculations have been made. As an example, we mention the work of Clark et al. (1965) on the (100), (110), and (111) surfaces of a face-centered cubic crystal with nearest neighbor central forces, a model which gives a reasonable representation for nickel. These calculations were carried out in the high-temperature limit. The anisotropy at the surface and the rapid fall off of the mean square displacement with increasing distance from the surface are illustrated in fig. 10 for the (111) surface. One sees that the mean square displacements have essentially assumed their bulk values at about five atomic layers from the surface. The (110) surface reveals an anisotropy in the tangential components as shown in table 1 that is not found with the other surfaces. Also shown in table 1 are the experimental values of MacRae (1964) for nickel. The agreement between theory and experiment is qualitatively satisfactory and can be understood on the basis of the number and orientation of bonds broken in creating the free surface.

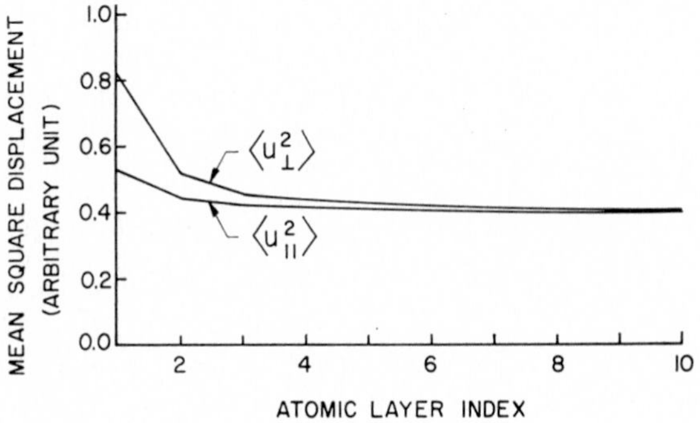

Fig. 10. Mean square displacement components versus atomic layer index for the (111) surface of nickel.

TABLE 1

Theoretical and experimental effective Debye temperatures associated with mean-square displacement components at the surface and in the bulk of a nickel crystal with a (110) free surface. The experimental data are due to MacRae (1964).

Method	[110] (K)	[1$\bar{1}$0] (K)	[001] (K)	Bulk (K)
Theoretical	290	325	281	415
Experimental	220	330	220	390

The discrepancies may be due to multiple scattering effects or to changes in the surface force constants as discussed in subsection 3.2.

The temperature dependence of mean square displacements reveals zero-point effects at low temperatures. This is shown in fig. 11 for the (110) surface of chromium, a body-centered cubic material. The theoretical curve is from the work of Wallis and Cheng (1972), and the experimental data is that of Kaplan and Somorjai (1971). The ratio of surface-to-bulk mean

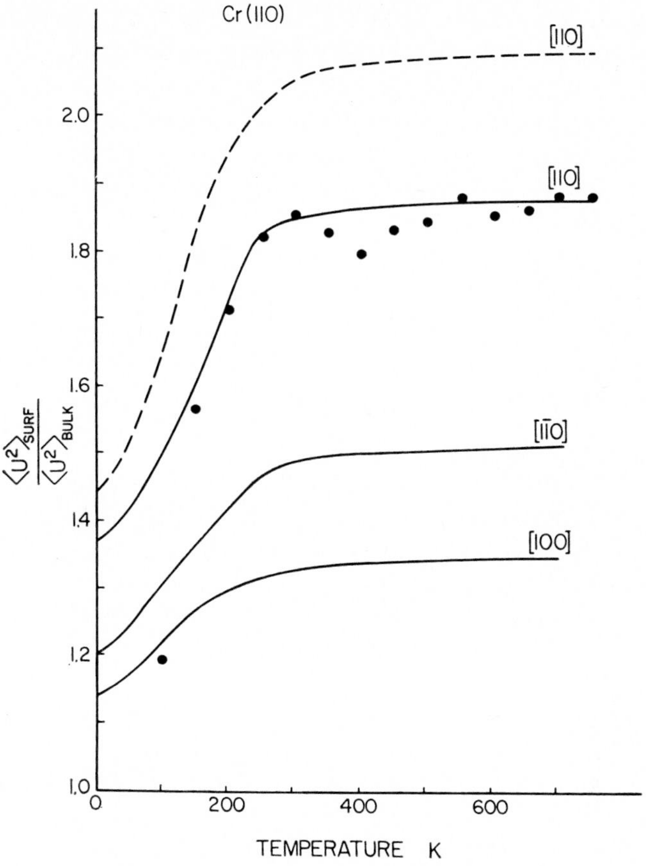

Fig. 11. Ratios of surface to bulk mean square displacements plotted as functions of temperature for the (110) surface of chromium. The points are experimental values (Kaplan and Somorjai 1971). The dashed and solid lines are calculated results using unchanged and changed surface force constants, respectively (Wallis and Cheng 1972).

square displacements drops sharply at low temperatures because zero-point effects become important at a higher temperature for the bulk motion than for the surface motion.

Extensive numerical calculations of surface atom mean square displacements have been reported by Allen and De Wette (1969) and by Allen et al. (1969) for various surfaces of noble gas crystals. This work has been extended to ionic crystals such as NaCl by Chen et al. (1972). On the experimental side, the early work of MacRae and Germer (1962) and MacRae (1964) has been extensively supplemented by Jones et al. (1966) for silver, by Lyon and Somorjai (1966) and Goodman et al. (1968) for various face-centered cubic metals, by Kaplan and Somorjai (1971) for chromium, and by Tabor and Wilson (1970) and Tabor et al. (1971) for several body-centered cubic metals. For further discussion of both experimental and theoretical work, the reader is referred to the review article by the present author (Wallis 1973).

We now take up the subject of mean square velocities of surface atoms. The second order Doppler shift has been shown by Pound and Rebka (1960) and by Josephson (1960) to lead to a temperature-dependent shift in the energy of the emitted gamma ray in the Mössbauer effect. This shift ΔE is related to the energy E by

$$\Delta E = E\left(\langle \dot{u}^2 \rangle / 2c^2\right), \tag{6.18}$$

where $\langle \dot{u}^2 \rangle$ is the mean square velocity of the emitting nucleus.

We can obtain theoretical expressions for the mean square velocity in a fashion similar to that for the mean square displacement (Wallis and Gazis 1962). In a normal mode of vibration of frequency ω_p, the velocity and displacement components of atom $l\kappa$ are related by

$$\dot{u}_\alpha(l\kappa) = \mathrm{i}\omega_p\, u_\alpha(l\kappa). \tag{6.19}$$

Consequently, the expression for $\langle \dot{u}_\alpha^2(l\kappa) \rangle$ analogous to eq. (6.10) is

$$\langle \dot{u}_\alpha^2(l\kappa) \rangle = (1/M_\kappa) \sum_p |e_{p\alpha}(l\kappa)|^2\, \bar{\varepsilon}(\omega_p). \tag{6.20}$$

Transforming eq. (6.20) using the theory of matrices, we obtain

$$\langle \dot{u}_\alpha^2(l\kappa) \rangle = (\hbar/2M_\kappa)\left[D^{1/2} \coth(\hbar D^{1/2}/2k_{\mathrm{B}}T\right]_{l\kappa\alpha,\, l\kappa\alpha}. \tag{6.21}$$

Equations analogous to eqs. (6.16) and (6.17) can be obtained in a similar manner.

It is helpful to consider the expansion of eq. (6.21) appropriate to high temperatures:

$$\langle \dot{u}_\alpha^2(l\kappa) \rangle = \frac{kT}{M_\kappa} + \frac{\hbar^2}{12M_\kappa kT}[D]_{l\kappa\alpha,\, l\kappa\alpha} + \cdots. \tag{6.22}$$

We note that in the extreme high-temperature limit, the mean square velocity has the equipartition value kT/M_κ and is independent of the position of the atom relative to the surface. The correction term in $1/T$ is proportional to the dynamical matrix D, so experimental measurement of this term should give the force constants at the surface directly. At low temperatures, the expansion of the mean square velocity has the leading term

$$\langle \dot{u}_\alpha^2(l\kappa)\rangle \approx (\hbar/2M_\kappa)\,[D^{1/2}]_{l\kappa\alpha,\,l\kappa\alpha} + \cdots . \tag{6.23}$$

The zero-point velocity consequently depends on the proximity of the atom to the surface through the $D^{1/2}$ factor in eq. (6.23). The mean square velocity is smaller for a surface atom than for an interior atom, as a consequence of the smaller number of interactions involving the surface atom compared to an interior atom.

Experimental studies of the second-order Doppler shift of surface atoms have been severely limited (Godwin 1966). Only a few radioactive atoms are suitable as ^{57}Fe and ^{119}Sn. It is difficult to prepare samples with the emitting atoms only in the surface layer, and even if this situation is achieved, the flux of γ-rays will be very weak. Excessive broadening of the lines associated with emitters at and near surfaces is another problem.

7. *Inelastic scattering from crystal surfaces*

A method for determining surface phonon energies which is receiving increasing attention is the inelastic scattering of particles such as electrons or atoms from crystal surfaces. Helium atoms are particularly suitable, since they are primarily scattered by the surface layer and since their energy is on the order of millivolts (in the range of phonon energies) when their De Broglie wavelength is on the order of a typical lattice spacing. The experimental difficulties are severe, however. Neutrons are of little use because they penetrate deeply into the crystal and do not sample only the surface. We shall focus our attention on electrons which have been used rather extensively in spite of their unfavorable energy – De Broglie wavelength relationship. Electron inelastic scattering is useful primarily in determining the large wave vector (unretarded) surface phonon frequencies.

Electron scattering may be dominated by short-range electron–atom interactions (non-polar solids) or by long-range Coulomb interactions (polar solids). The first case can be conveniently handled quantum mechanically, while the second case can be approached semiclassically.

Roundy and Mills (1972) have reported a quantum mechanical treatment whose outline we shall follow. Let us consider a semi-infinite monoatomic crystal with a surface in the x–y plane. The interaction energy of the electron of interest with the atom having position vector $\boldsymbol{R}(\boldsymbol{l})$ can be expanded in the Fourier series

$$v_{l_z}(\boldsymbol{r} - \boldsymbol{R}(l)) = \sum_{\boldsymbol{q}} v_{l_z}(\boldsymbol{q}) \exp[\mathrm{i}q\cdot(\boldsymbol{r} - \boldsymbol{R}(\boldsymbol{l}))], \tag{7.1}$$

where the subscript l_z takes into account the dependence of the atomic potential on the distance of the atom from the surface. We write the wave function of the system of electron plus phonons as a product of an electronic wave function ψ and a phonon wave function χ, the latter being itself a product of harmonic oscillator wave functions for the normal coordinates.

Let $\boldsymbol{R}(\boldsymbol{l})=\boldsymbol{R}^{(0)}(\boldsymbol{l})+\boldsymbol{u}(\boldsymbol{l})$, where $\boldsymbol{R}^{(0)}(\boldsymbol{l})$ is the equilibrium position vector and $\boldsymbol{u}(\boldsymbol{l})$ the displacement of the atom from equilibrium. The perturbation hamiltonian H' which produces the inelastic scattering can be written with the aid of eq. (7.1) in the form

$$H' = \sum_{\boldsymbol{l}} \sum_{\boldsymbol{q}} v_{l_z}(\boldsymbol{q}) \exp[\mathrm{i}\boldsymbol{q}\cdot(\boldsymbol{r} - \boldsymbol{R}^{(0)}(\boldsymbol{l}))] \{\exp[-\mathrm{i}\boldsymbol{q}\cdot\boldsymbol{u}(\boldsymbol{l})] - 1\}. \tag{7.2}$$

In the scattering process, the electron–phonon system makes a transition from an initial state i to a final state f. We consider only processes where one phonon of frequency ω_s is created. If the initial and final electron energies are ε_i and ε_f, then the transition rate R is given by

$$R_{\mathrm{fi}} = (2\pi/\hbar)|\langle f|H'|\,i\rangle|^2\, \delta(\varepsilon_\mathrm{f} - \varepsilon_\mathrm{i} + \hbar\omega_s), \tag{7.3}$$

where the delta function states the conservation of energy $\varepsilon_\mathrm{f}+\hbar\omega_s=\varepsilon_\mathrm{i}$. Utilizing the product form for the wave function, we can write the matrix element in eq. (7.3) as

$$\langle \mathrm{f}|\,H'\,|\mathrm{i}\rangle = \sum_{\boldsymbol{l}} \sum_{\boldsymbol{q}} v_{l_z}(\boldsymbol{q}) \exp[-\mathrm{i}\boldsymbol{q}\cdot\boldsymbol{R}^{(0)}(\boldsymbol{l})] \times \langle \Psi_\mathrm{f}|\exp(\mathrm{i}\boldsymbol{q}\cdot\boldsymbol{r})\,|\Psi_\mathrm{i}\rangle\, \langle\chi_\mathrm{f}|\exp[-\mathrm{i}\boldsymbol{q}\cdot\boldsymbol{u}(\boldsymbol{l})]\,|\chi_\mathrm{i}\rangle_\mathrm{T}, \tag{7.4}$$

where the subscript T on the phonon matrix element indicates that a thermal average over a canonical ensemble has been taken.

If we introduce a normal coordinate transformation

$$\boldsymbol{u}(\boldsymbol{l}) = \sum_p (\hbar/2M\omega_p)^{1/2}\, \boldsymbol{e}_p(\boldsymbol{l})\, (a_p + a_p^+), \tag{7.5}$$

where $\boldsymbol{e}_p(\boldsymbol{l})$ is the eigenvector of the pth vibrational mode and a_p and a_p^+ are annihilation and creation operators, we can rewrite the phonon matrix element as

$$\langle \chi_\mathrm{f} | \exp[-\mathrm{i}\boldsymbol{q}\cdot\boldsymbol{u}(\boldsymbol{l})] | \chi_\mathrm{i} \rangle_\mathrm{T} = -\mathrm{i}\left(\frac{1+n(\omega_s)}{2M\omega_s/\hbar}\right)^{1/2} \times \boldsymbol{q}\cdot\boldsymbol{e}_s(\boldsymbol{l}) \exp\{-\tfrac{1}{2}\langle[q\cdot u(l)]^2\rangle_\mathrm{T}\}. \quad (7.6)$$

In eq. (7.6), $n(\omega_s)$ is the mean phonon occupation number given by eq. (4.3), and it has been assumed that the phonon quantum numbers in χ_f and χ_i are the same except for mode s where they differ by unity.

The electronic matrix element can be evaluated by exploiting the translational periodicity parallel to the surface and writing the electronic wave functions as

$$\Psi_\mathrm{i}(\boldsymbol{r}_\parallel, z) = [\exp(-\mathrm{i}\boldsymbol{k}_\parallel^{(\mathrm{i})}\cdot\boldsymbol{r}_\parallel)]\, U_\mathrm{i}(\boldsymbol{k}_\parallel^{(\mathrm{i})}, \varepsilon_\mathrm{i}; \boldsymbol{r}_\parallel, z), \quad (7.7\mathrm{a})$$

$$\Psi_\mathrm{f}(\boldsymbol{r}_\parallel, z) = [\exp(-\mathrm{i}\boldsymbol{k}_\parallel^{(\mathrm{f})}\cdot\boldsymbol{r}_\parallel)]\, U_\mathrm{f}(\boldsymbol{k}_\parallel^{(\mathrm{f})}, \varepsilon_\mathrm{f}; \boldsymbol{r}_\parallel, z), \quad (7.7\mathrm{b})$$

where the subscript $_\parallel$ indicates a two-dimensional wave vector parallel to the surface and the U functions have the translational periodicity of the lattice parallel to the surface. Using eq. (7.7), we can write the electronic matrix element in the form

$$\langle \Psi_\mathrm{f} | \exp(\mathrm{i}\boldsymbol{q}\cdot\boldsymbol{r}) | \Psi_\mathrm{i} \rangle = A\delta_{\boldsymbol{k}_\parallel^{(\mathrm{f})}, \boldsymbol{k}_\parallel^{(\mathrm{i})} - \boldsymbol{q}_\parallel + \boldsymbol{G}_\parallel} M(q_z), \quad (7.8)$$

where A is the area, $\boldsymbol{G}_\parallel$ is that reciprocal lattice vector that places $\boldsymbol{k}_\parallel^{(\mathrm{i})} - q_\parallel + \boldsymbol{G}_\parallel$ in the first Brillouin zone and $M(q_z)$ is a matrix element involving the U functions. Utilizing eqs. (7.6) and (7.8) and carrying out the sum over $\boldsymbol{q}_\parallel$, we obtain

$$\langle \mathrm{f} | H' | \mathrm{i} \rangle = A \sum_{\boldsymbol{l}} \sum_{K_z} \Big\{ -\mathrm{i}\left[\frac{1+n(\omega_s)}{2M\omega_s/\hbar}\right]^{1/2} \times \tilde{v}_{l_z}(\boldsymbol{K})\, [\boldsymbol{K}\cdot\boldsymbol{e}_s(\boldsymbol{l})] \exp[-\mathrm{i}\boldsymbol{K}\cdot\boldsymbol{R}^{(0)}(\boldsymbol{l})]\, M(K_z) \Big\}, \quad (7.9)$$

where $\boldsymbol{K}$ is a vector with components $\boldsymbol{K}_\parallel = \boldsymbol{k}_\parallel^{(\mathrm{i})} - \boldsymbol{k}_\parallel^{(\mathrm{f})} + \boldsymbol{G}_\parallel$, $K_z = q_z$ and

$$\tilde{v}_{l_z}(\boldsymbol{K}) = v_{l_z}(\boldsymbol{K}) \exp\{-\tfrac{1}{2}\langle[\boldsymbol{K}\cdot\boldsymbol{u}(\boldsymbol{l})]^2\rangle_\mathrm{T}\}. \quad (7.10)$$

Again exploiting the translational symmetry parallel to the surface, we can utilize eq. (6.14) which we rewrite in the form

$$\boldsymbol{e}_s(\boldsymbol{l}) = (N_\mathrm{S})^{-1/2}\, \boldsymbol{e}_j(\boldsymbol{k}_\parallel, l_z) \exp[\mathrm{i}\boldsymbol{k}_\parallel\cdot\boldsymbol{R}_\parallel^{(0)}(\boldsymbol{l}_\parallel)]. \quad (7.11)$$

where j specifies the normal modes for given $\boldsymbol{k}_{\|}$. Substitution of eq. (7.11) into eq. (7.9) and evaluation of the sum over $\boldsymbol{l}_{\|}$ yields

$$\langle \mathrm{f}|\, H'\, |\mathrm{i}\rangle = -\sum_{l_z}\left(\frac{\hbar N_{\mathrm{S}}}{2M\omega_s}\right)^{1/2}[1+n(\omega_s)]^{1/2} \times \delta_{\boldsymbol{K}_{\|},\boldsymbol{k}_{\|}}[\boldsymbol{Q}\cdot\boldsymbol{e}_j(\boldsymbol{k}_{\|},l_z)]\, m(l_z), \quad (7.12)$$

where j now stands for the pair of indices $\boldsymbol{k}_{\|}$, j,

$$m(l_z) = \mathrm{i}A\sum_{K_z}\tilde{v}_{l_z}(\boldsymbol{K})\exp[-\mathrm{i}K_zR_z^{(0)}(l_z)]\, M(K_z), \quad (7.13)$$

$$\boldsymbol{Q} = \boldsymbol{k}_{\|} + \hat{z}Q_z(l_z), \quad (7.14)$$

$$Q_z(l_z) = \frac{\mathrm{i}}{m(l_z)}\frac{\partial m(l_z)}{\partial l_z}, \quad (7.15)$$

and the Kronecker delta states the conservation of parallel wave vector $\boldsymbol{k}_{\|} = \boldsymbol{k}_{\|}^{(\mathrm{i})} - \boldsymbol{k}_{\|}^{(\mathrm{f})} + \boldsymbol{G}_{\|}$. Substituting eq. (7.12) into eq. (7.3) and summing over all values of the wave vector of the final electron state, we obtain for the transition rate R_{i}

$$R_{\mathrm{i}} = \frac{2\pi}{\hbar}\sum_{k_z^{(\mathrm{f})}}\sum_{l_z}\sum_{l'_z}\frac{\hbar N_{\mathrm{S}}}{2M\omega_s}[1+n(\omega_s)]\,[\boldsymbol{Q}\cdot\boldsymbol{e}_j(\boldsymbol{k}_{\|},l_z)] \times [\boldsymbol{Q}\cdot\boldsymbol{e}_j(k_{\|},l'_z)]^*\, m(l_z)\, m^*(l'_z)\,\delta(\varepsilon_{\mathrm{f}}-\varepsilon_{\mathrm{i}}+\hbar\omega_s). \quad (7.16)$$

Transforming the sum over $k_z^{(\mathrm{f})}$ to an integral and carrying out the integration, we find

$$R_{\mathrm{i}} = \frac{L}{\hbar v_z}\frac{N_{\mathrm{S}}}{2M\omega_s}[1+n(\omega_s)] \times \sum_{l_z}\sum_{l'_z}[\boldsymbol{Q}\cdot\boldsymbol{e}_j(\boldsymbol{k}_{\|},l_z)]\,[\boldsymbol{Q}\cdot\boldsymbol{e}_j(\boldsymbol{k}_{\|},l'_z)]^*\, m(l_z)\, m^*(l'_z), \quad (7.17)$$

where v_z is the z-component of the group velocity of the outgoing electron and L is the thickness of the crystal. Since $\omega_s \ll \varepsilon_{\mathrm{i}}, \varepsilon_{\mathrm{f}}$, all phonons with the same $\boldsymbol{k}_{\|}$ scatter an incident electron into essentially the same outgoing direction. To get the total transition rate associated with an energy shift between $\hbar\omega$ and $\hbar\omega + \omega\Delta\omega$, we must multiply the right-hand side of eq. (7.17) by $\rho(\boldsymbol{k}_{\|},\omega)$, the density of phonon modes having fixed $\boldsymbol{k}_{\|}$ and frequency between ω and $\omega+\Delta\omega$:

$$R_{\mathrm{T}} = \frac{L}{\hbar v_z}\frac{N_{\mathrm{S}}}{2M\omega}[1+n(\omega)]\sum_{l_z}\sum_{l'_z}[\boldsymbol{Q}\cdot\boldsymbol{e}_j(\boldsymbol{k}_{\|},l_z)] \times [\boldsymbol{Q}\cdot\boldsymbol{e}_j(\boldsymbol{k}_{\|},l'_z)]^*\, m(l)_z\, m^*(l'_z)\,\rho(\boldsymbol{k}_{\|},\omega)\,\Delta\omega. \quad (7.18)$$

Introducing the phonon Green's function

$$U_{\alpha\beta}(\boldsymbol{k}_{\|}; l_z, l'_z; \omega) = \sum_j \frac{e_{\alpha j}(\boldsymbol{k}_{\|}, l_z)\, e_{\beta j}(\boldsymbol{k}_{\|}, l'_z)}{\omega^2 - \omega_j^2(\boldsymbol{k}_{\|})}, \tag{7.19}$$

and the spectral density function

$$A_{\alpha\beta}(\boldsymbol{k}_{\|}; l_z, l'_z; \omega) = (1/\pi \mathrm{i}) \times \lim_{\eta \to 0^+} [U_{\alpha\beta}(\boldsymbol{k}_{\|}; l_z, l'_z; \omega - \mathrm{i}\eta) - U_{\alpha\beta}(\boldsymbol{k}_{\|}; l_z, l'_z; \omega + \mathrm{i}\eta)], \tag{7.20}$$

we can rewrite R_{T} in the form

$$R_{\mathrm{T}} = \frac{L}{\hbar v_z} \frac{N_s}{2M} [1 + n(\omega)] \sum_{l_z} \sum_{l'_z} m(l_z)\, m^*(l'_z) \times \sum_{\alpha\beta} Q_\alpha Q_\beta^* A_{\alpha\beta}(\boldsymbol{k}_{\|}; l_z, l'_z; \omega)\, \Delta\omega. \tag{7.21}$$

For low-energy electrons scattered primarily by the surface layer, we take $l_z = l'_z = 0$. The matrix element $m(0)$ is essentially independent of the energy shift $\hbar\omega$. The differential scattering cross section $\mathrm{d}^2\sigma/\mathrm{d}\Omega\,\mathrm{d}\omega$ describing scattering of electrons into solid angle $\mathrm{d}\Omega$ is proportional to R_{T} and in view of the foregoing restrictions can be written as

$$\frac{\mathrm{d}^2\sigma}{\mathrm{d}\Omega\,\mathrm{d}\omega} = K[1 + n(\omega)] \sum_{\alpha\beta} Q_\alpha Q_\beta^* A_{\alpha\beta}(\boldsymbol{k}_{\|}; l_z, l'_z; \omega), \tag{7.22}$$

where K is independent of ω.

The scattering cross section in general has contributions from both surface and bulk phonons. This has been illustrated by Roundy and Mills (1972) who evaluated the spectral density for a slab of a face-centered cubic material with (100) surfaces. Their results, presented in fig. 12 for a particular value of $\boldsymbol{k}_{\|}$, show clearly the delta-function-like contribution from surface

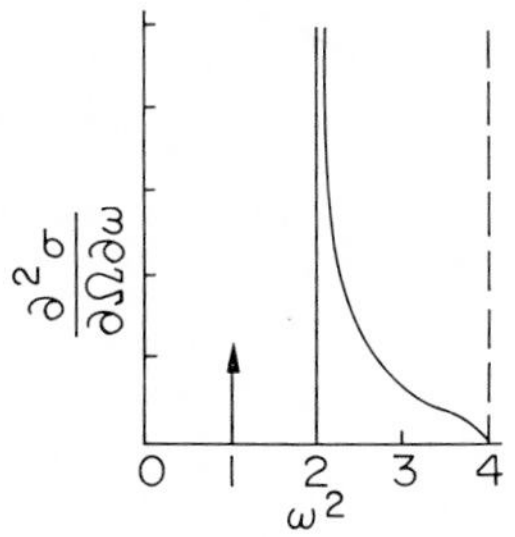

Fig. 12. Energy loss spectrum for a particular value of $\boldsymbol{k}_{\|}$. The line at $\omega^2 = 1$ corresponds to the surface mode and the broad band to the bulk modes (after Roundy and Mills 1972).

modes and the broad-band contribution from bulk modes. By varying $\boldsymbol{k}_{\|}$ (sampling various directions for the outgoing electrons) one can in principle determine the surface phonon dispersion curve and obtain information about the coupling constants at the surface.

In the case of ionic crystals, the scattering is caused primarily by the macroscopic electric field arising from the long-range Coulomb interactions. Since it is the surface optical phonons and not the bulk optical phonons which have a macroscopic field extending outside the crystal, low-energy electrons are predominately scattered inelastically by the surface optical phonons. Theories of the scattering have been given by Fujiwara and Ohtaka (1968), Lucas and Sunjic (1971, 1972), and by Evans and Mills (1972, 1973). The macroscopic electric field is also important in the scattering of low-energy electrons from covalent crystals having surface-induced effective charges on the surface.

Ibach (1970) has exploited inelastic low-energy electron scattering to determine the surface optical phonon energy for the $(1\bar{1}00)$ and (0001) surfaces of ZnO. The results are in good agreement with the Fuchs–Kliewer theory. Ibach (1971) extended this work to the (111) surface of silicon and inferred a value of $0.1e$ for the surface-induced effective charge. Relatively high energy electrons ($\sim$25 keV) have been used by Boersch et al. (1966) to study surface optical phonons on LiF surfaces.

8. *Effects of free surfaces on optical properties*

8.1. Infrared absorption

It is a well-known consequence of periodic boundary conditions (Born and Huang 1954) that the infrared absorption of an ionic crystal peaks strongly at the frequency ω_{T} of transverse optical phonons of long wavelength. If the periodic boundary conditions are modified so that free surfaces are present, the infrared absorption may exhibit peaks at frequencies other than ω_{T}.

Since infrared wavelengths are large compared to lattice spacings in crystals we can regard the wave vector of the radiation as negligible. Under these circumstances, the absorption coefficient of a crystal lattice is proportional to the quantity

$$I(\omega) = \sum_{\mathrm{i}} \sum_{\mathrm{f}} v_{\mathrm{i}} \left| \int \psi_{\mathrm{f}}^{*}(\boldsymbol{R})\, \boldsymbol{M}(\boldsymbol{R})\, \psi_{\mathrm{i}}(\boldsymbol{R})\, \mathrm{d}\boldsymbol{R} \right|^{2} \delta(E_{\mathrm{f}} - E_{\mathrm{i}} + \hbar\omega), \qquad (8.1)$$

where $\boldsymbol{R}$ stands for the set of nuclear coordinates, ψ_i and ψ_f are the vibrational wave functions for the initial and final states, E_i and E_f are the corresponding energy eigenvalues, v_i is the Boltzmann occupancy factor, and $\boldsymbol{M}(\boldsymbol{R})$ is the electric dipole moment.

The dipole moment can be expanded in power series in the displacements $\boldsymbol{u}(l\kappa)$ of the ions from their equilibrium positions:

$$M_\alpha(\boldsymbol{R}) = M_{0\alpha} + \sum_{l\kappa\beta} M_{\alpha\beta}(l\kappa)\, u_\beta(l\kappa) + \sum_{l\kappa\beta}\sum_{l'\kappa'\gamma} M_{\alpha\beta\gamma}(l\kappa, l'\kappa')\, u_\beta(l\kappa)\, u_\gamma(l'\kappa') + \cdots. \tag{8.2}$$

The constant term $M_{0\alpha}$ is of no concern for infrared absorption. The terms linear and quadratic in the displacements $\boldsymbol{u}(l\kappa)$ are the first order and second order terms. We shall confine our discussion to the first order terms, which are important in ionic crystals and are subject to strict selection rules if the crystal is periodic.

For a periodic crystal of the NaCl type, the coefficient $M_{\alpha\beta}(l\kappa)$ can be written as

$$M_{\alpha\beta}(l\kappa) = e_\kappa \delta_{\alpha\beta}, \tag{8.3}$$

where e_κ is the effective charge of ions of type κ. The situation can be illustrated simply in one dimension where the normal coordinate transformation can be taken to be

$$u(l\kappa) = (NM_\kappa)^{-1/2} \sum_{kj} e(\kappa|kj)\, \mathrm{e}^{ikal} Q(kj). \tag{8.4}$$

In eq. (8.4), $k = 2\pi n/Na$, n is an integer in the range $0 \leqslant n \leqslant N-1$, N is the number of ions of a given type and a is the lattice constant. Substitution of eqs. (8.3) and (8.4) into eq. (8.2) and carrying out the sum over l yields

$$M(R) = \sum_\kappa e_\kappa (N|M_\kappa)^{1/2} \sum_{kj} e(\kappa|kj)\, Q(kj)\, \delta_{k,0}. \tag{8.5}$$

We see that only the $k=0$ modes give a non-vanishing dipole moment. Since the acoustical modes with $k=0$ correspond to uniform translation and hence zero dipole moment, only the optical modes with $k=0$ yield a non-vanishing dipole moment for a periodic crystal. This result is very easily generalized to three dimensions.

When a free surface is present, other modes besides the fundamental (long-wavelength transverse optical mode) can give a non-vanishing dipole moment and optical absorption. This point has been investigated by Rosenstock (1955, 1957) using explicit lattice-dynamical models. For a linear chain of N ions of alternating charge but equal mass and nearest neighbor interactions, he obtained for the first-order dipole moment associated with normal mode s,

$$M_s = eu_0/\cos(\varphi_s/2), \quad s \text{ odd},$$
$$= 0, \quad s \text{ even},$$

where $\varphi_s = s\pi/N$, $s=0, 1, 2, \ldots, N-1$, and u_0 is an arbitrary amplitude. The dipole moment has a maximum at $s=N-1$ (the mode which has the maximum frequency ω_m and which would be the long-wave length optical mode if the lattice were made diatomic) and decreases in magnitude as s decreases. Thus, the free surfaces (ends) lead to absorption in frequency regions not allowed with periodic boundary conditions.

Since the fundamental absorption of infrared radiation by a crystal is primarily restricted to small wave vectors, it is possible to simplify the situation by applying macroscopic theory in the frequency region near the fundamental. This has been done by Ruppin and Englman (1970) who employed the Mie theory to calculate the absorption cross section σ_a for small spheres. The result is

$$\sigma_a = \frac{2}{(k_0 R)^2} \sum_{l=1} (2l+1)(-\operatorname{Re} a_l - |a_l|^2 - \operatorname{Re} b_l - |b_l|^2), \tag{8.6}$$

where

$$a_l = -\frac{j_l(x_i)[x_0 j_l(x_0)]' - j_l(x_0)[x_i j_l(x_i)]'}{j_l(x_i)[x_0 h_l(x_0)]' - h_l(x_0)[x_i j_l(x_i)]'}, \tag{8.7a}$$

$$b_l = -\frac{\varepsilon_M j_l(x_0)[x_i j_l(x_i)]' - \varepsilon j_l(x_i)[x_0 j_l(x_0)]'}{\varepsilon_M h_l(x_0)[x_i j_l(x_i)]' - \varepsilon j_l(x_i)[x_0 h_l(x_0)]'}, \tag{8.7b}$$

$x_0 = k_0 R$, $x_i = k_i R$, $k_0 = \varepsilon_M^{1/2}\omega/c$, $k_i = \varepsilon^{1/2}\omega/c$, ε_M is the dielectric constant of the medium surrounding the sphere, ε is the dielectric constant of the sphere, and j_l and k_l are the spherical Bessel and Hankel functions, and the prime denotes differentiation with respect to the argument of the Bessel or Hankel function. The scattering cross section is given by

$$\sigma_s = \frac{2}{(k_0 R)^2} \sum_{l=1} (2l+1)(|a_l|^2 + |b_l|^2), \tag{8.8}$$

and the total (extinction) cross section is given by

$$\sigma_t = \sigma_a + \sigma_s = -\frac{2}{(k_0 R)^2} \sum_{l=1} (2l+1) \operatorname{Re}(a_l + b_l). \tag{8.9}$$

Numerical calculations reveal that the extinction cross section possesses peaks at frequencies corresponding to the poles of a_l and b_l specified by eq. (7). The poles of a_l and b_l yield the so-called magnetic and electric modes, respectively (no radial components of the electric and magnetic fields, respectively). For very small spheres, $R \to 0$, only the electric mode with $l=1$ causes appreciable absorption. This mode is in fact the mode discussed by Fröhlich (1949) which has a frequency ω_F given by

$$\frac{\omega_F^2}{\omega_T^2} = \frac{\varepsilon_0 + 2\varepsilon_M}{\varepsilon_\infty + 2\varepsilon_M}, \tag{8.10}$$

where ε_0 and ε_∞ are the static and high-frequency dielectric constants of the sphere. It is clear from the Lyddane–Sachs–Teller relation $\omega_L^2/\omega_T^2 = \varepsilon_0/\varepsilon_\infty$ that ω_F lies between ω_L and ω_T. One should note that there is no significant peak in extinction at ω_T for very small spheres.

In the treatments of Fuchs and Kliewer and of Ruppin and Englman, the boundary conditions have been handled satisfactorily for the long-range forces but not the short-range forces. The task of calculating the dielectric tensor with proper account taken of the boundary conditions for both types of forces has been undertaken by Grim et al. (1970). They use the Kubo formalism (Kubo 1957) to write the imaginary part of the dielectric response tensor (which relates the polarization to the *external* electric field) in the form

$$\varepsilon_{\mu\nu}^{(2)}(\omega) = (2\pi/\hbar\Omega)\,(\mathrm{e}^{\beta\hbar\omega} - 1) \int_0^\infty \mathrm{d}t\, \mathrm{e}^{-\mathrm{i}\omega t} \langle M_\nu(t)\, M_\mu(0)\rangle, \tag{8.11}$$

where Ω is the volume of the crystal, $\beta = 1/k_B T$, $M_\mu(t)$ is given by eq. (8.2) with the displacements $u_\mu(l\kappa)$ taken to be time dependent, and the angular brackets denote an average over a canonical ensemble. By generalizing the normal coordinate transformation specified by eqs. (7.5) and (7.11) to two atoms per unit cell and writing the time dependence of the creation and annihilation operators as

$$a_j(\boldsymbol{k}_\parallel, t) = a_j(\boldsymbol{k}_\parallel, 0) \exp[-\mathrm{i}\omega_j(\boldsymbol{k}_\parallel)\, t] \tag{8.12a}$$

and

$$a_j^\dagger(-\boldsymbol{k}_\parallel, t) = a_j^\dagger(-\boldsymbol{k}_\parallel, 0) \exp[\mathrm{i}\omega_j(\boldsymbol{k}_\parallel)\, t], \tag{8.12b}$$

one can reduce the expression for $\varepsilon_{\mu\nu}^{(2)}(\omega)$ to the form

$$\varepsilon_{\mu\nu}^{(2)}(\omega) = \frac{\pi^2 e^2}{N(2r_0^3)} \sum_{j=1}^{6N} \frac{\delta[\omega - \omega_j(0)]}{\omega_j(0)} f_{\mu j} f_{\nu j}^*, \tag{8.13}$$

where

$$f_{\mu j} = \sum_{l_z} \sum_{\kappa=\pm} M_\kappa^{-1/2} \kappa \xi_{\mu j}(\mathbf{0}, \kappa, l_z). \tag{8.14}$$

Note that only $\boldsymbol{k}_\| = 0$ modes contribute to $\varepsilon_{\mu\nu}^{(2)}(\omega)$ and hence to the absorption. The tetragonal symmetry of the slab is reflected in $\varepsilon_{\mu\nu}^{(2)}(\omega)$ by the inequality of $\varepsilon_{xx}^{(2)}(\omega)$ and $\varepsilon_{zz}^{(2)}(\omega)$.

These calculations have been extended by Grimm et al. to include the real part of $\varepsilon_{\mu\nu}(\omega)$. By utilizing the results of Tong and Maradudin (1969) for the normal modes of an ionic crystal slab, they obtained explicit expressions for the diagonal components of $\varepsilon_{\mu\nu}(\omega)$ for a 100-layer slab of NaCl in the form

$$\varepsilon_{xx}(\omega) = 1 + \frac{1.229\omega_0^2}{(2.418\omega_0)^2 - \omega^2 - \mathrm{i}\gamma\omega} + \frac{26.65\omega_0^2}{(2.491\omega_0)^2 - \omega^2 - \mathrm{i}\gamma\omega}, \tag{8.15a}$$

$$\varepsilon_{zz}(\omega) = 1 + \frac{28.79\omega_0^2}{(2.298\omega_0)^2 - \omega^2 - \mathrm{i}\gamma\omega}, \tag{8.15b}$$

where $\omega_0 = 10^{13}\ \mathrm{sec}^{-1}$ and γ is the damping constant ($\sim 0.02\omega_0$ at room temperature). The poles of $\varepsilon_{xx}(\omega)$ in the limit $\gamma \to 0$ are at $\omega_\mathrm{T} = 2.491\omega_0$ and at a transverse surface mode, $\omega_\mathrm{TSM} = 2.418\omega_0$, which is localized within a few atomic layers of the surface and is distinct from the Fuchs–Kliewer mode. The zero of $\varepsilon_{zz}(\omega)$ when $\gamma \to 0$ is at $\omega_\mathrm{L} = 5.837\omega_0$. For normal incidence there is absorption at ω_T and at ω_TSM. For non-normal incidence there is also absorption at ω_L. The latter absorption was observed experimentally some time ago by Berreman (1963). The theoretical absorption coefficient for an NaCl slab is plotted against frequency in fig. 13 for an angle of incidence of 30°.

A variety of experimental results have been obtained on the infrared absorption of very small crystals. Generally speaking, the results can be understood on the basis of macroscopic theory and are discussed in detail by Ruppin and Englman (1970).

In the work of Grimm et al. on the ionic crystal slab, no absorption is found at the frequency of the Fuchs–Kliewer mode. This is related to the dispersion curve for the Fuchs–Kliewer modes lying to the right of the light line $\omega = kc$. However, by suitable experimental procedures, it is possible to make these modes accessible to experimental study.

One procedure is to study the infrared reflectance from a sample upon which a grating has been ruled (Marschall et al. 1971). If the spacing of the

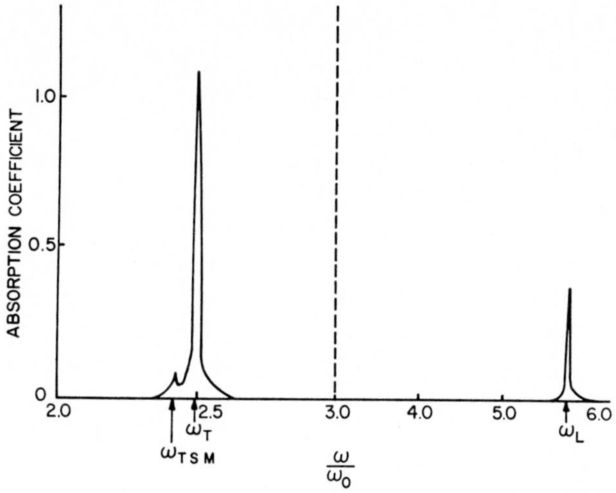

Fig. 13. Absorption coefficient plotted against frequency for a NaCl crystal slab 100 atomic layers thick (after Grim et al. 1970).

grooves is d, then the effective wave-vector component of the radiation parallel to the surface is augmented by $2\pi n/d$ where n is an integer. Thus, we have

$$k_{\parallel} = (\omega/c)\sin\theta + 2\pi n/d\,, \tag{8.16}$$

where θ is the angle of incidence. The reflectance curve exhibits dips at frequencies determined by the surface polariton dispersion curve and eq. (8.16). From the observed reflectance dips, an experimental dispersion curve can be constructed.

An alternative and perhaps more convenient procedure is attenuated total reflection (Otto 1968). This technique would be useful in the experimental investigation of non-radiative surface polaritons. The incrementation of the wave vector is achieved by placing a prism adjacent to the sample and separated from the sample by a few microns. In the absence of the sample, the radiation is totally internally reflected by the prism. In the presence of the sample, the exponential tail of radiation penetrating outside the prism couples with the surface polaritons in the sample and causes a dip in the intensity of the reflected radiation. Coupling is possible because the effective wave vector of the radiation parallel to the surface is specified by

$$k_{\parallel} = (\omega/c)\, n \sin\alpha\,, \tag{8.17}$$

where n is the refractive index of the prism and α is the angle of incidence in the prism. Since $n>1$, wave vectors to the right of the light line in vacuum can be attained. This technique has recently been exploited by Marschall and Fischer (1972) who determined the dispersion curve for surface optical phonons in GaP. An independent investigation along similar lines is that of Bryksin et al. (1972) on NaCl and CaF_2.

Infrared absorption by surface modes associated with adsorbed species has apparently been observed by Pliskin and Eischens (1960) for hydrogen adsorbed on platinum. They observed two absorption peaks which they attributed to two different types of bonding. The vibrational origin of the peaks was confirmed by the isotopic shift when hydrogen is replaced by deuterium.

8.2. Raman scattering

In the Raman effect, the frequency of the scattered radiation is down-shifted (Stokes) or up-shifted (anti-Stokes) from the frequency of the incident radiation. The advent of high intensity lasers has stimulated a great upsurge of experimental investigations of the Raman effect in bulk crystals; however, the use of the Raman effect to study surface phonons is in a very rudimentary state, although activity in this area can be expected to increase rapidly in the future.

If one considers scattering from a perfect periodic crystal, one finds that only optical modes with wave vector $\boldsymbol{k}\approx 0$ are active in the Raman effect. It turns out from symmetry considerations that crystals such as NaCl with every atom at a center of inversion are not Raman active in first order. However, crystals such as diamond which have centers of inversion midway between pairs of atoms do show a first-order Raman effect, as do III–V semiconductors which lack a center of inversion.

The creation of a free surface can result in the elimination of centers of inversion symmetry and leads to surface-induced Raman scattering. A theoretical analysis has been given by Ruppin and Englman (1969) who treated the case of the incident beam perpendicular to a thin slab and the scattered beam at an angle θ to the normal. Conservation of energy and of momentum components parallel to the surface yields the conditions for Stokes scattering

$$\omega_1 = \omega_2 + \omega\,, \qquad q_{\parallel} = k_{\parallel 2} = |\boldsymbol{k}_2| \sin\theta\,, \tag{8.18, 19}$$

where the subscripts 1 and 2 refer to the incident and scattered radiation and the unsubscripted quantities refer to the phonon. From eqs. (8.18) and (8.19), one obtains

$$\sin\theta = \frac{cq_{\parallel}}{\omega_1 - \omega(q_{\parallel})} . \qquad (8.20)$$

This relation between $q_{\parallel}$ and θ can be used in principle to determine the dispersion curve, $\omega(q_{\parallel})$, of surface modes.

The Fuchs–Kliewer modes of a slab of a NaCl-type crystal will not exhibit first-order Raman scattering, since the displacement patterns of these surface modes are similar to those of the bulk longitudinal and transverse optical modes which are Raman inactive. For crystals which are Raman active in the bulk, however, the Fuchs–Kliewer surface modes should also be Raman active. Very recently, Evans et al. (1973) have observed Raman scattering from surface polaritons in a thin film of gallium arsenide on a sapphire substrate. They found that the mode frequency is appropriate for the surface polariton of the film bounded by a sapphire substrate on one side and by air on the other side.

9. *Surface effects on thermal expansion*

We have seen in subsection 3.2 that the equilibrium spacings of the atomic layers near to a free surface are in general different from the bulk value. We may also anticipate that the change in equilibrium spacing with temperature, i.e., the thermal expansion, will also be different near a surface from that in the bulk.

Experimental information concerning surface thermal expansion can be obtained in principle from the temperature shifts of Bragg peaks in LEED data, provided the kinematic approximation is valid. Multiple scattering effects will tend to obscure the extraction of surface thermal expansion values from the data, however.

A survey of experimental and theoretical aspects of surface thermal expansion has been given by Wilson and Bastow (1971). The positions of normal incidence diffraction peaks are specified in the kinematic approximation by

$$|\boldsymbol{Q}| = 4\pi/\lambda = n\pi/a_{\perp} , \qquad (9.1)$$

where $\boldsymbol{Q}$ is the scattering vector, λ is the electron wavelength, n is an integer, and $a_{\perp}$ is the spacing between equivalent layers in the direction normal to the surface. The electron accelerating potential E_p and the inner potential V_i are related to λ by the relation

$$\lambda = [150.4/E'_p(\mathrm{eV})]^{1/2}, \tag{9.2}$$

where $E'_p = E_p + V_i$. The thermal expansion α_s is then given

$$\alpha_s = \frac{1}{a_\perp}\frac{\mathrm{d}a_\perp}{\mathrm{d}T} = -\tfrac{1}{2}\frac{1}{E'_p}\frac{\mathrm{d}E'_p}{\mathrm{d}T}. \tag{9.3}$$

For low values of E_p, the scattering is primarily from the surface and the surface thermal expansion is obtained.

Experimental results have been obtained by various workers. Gelatt et al. (1969) reported values of α_s/α_b (α_b is the bulk value) on the order of one to two for Ag and Ni. However, temperature-dependent asymmetries of the Bragg peaks due to absorption and the variation of the Debye–Waller factor with distance from the surface complicate the determination of α_s/α_b. Wilson and Bastow (1971) have investigated the (100) surfaces of Cr and Mo and found values of α_s/α_b in the range between two and three. Ignatiev and Rhodin (1973) have studied the (111) surface of Xe and found α_s/α_b values of about four or five.

A simple theoretical treatment of surface thermal expansion has been given by Wilson and Bastow (1971) based on the Grüneisen expression for thermal expansion which they write in the approximate form

$$\alpha = 2\gamma C_v/3Ea_0^2, \tag{9.4}$$

where γ is the Grüneisen constant, C_v is the specific heat per atom at constant volume, E is Young's modulus, and a_0 is the lattice constant. At high temperatures, $C_v = 3k_B$; furthermore, we can regard Ea_0 as a force constant. Introducing the Debey frequency ω_D and Debye temperature Θ_D, we have

$$Ea_0 = M\omega_D^2 = M(k_B\Theta_D/\hbar)^2, \tag{9.5}$$

where M is the atomic mass. Eq. (9.4) can now be rewritten in the form

$$\alpha = \frac{k_B\gamma}{a_0^2 M}\left(\frac{\hbar}{k_B\Theta_D}\right)^2. \tag{9.6}$$

If γ is the same for surface layers as for bulk layers, then

$$\alpha_s/\alpha_b = (\Theta_{Db}/\Theta_{Ds})^2 = \langle u_s^2\rangle/\langle u_b^2\rangle. \tag{9.7}$$

This relation seems to be in rough agreement with the available experimental data.

In a more complete theory, one would minimize the Helmholtz free energy with respect to variatious in the various layer spacings. This has been done by Allen (1972) who finds in the high-temperature region that

$$\alpha_s/\alpha_b \approx 0.75 \langle u_\perp^2 \rangle_s / \langle u_\perp^2 \rangle_b , \tag{9.8}$$

where$\langle u_\perp^2 \rangle$ is the mean square displacement perpendicular to the surface. An alternative formulation of surface thermal expansion has been presented by Dobrzynski and Maradudin (1973) who evaluate the Helmholtz free energy including anharmonic terms with the aid of many-body techniques. Specific calculations for the (100) surface of α-iron are not inconsistent with eqs. (9.7) or (9.8) at high temperature, but exhibit a rapid rise in α_s/α_b at low temperatures (below 50 K).

Acknowledgements

This work (Technical Report No. 74-31) was supported in part by the Office of Naval Research under Contract No. N00014-69-A-0200-9003.

References

Allen, R.E. (1972), J. Vac. Sci. Tech. **9**, 934.
Allen, R.E., G.P. Alldredge and F.W. De Wette (1971), Phys. Rev. **B4**, 1648, 1661.
Allen, R.E. and F.W. De Wette (1969), Phys. Rev. **179**, 873.
Allen, R.E., F.W. De Wette and A. Rahman (1969), Phys. Rev. **179**, 887.
Barkman, J.H., R.L. Anderson and T.E. Brackett (1965), J. Chem. Phys. **42**, 1112.
Berreman, D.W. (1963), Phys. Rev. **130**, 2193.
Bleustein, J.L. (1968), Appl. Phys. Lett. **13**, 412.
Boersch, H., J. Geiger and W. Stickel (1966), Phys. Rev. Lett. **17**, 379.
Born, M. (1942), Rep. Progr. Phys. **9**, 294.
Born, M. and K. Huang (1954), *Dynamical theory of crystal lattices* (Oxford University Press, Oxford).
Bryksin, V.V., Yu.M. Gerbshtein and D.N. Mirlin (1972), Fiz. Tverd. Tela **14**, 543, 3368 [Sov. Phys. Solid State **14**, 453, 2849].
Budreau, A.J. and P.H. Carr (1971), Appl. Phys. Lett. **18**, 239.
Cady, W.G. (1964), *Piezoelectricity*, Vol. 1 (Dover Publications, Inc., New York).
Chen, T.S., G.P. Alldredge, F.W. De Wette and R.E. Allen (1971a), Phys. Rev. Lett. **26**, 1543.
Chen, T.S., G.P. Alldredge, F.W. De Wette and R.E. Allen (1971b), J. Chem. Phys. **55**, 3121.

CHEN, T.S., G.P. ALLDREDGE, F.W. DE WETTE and R.E. ALLEN (1972), Phys. Rev. **B6**, 623.
CLARK, B.C., R. HERMAN, D.C. GAZIS and R.F. WALLIS (1967), *Ferroelectricity*, ed. by E.F. Weller (Elsevier Publishing Co., Amsterdam), p. 101.
CLARK, B.C., R. HERMAN and R.F. WALLIS (1965), Phys. Rev. **139**, A860.
DOBRZYNSKI, L. and G. LEMAN (1969), J. de Physique **30**, 116.
DOBRZYNSKI, L. and A.A. MARADUDIN (1973), Phys. Rev. **B7**, 1207.
DRANSFELD, K. and E. SALZMANN (1970), in *Physical acoustics*, Vol. 7, ed. by W.R. Mason and R.N. Thurston (Academic Press, Inc., New York), p. 219.
DUKE, C.B. and G.E. LARAMORE (1970), Phys. Rev. **B2**, 4765, 4783.
DUPUIS, M., R. MAZO and L. ONSAGER (1960), J. Chem. Phys. **33**, 1452.
EVANS, D.J., S. USHIODA and J.D. MCMULLEN (1973), Phys. Rev. Lett. **31**, 369.
EVANS, E. and D.L. MILLS (1972), Phys. Rev. **B5**, 4126.
EVANS, E. and D.L. MILLS (1973), Phys. Rev. **B7**, 853.
FARNELL, G.W. (1970), in *Physical acoustics*, Vol. VI, ed. by W.R. Mason and R.N. Thurston (Academic Press, Inc., New York), p. 109.
FARNELL, G.W. and E.L. ADLER (1972), *Physical acoustics*, Vol. IX, ed. by W.P. Mason and R.N. Thurston (Academic Press, Inc., New York), p. 35.
FEUCHTWANG, T.E. (1967), Phys. Rev. **155**, 715, 731.
FRÖHLICH, H. (1949), *Theory of dielectrics* (Oxford University Press, Oxford).
FUCHS, R. and K.L. KLIEWER (1965), Phys. Rev. **140**, A2076.
FUJIWARA, T. and K. OHTAKA (1968), J. Phys. Soc. Japan **24**, 1326.
GAZIS, D.C., R. HERMAN and R.F. WALLIS (1960), Phys. Rev. **119**, 533.
GAZIS, D.C. and R.F. WALLIS (1965), Surf. Sci. **3**, 19.
GELATT, C.D., M.G. LAGALLY and M.B. WEBB (1969), Bull. Am. Phys. Soc. **14**, 793.
GODWIN, R.P. (1966), Thesis, University of Illinois.
GOODMAN, R.H., H.H. FARRELL and G.A. SOMORJAI (1968), J. Chem. Phys. **48**, 1046.
GRIM, A., A.A. MARADUDIN and S.Y. TONG (1970), J. Phys. Coll C1, suppl. to No. 4, C1–9.
GULYAEV, YU.V. (1969),. Zh. Eksp. Teor. Fiz. Pis. v. Red. **9**, 63 [English transl.: Sov. Phys. JETP Lett. **9**, 37].
IBACH, H. (1970), Phys. Rev. Lett. **24**, 1416.
IBACH, H. (1971), Phys. Rev. Lett. **27**, 253.
IGNATIEV, A. and T.N.RHODIN (1973), Phys. Rev. **B8**, 893.
JEPSEN, D.W., P.M. MARCUS and F. JONA (1973), Surface Sci. **39**, 27.
JONES, E.R, J.T.MCKINNEY and M.B. WEBB (1966), Phys. Rev. **151**, 476.
JONES, W.E. and R. FUCHS (1971), Phys. Rev. **B4**, 3581.
JOSEPHSON, B.D. (1960), Phys. Rev. Lett. **4**, 341.
KAPLAN, R. and G.A. SOMORJAI (1971), Solid State Commun. **9**, 505.
KING, P.J. and F.W. SHEARD (1969), J. Appl. Phys. **40**, 5189.
KING, P.J. and F.W. SHEARD (1970), Proc. Roy. Soc. (London) **A320**, 175.
KLIEWER, K.L. and R. FUCHS (1966), Phys. Rev. **144**, 495.
KUBO, R. (1957), J. Phys. Soc. Japan **12**, 570.
LANDAU, L. and E.M. LIESHITY, *Theory of elastici* (Pergamon Press, Oxford), pp. 155–157.
LANDAU, L. and G. RUMER (1937), Phys. Z. Sowjetunion **11**, 18.
LIM, T.C. and G.W. FARNELL (1968), J. Appl. Phys. **39**, 4319.
Lord RAYLEIGH (1887), Proc. London Math. Soc. **17**, 4
LOVE, A.E.H. (1911), *Some problems of geodynamics* (Cambridge Univ. Press, London and New York).

LOVE, A.E.H. (1944), *A treatise on the mathematical theory of elasticity*, fourth ed. (Dover Publications, New York), p. 309.

LOW, G.G.E. (1962), Proc. Phys. Soc. (London) **79**, 479.

LUCAS, A.A. and M. SUNJIC (1971), Phys. Rev. Lett. **26**, 229.

LUCAS, A.A. and M. SUNJIC (1972), Prog. Surf. Sci. **2**, 75.

LYON, H.B. and G.A. SOMORJAI (1966), J. Chem. Phys. **44**, 3707.

MACRAE, A.U. (1964), Surf. Sci. **2**, 522

MACRAE, A.U. and L.H. GERMER (1962), Phys. Rev. Lett. **8**, 489.

MARADUDIN, A.A. and J. MELNGAILIS (1964), Phys. Rev. **133**, A1188.

MARADUDIN, A.A. and D.L. MILLS (1968), Phys. Rev. **173**, 881.

MARADUDIN, A.A., E.W. MONTROLL, G.H. WEISS and I.P. IPATOVA (1971), *Theory of lattice dynamics in the harmonic approximation*, second ed. (Academic Press, Inc., New York).

MARADUDIN, A.A. and R.F. WALLIS (1966), Phys. Rev. **148**, 945.

MARSCHALL, N. and B. FISCHER (1972), Phys. Rev. Lett. **28**, 811.

MARSCHALL, N., B. FISCHER and H.J. QUEISSER (1971), Phys. Rev. Lett. **27**, 95.

MASRI, P. and L. DOBRZYNSKI (1971), J. de Physique **32**, 939.

OTTO, A. (1968), Z. Physik **216**, 398.

PLISKIN, W.A. and R.P. EISCHENS (1960), Z. Physik. Chem. **24**, 11.

POUND, R.V. and G.A. REBKA (1960), Phys. Rev. Lett. **4**, 274.

PRESS, F. and I. HEALY (1957), J. Appl. Phys. **28**, 1323.

RICH, M. (1963), Phys. Lett. **4**, 153.

ROSENSTOCK, H.B. (1955), J. Chem. Phys. **23**, 2415.

ROSENSTOCK, H.B. (1957), J. Chem. Phys. **27**, 1194.

ROSENSTOCK, H.B. and G.F. NEWELL (1953), J. Chem. Phys. **21**, 1607.

ROUNDY, V. and D.L. MILLS (1972), Phys. Rev. **B5**, 1347.

RUPPIN, R. and R. ENGLMAN (1969), in *Light scattering spectra of solids*, ed. by G.B. Wright (Springer-Verlag, New York), p. 157.

RUPPIN, R. and R. ENGLMAN (1970), Repts. on Prog. Phys. **33**, 149.

SALZMANN, E., T. PLIENINGER and K. DRANSFELD (1968), Appl. Phys. Lett. **13**, 14.

SCHOLTE, J.G. (1947), Mon. Not. Roy. Astron. Soc. Geophys. Suppl. **5**, 120.

STEG, R.G. and P.G. KLEMENS (1970), Phys. Rev. Lett. **24**, 381.

STONELEY, R. (1924), Proc. Roy. Soc. (London) **A106**, 416.

STONELEY, R. (1955), Proc. Roy. Soc. (London) **A232**, 447.

STRATTON, R. (1953), Phil. Mag. **44**, 519.

STRATTON, R. (1962), J. Chem. Phys. **37**, 2972.

TABOR, D. and J. WILSON (1970), Surf. Sci. **20**, 203.

TABOR, D., J.M. WILSON and T.J. BASTOW (1971), Surf. Sci. **26**, 471.

TONG, S.Y. and A.A. MARADUDIN (1969), Phys. Rev. **181**, 1318.

TSENG, C.C. (1967), J. Appl. Phys. **38**, 4281.

TSENG, C.C. and R.M. WHITE (1967), J. Appl. Phys. **38**, 4274.

WALLIS, R.F. (1957), Phys. Rev. **105**, 540.

WALLIS, R.F. (1973), Prog. Surf. Sci. **4**, 233.

WALLIS, R.F. and D.J. CHENG (1972), Solid State Commun. **11**, 221.

WALLIS, R.F. and D.C. GAZIS (1962), Phys. Rev. **128**, 106.

WILSON, J.M. and T.J. BASTOW (1971), Surf. Sci. **26**, 461.

Subject Index

Author Index